D0371666

# The Changing Shape of Metropolitan America:

## DECONCENTRATION SINCE 1920

# The Changing Shape of Metropolitan America:

## DECONCENTRATION SINCE 1920

By AMOS H. HAWLEY

The Free Press, Glencoe, Illinois

PRINTED IN THE UNITED STATES OF AMERICA

## FOREWORD

This monograph is the second report in a series dealing with patterns of growth and change in metropolitan areas of the United States, It was begun as a part of the Scripps Foundation's program of research in the field of population distribution, the funds for which were provided by the Rockefeller Foundation. A four year contract granted the Scripps Foundation For Research in Population Problems by the Housing and Home Finance Agency made it possible to greatly enlarge the scope and increase the detail of the work for the study. Hence the Housing and Home Finance Agency shares its financial sponsorship with the Rockefeller Foundation.

The first report, prepared by Dr. Donald J. Bogue, bears the title *Population Growth in Standard Metropolitan Areas, 1900-1950, with an Explanatory Analysis of Urbanized Areas.* In his study Dr. Bogue analyzed growth trends in metropolitan areas which in each census year, beginning with 1900, conformed to the 1950 definition of Standard Metropolitan Area. He observed the effects of size, regional location, and other factors on differential growth as between central cities and metropolitan rings. This study complements Dr. Bogue's in that it also treats population redistribution within metropolitan areas for the period 1900 to 1950. It differs, however, in giving close attention to the relation of population change to distance from central cities and in the selection of independent variables analyzed. These and other monographs to follow in this series are intended to provide a fuller knowledge of the patterns of and factors associated with metropolitan development than has been available heretofore.

The author wishes to express his indebtedness to Dr. Warren Thompson and Dr. Donald J. Bogue for their assistance in the preparation of this monograph. Mr. Howard Brunsman, Dr. Henry Shryock, and their colleagues in the Population Division, U. S. Bureau of the Census, gave substantial aid to the research on numerous occasions.

Sarah Jacobson, Thelma Batten, Lois Pratt, Leo Schnore, and Maria Cohn performed the statistical operations required. Marian Rickel typed the manuscript. All offered many helpful suggestions for improving the monograph.

Amos H. Hawley
Ann Arbor, Michigan
October, 1955

## CONTENTS

CHAPTER I

# INTRODUCTION

Few phenomena are more representative of the trend of modern society with its increasing emphasis on large-scale organization than is the emergence and rapid development of the metropolitan community during the past fifty odd years. Following quickly upon reductions of the time and cost involved in local movements, which resulted from the introduction of the motor vehicle and the hard-surfaced road, improvements in the transmission of electric power, the telephone, the radio and more recently television, the urban community burst its narrow bounds and expanded over the surrounding country.[1] In contrast to the compact city of the nineteenth century the radial scope of which seldom exceeded ten miles, the expanded or metropolitan community embraces in a single organization the cities, villages and other minor civil divisions lying within a radial distance of thirty-five miles or more from a central or core city. This new type of unit has assumed a dominant position in the urban settlement pattern of the United States.

The growth of metropolitan population has been one of the most conspicuous features of population movement in the United States during the first half of the twentieth century. In every decade since metropolitan areas[2] were first identified and reported separately in census volumes the part of the population so classified has maintained a higher growth rate than has any other part of the nation's population. As may be observed in Table 1, the rate of metropolitan population growth exceeded, in almost every decade, the rate of total population growth by 50 per cent or more, and it exceeded the growth rate of population residing outside of metropolitan areas by 100 to 300 per cent. Thus, in contrast to the 40 per cent of the total population that was classified as urban in 1900, the 168 metropolitan areas in 1950 contained 56 per cent of the nation's population, or about 86 million people. The United States population is living, to an increasing extent, in community aggregates of unprecendented size.

TABLE 1. PER CENT CHANGE OF POPULATION IN THE UNITED STATES, IN METROPOLITAN AREAS, AND IN AREA OUTSIDE OF METROPOLITAN AREAS, 1900-1950

| *Type of place* | *1940-1950*[a] | *1930-1940*[b] | *1920-1930*[b] | *1910-1920*[b] | *1900-1910*[b] |
|---|---|---|---|---|---|
| Total United States population | 14.5 | 7.2 | 16.1 | 14.9 | 21.0 |
| All metropolitan areas reported | 22.0 | 8.1 | 28.3 | 26.9 | 34.6 |
| Central cities | 13.9 | 5.1 | 22.3 | 25.2 | 33.6 |
| Satellite areas | 35.6 | 15.1 | 44.0 | 32.0 | 38.2 |
| Area outside metropolitan areas | 6.1 | 6.5 | 7.9 | 9.6 | 16.4 |
| Number of metropolitan areas | 168 | 140 | 97 | 58 | 44 |

[a] Seventeenth Census of the United States.

[b] W. S. Thompson, The Growth of Metropolitan Districts in the United States: 1900-1940. (Washington, D. C., U. S. Government Printing Office, 1947).

Just as interesting, however, is the fact of differential growth, or population redistribution, within metropolitan areas. It is to be noted in Table 1 that the ratio of central city growth to satellite growth has tended to become progressively smaller. High growth rates, in other words, have shifted from the centers to the outlying parts of metropolitan areas. Consequently the proportion of metropolitan population occupying satellite area has increased steadily from 23 per cent, in the 44 districts reported in 1910, to 42 per cent in the 168 areas of 1950. Table 2 describes that trend.

TABLE 2. PER CENT DISTRIBUTION OF POPULATION IN METROPOLITAN AREAS, BY TYPE OF PLACE, 1910-1950

| *Type of place* | *1950*[a] | *1940*[b] | *1930*[b] | *1920*[b] | *1910*[b] |
|---|---|---|---|---|---|
| Metropolitan areas | 100.0 | 100.0 | 100.0 | 100.0 | 100.0 |
| Central cities | 58.4 | 68.0 | 69.1 | 74.4 | 76.7 |
| Satellite areas | 41.6 | 32.0 | 30.9 | 25.6 | 23.3 |
| Number of metropolitan areas | 168 | 140 | 97 | 58 | 44 |

[a] Seventeenth Census of the United States.

[b] W. S. Thompson, *op. cit.*

The enlarged scale of community size presents many problems most of which seem to arise from the dislocations and stresses incident to unequal rates of change. Urban expansion has involved both (1) a release of industry, residence, and related activities from close confinement in a comparatively small area and (2) a reorientation of the activities of the population occupying areas recently brought within daily access of the central city. Apparently such changes encounter a relatively slight inertia, for they began immediately and their effects have accumulated rapidly. Quite different has been the experience with the capital equipment of urban living, with forms of local government, and with other institutional systems. These have been slow to adapt to the altered situation, tending rather to persist in their early patterns. Hence large sections of metropolitan areas have lacked adequate roads, public water and sewage facilities, and buildings to house community service; the multiplicities of government units have preserved administrative confusion and revenue inequities; and welfare and many other institutions have made only belated attempts to serve the more widely scattered populations. The disparity between the actual scope of the metropolitan community and the development of its service structure constitutes a problem of major importance. But a proper measure of its magnitude as well as decisions concerning how the problem should be treated require more detailed knowledge of the trends and patterns of redistributions within metropolitan areas than has been available to date.

In this study attention is directed to the analysis of population redistribution within metropolitan areas. Although population redistribution is but one phase of the general movement that is involved in the maturation of metropolitan communities, it is more readily accessible to observation than are many other relocation tendencies. Population change, moreover, is one of the most precise indicators of social change.

Metropolitan population redistribution has been treated broadly in varvarious reports.[3] Here, however, the amount and rate of redistribution will be examined with special reference to distance from central city. The growth of metropolitan organization, it has been pointed out, has resulted from the conquest of distance as a barrier to community size. It was noted also that the reduction of the limiting effects of distance has made possible an extension of the radius of community area from about ten to approximately thirty-five miles. Those radii are approximate maximum distances that can be travelled in an hour's time with the transportation facilities available in the respective periods. It is helpful to think of distance as a friction, which, though it can be reduced by technological improvements, may never be eliminated. The friction mounts with additions to distance, assuming a given transportation technology; that is, the time

and energy that must be expended to pass over space increase as the space to be overcome is lengthened. Hence the familiar gradient pattern observed in the spatial distributions of community components. Thus it might be expected that the gradients plotted for the distributions of metropolitan population at successive intervals from a selected date, 1900 for example, would tend to grow longer and flatter. But space is not the only source of friction. The time and energy consumed in moving from point to point may be increased over what would be required on an unobstructed plane by obstacles of various kinds, such as hills, rivers and other topographic features. Urban communities develop a unique friction known as traffic density or congestion. The efficiency of modern forms of transportation and communication may be, in fact are, reduced well below their potentials by traffic density. A friction of this kind may operate as both a propulsive factor, encouraging the deconcentration of dense aggregates, and a limiting factor on the linear extent of deconcentration. In any event, there is no simple way of anticipating a priori the emerging pattern of population distribution in metropolitan areas.

The distance involved in the deconcentration of metropolitan population impinges upon the economics of metropolitan development at many points. It describes the areas of shifting housing demand, it affects the feasibility of extending municipal utilities to unserviced localities, and it indicates the dimensions of the changing market for services of all kinds, to mention but a few examples. Intelligent planning of metropolitan communities, therefore, demands as full a knowledge of the scope of population redistribution as can be obtained.

## The Problem and the Data

Specifically, this monograph analyzes population redistribution trends in the United States, from 1900 through 1950, by distance from central city, by type of satellite unit, and by selected characteristics of areas, for all metropolitan areas identified in the census of 1950 and for which comparable data for two or more census years are available. The characteristics employed as independent variables include: size of central city; growth rate of central city; proximity of central cities to one another; geographic location of central city; amount of manufacturing employment in area; industrial relocation trend; and regional location.

All data employed in the investigation of the problem as stated are taken from official publications of the Bureau of the Census. The population data are derived from the Series 1 tables which show total population figures for states and minor civil divisions. The location of areas

and the delimitation of zones are based on the State and Minor Civil Division maps prepared by the Geography Division of the Bureau of the Census. Various other Bureau of the Census publications, particularly the Census of Manufactures, are used for the classifications of metropolitan areas.

## The Definition of Metropolitan Area

Two definitions of metropolitan area are employed in the analysis, one termed the Standard Metropolitan Area and the second described as the Extended Metropolitan Area. The former represents a new concept of metropolitan area introduced into the Census of Population in 1950. It replaces the older Metropolitan District term which had been in use from 1910 through 1940. The latter, that is, the Extended Metropolitan Area, was developed for purposes of the present study and for reasons to be discussed in later paragraphs.

The definition of the Standard Metropolitan Area is stated as follows:

> A standard metropolitan area contained at least one city of 50,000 or more in 1950, and each city of this size is included in one standard metropolitan area.....When two cities of 50,000 or more are within 20 miles of one another they have ordinarily been included in the same standard metropolitan area. .....In general, each standard metropolitan area comprises the county containing the city and any other contiguous counties which are deemed to be closely economically integrated with that city.
>
> Contiguous counties are included in a standard metropolitan area when they qualify on two types of criteria. One type is concerned with the character of the county as a place of work for nonagricultural workers and with the density of population, The other type is concerned with the extent to which contiguous counties are socially and economically integrated with the central city. Specifically, these criteria are:
>
> 1. The county must have
>     a. 10,000 nonagricultural workers, or
>     b. 10 percent of the nonagricultural workers in the standard metropolitan area, or
>     c. At least half of its population residing in contiguous minor civil divisions with a population density of 150 or more per square mile.
> 2. Nonagricultural workers must constitute at least two-thirds of the total employed labor force of the county.

3. There must be evidence of social and economic integration of the county with the central city as indicated by such criteria as the following:
   a. 15 percent or more of the workers residing in the contiguous county work in the county containing the largest city in the standard metropolitan area, or
   b. 25 percent or more of the persons working in the contiguous county reside in the county containing the largest city in the standard metropolitan area, or
   c. An average of four or more telephone calls per subscriber per month from the contiguous county to the county containing the largest city in the standard metropolitan area.

In New England, where the city and town rather than the county were used to define standard metropolitan areas, the first and second criteria set forth above could not be applied. In their place, a population density criterion of 150 or more persons per square mile, or 100 or more persons per square mile where strong integration was evident, has been used.[4]

On the basis of this definition, 168 Standard Metropolitan Areas in continental United States have been identified.

On the supposition that the scope of the Standard Metropolitan Area may not be adequate to encompass the full range of metropolitan influence, and as a test of that probability, the concept of the Extended Metropolitan Area is also used. This is an area having the same central city as the Standard Metropolitan Area, and includes all counties, or, in New England, all minor civil divisions, with centers within 35 miles of the inner core of the central city. There are thus as many Extended Metropolitan Areas as Standard Metropolitan Areas. Beyond its use as a test of the adequacy of the Standard Metropolitan Area concept, the Extended Metropolitan Area has independent value in description of the scope of metropolitan influence. The mass of detail involved in duplicating all tabulations for both concepts, however, would soon become so great as to invite confusion. Hence the analysis of Extended Metropolitan Areas is carried only into Chapter III.

The locations of the central cities of the 168 metropolitan areas are shown in Fig. 1.

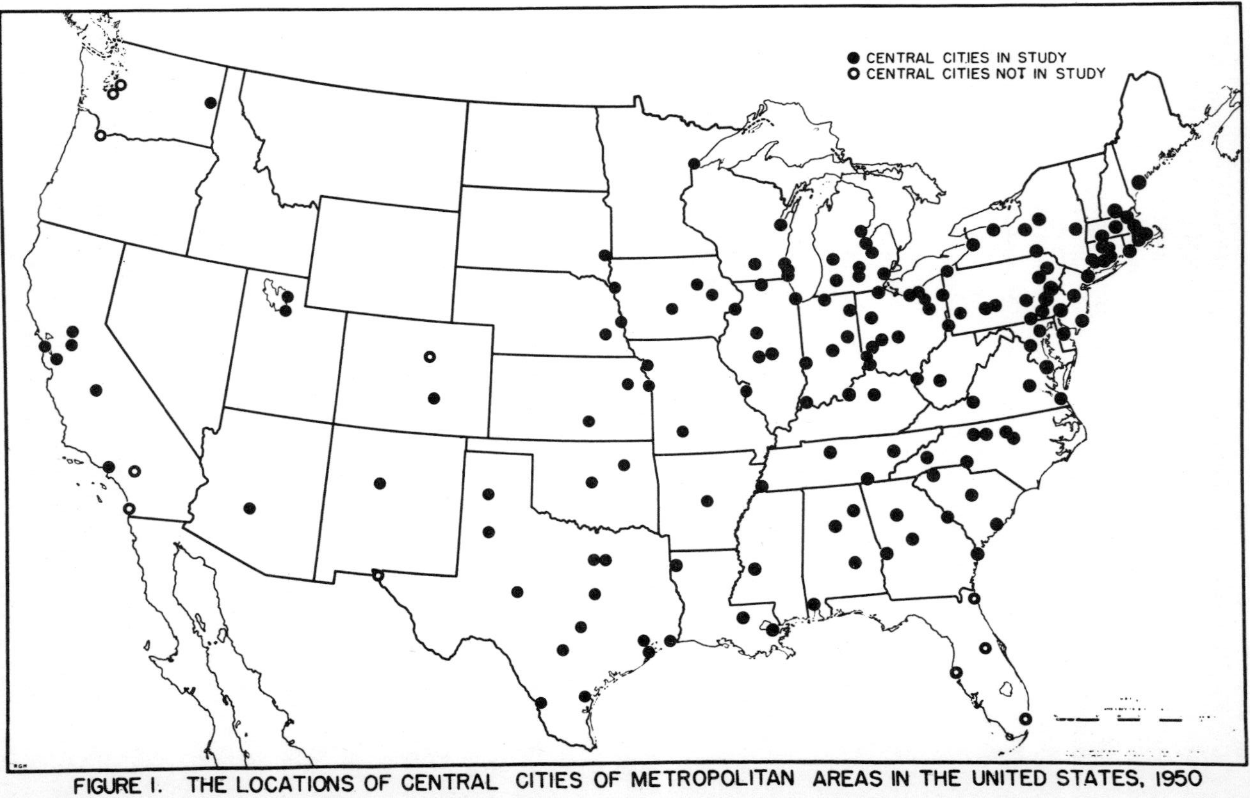


FIGURE I. THE LOCATIONS OF CENTRAL CITIES OF METROPOLITAN AREAS IN THE UNITED STATES, 1950

## Number of Metropolitan Areas in Study

The definitions stated above are applied uniformly in all decades, though many of the areas were not identified as metropolitan in earlier years and many could not have qualified as metropolitan even on the basis of the liberal census definitions of 1940 and 1950. Nevertheless, it has not been possible to include all 168 areas; in fact, the number of areas in the study differ from one decade to the next in the following manner:

| Decade | Number |
|---|---|
| 1940-50 | 143 |
| 1930-40 | 157 |
| 1920-30 | 155 |
| 1910-20 | 153 |
| 1900-10 | 148 |

Several circumstances are responsible for this. For example, since Oklahoma, New Mexico, and Arizona were not organized as states until after 1900, no data for minor civil divisions are available until later censuses A more important factor affecting the number of metropolitan areas in the study, however, is the practice in some States of frequent redistricting of minor civil divisions, thus eliminating any possibility of comparability between succeeding census years. For this reason eleven metropolitan areas are completely excluded from this study. Some metropolitan areas, notably Los Angeles, are included for only the latter part of the 50-year period because of extensive redistricting in earlier years. On the other hand, fourteen areas, which are included from 1900 to 1940, are omitted for the 1940-50 decade. The metropolitan areas in the study, together with selected characteristics of the areas, are shown in Appendix Table 1.

## The Measurement of Distance

Distance from the central city is measured from the approximate site of the city hall of the central city and is expressed in 5-mile intervals. Where two or more central cities are recognized by the Bureau of the Census, the city hall location of the largest city is used as the center. In the few instances in which the companion central cities are of about equal size a point midway between them is selected as the center.

In many metropolitan areas it is possible to identify eight distance zones, beginning with 0-5 miles and ending with 35 miles and over. The exceptions occur where metropolitan areas are surrounded by other

metropolitan areas whose centers are less than 75 miles distant and by coastal waters less than 35 miles distant. The New Britain-Bristol metropolitan area, for example, has but a 15-mile radius. Similar limitations of territory occur in other New England metropolitan areas.[5] It should be noted also that, as a result of proximity of central cities as well as of bodies of water, the concentric zones are rarely full circles. Fig. 2, which shows the metropolitan areas and their respective distance zones in northeastern Ohio, illustrates the interruption of zones. As a result of these two kinds of limitations the amount of land area in each distance zone is less than is to be expected in fully circular belts. Thus, as may be observed in Table 3, the proportion of the expected square miles of area contained in each zone declines rapidly with distance. Even the 0-5 mile zone contains no more than four-fifths of the land area expected, a consequence of the location of many central cities on water edges. The greater inclusiveness of the Extended Metropolitan area is apparent.

TABLE 3. EXPECTED AND ACTUAL NUMBER OF SQUARE MILES IN 157 METROPOLITAN AREAS, BY DISTANCE ZONES, 1940

| *Distance zone* | *Expected number of square miles* | *Actual number of square miles* | | *Proportion that actual is of expected* | |
|---|---|---|---|---|---|
| | | *Standard Metropolitan Areas* | *Extended Metropolitan Areas* | *Standard Metropolitan Areas* | *Extended Metropolitan Areas* |
| Central cities | 4,944 | 4,944 | 4,944 | 100 | 100 |
| 0 - 5 miles | 7,691 | 6,007 | 6,158 | 78 | 80 |
| 5 - 10 " | 37,052 | 26,761 | 30,174 | 72 | 81 |
| 10 - 15 " | 61,701 | 33,848 | 50,900 | 55 | 82 |
| 15 - 20 " | 86,350 | 28,552 | 63,755 | 33 | 74 |
| 20 - 25 " | 110,999 | 26,263 | 77,375 | 24 | 70 |
| 25 - 30 " | 135,648 | 12,413 | 71,338 | 9 | 53 |
| 30 - 35 " | 160,297 | 7,854 | 62,832 | 5 | 39 |
| 35 miles and over | 184,946 | 22,132 | 92,934 | 12 | 50 |
| Total | 789,628 | 168,774 | 460,410 | 21 | 58 |

Two distance zones require special comment. The 0-5 mile zone is defined to include only that part of the area within the 5-mile radius that lies outside the incorporated boundaries of the central city. Hence in the

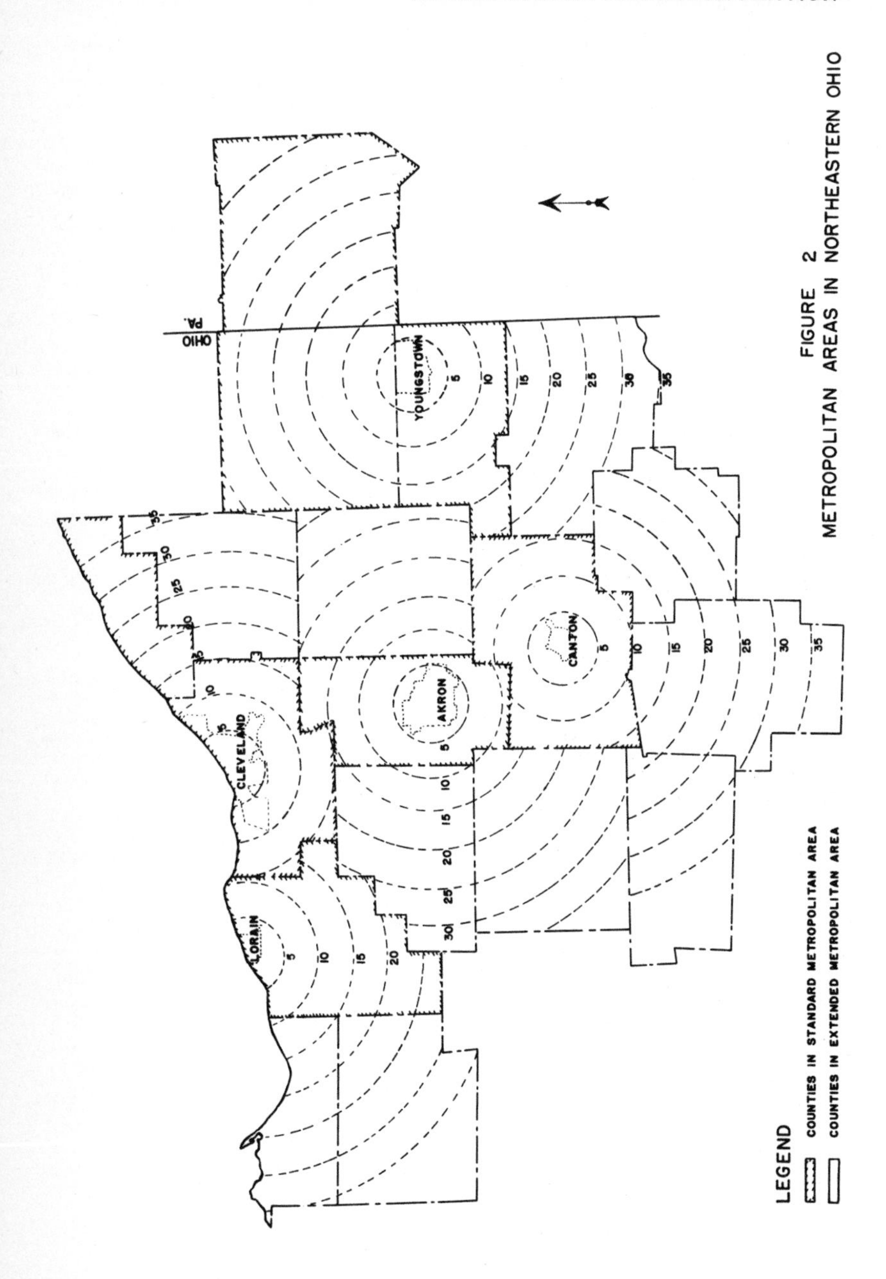


FIGURE 2
METROPOLITAN AREAS IN NORTHEASTERN OHIO

Cleveland area, shown in Fig. 2, the 0-5 mile zone contains but .7 square mile in contrast to an average of 48.9 square miles. An even more extreme case is that of the Chicago area in which the central city occupies all of the area within 5 miles of the city hall and, as does the city of Cleveland, extends into the 5-10 mile zone. Thus the 0-5 mile zones differ in area with variations in the amounts of area contained in central cities. The 35 mile and over zone is of irregular size by virtue of its being an open-ended class. It comprises the parts, that lie more than 35 miles from central cities, of all counties that (a) are included in Standard Metropolitan Areas and (b) are included in Extended Metropolitan Areas, i.e., the centers of which are within 35 miles of central cities.

The area and population of each distance zone are the same as those in the minor civil divisions, e.g., incorporated places, townships, towns, precincts, etc., the centers of which are within the specified distance from the core of the central city. Consequently, the area and the population attributed to each zone differ from what they would be if it were possible to apply a rigorous mileage measure. Such errors, however, tend to cancel one another in averages for a number of metropolitan areas.

The preservation of comparability of distance zones from one census year to another is complicated by numerous minor civil division boundary changes resulting from annexations, consolidations, and redistrictings. Reference has been made already to the effects of broad scale changes of boundaries on the number of metropolitan areas that lend themselves to a given definition. There are also many occasional changes which in general present a less serious problem, for the information required in the making of adjustments is frequently available.

The corrections for boundary changes result in two tabulations of population by distance zones for each decade: one for the end of the decade which states the population distribution as enumerated in the census of that year, and one for the beginning of the decade which states the distribution of population of the preceding census year as it would have been if minor civil division boundaries had been as they were at the end of that decade. Appendix Table 2 shows the total populations for the beginning and the end of each decade for all of both Standard and Extended Metropolitan Areas. Caution should be observed in the use of these absolute numbers. Because the number of areas changes in each successive decade, figures for total populations are comparable only as between the beginning and the end of a given decade.

CHAPTER II

# POPULATION REDISTRIBUTION WITHIN ALL METROPOLITAN AREAS

## Central Cities and Satellite Areas

The general tendency has been for the rate of growth of metropolitan population to decline through the 50 years since 1900. As may be observed in Table 4, the trend has followed the same pattern, though at different levels, in both Standard and Extended Metropolitan Areas. In both classes of areas the trend has been erratic, reflecting the influences of a number of historic events on population growth and distribution.

A more consistent trend, noticeable in Table 4 and shown graphically in Fig. 3, may be described as a shift of high growth rates from central cities to those parts of metropolitan areas not included in central cities, commonly referred to as satellite areas. The deconcentration movement is not conspicuous, however, until after 1920. The sharp reductions in growth rates in 1910-20 below those of 1900-10 doubtlessly are a consequence of the curtailment of foreign immigration incident to World War I. Although foreign immigration was not resumed on its former scale in the 1920-30 decade, the continued decline of central city growth rates was brought about by the preemptive increase of satellite rates. Again in 1930-40 metropolitan rates of increase were depressed by a failure of migration, though this time it was a failure of rural to urban migration which after 1920 had replaced foreign migration as a source of urban population growth. The absence of job opportunities in urban areas during the 1930's removed a primary incentive to urbanward migration. But depression conditions appear to have provoked an acceleration of the centrifugal[1] movement to satellite areas, for the difference between central city and satellite growth rates widened during 1930-40. And in the 1940-50 decade an equivalent difference remained despite the resumption of relatively rapid increase of metropolitan population. Deconcentration was more pronounced in Standard than in Extended Metropolitan Areas.

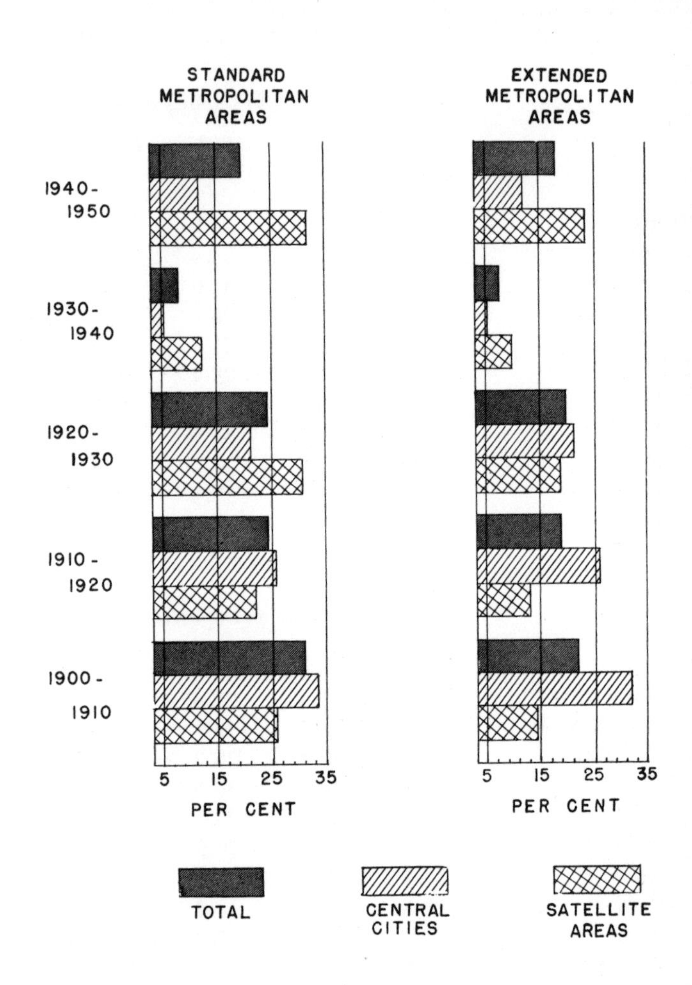


FIGURE 3

PER CENT CHANGE OF POPULATION IN METROPOLITAN AREAS, 1900-1950

TABLE 4. PER CENT CHANGE OF POPULATION IN STANDARD AND EXTENDED METROPOLITAN AREAS, BY TYPE OF PLACE AND DISTANCE FROM CENTRAL CITY, 1900-1950

| *Distance zone* | *1940-50* | *1930-40* | *1920-30* | *1910-20* | *1900-10* |
|---|---|---|---|---|---|
| | *Standard Metropolitan Areas* | | | | |
| All area* | 19.7 | 8.0 | 24.9 | 24.5 | 29.4 |
| Central cities* | 11.8 | 5.1 | 21.4 | 25.9 | 31.5 |
| Satellite areas* | 31.6 | 12.6 | 31.0 | 22.2 | 26.0 |
| 0-5 miles | 23.6 | 10.4 | 26.3 | 29.3 | 27.9 |
| 5-10 " | 36.3 | 15.0 | 41.2 | 23.4 | 29.4 |
| 10-15 " | 32.2 | 11.6 | 25.4 | 20.3 | 24.9 |
| 15-20 " | 32.9 | 13.4 | 32.7 | 21.8 | 22.9 |
| 20-25 " | 30.6 | 13.5 | 34.9 | 20.8 | 24.1 |
| 25-30 " | 23.2 | 9.6 | 24.2 | 19.0 | 23.7 |
| 30-35 " | 36.8 | 11.0 | 17.5 | 15.6 | 14.2 |
| 35 miles and over | 27.2 | 9.5 | 18.7 | 9.3 | 25.2 |
| | *Extended Metropolitan Areas* | | | | |
| All area | 17.7 | 7.4 | 20.1 | 19.1 | 21.9 |
| Central cities | 11.8 | 5.1 | 21.4 | 25.9 | 31.5 |
| Satellite areas | 23.2 | 9.7 | 18.9 | 13.2 | 14.7 |
| 0-5 miles | 23.6 | 10.4 | 26.3 | 29.3 | 27.9 |
| 5-10 " | 35.8 | 14.7 | 39.5 | 22.5 | 27.9 |
| 10-15 " | 29.9 | 10.8 | 21.6 | 16.9 | 19.8 |
| 15-20 " | 24.5 | 10.2 | 20.0 | 12.2 | 13.1 |
| 20-25 " | 18.5 | 8.9 | 14.1 | 8.2 | 10.0 |
| 25-30 " | 12.6 | 6.7 | 8.1 | 7.3 | 8.2 |
| 30-35 " | 11.9 | 5.7 | 7.0 | 6.7 | 6.0 |
| 35 miles and over | 9.4 | 4.4 | 5.5 | 4.3 | 8.1 |

*The differences between the figures in these rows and those reported by Donald J. Bogue in *Population Growth in Standard Metropolitan Areas, 1900-1950* (Washington: U. S. Government Printing Office, 1953) are due to (1) Bogue's inclusion of all metropolitan areas in contrast to the use in this study of only those for which comparable data could be assembled for the 50-year period, and (2) his substitution of county equivalents for New England metropolitan areas instead of using the town based areas as defined by the Bureau of the Census.

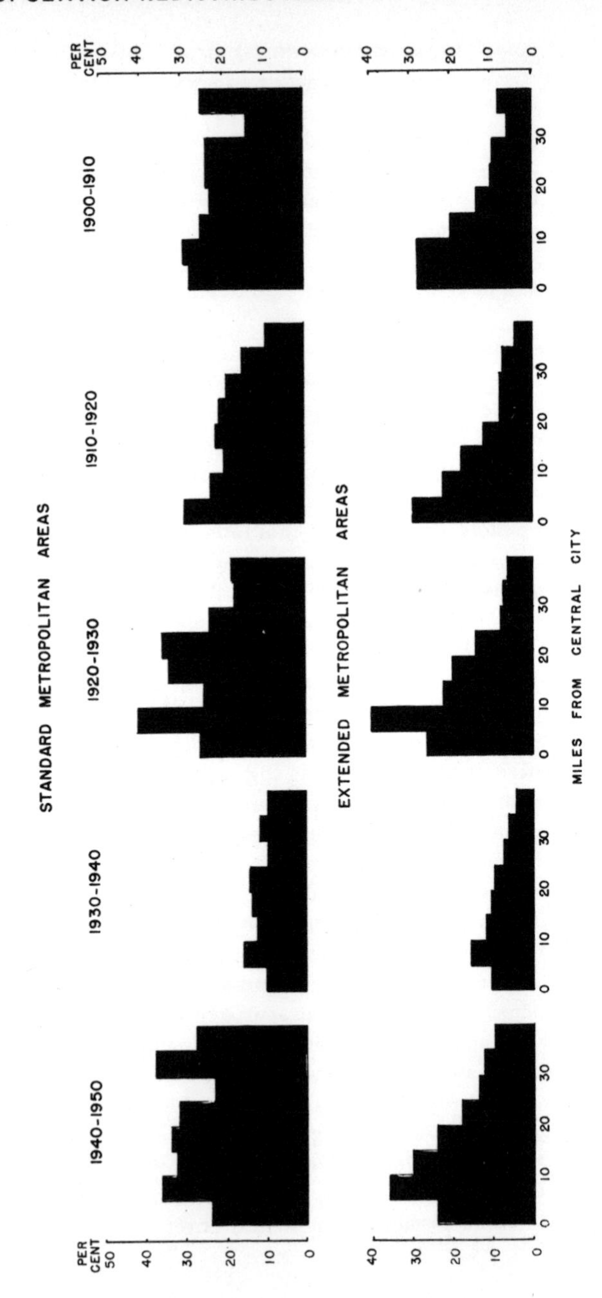


FIGURE 4
PER CENT CHANGE OF POPULATION IN METROPOLITAN AREAS, BY DISTANCE FROM CENTRAL CITIES,
1900 - 1950

The patterns of growth by distance zones, shown in Table 4 and Fig. 4, differ as between the two types of metropolitan areas. In the Standard Metropolitan Areas, growth rates show no consistent variation with distance from central cities. In the Extended Metropolitan Areas, on the other hand, there is a rather uniform gradient, i.e., growth rates decline with distance. The latter, which are considerably larger than the Standard Metropolitan Areas, permit a fuller expression of the effect of distance on metropolitan influence. Stated differently, the definition of the Standard Metropolitan Area tends to select the most rapidly growing portion of each distance zone.

Over the fifty year period high growth rates have moved outward. In 1900-10 the most rapidly growing parts of metropolitan areas were the central cities. In the next decade maximum growth rates occurred in the 0-5 mile zones. Peak rates of growth shifted to the 5-10 mile zones in 1920-30, where they remained through the last two decades. In the meantime population growth was accelerating in many of the more distant zones. But this is more adequately demonstrated in a later connection. The declining rates of increases in the 0-5 mile zones cannot be attributed to the absorption of progressively larger proportions of the land and population of those zones by central cities, for boundaries have been held constant within each decade. It seems likely that the circumstances which have depressed population growth in central cities have operated also on their immediately adjacent areas. Changes in the 35 mile and over zones suggest an interesting possibility. It seems likely that population changes in areas beyond 35 miles of central cities in the early decades may have occured independently of events in the interiors of metropolitan areas. The distant areas may have remained in relative isolation from the influences of central cities until substantial improvements of highway transportation accumulated in subsequent decades.

Some of the variations in rates of population change from decade to decade undoubtedly result from variations in the growth rates of the total national population. If the rates of change in metropolitan areas are expressed in relative terms, as in Fig. 5, that source of disturbance is removed. Thus it may be observed that the ratios for central cities increased from 1900 to 1920 and then declined through the remainder of the period, falling below unity after 1930. The centrifugal movements of highest rates of change, noted above, is again apparent.

In the Standard Metropolitan Areas, growth rates in the satellite areas fall below those for the nation as a whole only in the earlies decades, and then only in the area beyond 30 miles from central cities. The ratios for

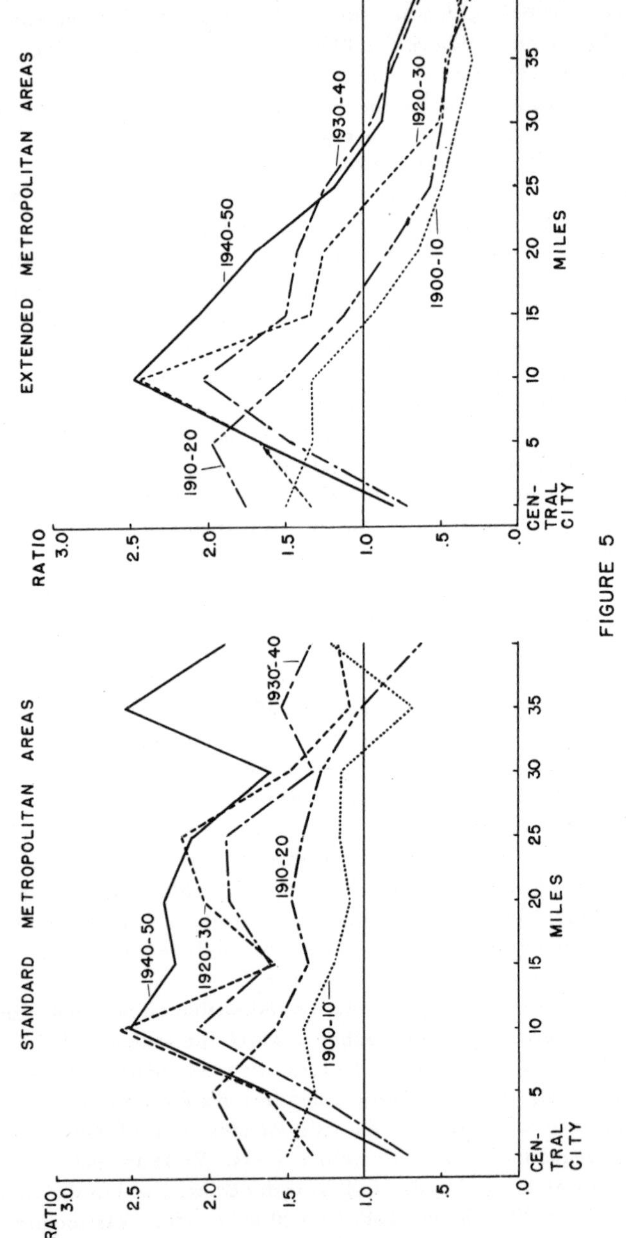


FIGURE 5

RATIO OF PER CENT CHANGE OF POPULATION IN METROPOLITAN AREAS TO PER CENT CHANGE OF TOTAL UNITED STATES POPULATION, BY DISTANCE FROM CENTRAL CITY, 1900-1950

each distance zone beyond 5 miles from central cities tend to increase in each succeeding decade, though the 1930-40 decade remains an exception in all but the zones 30 miles or more from central cities.

Growth rate ratios in the Extended Metropolitan Areas display a somewhat more consistent tendency to increase in succeeding decades. Of greater importance, however, is the evidence of the changing scope of metropolitan influence as shown in the second panel of Fig. 5. In 1900-10 metropolitan growth rates exceeded that of the total United States population only within a radius of 10 miles of central cities. In zones beyond that distance growth rates were less than the national average. During the next four decades approximately 15 miles were added to the radius within which higher than expected growth rates occurred. Thus it appears that, measured on this basis, the radius of metropolitan influence has moved from 10 to 25 or 30 miles in the 50 year period.

A comparison of the rates of change in distance zones with those of central cities, as shown in Fig. 6, reveals the growing importance of the satellite area even more clearly. In 1900-10 the population of central cities increased more rapidly than that of any distance zone. In the next decade, 1910-20, the 0-5 mile zones alone had higher rates of increase than did central cities. As may be observed, the distributions of the ratios for the two types of metropolitan areas are quite similar for 1900-10 and 1910-20. After 1920 their distributions differ markedly. During 1920-30 the area within which the growth rate ratios exceeded unity reach to 30 miles in Standard Metropolitan Areas and to 15 miles in Extended Metropolitan Areas. In the two decades following 1930 the ratios were considerably higher than in preceding decades and the distances over which ratios greater than 1.0 obtained were increased, especially in Extended Metropolitan Areas. It is noteworthy that in the latter class of areas, satellite growth was more concentrated in 1940-50 than in 1930-40. The curve for 1930-40 rises above that for 1940-50 beyond the 20 mile zone. In other words, in the decade of slowest metropolitan growth, the depression years of 1930 to 1940, the relative rates of growth of satellite areas were exceeded only by those of the 1940-50 decade.

The centrifugal tendency in population redistribution within metropolitan areas is also reflected in the manner in which the amounts of change in each decade are distributed over the total area, as shown in Table 5. The proportion of all increase that occurred in central cities declined from three-fifths or more to one third in the five decades, and, of course, a complementary increase took place in satellite areas. While in 1900-10 and 1910-20 three-fifths to two-thirds of all growth occurred within the bounds of central cities, in 1930-40 and 1940-50 a 10-mile radius was required to

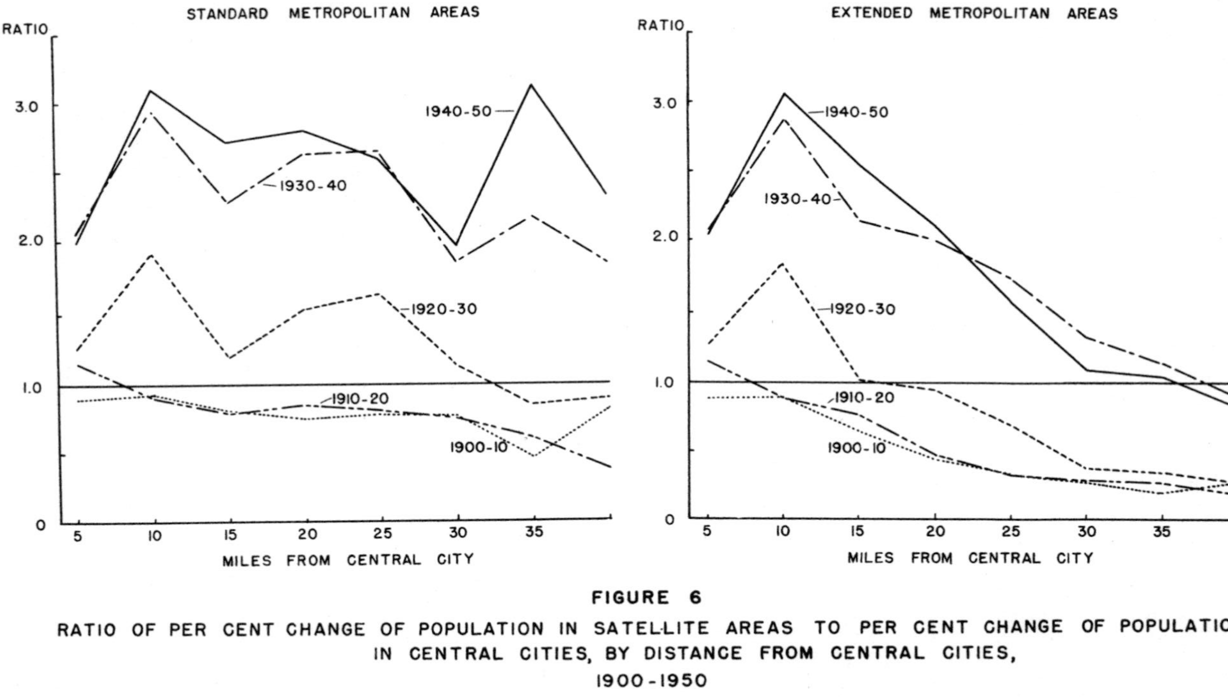


FIGURE 6

RATIO OF PER CENT CHANGE OF POPULATION IN SATELLITE AREAS TO PER CENT CHANGE OF POPULATION IN CENTRAL CITIES, BY DISTANCE FROM CENTRAL CITIES, 1900-1950

TABLE 5. PER CENT DISTRIBUTION OF AMOUNT OF POPULATION CHANGE IN STANDARD AND EXTENDED METROPOLITAN AREAS, BY DISTANCE ZONE, 1900-1950

| *Metropolitan Area and distance zone* | *Per cent distribution* | | | | | *Cumulative per cent distribution* | | | | |
|---|---|---|---|---|---|---|---|---|---|---|
| | *1940-50* | *1930-40* | *1920-30* | *1910-20* | *1900-10* | *1940-50* | *1930-40* | *1920-30* | *1910-20* | *1900-10* |
| Standard Metropolitan Areas | 100.0 | 100.0 | 100.0 | 100.0 | 100.0 | | | | | |
| Central cities | 35.8 | 39.5 | 54.8 | 66.4 | 65.9 | 35.8 | 39.5 | 54.8 | 66.4 | 65.9 |
| 0-5 miles | 7.5 | 8.0 | 6.5 | 7.2 | 6.0 | 43.3 | 47.5 | 61.3 | 73.6 | 71.9 |
| 5-10 " | 22.6 | 21.6 | 16.6 | 10.0 | 10.6 | 65.9 | 69.1 | 77.9 | 83.6 | 82.5 |
| 10-15 " | 14.4 | 12.3 | 8.6 | 7.2 | 7.8 | 80.3 | 81.4 | 86.5 | 90.8 | 90.3 |
| 15-20 " | 8.7 | 8.3 | 5.9 | 4.1 | 3.7 | 89.0 | 89.7 | 92.4 | 94.9 | 94.0 |
| 20-25 " | 5.0 | 5.0 | 4.0 | 2.4 | 2.4 | 94.0 | 94.7 | 96.4 | 97.3 | 96.4 |
| 25-30 " | 2.2 | 2.2 | 1.7 | 1.4 | 1.6 | 96.2 | 96.9 | 98.1 | 98.7 | 98.0 |
| 30-35 " | 1.8 | 1.3 | .7 | .6 | .5 | 98.0 | 98.2 | 98.8 | 99.3 | 98.5 |
| 35 miles and over | 2.0 | 1.8 | 1.2 | .7 | 1.5 | 100.0 | 100.0 | 100.0 | 100.0 | 100.0 |
| Extended Metropolitan Areas | 100.0 | 100.0 | 100.0 | 100.0 | 100.0 | | | | | |
| Central cities | 32.2 | 34.2 | 52.0 | 62.5 | 61.2 | 32.2 | 34.2 | 52.0 | 62.5 | 61.2 |
| 0-5 miles | 6.9 | 7.0 | 6.3 | 6.9 | 5.6 | 39.1 | 41.2 | 58.3 | 69.4 | 66.8 |
| 5-10 " | 20.9 | 19.1 | 16.0 | 9.6 | 10.1 | 60.0 | 60.3 | 74.3 | 79.0 | 76.9 |
| 10-15 " | 14.5 | 12.0 | 8.7 | 7.3 | 7.6 | 74.5 | 72.3 | 83.0 | 86.3 | 84.5 |
| 15-20 " | 9.8 | 9.4 | 6.7 | 4.6 | 4.6 | 84.3 | 81.7 | 89.7 | 90.9 | 89.1 |
| 20-25 " | 6.3 | 7.0 | 4.4 | 3.0 | 3.5 | 90.6 | 88.7 | 94.1 | 93.9 | 92.6 |
| 25-30 " | 4.0 | 5.0 | 2.5 | 2.6 | 2.9 | 94.6 | 93.7 | 96.6 | 96.5 | 95.5 |
| 30-35 " | 2.9 | 3.4 | 1.8 | 2.0 | 1.8 | 97.5 | 97.1 | 98.4 | 98.5 | 97.3 |
| 35 miles and over | 2.5 | 2.9 | 1.6 | 1.5 | 2.7 | 100.0 | 100.0 | 100.0 | 100.0 | 100.0 |

contain a like amount of the total increments. The minimum area required to account for 90 per cent of all growth, however, changed very little for Standard Metropolitan Areas, shifting from an area with a radius of 20 miles to one with a radius of less than 25 miles. In the Extended Metropolitan Areas the radius of the area within which 90 per cent of the growth occurred varied from less than 25 to less than 30 miles. In other words, it appears that the centrifugal tendency, so far as amounts of growth are concerned, operated primarily within rather short distances. Of interest in this connection is the fact that that tendency was actually reversed in both classes of metropolitan areas, in 1910-20. Some evidence of reversal is also noticeable in the Extended Metropolitan Areas after 1940.

The effect of differential growth rates, of course, is to change the pattern of population distribution within metropolitan areas. As may be observed in Table 6, redistribution in Standard Metropolitan Areas moved toward increased concentration through the first 20 years of the 50 year period. After 1920 the prevailing movement was toward dispersion. But the shift in the direction of redistribution after 1920 applies only to the area within a 15 mile radius. Dispersion did not begin to operate in the more distant zones until after 1930.

The proportion of the total population found in central cities, when Extended Metropolitan Areas are employed as units of observation, increased to 1930, 10 years beyond the peak for central cities of Standard Metropolitan Areas. The distribution of population over the several distance zones of the satellite areas was fairly uniform in 1900. From that date to 1950 the prevailing tendency has been toward concentration, particularly within the 25-mile boundary. Thus, if increases in the population in the satellite area be regarded as indicating metropolitan influence, it would seem that the scope of metropolitan areas does not extend beyond 25 miles from the centers of central cities. On this basis it may be argued that, in 1900, metropolitan areas had not in fact emerged, and that their development involved, first, a growth of central cities and immediately adjacent areas, and subsequently, the growth of population in more remote areas within the 25-mile radius.

Although the difference in population distribution between the beginning and the end of the 50-year span is considerable, the amount of change from one census year to the next is fairly small. This is evident in Table 5. It is shown more clearly, however, by a summation of the positive or negative percentage point differences between the percentage distributions of two consecutive census years. The coefficient of redistribution[2], as that summation has been designated, indicates the proportion of the population that would have to be redistributed to make the distribution at the end

TABLE 6. PER CENT DISTRIBUTION OF POPULATION IN STANDARD AND EXTENDED METROPOLITAN AREAS, BY DISTANCE ZONES, 1900-1950

| *Type of metropolitan area and distance zone* | *Per cent distribution* | | | | | | *Cumulative per cent distribution* | | | | | |
|---|---|---|---|---|---|---|---|---|---|---|---|---|
| | *1950* | *1940* | *1930* | *1920* | *1910* | *1900* | *1950* | *1940* | *1930* | *1920* | *1910* | *1900* |
| Standard Metropolitan Areas | 100.0 | 100.0 | 100.0 | 100.0 | 100.0 | 100.0 | | | | | | |
| Central cities | 55.9 | 59.9 | 61.7 | 63.7 | 62.8 | 61.4 | 55.9 | 59.9 | 61.7 | 63.7 | 62.8 | 61.4 |
| 0-5 miles | 6.5 | 6.3 | 6.1 | 6.2 | 6.1 | 6.3 | 62.4 | 66.2 | 67.8 | 69.9 | 68.9 | 67.7 |
| 5-10 " | 14.0 | 12.3 | 11.5 | 10.0 | 10.4 | 10.6 | 76.4 | 78.5 | 79.3 | 79.9 | 79.3 | 78.3 |
| 10-15 " | 9.8 | 8.9 | 8.5 | 8.4 | 8.7 | 9.1 | 86.2 | 87.4 | 87.8 | 88.3 | 88.0 | 87.4 |
| 15-20 " | 5.7 | 5.1 | 5.0 | 4.5 | 4.6 | 4.8 | 91.9 | 92.5 | 92.8 | 92.8 | 92.6 | 92.2 |
| 20-25 " | 3.5 | 3.2 | 3.0 | 2.8 | 2.8 | 2.9 | 95.4 | 95.7 | 95.8 | 95.6 | 95.4 | 95.1 |
| 25-30 " | 1.9 | 1.8 | 1.8 | 1.8 | 1.8 | 2.0 | 97.3 | 97.5 | 97.6 | 97.4 | 97.2 | 97.1 |
| 30-35 " | 1.1 | 1.0 | .9 | .9 | 1.0 | 1.1 | 98.4 | 98.5 | 98.5 | 98.3 | 98.2 | 98.2 |
| 35 miles and over | 1.6 | 1.5 | 1.5 | 1.7 | 1.8 | 1.8 | 100.0 | 100.0 | 100.0 | 100.0 | 100.0 | 100.0 |
| Extended Metropolitan Areas | 100.0 | 100.0 | 100.0 | 100.0 | 100.0 | 100.0 | | | | | | |
| Central cities | 45.9 | 48.3 | 49.6 | 48.9 | 46.0 | 42.4 | 45.9 | 48.3 | 49.6 | 48.9 | 46.0 | 42.4 |
| 0-5 miles | 5.4 | 5.1 | 4.9 | 4.7 | 4.4 | 4.4 | 51.3 | 53.4 | 54.5 | 53.6 | 50.4 | 46.8 |
| 5-10 " | 11.9 | 10.3 | 9.6 | 8.1 | 8.1 | 7.9 | 63.2 | 63.7 | 64.1 | 61.7 | 58.5 | 54.7 |
| 10-15 " | 9.5 | 8.6 | 8.2 | 8.1 | 8.2 | 8.4 | 72.7 | 72.3 | 72.3 | 69.8 | 66.7 | 63.1 |
| 15-20 " | 7.4 | 7.0 | 6.9 | 6.8 | 7.2 | 7.7 | 80.1 | 79.3 | 79.2 | 76.6 | 73.9 | 70.8 |
| 20-25 " | 6.1 | 6.1 | 5.9 | 6.3 | 6.9 | 7.6 | 86.2 | 85.4 | 85.1 | 82.9 | 80.8 | 78.4 |
| 25-30 " | 5.3 | 5.5 | 5.5 | 6.2 | 6.8 | 7.6 | 91.5 | 90.9 | 90.6 | 89.1 | 87.6 | 86.0 |
| 30-35 " | 4.1 | 4.4 | 4.5 | 5.1 | 5.8 | 6.6 | 95.6 | 95.3 | 95.1 | 94.2 | 93.4 | 92.6 |
| 35 miles and over | 4.4 | 4.7 | 4.9 | 5.8 | 6.6 | 7.4 | 100.0 | 100.0 | 100.0 | 100.0 | 100.0 | 100.0 |

of a decade identical to that of the beginning of the decade. Trends in the rates of redistribution as measured by the coefficient of redistribution are shown in Fig. 7 for both Standard and Extended Metropolitan areas. The rate of redistribution in Standard Metropolitan Areas has accelerated over the 50-year period, though that trend was offset in 1910-20 and again in 1930-40. Contrariwise, the trend in the rate of redistribution within Extended Metropolitan Areas moved steadily downward to 1940, and it is of interest to note that the rate for 1930-40 fits the trend established in the preceding decades. After 1940 the rate increased abruptly.

**Size and Type of Satellite Place**

In view of the increasing importance of the satellite area as a location of residence of metropolitan population, it is desirable to know the trends of redistribution among the different sizes and types of places comprising satellite areas. Two classifications are used in the following analysis: incorporated and unincorporated. Incorporated places are not to be confused with urban places; they include all localities listed in census reports as having a distinct political identity, and they exclude all special rule urban places and other unincorporated concentrations of population.

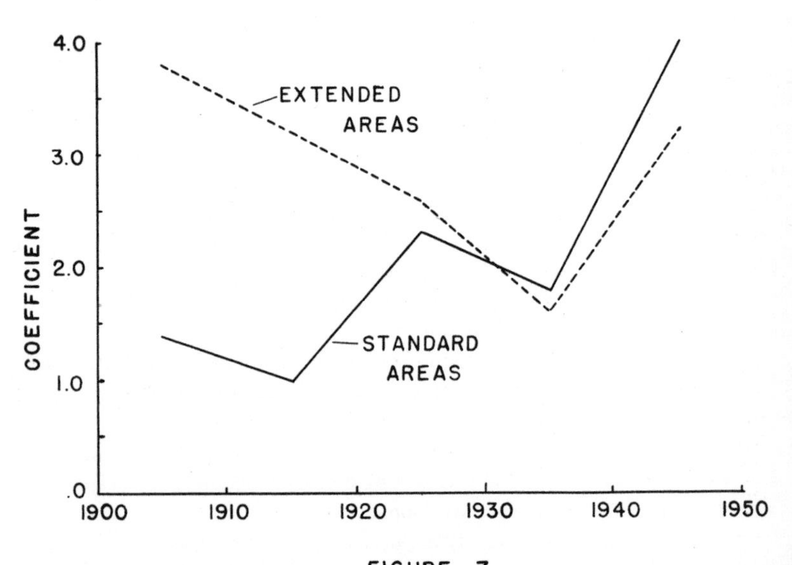


FIGURE 7

COEFFICIENTS OF REDISTRIBUTION, 1900-1950

The latter, despite their greater similarity to urban rather than to rural areas, lack the distinctness required for tracing them through five decades of change. Unincorporated places are included in all unincorporated area.

All satellite incorporated places with populations of 1,000 or more have experienced declining rates of growth, as may be seen in Table 7. The largest and most consistent declines have occurred in places of 25,000 or more population. In cities and towns with less than 5,000 population the rates of increase rose to 1930 and then subsided. Only in unincorporated area was there a constant trend of increase in growth rates. At the end of the 50 years the rate in unincorporated areas within Standard Metropolitan Areas was 160 per cent larger than that at the beginning of the period, while in Extended Metropolitan Areas the difference amounted to 260 per cent. Thus the increased rates of change in all satellite area, in 1940-50 over 1920-30, were entirely a function of rate increases in unincorporated area. The same statement cannot be made, however, of the rate changes from 1900-10 to 1920-30, since incorporated places of less than 5,000 population also increased their growth rates during those decades.

A second aspect of change concerns the relationship of growth rate to size of satellite place. In 1900-10, growth rates varied directly with size of place, particularly in Extended Metropolitan Areas. By 1930-40 that pattern of association had been reversed, -- rates varied inversely with size of place.

Some insight into the basis of growth in satellite places may be gained from the data, in Table 7, showing the average number of incorporated places per metropolitan area. The two decades of slowest growth rates, 1910-20 and 1930-40, correspond to the periods in which the smallest changes in number of satellite places took place. On the other hand, the decades of highest growth rates are those in which the frequencies of incorporation were highest. It is probably unnecessary to point out that rate of population growth and rate of incorporation are, rather than cause and effect, doubtlessly companion effects of another factor or factors. The declines in the numbers of places of less than 1,000 population are due both to the growth into larger size classes and to the frequent annexation or disincorporation of such places.

The growth rates of all incorporated satellite population shown in Table 8 have declined and increased again in succeeding decades, following the pattern of all satellite population (see Table 4). A line drawn through the decades 1900-10, 1920-30, and 1940-50, however, describes a general tendency toward decline in all distance zones. The diminishing importance of incorporated areas in the growth of all satellite population

TABLE 7. RATE OF CHANGE IN SATELLITE AREA AND AVERAGE NUMBER OF INCORPORATED SATELLITE PLACES PER METROPOLITAN AREA, BY TYPE OF METROPOLITAN AREA AND SIZE AND TYPE OF SATELLITE PLACE, 1900-1950

| *Type of metropolitan area and size[a] and type of satellite place* | *Rate of Change* | | | | | *Average number of places per metropolitan area* | | | | | |
|---|---|---|---|---|---|---|---|---|---|---|---|
| | *1940-1950* | *1930-1940* | *1920-1930* | *1910-1920* | *1900-1910* | *1950* | *1940* | *1930* | *1920* | *1910* | *1900* |
| Standard Metropolitan Areas | 31.6 | 12.6 | 31.0 | 22.2 | 26.0 | 17.9 | 15.5 | 16.0 | 14.7 | 13.4 | 10.2 |
| 50,000 and over | 10.8 | 1.2 | 13.1 | 17.5 | 35.5 | .4 | .3 | .3 | .2 | .1 | .1 |
| 25,000 - 50,000 | 12.0 | 2.7 | 31.2 | 21.9 | 37.1 | .6 | .4 | .4 | .3 | .2 | .1 |
| 10,000 - 25,000 | 19.4 | 7.9 | 30.0 | 34.1 | 32.4 | 1.7 | 1.2 | 1.2 | .8 | .6 | .5 |
| 5,000 - 10,000 | 29.3 | 9.2 | 39.0 | 27.0 | 43.1 | 2.4 | 1.7 | 1.5 | 1.3 | .9 | .6 |
| 2,500 - 5,000 | 35.9 | 10.7 | 44.3 | 38.8 | 42.2 | 2.4 | 2.1 | 2.3 | 2.2 | 1.5 | 1.0 |
| 1,000 - 2,500 | 31.7 | 14.7 | 52.6 | 31.2 | 37.6 | 4.3 | 3.6 | 3.5 | 3.3 | 3.2 | 2.3 |
| Under 1,000 | 32.2 | 14.0 | 36.3 | 21.5 | 30.6 | 6.1 | 6.2 | 6.8 | 6.6 | 6.9 | 5.6 |
| Unincorporated area | 47.6 | 21.8 | 31.5 | 17.3 | 18.0 | | | | | | |
| Extended Metropolitan Areas | 23.2 | 9.7 | 18.9 | 13.2 | 14.7 | 40.4 | 37.2 | 37.0 | 33.8 | 33.2 | 28.0 |
| 50,000 and over | 10.8 | 1.2 | 13.1 | 17.5 | 35.5 | .4 | .3 | .3 | .2 | .1 | .1 |
| 25,000 - 50,000 | 12.2 | 2.9 | 24.7 | 19.4 | 32.8 | .8 | .7 | .6 | .4 | .3 | .2 |
| 10,000 - 25,000 | 17.6 | 7.6 | 20.9 | 25.1 | 23.5 | 2.5 | 2.1 | 2.0 | 1.4 | 1.2 | .9 |
| 5,000 - 10,000 | 23.3 | 8.0 | 27.8 | 21.3 | 31.0 | 3.5 | 2.9 | 2.6 | 2.1 | 1.8 | 1.4 |
| 2,500 - 5,000 | 27.7 | 10.2 | 29.6 | 28.6 | 27.0 | 4.3 | 3.8 | 3.8 | 3.6 | 3.1 | 2.7 |
| 1,000 - 2,500 | 23.3 | 10.1 | 29,7 | 18.6 | 21.5 | 9.7 | 7.8 | 7.6 | 7.5 | 7.2 | 6.2 |
| Under 1,000 | 18.6 | 8.5 | 15.9 | 11.2 | 19.5 | 19.2 | 19.6 | 20.1 | 19.6 | 19.5 | 16.5 |
| Unincorporated area | 28.7 | 13.4 | 15.3 | 7.5 | 7.9 | | | | | | |

[a] Places classified by size as of beginning of decade.

TABLE 8. RATES OF POPULATION CHANGE IN INCORPORATED PLACES AND AVERAGE NUMBER OF INCORPORATED PLACES PER METROPOLITAN AREA, BY TYPE OF METROPOLITAN AREA, AND DISTANCE ZONE, 1900-1950

| *Type of metropolitan area and distance zone* | *Rate of Change* | | | | | *Average number of places per metropolitan area* | | | | | |
|---|---|---|---|---|---|---|---|---|---|---|---|
| | *1940-50* | *1930-40* | *1920-30* | *1910-20* | *1900-10* | *1950* | *1940* | *1930* | *1920* | *1910* | *1900* |
| Standard Metropolitan Areas | 19.4 | 6.0 | 30.6 | 26.7 | 36.5 | 17.9 | 15.5 | 16.0 | 14.7 | 13.4 | 10.2 |
| 0-5 miles | 7.6 | 2.7 | 20.4 | 25.4 | 31.4 | 1.8 | 1.5 | 1.6 | 1.4 | 1.4 | 1.1 |
| 5-10 " | 19.9 | 6.4 | 37.9 | 27.6 | 42.0 | 4.0 | 3.3 | 3.4 | 3.0 | 2.7 | 2.1 |
| 10-15 " | 24.8 | 5.4 | 26.7 | 26.8 | 36.5 | 4.1 | 3.5 | 3.6 | 3.3 | 2.9 | 2.3 |
| 15-20 " | 27.4 | 10.5 | 45.9 | 32.7 | 38.4 | 3.0 | 2.7 | 2.8 | 2.6 | 2.4 | 1.6 |
| 20-25 " | 14.3 | 8.4 | 32.1 | 26.3 | 41.5 | 1.9 | 1.7 | 1.7 | 1.6 | 1.5 | 1.1 |
| 25-30 " | 17.9 | 5.4 | 27.6 | 28.5 | 29.5 | 1.2 | 1.2 | 1.2 | 1.1 | 1.0 | .8 |
| 30-35 " | 27.6 | 4.4 | 26.3 | 22.6 | 30.2 | .7 | .6 | .6 | .6 | .6 | .5 |
| 35 miles and over | 16.1 | 4.1 | 16.0 | 11.7 | 28.2 | 1.2 | 1.0 | 1.1 | 1.1 | .9 | .7 |
| Extended Metropolitan Areas | 17.7 | 6.1 | 22.8 | 20.8 | 26.6 | 40.4 | 37.2 | 37.0 | 33.8 | 33.2 | 28.0 |
| 0-5 miles | 11.6 | 2.6 | 20.7 | 24.0 | 31.1 | 1.9 | 1.8 | 1.7 | 1.5 | 1.5 | 1.2 |
| 5-10 " | 19.5 | 6.5 | 36.4 | 26.8 | 38.4 | 4.4 | 4.0 | 3.8 | 3.2 | 3.0 | 2.4 |
| 10-15 " | 23.8 | 5.5 | 24.3 | 25.5 | 33.2 | 5.5 | 4.9 | 4.9 | 4.3 | 4.2 | 3.5 |
| 15-20 " | 21.6 | 9.4 | 30.5 | 23.8 | 25.0 | 5.8 | 5.5 | 5.4 | 4.9 | 4.7 | 3.9 |
| 20-25 " | 14.7 | 7.4 | 18.8 | 16.0 | 22.6 | 6.0 | 5.4 | 5.5 | 5.1 | 5.0 | 4.3 |
| 25-30 " | 14.6 | 7.0 | 14.1 | 16.1 | 20.3 | 5.9 | 5.4 | 5.4 | 5.1 | 5.1 | 4.3 |
| 30-35 " | 14.6 | 6.2 | 12.5 | 12.6 | 14.3 | 4.7 | 4.5 | 4.5 | 4.3 | 4.3 | 3.8 |
| 35 miles and over | 11.9 | 3.8 | 9.4 | 13.5 | 26.6 | 6.2 | 5.7 | 5.8 | 5.4 | 5.4 | 4.6 |

has been noted previously. It is also to be observed that maximum rates have been held, for the most part, within 20 miles of central cities. This inner portion of satellite area has contained in all census years at least 70 per cent of all incorporated places in Standard Metropolitan Areas, but less than 50 per cent in Extended Metropolitan Areas.

Figs. 8 and 9 describe growth rates for different sizes of places, by distance zone, for selected decades. Large increases of growth rates in unincorporated areas are apparent in all but the farthest distance zone. On the other hand, no clear trend of change in incorporated places of less than 1,000 population is observable. The gradient pattern of growth in this size class is clearly marked. With each increase in size above 1,000 population the tendency for growth rates to decline in later years becomes increasingly pronounced. In the largest size classes, 25,000 and over, while rates have been reduced, it also seems that high growth rates have shifted to more distant mile zones. In fact, in all sizes of incorporated places gradients have tended to flatten; that is, growth rates in outlying zones have approximated those in inner zones.

The data shown in Figs. 10 and 11, however, indicate that increases in growth rates, relative to central city rates, have occurred in all satellite places up to 5,000 population and in places of 10,000-25,000 population. In some of the largest satellites increases in relative rates have taken place in outlying distance zones. The largest changes occurred in the smallest places, and within 15 miles of central cities in most size classes of incorporated places. But the spread of metropolitan influence on the growth of satellite places is clearly revealed.

The effects of differential rates of change on the satellite composition of each distance zone are shown in Figs. 12 and 13. The proportion of the population in unincorporated area declined in every distance zone from 1900 through 1930. After that it increased, returning to its 1900 level only in the 0-5 mile zone. No doubt the post-1930 trends of increase in the unincorporated area beyond the 0-5 mile zone will continue in the decades after 1950. Incorporated places of less than 2,500 population in Standard Metropolitan areas contained a progressively smaller proportion of the population of each zone, the amount of the decline varying with distance from the central city. Satellite places of this size in Extended Metropolitan Areas, however, held a fairly constant share of the population of each zone. The proportion of the population contained in satellite places of the 2,500-10,000 class remained rather stable in the 0-5 mile zone but increased in all other zones. The largest changes have occurred in the proportion within satellites of 25,000 or more population particularly in outlying zones.

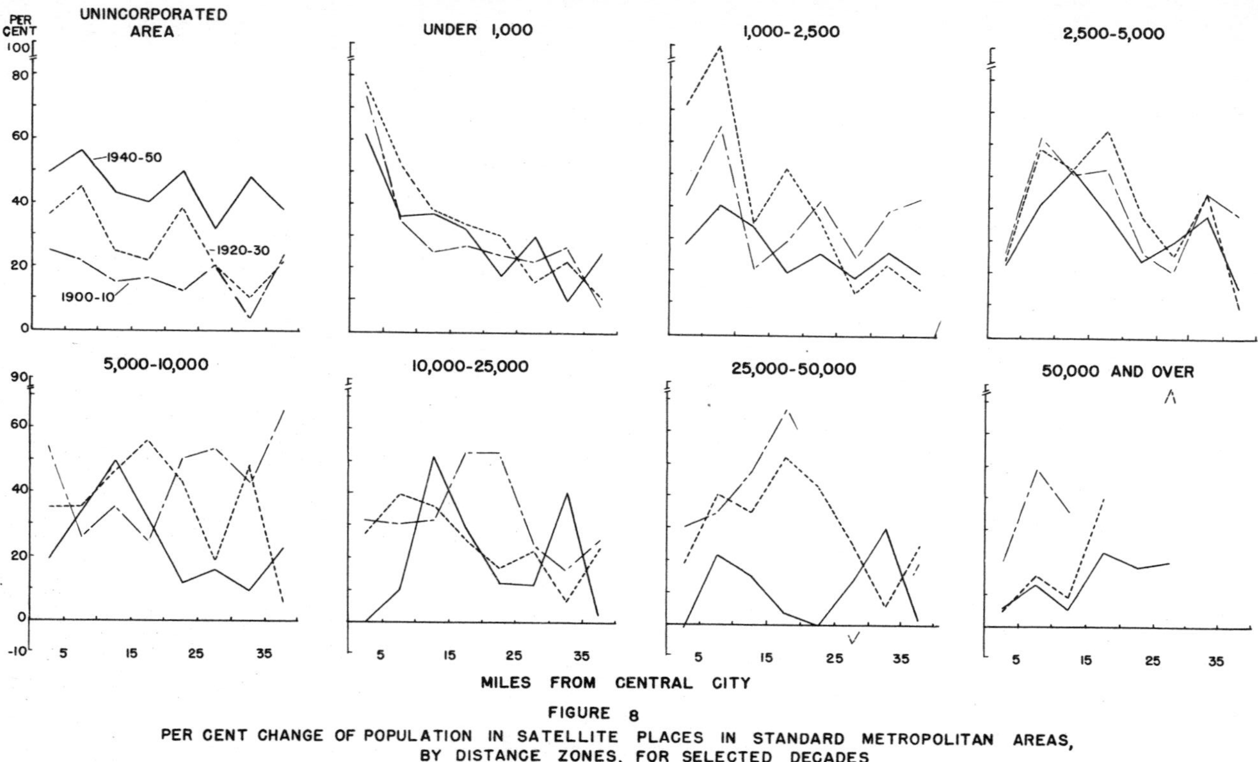


FIGURE 8

PER CENT CHANGE OF POPULATION IN SATELLITE PLACES IN STANDARD METROPOLITAN AREAS, BY DISTANCE ZONES, FOR SELECTED DECADES

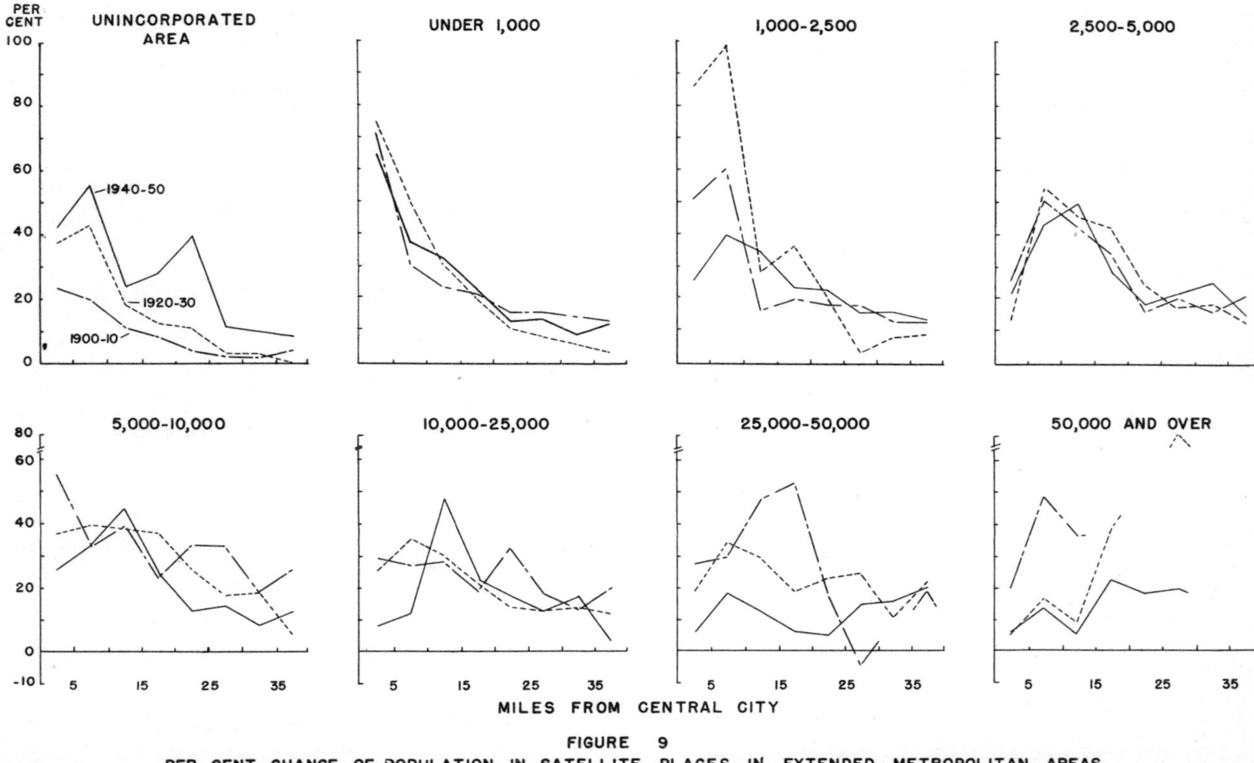


FIGURE 9

PER CENT CHANGE OF POPULATION IN SATELLITE PLACES IN EXTENDED METROPOLITAN AREAS, BY DISTANCE ZONES, FOR SELECTED DECADES

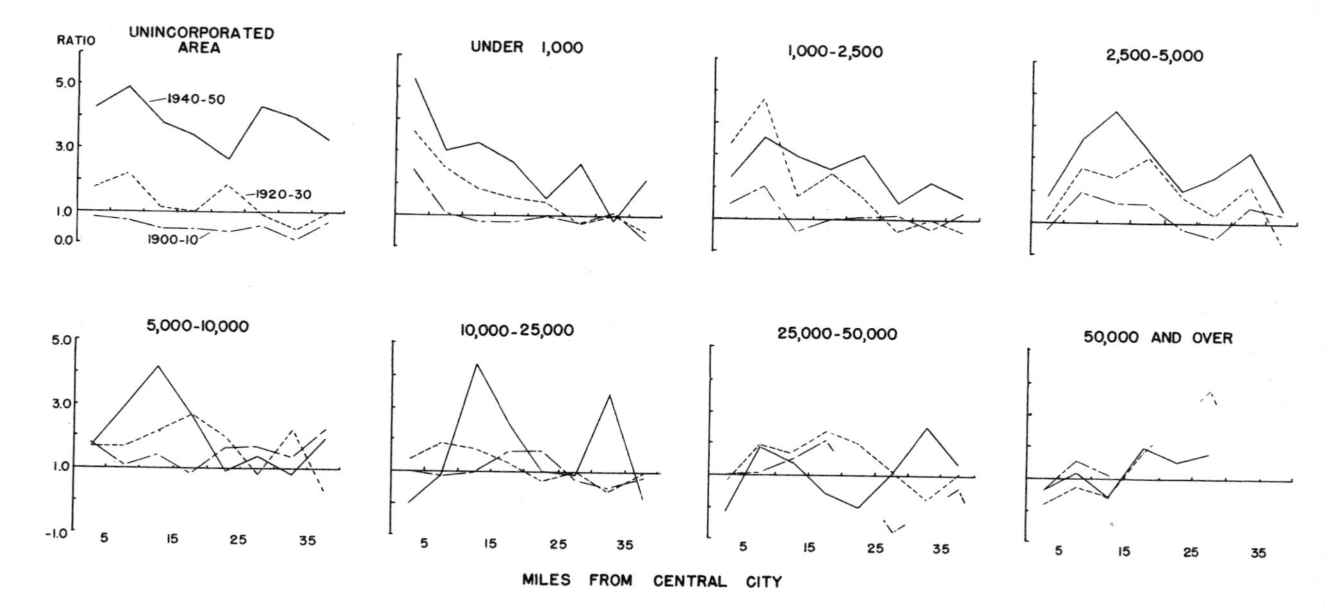


FIGURE 10
RATIO OF RATE OF CHANGE IN SATELLITE PLACES TO RATE OF CHANGE IN CENTRAL CITIES IN STANDARD METROPOLITAN AREAS, BY DISTANCE ZONES, FOR SELECTED DECADES

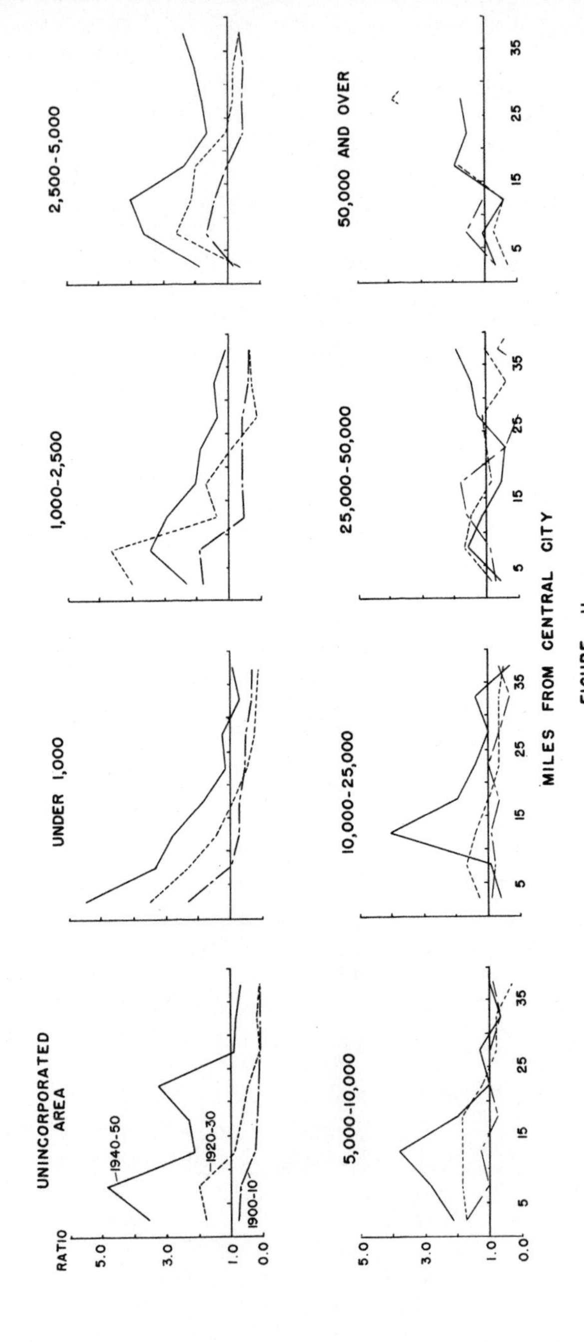


FIGURE 11

RATIO OF RATE OF CHANGE IN SATELLITE PLACES TO RATE OF CHANGE IN CENTRAL CITIES IN EXTENDED METROPOLITAN AREAS, BY DISTANCE ZONES, FOR SELECTED DECADES

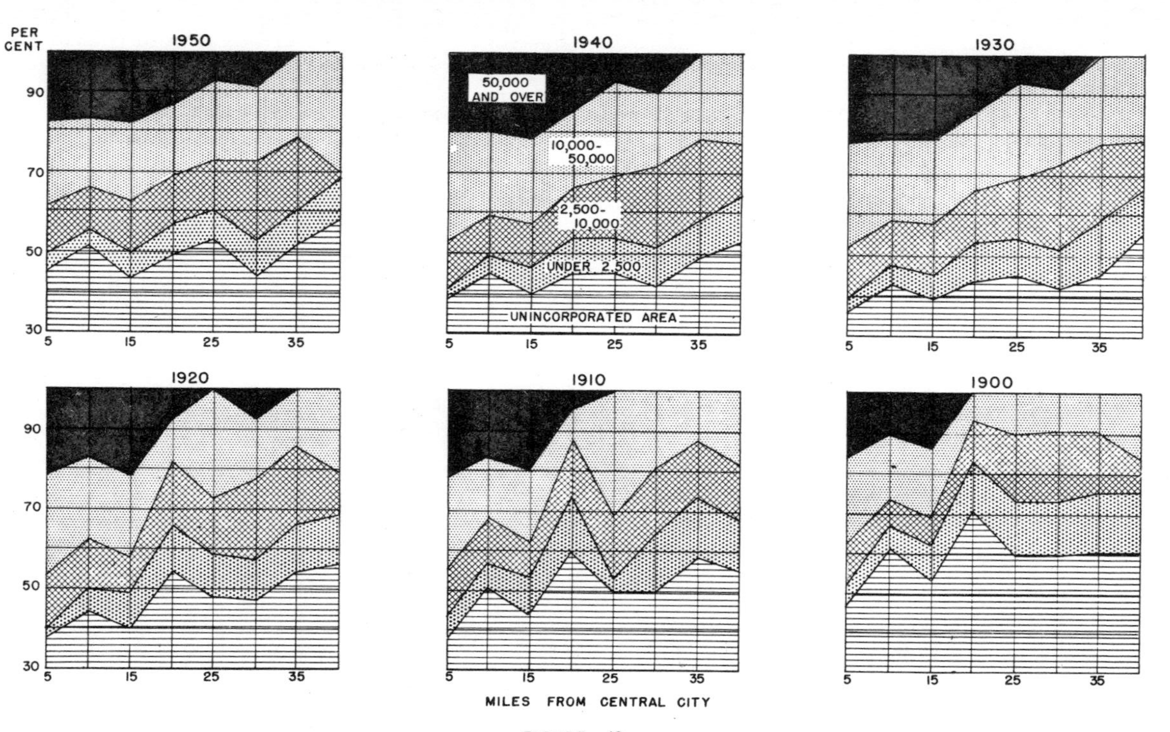


FIGURE 12

PER CENT DISTRIBUTION OF POPULATION IN DISTANCE ZONES OF STANDARD METROPOLITAN AREAS, BY SIZE AND TYPE OF SATELLITE PLACE, 1900-1950

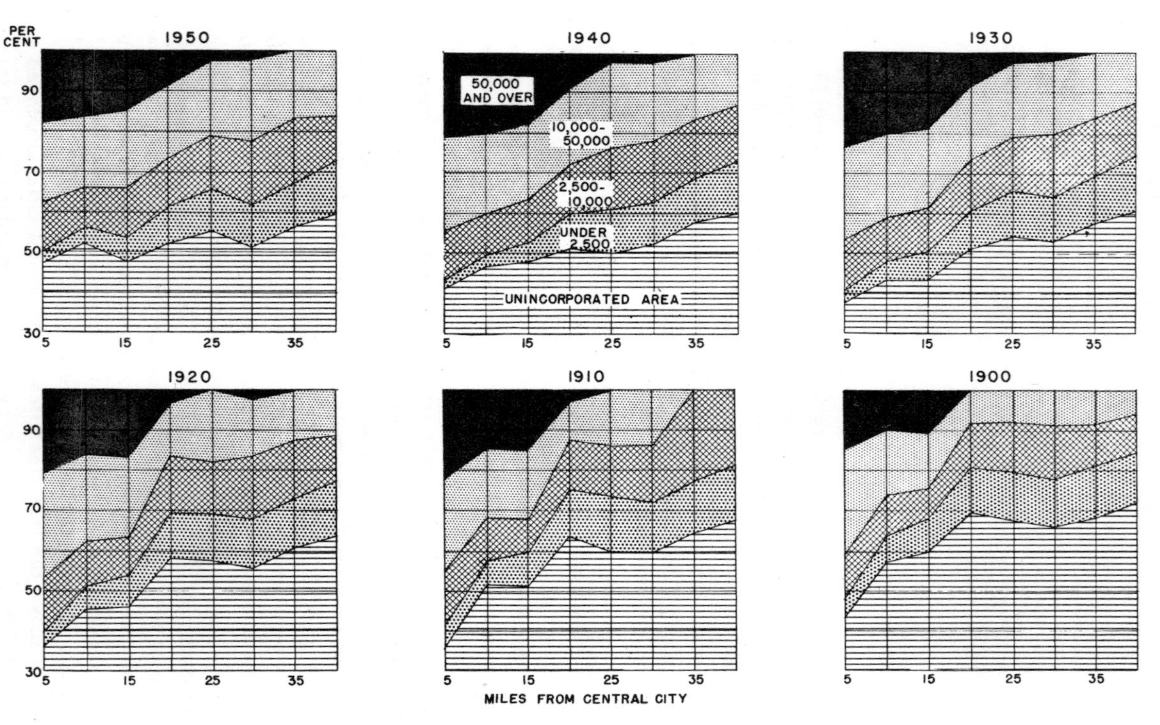


FIGURE 13

PER CENT DISTRIBUTION OF POPULATION IN DISTANCE ZONES OF EXTENDED METROPOLITAN AREAS, BY SIZE AND TYPE OF SATELLITE PLACE, 1900-1950

CHAPTER III

# SIZE OF CENTRAL CITY AND POPULATION REDISTRIBUTION

It was pointed out in the preceding chapter that rapid growth is associated with a concentration tendency. A small area, for example, is perhaps a newly emergent metropolitan area and therefore may be in a rapid growth phase. On the other hand, a large area, having attained a greater maturity, may be near the completion of its growth cycle. Maturity may mean, among other things, the development of a high population density in the inner zones, an effect of which may be to encourage an acceleration of growth in the outlying parts of the area. Maturity may also mean, however, a more fully developed transportation system and a more ramified network of intra-area relationships. Thus there is the further probability that the larger the area the greater is its scope of influence as reflected in a centrifugal movement of population. Thus a direct relationship between population redistribution and size of metropolitan area may be inferred from two different sets of assumptions. The present chapter is concerned with exploring this hypothesis.

The population size of a metropolitan area may be represented either by the size of its central city population or by the size of the total population of the area. But while the ratio of the one measure of size to the other varies considerably in comparisons of individual areas, a classification based on one measure of size produces a distribution which differs in only a few respects from that obtained by the use of the other. Hence either measure may be used without appreciably altering the results. Because many of the characteristics of metropolitan areas later to be analyzed are also characteristics of central cities it seems advisable, in the interest of consistency, to employ size of central city as the basis for a size classification of metropolitan areas.

Table 9 shows the size classification of central cities employed and the number of areas in each class, by decades. In order to obtain true measures of change for each decade metropolitan areas are reclassified

for each inter-censal interval on the basis of size of central city at the beginning of the respective decade. The "under 100,000" class merits special comment. This includes all metropolitan areas with central cities of less than 100,000, even though many such cities in census years prior to 1940 were too small to have qualified as central cities of metropolitan areas, i.e., less than 50,000 population. Since this report is concerned with the growth history of all places classified as metropolitan in 1950, these areas are included.

TABLE 9. NUMBER OF METROPOLITAN AREAS IN STUDY, BY SIZE OF CENTRAL CITY, AND BY DECADE, 1900 - 1950

| *Size of central city* | *1940-1950* | *1930-1940* | *1920-1930* | *1910-1920* | *1900-1910* |
|---|---|---|---|---|---|
| Total | 143 | 157 | 155 | 153 | 148 |
| 1,000,000 and over | 5 | 5 | 4 | 3 | 3 |
| 500,000 - 1,000,000 | 10 | 10 | 8 | 6 | 3 |
| 250,000 - 500,000 | 11 | 15 | 7 | 8 | 11 |
| 100,000 - 250,000 | 41 | 41 | 37 | 24 | 15 |
| Under 100,000 | 76 | 86 | 99 | 112 | 116 |

### Central Cities and Satellite Areas

In Table 10 it is evident that there is no clear relationship between size of central city and rate of population change in metropolitan areas. High rates prevailed in the largest, the middle-sized, and the smallest areas, while the two intervening size classes grew at comparatively low rates. The 250,000-500,000 class alternates with the 1,000,000 and over class as the most rapidly growing class of metropolitan areas.

A more consistent variation with size appears in the rates of change of parts of areas. The rates of population change in central cities tend to vary inversely with size, though the 1,000,000 and over and the 250,000-500,000 classes, particularly the former, are exceptions to this generalization. Conversely, growth rates in satellite areas vary directly with size of central city. The principal exception in this instance is the 250,000-500,000 class. Especially noteworthy are the high rates of growth in both central cities and satellite areas of that class in the 1930-40 decade. But much of the exceptional character of the middle-sized class seems to disappear when the boundaries of Extended rather

Table 10. Per Cent Change of Population, by Size of Central City, Distance Zone, Type of Metropolitan Area, and Decade, 1900-1950

| Size of central city and distance zone | Standard Metropolitan Areas | | | | | Extended Metropolitan Areas | | | | |
|---|---|---|---|---|---|---|---|---|---|---|
| | 1940-1950 | 1930-1940 | 1920-1930 | 1910-1920 | 1900-1910 | 1940-1950 | 1930-1940 | 1920-1930 | 1910-1920 | 1900-1910 |
| 1,000,000 and over | 18.0 | 7.8 | 30.0 | 22.0 | 33.5 | 18.3 | 8.1 | 29.9 | 21.6 | 33.3 |
| Central cities | 9.4 | 5.6 | 24.0 | 19.3 | 32.2 | 9.4 | 5.6 | 24.0 | 19.3 | 32.2 |
| Satellite area | 33.0 | 11.8 | 43.8 | 28.5 | 36.7 | 33.2 | 12.5 | 42.6 | 26.9 | 35.8 |
| 0-5 miles | 3.2 | -1.0 | 11.4 | 21.4 | 39.0 | 3.2 | -1.0 | 11.4 | 21.4 | 39.0 |
| 5-10 miles | 28.6 | 10.8 | 55.5 | 37.2 | 46.6 | 28.6 | 10.8 | 55.5 | 37.2 | 46.6 |
| 10-15 miles | 34.8 | 9.9 | 36.6 | 29.1 | 39.8 | 34.8 | 9.9 | 36.6 | 29.1 | 39.8 |
| 15-20 miles | 40.7 | 17.8 | 68.9 | 38.8 | 48.0 | 40.7 | 17.8 | 68.9 | 38.8 | 48.0 |
| 20-25 miles | 41.2 | 17.1 | 67.3 | 29.0 | 38.7 | 41.4 | 17.1 | 67.3 | 29.0 | 38.7 |
| 25-30 miles | 32.8 | 13.0 | 41.4 | 29.2 | 36.3 | 35.4 | 13.1 | 40.8 | 27.8 | 34.2 |
| 30-35 miles | 43.8 | 13.9 | 26.9 | 26.0 | 18.3 | 44.5 | 14.1 | 27.8 | 24.0 | 19.4 |
| 35 miles and over | 26.9 | 10.6 | 26.6 | 8.2 | 15.5 | 27.9 | 10.8 | 23.9 | 5.9 | 17.8 |
| 500,000 - 1,000,000 | 20.9 | 4.9 | 20.3 | 20.3 | 20.5 | 20.0 | 4.9 | 19.1 | 18.7 | 18.9 |
| Central cities | 8.9 | 1.0 | 11.4 | 19.8 | 16.5 | 8.9 | 1.0 | 11.4 | 19.8 | 16.5 |
| Satellite area | 36.2 | 10.1 | 32.9 | 21.0 | 26.5 | 32.0 | 9.4 | 28.5 | 17.5 | 22.1 |
| 0-5 miles | 10.4 | 2.2 | 19.4 | 24.2 | 29.0 | 10.4 | 2.2 | 19.4 | 24.2 | 29.0 |
| 5-10 miles | 41.6 | 11.8 | 51.0 | 22.5 | 37.8 | 41.7 | 11.7 | 50.9 | 22.4 | 37.5 |
| 10-15 miles | 51.7 | 14.6 | 35.2 | 15.2 | 19.7 | 51.6 | 14.8 | 34.6 | 14.8 | 18.8 |
| 15-20 miles | 35.8 | 11.2 | 30.2 | 27.8 | 16.9 | 33.9 | 11.4 | 27.8 | 22.9 | 15.1 |
| 20-25 miles | 31.5 | 10.8 | 11.7 | 20.9 | 4.3 | 28.1 | 10.7 | 9.4 | 15.0 | -4.2 |
| 25-30 miles | 20.4 | 6.6 | 17.6 | 19.9 | -3.5 | 16.7 | 5.7 | 11.1 | 10.8 | -27.1 |
| 30-35 miles | 31.8 | 2.3 | 4.1 | 3.8 | 21.9 | 14.0 | 2.8 | 5.3 | 8.4 | 5.0 |
| 35 miles and over | 33.2 | 6.4 | 11.7 | 5.1 | 8.2 | 5.1 | 3.9 | 5.1 | 4.8 | -0.3 |
| 250,000 - 500,000 | 23.4 | 13.2 | 23.3 | 34.9 | 31.8 | 20.0 | 11.2 | 19.5 | 31.0 | 28.1 |
| Central cities | 17.7 | 9.3 | 16.8 | 34.2 | 29.0 | 17.7 | 9.3 | 16.7 | 34.2 | 29.0 |
| Satellite area | 34.3 | 22.7 | 50.8 | 36.8 | 37.9 | 22.2 | 13.5 | 24.8 | 25.2 | 27.0 |
| 0-5 miles | 21.7 | 11.1 | 47.2 | 73.2 | 39.5 | 22.0 | 11.1 | 47.2 | 73.2 | 39.5 |
| 5-10 miles | 48.0 | 29.2 | 72.2 | 36.7 | 60.0 | 49.9 | 29.1 | 72.0 | 36.6 | 59.5 |
| 10-15 miles | 24.1 | 26.4 | 39.2 | 39.4 | 26.1 | 23.5 | 22.1 | 32.5 | 34.1 | 23.5 |
| 15-20 miles | 42.8 | 14.2 | 11.7 | 26.9 | 34.3 | 27.3 | 8.9 | 12.3 | 19.8 | 24.6 |
| 20-25 miles | 31.1 | 35.1 | 12.6 | 35.1 | 30.6 | 12.8 | 9.0 | 2.8 | 20.8 | 18.2 |
| 25-30 miles | 9.5 | 14.7 | -1.0 | 0.4 | 27.1 | 8.2 | 6.1 | 1.8 | 1.1 | 17.0 |
| 30-35 miles | ---- | 12.2 | -4.4 | 5.8 | 16.7 | 7.7 | 5.0 | -0.3 | -3.7 | 11.6 |
| 35 miles and over | ---- | ---- | ---- | 5.5 | 3.5 | 3.0 | 3.2 | 0.3 | 0.1 | 23.5 |
| 100,000 - 250,000 | 19.9 | 5.9 | 21.5 | 20.0 | 22.5 | 16.9 | 5.2 | 15.7 | 13.5 | 14.2 |
| Central cities | 12.7 | 2.7 | 20.6 | 22.4 | 24.1 | 12.7 | 2.7 | 20.6 | 22.4 | 24.1 |
| Satellite area | 30.8 | 11.1 | 23.2 | 15.4 | 19.1 | 19.8 | 7.0 | 11.9 | 7.2 | 7.7 |
| 0-5 miles | 39.4 | 14.4 | 31.9 | 27.6 | 27.0 | 39.4 | 14.4 | 32.2 | 27.8 | 26.9 |
| 5-10 miles | 38.8 | 15.2 | 30.1 | 17.1 | 22.2 | 37.9 | 14.6 | 29.1 | 17.0 | 20.5 |
| 10-15 miles | 23.7 | 5.8 | 10.4 | 11.2 | 13.9 | 23.3 | 6.6 | 9.2 | 8.3 | 9.7 |
| 15-20 miles | 15.9 | 11.9 | 19.2 | 3.5 | 2.1 | 16.9 | 7.1 | 11.3 | 2.4 | 4.9 |
| 20-25 miles | 9.5 | 3.7 | 22.7 | -5.1 | -3.8 | 11.2 | -6.4 | 4.4 | 3.4 | 3.0 |
| 25-30 miles | 7.8 | -0.5 | 1.0 | -4.4 | -2.9 | 7.9 | 6.3 | 2.6 | 0.1 | -0.8 |
| 30-35 miles | 9.2 | 2.9 | 1.4 | -2.5 | -12.0 | 6.7 | 3.6 | 5.2 | 5.4 | 3.6 |
| 35 miles and over | -7.3 | -0.4 | -2.9 | -1.9 | -9.3 | -1.3 | 0.2 | -1.5 | -1.7 | -1.7 |
| Under 100,000 | 20.7 | 10.8 | 24.2 | 28.0 | 28.7 | 14.6 | 8.6 | 15.2 | 17.0 | 16.6 |
| Central cities | 18.1 | 8.2 | 29.2 | 38.5 | 42.0 | 18.1 | 8.2 | 29.2 | 38.5 | 42.0 |
| Satellite area | 23.3 | 13.8 | 18.6 | 17.2 | 17.2 | 13.2 | 8.8 | 9.6 | 9.4 | 9.3 |
| 0-5 miles | 29.9 | 19.2 | 29.9 | 28.3 | 22.7 | 30.6 | 19.2 | 30.2 | 28.4 | 22.6 |
| 5-10 miles | 29.1 | 17.3 | 23.9 | 16.7 | 14.1 | 27.3 | 15.8 | 21.9 | 15.5 | 13.7 |
| 10-15 miles | 19.5 | 11.4 | 15.3 | 15.0 | 18.2 | 16.8 | 9.3 | 11.7 | 11.9 | 13.3 |
| 15-20 miles | 13.6 | 6.2 | 7.4 | 12.4 | 11.5 | 9.3 | 6.1 | 6.9 | 7.3 | 8.0 |
| 20-25 miles | 10.6 | 8.7 | 18.2 | 10.7 | 13.3 | 8.2 | 7.4 | 7.0 | 4.5 | 7.4 |
| 25-30 miles | -0.3 | 6.3 | 9.6 | 14.6 | 12.5 | 6.1 | 6.8 | 4.4 | 6.8 | 6.7 |
| 30-35 miles | -4.6 | 9.2 | -5.2 | -1.6 | -0.2 | 4.6 | 5.2 | 5.1 | 5.5 | 4.4 |
| 35 miles and over | 57.1 | 11.0 | 0.1 | 14.7 | 80.1 | 5.7 | 3.6 | 1.8 | 6.0 | 6.9 |

than Standard Metropolitan Areas are used. It is possible that the definition of the Standard Metropolitan Area is more selective of rapidly growing places in the 250,000-500,000 class than in the other four size classes.

When the 50-year trends of growth rates in metropolitan areas are analyzed, it is apparent that there are certain differentials in the general tendency to decline that was noted in the preceding chapter. Growth rates in areas with central cities of 1,000,000 population or more declined by almost half from 1900 to 1950, though the trend was irregular. No appreciable difference exists between Standard and Extended Metropolitan Areas in this respect. But in the former, areas with central cities of 500,000-1,000,000 population maintained a relatively constant growth rate, if the 1930-40 decade may be treated as an unrepresentative period, on the other hand, in the Extended Metropolitan Areas of the same size class, a trend toward increasing rates of growth is observable. In the third size class, 250,000-500,000 population, growth rates in both types of metropolitan areas increased in the second decade of the 50-year period after which they dropped by about 33 per cent. No trend of change is evident after 1920. The pattern of changes in growth rates in the 100,000-250,000 size class of Standard Metropolitan Areas is very similar to that in the largest size class. The trend for this same size class of Extended Metropolitan Areas, however, was in the direction of increasing rates of growth. And in the smallest size class growth rates declined through the period, though by a greater extent in Standard than in Extended Metropolitan Areas.

All sizes of central cities experienced declining rates of growth. The greatest amounts of reduction occurred in the largest and in the smallest central cities. The least reduction of growth rate over the 50-year period occurred in central cities of 250,000-500,000 population. It was also in this size class that the retardation of growth of the 1930-40 decade was least.

Growth rate trends in satellite areas display no consistent pattern. In metropolitan areas with central cities of 1,000,000 population and over, and in those of 250,000-500,000 the tendency was toward reduction, though the peak rates of growth took place in 1920-30. All other size classes show rising growth rates in satellite areas, with somewhat larger increases in those of the Extended Metropolitan Areas.

The rates of change in each distance zone, shown in Table 10, reveal several kinds of variation with size of central city. In the largest size classes rates of increase have declined steadily in the innermost zones. The zone of decline extends out to 10 miles from centers in the 1,000,000 and over areas, but to only 5 miles in areas with central cities of 250,000 to 1,000,000 population. Areas with central cities below 250,000 population, however, had trends of increase in rates of change within the 0-5 mile

and adjacent zones. A second characteristic is that the larger the size of central city the more extensive is the area over which growth rates were equal to or in excess of the average growth of satellite areas. For the largest size class that included all area within 30 miles, in 1900-10, and most of the satellite territory beyond 10 miles of central cities after 1930. In the 500,000-1,000,000 metropolitan areas the average growth was exceeded within a lengthening radius, beginning at 10 miles, in 1900-10, and embracing more distant zones in succeeding decades. A similar change took place in the 250,000-500,000 with the difference that at no time did the zone of greater than average growth reach beyond 30 miles of the central city. In the next smaller size class that radius changed from 10 miles at the beginning of the period to 20 miles at the end, while in metropolitan areas of the under 100,000 class the radius moved from 5 miles or less to 15 miles.

The small, and frequently negative, rates of change in the more remote distance zones, especially in the smaller areas, suggest that in the formative stages of metropolitan development central cities and inner zones grew at the expense in part at least, of their outlying zones. Apparently only in areas with central cities greater than 500,000, and there only since 1930, has growth occurred without loss to distance zones near metropolitan peripheries.

That the differences in growth rates in different size classes of metropolitan areas may be due partly to variations in densities of population is indicated by Table 11. The variation of density with size, both in central cities and in each distance zone, is close, much closer in fact than in the relationship between rate of change and size. The linear correlation coefficient for density (1940) and rate of change (1940-50) in Standard Metropolitan Areas is -.358, and in Extended Metropolitan Areas -.240. Although these values reveal the type of relationships expected, they are not high. Variations in density do not account for more than 13 per cent of the variations in rate of change. Most of the variation, therefore, is a function of other factors.

A comparison of rates of change in parts of metropolitan areas with rates of change in the total population of the nation casts further light on size variations. According to Table 12 there is no clear relationship between the ratios and sizes of areas, though there is some evidence of a direct association in the satellite areas. Growth seems to have favored first one size class of metropolitan areas and then another in different decades. Thus the highest relative rates of change in 1,000,000 and over areas occurred in 1920-30; the 500,000-1,000,000 areas attained their peak growth, relative to that of the nation, in 1940-50, as did also the 100,000-250,000 class of areas; while the remaining two classes of areas had their

TABLE 11. POPULATION PER SQUARE MILE IN METROPOLITAN AREAS, BY SIZE OF CENTRAL CITY, AND DISTANCE ZONE, 1940

| *Type of metropolitan area* | *Total* | *Central cities* | *Distance from central city* 0-5 | 5-10 | 10-15 | 15-20 | 20-25 | 25-30 | 30-35 | 35 and over | All satellite areas |
|---|---|---|---|---|---|---|---|---|---|---|---|
| Standard Metropolitan Areas | | | | | | | | | | | |
| 1,000,000 and over | 1,359 | 13,846 | 11,143 | 3,915 | 1,977 | 841 | 458 | 289 | 186 | 100 | 530 |
| 500,000 - 1,000,000 | 732 | 11,397 | 4,552 | 1,133 | 365 | 259 | 778 | 107 | 97 | 46 | 342 |
| 250,000 - 500,000 | 619 | 6,198 | 1,736 | 369 | 142 | 65 | 59 | 29 | — | 4 | 205 |
| 100,000 - 250,000 | 249 | 5,422 | 555 | 184 | 179 | 55 | 34 | 29 | 25 | 17 | 103 |
| Under 100,000 | 134 | 4,882 | 341 | 105 | 58 | 43 | 27 | 47 | 14 | 18 | 65 |
| Extended Metropolitan Areas | | | | | | | | | | | |
| 1,000,000 and over | 1,172 | 13,846 | 11,143 | 3,915 | 1,977 | 841 | 458 | 297 | 194 | 94 | 463 |
| 500,000 - 1,000,000 | 460 | 11,397 | 4,552 | 1,087 | 319 | 207 | 129 | 95 | 80 | 61 | 229 |
| 250,000 - 500,000 | 195 | 6,198 | 1,454 | 346 | 115 | 64 | 64 | 57 | 64 | 49 | 94 |
| 100,000 - 250,000 | 123 | 5,422 | 555 | 175 | 108 | 69 | 59 | 49 | 59 | 30 | 73 |
| Under 100,000 | 64 | 4,882 | 290 | 89 | 48 | 42 | 34 | 39 | 34 | 28 | 44 |

TABLE 12. RATIO OF RATE OF POPULATION CHANGE IN METROPOLITAN AREAS TO RATE OF CHANGE OF TOTAL UNITED STATES POPULATION, BY TYPE OF PLACE, SIZE OF CENTRAL CITY, TYPE OF METROPOLITAN AREA, AND DECADE, 1900-1950

| *Type of place and size of central city* | *Standard Metropolitan Areas* | | | | | *Extended Metropolitan Areas* | | | | |
|---|---|---|---|---|---|---|---|---|---|---|
| | *1940-50* | *1930-40* | *1920-30* | *1910-20* | *1900-10* | *1940-50* | *1930-50* | *1920-30* | *1910-20* | *1900-10* |
| Total area | | | | | | | | | | |
| 1,000,000 and over | 1.24 | 1.08 | 1.86 | 1.48 | 1.60 | 1.26 | 1.13 | 1.86 | 1.45 | 1.59 |
| 500,000 - 1,000,000 | 1.44 | .68 | 1.26 | 1.36 | .98 | 1.38 | .68 | 1.19 | 1.26 | .90 |
| 250,000 - 500,000 | 1.61 | 1.83 | 1.45 | 2.32 | 1.51 | 1.38 | 1.56 | 1.21 | 2.08 | 1.34 |
| 100,000 - 250,000 | 1.37 | .82 | 1.34 | 1.34 | 1.07 | 1.17 | .72 | .98 | .91 | .68 |
| Under 100,000 | 1.43 | 1.50 | 1.50 | 1.88 | 1.37 | 1.01 | 1.19 | .94 | 1.14 | .79 |
| Central cities | | | | | | | | | | |
| 1,000,000 and over | .65 | .78 | 1.49 | 1.30 | 1.53 | .65 | .78 | 1.49 | 1.30 | 1.53 |
| 500,000 - 1,000,000 | .61 | .14 | .71 | 1.33 | .79 | .61 | .14 | .71 | 1.33 | .79 |
| 250,000 - 500,000 | 1.22 | 1.29 | 1.04 | 2.30 | 1.38 | 1.22 | 1.29 | 1.04 | 2.30 | 1.38 |
| 100,000 - 250,000 | .88 | .38 | 1.28 | 1.50 | 1.15 | .88 | .38 | 1.28 | 1.50 | 1.15 |
| Under 100,000 | 1.25 | 1.14 | 1.81 | 2.58 | 2.00 | 1.25 | 1.14 | 1.81 | 2.58 | 2.00 |
| Satellite areas | | | | | | | | | | |
| 1,000,000 and over | 2.28 | 1.64 | 2.72 | 1.91 | 1.75 | 2.29 | 1.74 | 2.65 | 1.81 | 1.70 |
| 500,000 - 1,000,000 | 2.50 | 1.40 | 2.04 | 1.41 | 1.26 | 2.21 | 1.31 | 1.77 | 1.17 | 1.05 |
| 250,000 - 500,000 | 2.37 | 3.15 | 3.16 | 2.47 | 1.80 | 1.53 | 1.88 | 1.54 | 1.69 | 1.29 |
| 100,000 - 250,000 | 2.12 | 1.54 | 1.44 | 1.03 | .91 | 1.37 | .97 | .74 | .48 | .37 |
| Under 100,000 | 1.61 | 1.92 | 1.16 | 1.15 | .82 | .91 | 1.22 | .60 | .63 | .44 |

highest ratios in the 1910-20 decade. All sizes of central cities had reached their highest relative growth rates by 1920, their ratios declining rapidly after that date. The ratios for satellite areas increased over the period, and for most of the areas the highest ratios occurred in the last 10-year interval. Both the largest and the middle-sized areas, however, maintained high ratios for satellite areas throughout the period. It is of interest to note that not until after 1930 did growth rates in the satellite areas of the two smallest classes of Extended Metropolitan Areas rise a above the national average.

Differentials in the centrifugal movement of population are described in detail in Figs. 14 and 15. The metropolitan areas with central cities of 1,000,000 or more population have maintained higher than average growth rates over most of their satellite areas throughout the 50-year period. Low ratios are found in the extreme distance zones in the first two decades, and ratios in the innermost zones dropped below unity after 1920. The progressive spread of higher than average growth rates over satellite areas is more clearly apparent in the 500,000 to 1,000,000 size class. In the next smaller size class that trend of change is observable only at the centers and the extremities of metropolitan areas: central city ratios declined while ratios in the zones beyond 25 miles showed some tendency to increase. The patterns of centrifugal change are similar in the two smallest size classes, though the area over which higher than average rates prevailed is greater by 5 miles in the larger of the two classes of areas. In general, the larger the size of central city the more extensive has been the area over which growth rates exceeded the decennial rate of the total population of the nation.

The ratio of satellite growth rates to central city rates provides, however, a better measure of centrifugal movement of population. Measured on this basis the rate of deconcentration appears to vary rather closely with size of central city in all decades but 1930-40, as may be seen in Table 13. Correspondingly, deconcentration has tended to accelerate in successive decades, with the 1930-40 decade off-setting the trend. There is also a noticeable tendency for the rates of deconcentration to have increased by larger amounts, over the five decades, in small than in large metropolitan areas. This is most apparent in Extended Metropolitan Areas.

Figs. 16 and 17, in which the ratios of distance zone rates to central city rates are presented, reveal that in metropolitan areas with central cities of over 1,000,000 the gradient aspect of deconcentration, such as is apparent in all other classes of areas, is lacking. Although the ratios have increased in successive decades, there are but slight variations among distance zones. The exceptional growth of satellite relative to central city population in the

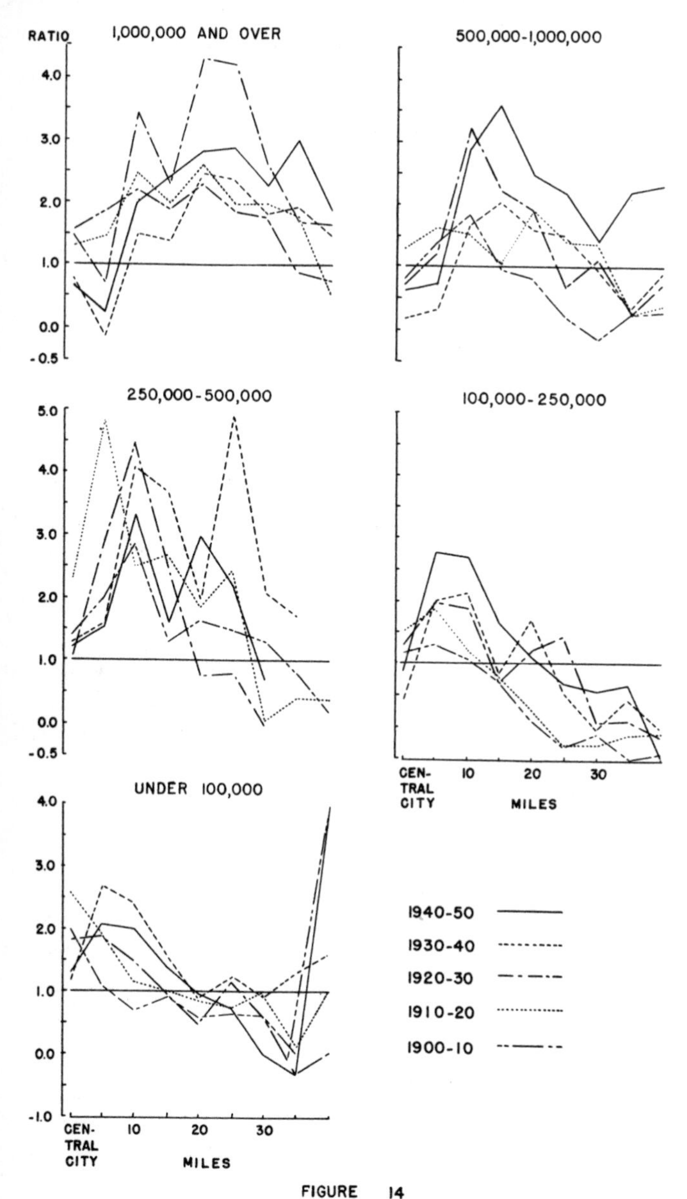


FIGURE 14

RATIO OF RATE OF POPULATION CHANGE IN STANDARD METROPOLITAN AREAS TO RATE OF CHANGE OF TOTAL UNITED STATES POPULATION, BY SIZE OF CENTRAL CITY AND BY DISTANCE ZONE, 1900-1950

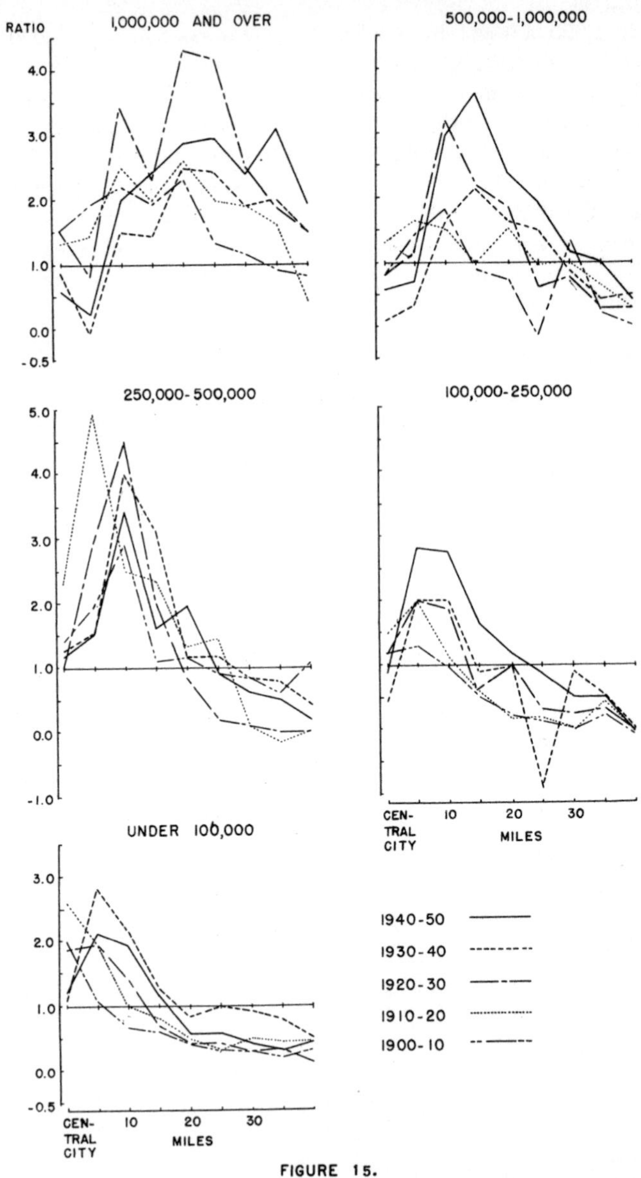


FIGURE 15.

RATIO OF RATE OF POPULATION CHANGE IN EXTENDED METROPOLITAN AREAS TO RATE OF CHANGE OF TOTAL UNITED STATES POPULATION, BY SIZE OF CENTRAL CITY AND BY DISTANCE ZONE, 1900-1950

500,000-1,000,000 and the 100,000-250,000 areas during the 1930-40 decade results from a defect of the ratio rather than from unusually high satellite growth rates. As the central city growth rate approaches zero the ratios assume increasingly larger values. It was shown in Table 10 that the 1930-40 rate for central cities of 500,000-1,000,000 was only 1.0 per cent, and the rate for central cities of 100,000-250,000 was 2.7 per cent. Actually the 1930-40 satellite growth rates in these two classes of metropolitan areas were slightly below those for other size classes. Thus a high ratio may be due to a failure of central city growth as well as to a relatively high rate of satellite growth.

TABLE 13. RATIO OF RATE OF CHANGE IN SATELLITE AREAS TO RATE OF CHANGE IN CENTRAL CITIES, BY TYPE OF METROPOLITAN AREA, SIZE OF CENTRAL CITY, AND DECADE, 1900-1950

| *Metropolitan area and size of central city* | *1940-50* | *1930-40* | *1920-30* | *1910-20* | *1900-10* |
|---|---|---|---|---|---|
| Standard Metropolitan Areas | 2.68 | 2.47 | 1.45 | .86 | .83 |
| 1,000,000 and over | 3.51 | 2.11 | 1.83 | 1.48 | 1.14 |
| 500,000 - 1,000,000 | 4.07 | 10.10 | 2.89 | 1.06 | 1.61 |
| 250,000 - 500,000 | 1.94 | 2.44 | 3.02 | 1.08 | 1.31 |
| 100,000 - 250,000 | 2.43 | 4.11 | 1.13 | .69 | .79 |
| Under 100,000 | 1.29 | 1.68 | .64 | .45 | .41 |
| Extended Metropolitan Areas | 1.97 | 1.90 | .88 | .51 | .47 |
| 1,000,000 and over | 3.53 | 2.23 | 1.78 | 1.39 | 1.11 |
| 500,000 - 1,000,000 | 3.60 | 9.40 | 2.50 | .88 | 1.34 |
| 250,000 - 500,000 | 1.25 | 1.45 | 1.49 | .74 | .93 |
| 100,000 - 250,000 | 1.56 | 2.59 | .58 | .32 | .32 |
| Under 100,000 | .73 | 1.07 | .33 | .24 | .22 |

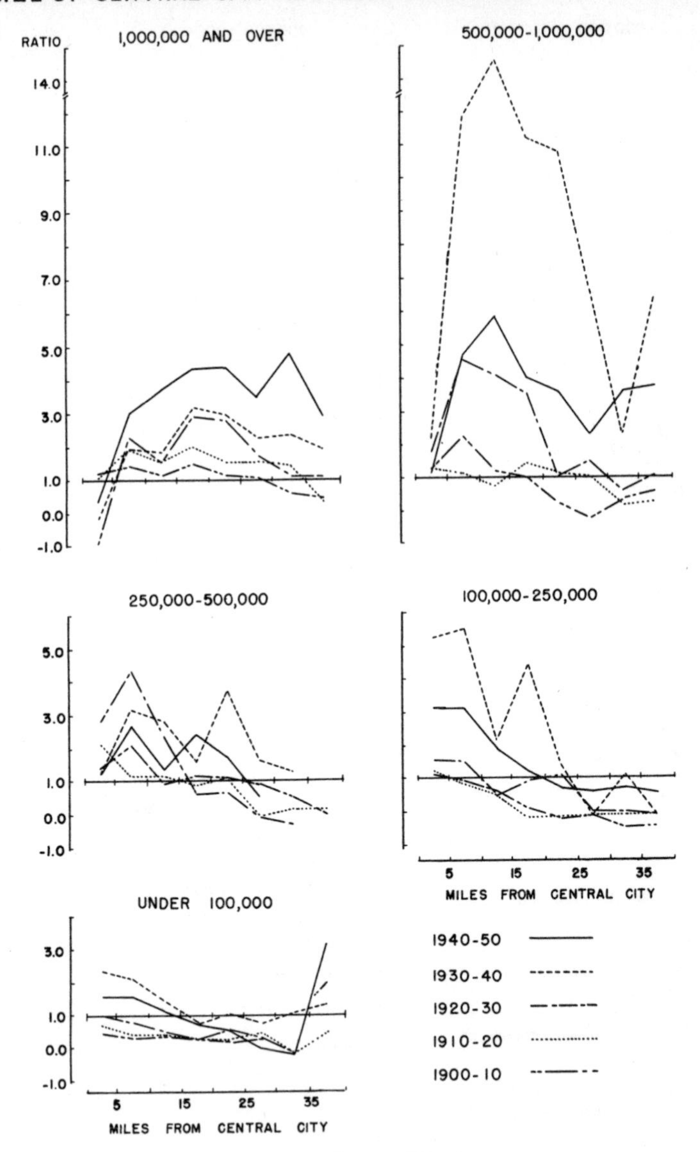


FIGURE 16
RATIO OF RATE OF POPULATION CHANGE IN SATELLITE AREA OF STANDARD METROPOLITAN AREAS TO RATE OF CHANGE IN CENTRAL CITY, BY SIZE OF CENTRAL CITY AND BY DISTANCE ZONE, 1900-1950

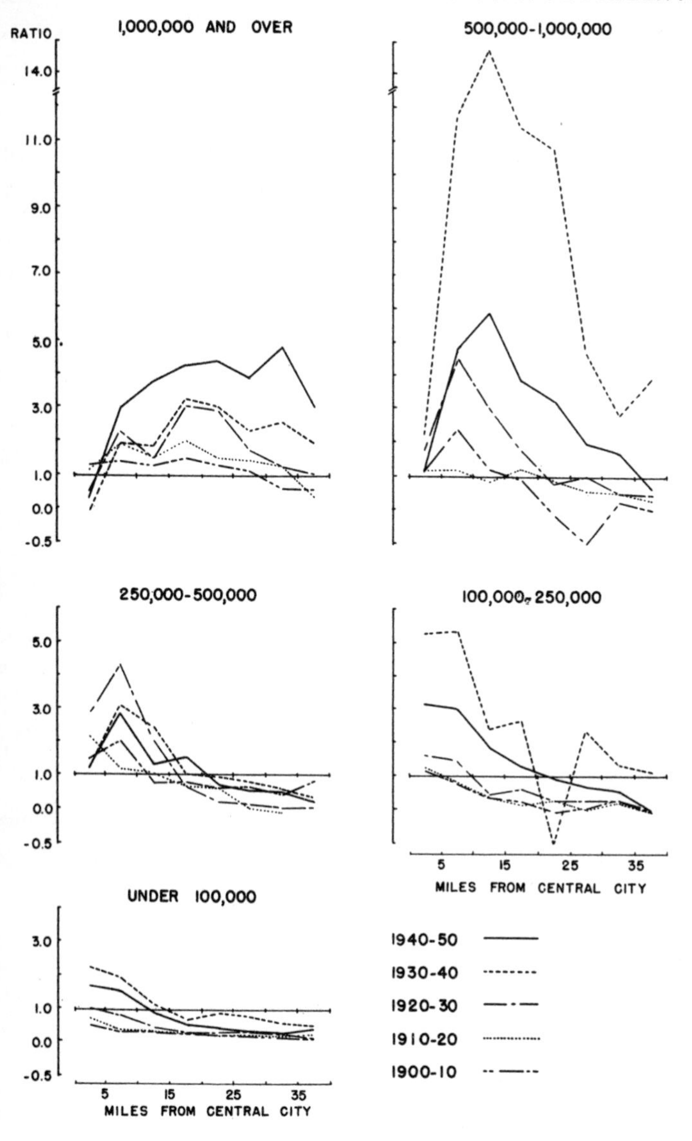


FIGURE 17.

RATIO OF RATE OF POPULATION CHAN IN SATELLITE AREA OF EXTENDED METROPOLITAN AREAS TO RATE OF CHANGE IN CENTRAL CITY, BY SIZE OF CENTRAL CITY AND BY DISTANCE ZONE, 1900-1950

The proportion of all population increase that accrued to central cities shows, in Table 14, a rough correspondence with city size. And the amount of decline in this respect, from 1900 through 1950, shows some tendency to vary inversely with size of area. Central cities of 250,000-500,000 were unusually successful in maintaining a large proportion of all increase in their areas. The proportions of growth attracted to satellite areas conform to a converse pattern.

Although satellite areas received increasingly large shares of all growth, most of the increase was contained within a closely circumscribed space, as Table 15 clearly shows. The 10-15 mile distance zone, in the largest class of metropolitan areas, has consistently absorbed the largest proportion of all satellite growth. In the four other size classes the 5-10 mile zone has continued to attract the largest share of growth occurring outside central cities. But while there has been concentration of population increase within a given zone, there also have been rapid increases in the proportions received by more distant zones. Size of central city appears to have been an important factor in the radius over which population increments have been scattered.

Differences in rates of change have not been large enough to significantly alter the distribution of population within metropolitan areas. The cumulative percentage distributions, shown in Table 16, demonstrate that in few instances has the distance required to contain any given proportion of the total population shifted by more than five miles. This applies not only to each decade, but to the entire 50-year period as well. In several cases the shifts have been toward reduction rather than increase of the distance.

It will be observed that in Extended Metropolitan Areas, concentration varies directly with size of area. This, of course, is largely a result of the direct variation of the proportion of population in central cities with size of central city. Such an association appears only as a tendency in Standard Metropolitan Areas.

Coefficients of redistribution, shown graphically in Fig. 18, indicates that the highest incidence of redistribution occurred in the 250,000-500,000 class. Referring to Table 16 it will be seen that movement in that size class of areas was toward concentration. Relatively constant rates of redistribution obtained in the two smallest size classes, and the data in Table 16 show very slight shifts toward a scattering or deconcentration of population. The rather erratic patterns of redistribution shown for the remaining two classes of metropolitan areas are due largely to sharp declines in the proportions of population within 10 miles of central cities.

TABLE 14. PER CENT DISTRIBUTION OF POPULATION INCREASE BY TYPE OF PLACE, AND BY SIZE OF CENTRAL CITY, TYPE OF METROPOLITAN AREA, AND DECADE, 1900-1950

| Size of central city and type of place | *Standard Metropolitan Areas* | | | | | *Extended Metropolitan Areas* | | | | |
|---|---|---|---|---|---|---|---|---|---|---|
| | *1940-50* | *1930-40* | *1920-20* | *1910-20* | *1900-10* | *1940-50* | *1930-40* | *1920-30* | *1910-20* | *1900-10* |
| 1,000,000 and over | 100.0 | 100.0 | 100.0 | 100.0 | 100.0 | 100.0 | 100.0 | 100.0 | 100.0 | 100.0 |
| Central cities | 33.3 | 46.8 | 55.6 | 61.7 | 68.4 | 32.2 | 45.7 | 54.9 | 61.6 | 67.4 |
| Satellite areas | 66.7 | 53.2 | 44.4 | 38.3 | 31.6 | 67.8 | 54.3 | 45.1 | 38.4 | 32.6 |
| 500,000 - 1,000,000 | 100.0 | 100.0 | 100.0 | 100.0 | 100.0 | 100.0 | 100.0 | 100.0 | 100.0 | 100.0 |
| Central cities | 23.8 | 11.9 | 33.1 | 57.3 | 47.9 | 22.9 | 11.0 | 32.9 | 56.6 | 49.9 |
| Satellite areas | 76.2 | 88.1 | 66.9 | 42.7 | 52.1 | 77.1 | 89.0 | 67.1 | 43.4 | 50.1 |
| 250,000 - 500,000 | 100.0 | 100.0 | 100.0 | 100.0 | 100.0 | 100.0 | 100.0 | 100.0 | 100.0 | 100.0 |
| Central cities | 50.2 | 50.3 | 58.0 | 70.5 | 62.0 | 44.0 | 44.8 | 56.3 | 70.9 | 59.6 |
| Satellite areas | 49.8 | 49.7 | 42.0 | 29.5 | 38.0 | 56.0 | 55.2 | 43.7 | 29.1 | 40.4 |
| 100,000 - 250,000 | 100.0 | 100.0 | 100.0 | 100.0 | 100.0 | 100.0 | 100.0 | 100.0 | 100.0 | 100.0 |
| Central cities | 38.4 | 28.1 | 61.9 | 74.1 | 72.4 | 30.9 | 22.1 | 57.2 | 69.0 | 67.4 |
| Satellite areas | 61.6 | 71.9 | 38.1 | 25.9 | 27.6 | 69.1 | 77.9 | 42.8 | 31.0 | 32.6 |
| Under 100,000 | 100.0 | 100.0 | 100.0 | 100.0 | 100.0 | 100.0 | 100.0 | 100.0 | 100.0 | 100.0 |
| Central cities | 45.0 | 40.4 | 63.8 | 69.7 | 67.8 | 36.5 | 28.6 | 54.7 | 59.4 | 56.6 |
| Satellite areas | 55.0 | 59.6 | 36.2 | 30.3 | 32.2 | 63.5 | 71.4 | 45.3 | 40.6 | 43.4 |

Table 15. Percentage Distribution of Population Increase in Standard Metropolitan Areas, by Distance Zone, by Size of Central City, Type of Metropolitan Area, and Decade, 1900-1950

| Size of central city and distance zone | Standard Metropolitan Areas | | | | | Extended Metropolitan Areas | | | | |
|---|---|---|---|---|---|---|---|---|---|---|
| | 1940-1950 | 1930-1940 | 1920-1930 | 1910-1920 | 1900-1910 | 1940-1950 | 1930-1940 | 1920-1930 | 1910-1920 | 1900-1910 |
| 1,000,000 and over | 100.0 | 100.0 | 100.0 | 100.0 | 100.0 | 100.0 | 100.0 | 100.0 | 100.0 | 100.0 |
| Central cities | 33.3 | 46.8 | 55.6 | 61.7 | 68.4 | 32.2 | 45.7 | 54.9 | 61.6 | 67.4 |
| 0-5 miles | 0.4 | -0.3 | 1.1 | 2.4 | 2.7 | 0.4 | -0.3 | 1.0 | 2.3 | 2.6 |
| 5-10 miles | 12.3 | 10.2 | 9.9 | 8.3 | 6.2 | 11.9 | 10.0 | 9.7 | 8.2 | 6.1 |
| 10-15 miles | 18.1 | 11.9 | 10.7 | 11.6 | 9.9 | 12.5 | 11.6 | 10.6 | 11.6 | 9.8 |
| 15-20 miles | 14.2 | 13.1 | 9.0 | 6.2 | 4.6 | 13.7 | 12.7 | 8.7 | 6.2 | 4.5 |
| 20-25 miles | 7.1 | 8.0 | 6.9 | 3.8 | 3.2 | 8.9 | 7.9 | 6.8 | 3.8 | 3.2 |
| 25-30 miles | 4.5 | 4.0 | 2.9 | 2.8 | 2.2 | 5.2 | 4.3 | 3.2 | 2.9 | 2.3 |
| 30-35 miles | 4.3 | 3.0 | 1.5 | 2.0 | 1.0 | 4.6 | 3.2 | 1.7 | 2.1 | 1.2 |
| 35 miles and over | 3.8 | 3.3 | 2.4 | 1.2 | 1.8 | 5.6 | 4.9 | 3.2 | 1.3 | 2.9 |
| 500,000 - 1,000,000 | 100.0 | 100.0 | 100.0 | 100.0 | 100.0 | 100.0 | 100.0 | 100.0 | 100.0 | 100.0 |
| Central cities | 23.8 | 11.9 | 33.1 | 57.3 | 47.9 | 22.9 | 11.0 | 32.9 | 56.6 | 49.9 |
| 0-5 miles | 3.0 | 2.9 | 6.7 | 10.5 | 17.9 | 2.9 | 2.7 | 6.6 | 10.3 | 18.6 |
| 5-10 miles | 36.6 | 41.1 | 36.2 | 13.9 | 22.9 | 35.5 | 38.3 | 36.0 | 13.8 | 23.8 |
| 10-15 miles | 18.3 | 20.6 | 11.1 | 5.2 | 6.9 | 18.3 | 20.0 | 11.1 | 5.2 | 7.1 |
| 15-20 miles | 8.9 | 12.0 | 7.9 | 6.5 | 3.5 | 9.4 | 12.8 | 7.8 | 6.2 | 3.7 |
| 20-25 miles | 4.9 | 7.1 | 2.1 | 3.5 | 0.4 | 5.6 | 7.9 | 2.0 | 3.1 | -0.6 |
| 25-30 miles | 2.3 | 3.1 | 2.2 | 2.6 | -0.1 | 3.2 | 3.8 | 2.0 | 2.3 | -2.8 |
| 30-35 miles | 1.2 | 0.4 | 0.2 | 0.3 | 0.4 | 1.4 | 1.1 | 0.6 | 1.3 | 0.3 |
| 35 miles and over | 1.0 | 0.9 | 0.5 | 0.2 | 0.2 | 0.8 | 2.4 | 1.0 | 1.2 | ----- |
| 250,000 - 500,000 | 100.0 | 100.0 | 100.0 | 100.0 | 100.0 | 100.0 | 100.0 | 100.0 | 100.0 | 100.0 |
| Central cities | 50.2 | 50.3 | 58.0 | 70.5 | 62.0 | 44.0 | 44.8 | 56.3 | 70.9 | 59.6 |
| 0-5 miles | 8.3 | 6.5 | 10.6 | 7.5 | 4.2 | 7.6 | 5.9 | 10.3 | 7.5 | 4.0 |
| 5-10 miles | 26.3 | 26.2 | 24.5 | 12.0 | 17.8 | 24.2 | 23.8 | 23.7 | 12.1 | 17.1 |
| 10-15 miles | 8.2 | 12.3 | 5.8 | 4.3 | 4.5 | 8.3 | 11.5 | 6.4 | 4.3 | 4.3 |
| 15-20 miles | 5.5 | 2.2 | 0.8 | 2.7 | 4.6 | 7.5 | 3.6 | 2.3 | 2.8 | 4.4 |
| 20-25 miles | 1.4 | 2.2 | 0.3 | 2.8 | 3.6 | 3.4 | 3.7 | 0.5 | 2.6 | 3.2 |
| 25-30 miles | 0.1 | 0.3 | 0.0 | 0.0 | 2.5 | 2.4 | 3.0 | 0.5 | 0.1 | 3.3 |
| 30-35 miles | ----- | 0.0 | 0.0 | 0.1 | 0.7 | 1.9 | 2.2 | -0.1 | -0.3 | 1.6 |
| 35 miles and over | ----- | 0.0 | ----- | 0.1 | 0.1 | 0.7 | 1.5 | 0.1 | ----- | 2.5 |
| 100,000 - 250,000 | 100.0 | 100.0 | 100.0 | 100.0 | 100.0 | 100.0 | 100.0 | 100.0 | 100.0 | 100.0 |
| Central cities | 38.4 | 28.1 | 61.9 | 74.1 | 72.4 | 30.9 | 22.1 | 57.2 | 69.0 | 67.4 |
| 0-5 miles | 18.0 | 20.5 | 11.9 | 8.9 | 9.8 | 14.5 | 16.2 | 11.3 | 8.5 | 9.2 |
| 5-10 miles | 29.8 | 33.1 | 17.3 | 12.0 | 12.7 | 24.9 | 27.0 | 16.7 | 12.1 | 12.4 |
| 10-15 miles | 10.4 | 8.7 | 4.6 | 4.8 | 5.2 | 12.6 | 11.2 | 5.2 | 4.9 | 5.7 |
| 15-20 miles | 2.8 | 8.8 | 3.0 | 0.5 | 0.2 | 7.7 | 10.8 | 5.0 | 1.3 | 2.7 |
| 20-25 miles | 0.6 | 0.9 | 1.3 | -0.2 | -0.1 | 4.6 | 4.2 | 1.9 | 2.0 | 1.9 |
| 25-30 miles | 0.3 | -0.1 | 0.0 | -0.1 | 0.0 | 2.9 | 3.7 | 1.0 | 0.1 | -0.4 |
| 30-35 miles | 0.1 | 0.1 | 0.0 | 0.0 | -0.1 | 2.4 | 4.6 | 2.3 | 2.9 | 1.9 |
| 35 miles and over | -0.4 | -0.1 | 0.0 | 0.0 | -0.1 | -0.5 | 0.2 | -0.6 | -0.8 | -0.8 |
| Under 100,000 | 100.0 | 100.0 | 100.0 | 100.0 | 100.0 | 100.0 | 100.0 | 100.0 | 100.0 | 100.0 |
| Central cities | 45.0 | 40.4 | 63.8 | 69.7 | 67.8 | 36.5 | 28.6 | 54.7 | 59.4 | 56.6 |
| 0-5 miles | 18.3 | 19.9 | 11.8 | 9.7 | 7.6 | 15.4 | 14.3 | 10.3 | 8.4 | 6.3 |
| 5-10 miles | 18.3 | 20.3 | 12.3 | 8.1 | 8.0 | 16.2 | 15.3 | 11.2 | 7.3 | 7.3 |
| 10-15 miles | 9.8 | 10.6 | 6.6 | 6.2 | 8.1 | 10.3 | 9.5 | 6.9 | 6.7 | 7.8 |
| 15-20 miles | 3.4 | 3.1 | 2.0 | 3.1 | 3.1 | 6.2 | 7.0 | 4.8 | 4.7 | 5.4 |
| 20-25 miles | 2.2 | 3.3 | 2.9 | 1.3 | 1.6 | 5.9 | 9.2 | 5.0 | 2.8 | 5.1 |
| 25-30 miles | 0.0 | 1.0 | 0.7 | 1.0 | 0.9 | 4.4 | 8.2 | 3.2 | 4.5 | 4.8 |
| 30-35 miles | -0.1 | 0.4 | -0.1 | ----- | ----- | 2.5 | 4.9 | 2.9 | 3.0 | 2.7 |
| 35 miles and over | 3.1 | 1.0 | ----- | 0.9 | 2.9 | 2.6 | 3.0 | 1.0 | 3.2 | 4.0 |

Table 16. Cumulative Percentage Distribution of Population in Standard Metropolitan Areas, by Distance Zone, Size of Central City, Type of Metropolitan Area, and Decade, 1900-1950.

| Size of central city and distance zone | Standard Metropolitan Areas | | | | | | Extended Metropolitan Areas | | | | | |
|---|---|---|---|---|---|---|---|---|---|---|---|---|
| | 1950 | 1940 | 1930 | 1920 | 1910 | 1900 | 1950 | 1940 | 1930 | 1920 | 1910 | 1900 |
| 1,000,000 and over | | | | | | | | | | | | |
| Central city | 59.0 | 63.7 | 65.0 | 69.5 | 70.4 | 71.1 | 58.0 | 62.7 | 64.0 | 68.3 | 69.1 | 69.6 |
| 0-5 miles | 61.0 | 65.9 | 67.4 | 72.3 | 72.8 | 73.4 | 59.9 | 64.9 | 66.4 | 71.1 | 71.5 | 71.9 |
| 5-10 miles | 69.4 | 73.6 | 74.8 | 77.6 | 77.7 | 77.8 | 68.2 | 72.5 | 73.7 | 76.3 | 76.3 | 76.3 |
| 10-15 miles | 80.1 | 82.9 | 84.1 | 86.4 | 86.5 | 86.2 | 78.7 | 81.7 | 82.8 | 84.9 | 84.9 | 84.5 |
| 15-20 miles | 87.6 | 89.2 | 89.8 | 90.3 | 90.0 | 89.4 | 86.0 | 87.8 | 88.4 | 88.8 | 88.3 | 87.6 |
| 20-25 miles | 92.4 | 93.2 | 93.4 | 93.4 | 92.9 | 92.2 | 90.7 | 91.7 | 92.0 | 91.8 | 91.1 | 90.3 |
| 25-30 miles | 95.2 | 95.7 | 95.8 | 95.5 | 95.0 | 94.3 | 93.8 | 94.4 | 94.6 | 94.1 | 93.4 | 92.6 |
| 30-35 miles | 97.3 | 97.5 | 97.5 | 97.2 | 96.7 | 96.2 | 96.1 | 97.3 | 96.4 | 95.9 | 95.3 | 94.7 |
| 35 miles and over | 100.0 | 100.0 | 100.0 | 100.0 | 100.0 | 100.0 | 100.0 | 100.0 | 100.0 | 100.0 | 100.0 | 100.0 |
| 500,000 - 1,000,000 | | | | | | | | | | | | |
| Central city | 50.4 | 56.0 | 57.3 | 58.8 | 58.4 | 59.7 | 47.0 | 51.8 | 53.6 | 55.0 | 53.5 | 57.2 |
| 0-5 miles | 55.9 | 62.0 | 63.8 | 65.8 | 67.1 | 72.4 | 5.2 | 57.3 | 59.7 | 61.5 | 61.5 | 69.3 |
| 5-10 miles | 77.4 | 80.4 | 81.0 | 80.2 | 79.6 | 84.8 | 72.2 | 74.3 | 75.8 | 75.0 | 73.1 | 81.3 |
| 10-15 miles | 86.7 | 87.8 | 87.9 | 86.6 | 86.5 | 91.9 | 81.1 | 81.4 | 82.5 | 81.1 | 79.7 | 88.5 |
| 15-20 miles | 92.6 | 93.0 | 93.1 | 91.9 | 91.3 | 96.2 | 87.3 | 87.0 | 88.0 | 86.5 | 84.8 | 93.1 |
| 20-25 miles | 96.1 | 96.2 | 96.3 | 95.6 | 94.8 | 98.3 | 91.6 | 91.0 | 91.6 | 90.5 | 88.7 | 95.8 |
| 25-30 miles | 98.4 | 98.5 | 98.5 | 98.1 | 97.4 | 99.1 | 95.3 | 94.8 | 94.9 | 94.0 | 92.7 | 97.8 |
| 30-35 miles | 99.3 | 99.3 | 99.3 | 99.2 | 98.8 | 99.5 | 97.3 | 96.9 | 96.9 | 96.3 | 95.5 | 98.9 |
| 35 miles and over | 100.0 | 100.0 | 100.0 | 100.0 | 100.0 | 100.0 | 100.0 | 100.0 | 100.0 | 100.0 | 100.0 | 100.0 |
| 250,000 - 500,000 | | | | | | | | | | | | |
| Central city | 63.1 | 66.1 | 71.2 | 80.8 | 72.0 | 68.1 | 48.6 | 49.5 | 54.1 | 65.6 | 64.2 | 57.9 |
| 0-5 miles | 71.9 | 75.0 | 78.9 | 86.0 | 75.5 | 71.4 | 55.6 | 56.4 | 60.1 | 69.9 | 67.4 | 60.7 |
| 5-10 miles | 87.2 | 87.8 | 90.7 | 93.9 | 86.9 | 80.8 | 67.9 | 66.3 | 69.3 | 76.3 | 77.6 | 68.8 |
| 10-15 miles | 95.2 | 95.7 | 96.8 | 97.4 | 90.7 | 86.3 | 75.2 | 73.4 | 75.2 | 80.2 | 81.5 | 74.0 |
| 15-20 miles | 98.6 | 98.7 | 98.9 | 98.9 | 94.2 | 90.6 | 81.0 | 78.8 | 79.8 | 83.8 | 85.8 | 79.1 |
| 20-25 miles | 99.8 | 99.8 | 99.7 | 99.5 | 97.0 | 94.3 | 86.0 | 84.1 | 84.4 | 87.3 | 89.7 | 84.0 |
| 25-30 miles | 100.0 | 100.0 | 100.0 | 100.0 | 98.5 | 97.3 | 91.2 | 89.9 | 89.8 | 92.6 | 93.3 | 89.4 |
| 30-35 miles | ----- | ----- | ----- | ----- | 99.6 | 98.7 | 95.6 | 94.9 | 94.8 | 96.1 | 96.0 | 93.3 |
| 35 miles and over | ----- | ----- | ----- | ----- | 100.0 | 100.0 | 100.0 | 100.0 | 100.0 | 100.0 | 100.0 | 100.0 |
| 100,000 - 250,000 | | | | | | | | | | | | |
| Central cities | 56.2 | 60.2 | 61.8 | 64.6 | 66.2 | 67.6 | 39.6 | 41.0 | 42.5 | 43.7 | 41.6 | 39.8 |
| 0-5 miles | 67.2 | 69.3 | 70.2 | 72.6 | 72.7 | 75.7 | 47.0 | 47.2 | 48.3 | 49.2 | 45.7 | 44.7 |
| 5-10 miles | 84.9 | 84.6 | 83.2 | 85.0 | 86.8 | 88.6 | 60.1 | 58.3 | 57.9 | 58.2 | 55.3 | 53.2 |
| 10-15 miles | 93.8 | 93.3 | 92.0 | 94.4 | 95.4 | 97.0 | 69.7 | 67.4 | 66.6 | 67.1 | 63.3 | 61.6 |
| 15-20 miles | 96.2 | 96.8 | 96.4 | 97.8 | 98.5 | 99.1 | 77.4 | 75.1 | 74.5 | 74.0 | 70.5 | 69.5 |
| 20-25 miles | 97.3 | 98.0 | 97.8 | 99.0 | 99.3 | 99.5 | 83.9 | 82.0 | 81.2 | 80.8 | 78.7 | 78.4 |
| 25-30 miles | 98.0 | 98.8 | 98.8 | 99.7 | 99.8 | 99.7 | 89.6 | 88.2 | 87.6 | 87.2 | 86.1 | 86.0 |
| 30-35 miles | 98.2 | 99.0 | 99.0 | 99.9 | 99.9 | 99.9 | 95.2 | 94.3 | 94.1 | 94.0 | 93.3 | 93.5 |
| 35 miles and over | 100.0 | 100.0 | 100.0 | 100.0 | 100.0 | 100.0 | 100.0 | 100.0 | 100.0 | 100.0 | 100.0 | 100.0 |
| Under 100,000 | | | | | | | | | | | | |
| Central cities | 50.1 | 51.2 | 53.3 | 52.9 | 50.8 | 46.4 | 30.4 | 29.5 | 30.0 | 28.4 | 26.3 | 22.3 |
| 0-5 miles | 63.7 | 63.8 | 64.5 | 62.4 | 60.4 | 56.0 | 38.8 | 36.9 | 36.4 | 33.6 | 31.3 | 26.9 |
| 5-10 miles | 77.6 | 76.8 | 77.2 | 74.9 | 73.9 | 72.2 | 48.4 | 45.6 | 44.7 | 41.3 | 39.3 | 35.7 |
| 10-15 miles | 87.9 | 87.2 | 87.3 | 85.4 | 85.6 | 85.0 | 57.5 | 54.5 | 53.5 | 50.2 | 48.8 | 45.5 |
| 15-20 miles | 92.8 | 92.4 | 92.8 | 92.0 | 92.5 | 92.7 | 66.7 | 64.1 | 63.4 | 60.8 | 59.7 | 56.7 |
| 20-25 miles | 96.8 | 96.7 | 96.9 | 95.8 | 95.8 | 96.2 | 76.6 | 74.6 | 74.1 | 71.7 | 70.4 | 68.1 |
| 25-30 miles | 98.2 | 98.4 | 98.6 | 97.6 | 97.7 | 98.3 | 86.4 | 85.2 | 84.6 | 82.7 | 81.5 | 80.0 |
| 30-35 miles | 98.6 | 98.9 | 99.0 | 98.1 | 98.3 | 99.0 | 93.8 | 93.3 | 92.7 | 91.4 | 90.9 | 90.2 |
| 35 miles and over | 100.0 | 100.0 | 100.0 | 100.0 | 100.0 | 100.0 | 100.0 | 100.0 | 100.0 | 100.0 | 100.0 | 100.0 |

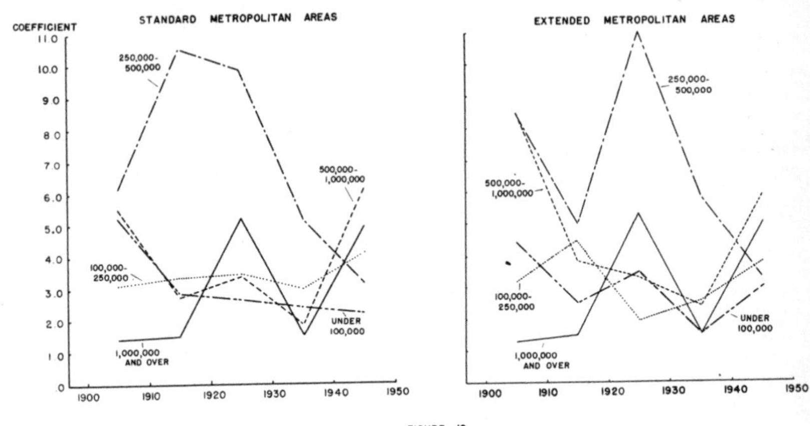


FIGURE 18
COEFFICIENTS OF POPULATION REDISTRIBUTION IN METROPOLITAN AREAS, 1900-1950

The comparisons of Standard and Extended Metropolitan Areas have shown, by virtually all measures, a more pronounced gradient aspect in the latter than in the former. And this is indicative of the inclusion within Standard Metropolitan Areas of most of the rapidly growing territories surrounding central cities. Even so, the difference between comparable zones have been small in most cases. It seems unnecessary, therefore, to carry the Extended Metropolitan Area concept beyond the present point.

## Size and Type of Satellite Place

It is of interest to know whether the trends of change in metropolitan areas that were observed when all satellite population was considered apply to population in each size and type of satellite place. That they do not apply uniformly is apparent in Table 17. For example, while there has been a general tendency for rates of change in all sizes and types of places to vary with the size of central city, that association has been most definite among small incorporated places and unincorporated areas. Perhaps such places are more dependent on and therefore more responsive to central city influence than are large satellite places. Unfortunately the data at hand do not permit direct observation of that relationship.

TABLE 17. PER CENT CHANGE OF POPULATION IN STANDARD METROPOLITAN AREAS, BY SIZE AND TYPE OF SATELLITE PLACE, BY SIZE OF CENTRAL CITY AND DECADE 1900 - 1950

| *Size of central city and size and type of satellite place* | *1940-50* | *1930-40* | *1920-30* | *1910-20* | *1900-10* |
|---|---|---|---|---|---|
| 1,000,000 and over | | | | | |
| 50,000 and over | 9.6 | 1.3 | 11.1 | 17.1 | 31.4 |
| 25,000 - 50,000 | 12.7 | 5.1 | 40.2 | 28.4 | 53.3 |
| 10,000 - 25,000 | 23.9 | 12.2 | 50.2 | 55.0 | 36.3 |
| 5,000 - 10,000 | 37.1 | 14.8 | 61.5 | 33.1 | 52.0 |
| 2,500 - 5,000 | 45.6 | 12.8 | 66.7 | 30.1 | 46.8 |
| 1,000 - 2,500 | 44.6 | 18.4 | 110.5 | 47.1 | 46.4 |
| Under 1,000 | 58.2 | 26.0 | 84.3 | 38.9 | 52.1 |
| Unincorporated area | 70.5 | 27.5 | 60.2 | 23.9 | 29.7 |
| 500,000 - 1,000,000 | | | | | |
| 50,000 and over | 13.0 | 2.5 | 20,8 | 11.7 | 22.2 |
| 25,000 - 50,000 | 16.2 | 0.0 | 30.2 | 8.9 | 26.0 |
| 10,000 - 25,000 | 24.1 | 7.1 | 24.4 | 30.3 | 33.6 |
| 5,000 - 10,000 | 39.0 | 9.4 | 37.9 | 31.3 | 22.9 |
| 2,500 - 5,000 | 40.3 | 15.0 | 74.1 | 42.5 | 88.1 |
| 1,000 - 2,500 | 48.2 | 16.2 | 55.1 | 42.4 | 68.1 |
| Under 1,000 | 36.1 | 17.9 | 30.8 | 32.3 | 28.1 |
| Unincorporated area | 57.6 | 18.1 | 33.6 | 17.1 | 20.8 |
| 250,000 - 500,000 | | | | | |
| 50,000 and over | 5.9 | -3.2 | 14.2 | 34.4 | 124.3 |
| 25,000 - 50,000 | 7.6 | -0.3 | 1.5 | 34.5 | 19.7 |
| 10,000 - 25,000 | 27.8 | 15.1 | 57.1 | 46.7 | 50.9 |
| 5,000 - 10,000 | 31.7 | 11.6 | 62.3 | 40.7 | 51.4 |
| 2,500 - 5,000 | 54.3 | 15.9 | 62.4 | 154.1 | 61.3 |
| 1,000 - 2,500 | 63.9 | 26.5 | 48.7 | 54.8 | 50.7 |
| Under 1,000 | 42.3 | 20.4 | 63.5 | 28.0 | 36.4 |
| Unincorporated area | 39.8 | 32.3 | 55.6 | 16.0 | 25.7 |
| 100,000 - 250,000 | | | | | |
| 50,000 and over | 17.1 | -6.3 | 4.3 | 11.8 | - |
| 25,000 - 50,000 | 11.4 | 1.5 | 23.1 | 24.8 | 33.1 |
| 10,000 - 25,000 | 3.7 | -1.6 | 14.8 | 12.3 | 28.7 |
| 5,000 - 10,000 | 4.2 | 2.1 | 20.6 | 7.5 | 32.0 |
| 2,500 - 5,000 | 17.9 | 1.0 | 17.8 | 3.2 | 40.2 |
| 1,000 - 2,500 | 14.9 | 10.0 | 26.6 | 20.5 | 26.6 |
| Under 1,000 | 17.4 | 8.2 | 33.9 | 15.5 | 32.3 |
| Unincorporated area | 46.6 | 19.6 | 27.8 | 17.0 | 14.2 |
| Under 100,000 | | | | | |
| 50,000 and over | - | - | - | - | - |
| 25,000 - 50,000 | 5.5 | 4.1 | 9.4 | 25.6 | 47.0 |
| 10,000 - 25,000 | 11.6 | 5.7 | 24.0 | 22.2 | 20.9 |
| 5,000 - 10,000 | 11.2 | -3.8 | 15.0 | 21.9 | 30.5 |
| 2,500 - 5,000 | 26.6 | 9.6 | 6.7 | 23.0 | 27.5 |
| 1,000 - 2,500 | 11.3 | 9.1 | 20.6 | 14.2 | 25.1 |
| Under 1,000 | 22.4 | 7.1 | 16.6 | 14.5 | 22.5 |
| Unincorporated area | 27.9 | 18.1 | 20.0 | 15.9 | 13.4 |

In all metropolitan area size classes, satellite incorporated places of 25,000 or more population have experienced declining rates of growth continuously since 1900. That trend reaches into satellite places of 10,000-25,000 population in metropolitan areas with central cities of less than 250,000 population. In all other sizes of incorporated places the trend has been irregular. Growth rates reached their highest point in the 1920-30 decade in most instances and then subsided. Only in unincorporated areas have growth rates shown any tendency toward continuous increase. For the most part, 1940-50 and 1930-40 growth rates varied inversely with size of incorporated place and were highest in unincorporated area. But in earlier decades that pattern of variation obtained only among incorporated places of 2,500 population and over, and only in metropolitan areas with central cities of 250,000 or more population.

The rates of change of all incorporated population, by distance zones, as shown in Table 18, reveal few instances of uninterrupted increase. Irregularity of rate from decade to decade has been the prevalent characteristic. The most notable instances of consistent change are found in the 0-5 and 5-10 mile zones where the trend has been downward. In these zones are located most of the large satellites, i.e., 25,000 population and over, which have been growing at progressively lower rates. Sharp declines are also observable in the outermost zones of the smaller metropolitan areas in which small incorporated places predominate. The zones between 10 and 20 miles from central cities, where the concentration of satellite incorporated places is pronounced (Table 19), have generally maintained the highest rates.

No clear association of rates of change of incorporated population with size of central city is observable for any distance zone in Table 18. The highest rates occurred in the 250,000-500,000 class, while in the two adjacent size classes rates are relatively low. It is apparent, however, that the larger the central city the more distant from it are the zones of highest rates of change.

The relation of growth rates in satellite places to size of central city is made clearer when they are expressed as ratios to central city growth rates, as in Fig. 19. It is immediately apparent that the smaller the size of central city the lower has been the relative growth rates of all sizes and types of satellite places. This is true of each of the three decades shown. Only in a few instances, and those mainly in 1900-10, do any of the curves for the 1,000,000 and over class of areas drop below unity. A striking exception to the general pattern in that size class is presented by the satellites of 50,000 or more population the ratios of which are below unity in the inner zones and above unity in outer zones. In the 500,000-1,000,000

TABLE 18. PER CENT CHANGE OF SATELLITE INCORPORATED POPULATION IN STANDARD METROPOLITAN AREAS, BY SIZE OF CENTRAL CITY, DISTANCE ZONES, AND DECADE, 1900-1950

| *Size of central city and distance zones* | *1940-50* | *1930-40* | *1920-30* | *1910-20* | *1900-10* |
|---|---|---|---|---|---|
| 1,000,000 and over | 20.4 | 7.2 | 39.1 | 30.0 | 39.9 |
| 0 - 5 miles | -15.5 | -1.8 | 15.6 | 20.5 | 32.4 |
| 5 - 10 " | 17.5 | 8.1 | 47.2 | 34.2 | 38.1 |
| 10 - 15 " | 24.3 | 5.8 | 30.1 | 29.0 | 40.4 |
| 15 - 20 " | 31.1 | 12.5 | 65.1 | 39.6 | 64.7 |
| 20 - 25 " | 22.4 | 9.8 | 59.3 | 28.5 | 44.2 |
| 25 - 30 " | 22.6 | 7.7 | 39.3 | 42.8 | 40.7 |
| 30 - 35 " | 32.3 | 5.8 | 31.3 | 28.6 | 31.5 |
| 35 miles and over | 18.3 | 3.7 | 24.5 | 10.4 | 23.5 |
| 500,000 - 1,000,000 | 23.1 | 5.9 | 32.6 | 23.7 | 29.4 |
| 0 - 5 miles | 9.3 | 1.4 | 18.2 | 22.1 | 29.1 |
| 5 - 10 " | 25.0 | 6.8 | 44.8 | 26.0 | 36.7 |
| 10 - 15 " | 48.9 | 9.0 | 33.2 | 15.7 | 27.9 |
| 15 - 20 " | 19.3 | 8.9 | 49.3 | 49.5 | 24.9 |
| 20 - 25 " | 14.3 | 7.2 | 11.5 | 24.1 | 16.9 |
| 25 - 30 " | 11.4 | 1.2 | 15.8 | 19.2 | -2.6 |
| 30 - 35 " | 9.5 | 1.4 | 17.9 | 3.6 | 37.8 |
| 35 miles and over | 52.3 | 9.6 | 16.3 | 2.5 | 43.1 |
| 250,000 - 500,000 | 25.4 | 8.6 | 45.7 | 51.6 | 53.3 |
| 0 - 5 miles | 15.0 | 5.7 | 39.7 | 78.8 | 38.7 |
| 5 - 10 " | 41.7 | 12.2 | 67.3 | 43.0 | 81.9 |
| 10 - 15 " | 20.5 | 6.5 | 23.7 | 50.7 | 30.9 |
| 15 - 20 " | 70.1 | 8.8 | 17.9 | 44.2 | 37.4 |
| 20 - 25 " | -51.0 | 22.4 | 5.7 | 64.9 | 52.0 |
| 25 - 30 " | 30.8 | 7.6 | 3.1 | 5.7 | 39.8 |
| 30 - 35 " | – | – | -13.9 | 23.8 | 38.4 |
| 35 miles and over | – | – | – | 16.1 | 0.0 |
| 100,000 - 250,000 | 10.6 | 1.3 | 17.0 | 13.2 | 31.6 |
| 0 - 5 miles | 16.4 | 6.0 | 18.1 | 16.1 | 47.1 |
| 5 - 10 " | 7.3 | 0.2 | 20.2 | 12.7 | 30.0 |
| 10 - 15 " | 10.3 | -0.8 | 13.5 | 18.1 | 22.7 |
| 15 - 20 " | 17.5 | 2.4 | 25.2 | -2.2 | 2.5 |
| 20 - 25 " | 4.6 | 0.8 | 12.1 | -5.1 | -2.9 |
| 25 - 30 " | 10.6 | -1.4 | 7.0 | 2.2 | 14.2 |
| 30 - 35 " | 12.5 | 4.4 | 1.9 | -0.7 | -7.0 |
| 35 miles and over | -5.7 | -2.7 | -9.7 | 12.8 | 8.2 |
| Under 100,000 | 14.2 | 5.4 | 16.1 | 19.8 | 27.2 |
| 0 - 5 miles | 19.8 | 5.0 | 21.7 | 18.5 | 25.2 |
| 5 - 10 " | 11.7 | 1.3 | 14.5 | 18.9 | 22.9 |
| 10 - 15 " | 19.0 | 7.7 | 24.9 | 28.2 | 36.0 |
| 15 - 20 " | 16.3 | 7.7 | 7.9 | 17.1 | 13.6 |
| 20 - 25 " | -4.2 | 7.9 | 12.1 | 14.6 | 35.8 |
| 25 - 30 " | 0.6 | 3.3 | 10.1 | 10.1 | 17.7 |
| 30 - 35 " | 4.5 | -11.4 | 4.1 | 2.5 | 8.8 |
| 35 miles and over | 8.3 | 19.9 | -4.9 | 19.0 | 72.1 |

class there are also few cases in which the curves fall below unity. The gradients, however, are steeper than are those of the 1,000,000 and over class, i.e., ratios change more rapidly with distance. The 250,000-500,000 class, which has had the most rapid growth of satellite population of any size class (See Tables 10 and 18), nevertheless had ratios below those of the two larger classes of metropolitan areas. In the two smallest size classes of metropolitan areas, high relative rates of growth in satellite places have been held within 20 miles of central cities for the most part, though only in two or three cases have the ratios exceeded 2.0.

Increases of ratios, from 1900-10 to 1940-50, have been general over all size classes of metropolitan areas and in most sizes and types of satellite places. The increases are particularly striking in areas with central cities of 1,000,000 or more population, especially in unincorporated areas. On the other hand, increases have been moderate in small metropolitan areas. The largest satellite places have been least affected by the tendency toward increase of relative growth rates. In the three smallest metropolitan areas the trend has actually worked in the opposite direction. It is also noteworthy that the largest increases of ratios have occurred within 15 miles of central cities. And at greater distances, particularly in small metropolitan areas, 1940-50 ratios frequently drop below those of earlier decades.

The changing patterns of population distribution in each distance zone are shown in Fig. 20. The proportion of the population occupying unincorporated area, as well as that in incorporated places of less than 10,000 population, decreases with increases in the size of central cities. These differences tend to diminish as distance from the central city is lengthened. The proportion represented by the population in incorporated places of 10,000 or more population varies directly with size of city.

In large metropolitan areas, those with central cities of 500,000 or more population, the proportion of the population in unincorporated area in each distance zone declined from 1900 to 1950. The proportions in incorporated places of less than 2,500 population increased to 1910 and then declined through the next four decades. Increases in places of 2,500 or more population were sustained throughout the period.

Unincorporated areas in the 250,000-500,000 class gained increased proportions more or less steadily. In fact, it appears that the proportions in unincorporated areas were enlarged at the expense of all sizes of incorporated satellite places. The principal change of unincorporated area population in metropolitan areas with central cities of 100,000-250,000 population involved increase within inner zones and decline in outer zones. This was accompanied by a decline in the proportion in places

TABLE 19. AVERAGE NUMBER OF SATELLITE INCORPORATED PLACES IN STANDARD METROPOLITAN AREAS, BY SIZE OF CENTRAL CITY, DISTANCE ZONE, AND CENSUS YEAR, 1900-1950

| *Size of central city and distance zone* | *1950* | *1940* | *1930* | *1920* | *1910* | *1900* |
|---|---|---|---|---|---|---|
| 1,000,000 and over | 149.4 | 144.8 | 174.5 | 197.6 | 141.3 | 107.0 |
| 0 - 10 miles | 21.6 | 22.2 | 27.2 | 30.3 | 21.3 | 17.0 |
| 10 - 20 " | 59.0 | 56.8 | 67.6 | 72.0 | 51.0 | 36.0 |
| 20 - 30 " | 36.4 | 35.6 | 42.5 | 48.3 | 36.0 | 27.3 |
| 30 miles and over | 32.4 | 30.2 | 37.2 | 47.0 | 33.0 | 26.7 |
| 500,000 - 1,000,000 | 45.8 | 44.9 | 59.6 | 65.0 | 92.7 | 20.3 |
| 0 - 10 miles | 18.7 | 15.4 | 19.5 | 20.5 | 29.0 | 7.7 |
| 10 - 20 " | 14.2 | 14.5 | 19.1 | 19.8 | 25.7 | 5.0 |
| 20 - 30 " | 9.8 | 11.5 | 15.0 | 17.0 | 28.0 | 4.3 |
| 30 miles and over | 3.1 | 3.5 | 6.0 | 7.7 | 10.0 | 3.3 |
| 250,000 - 500,000 | 15.3 | 11.4 | 29.7 | 14.2 | 16.1 | 23.6 |
| 0 - 10 miles | 7.3 | 6.7 | 16.5 | 7.3 | 5.8 | 6.5 |
| 10 - 20 " | 6.6 | 4.0 | 11.1 | 4.8 | 4.9 | 6.7 |
| 20 - 30 " | 1.2 | .7 | 2.1 | 2.0 | 3.1 | 7.1 |
| 30 miles and over | .2 | — | — | .1 | 2.3 | 3.3 |
| 100,000 - 250,000 | 9.7 | 11.3 | 12.2 | 14.1 | 13.5 | 6.7 |
| 0 - 10 miles | 3.4 | 3.8 | 4.0 | 5.2 | 5.3 | 3.0 |
| 10 - 20 " | 4.3 | 5.1 | 5.5 | 6.9 | 6.5 | 3.0 |
| 20 - 30 " | 1.3 | 1.5 | 1.8 | 1.8 | 1.5 | .5 |
| 30 miles and over | .7 | .9 | .9 | .2 | .2 | .2 |
| Under 100,000 | 9.4 | 7.3 | 6.4 | 7.1 | 7.7 | 6.7 |
| 0 - 10 miles | 3.6 | 2.8 | 2.4 | 2.5 | 2.7 | 2.4 |
| 10 - 20 " | 4.1 | 3.2 | 2.8 | 3.2 | 3.4 | 3.0 |
| 20 - 30 " | 1.2 | .9 | .8 | .9 | 1.0 | .9 |
| 30 miles and over | .5 | .4 | .4 | .5 | .6 | .4 |

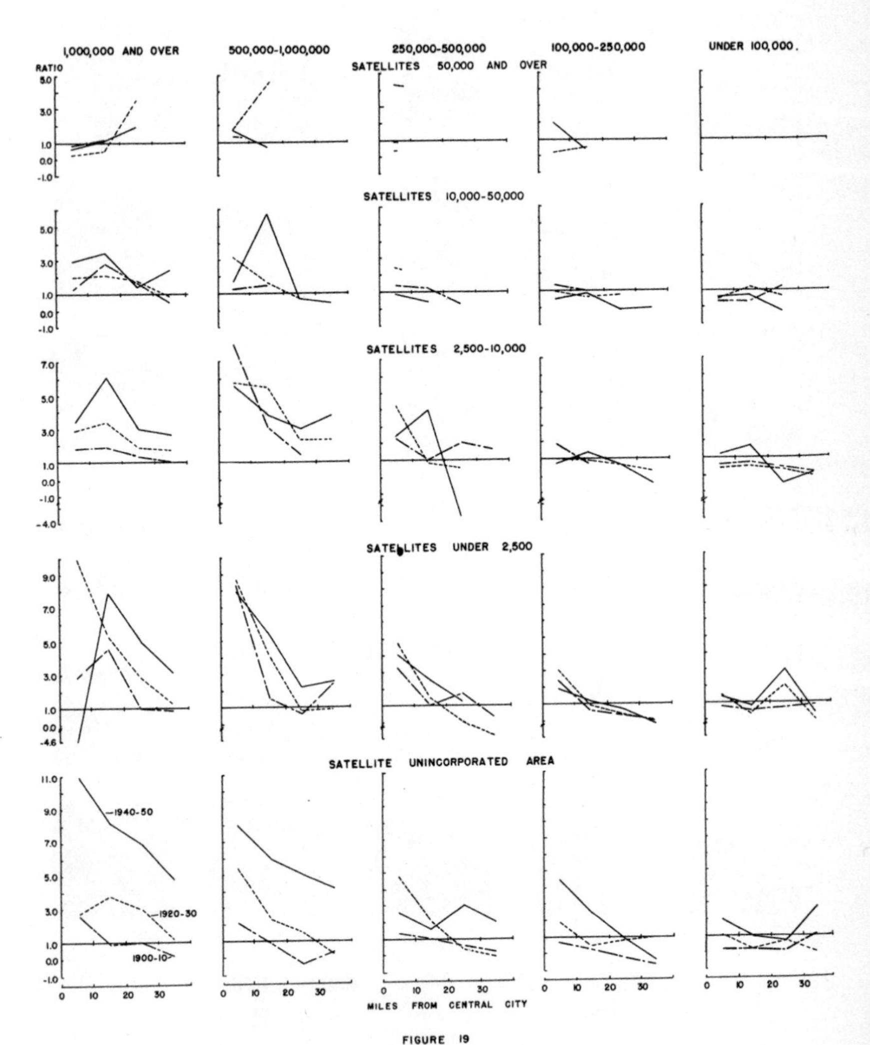


FIGURE 19

RATIO OF RATE OF CHANGE IN SATELLITE PLACES TO RATE OF CHANGE IN CENTRAL CITIES OF STANDARD METROPOLITAN AREAS, BY SIZE OF CENTRAL CITY AND BY DISTANCE ZONE, FOR SELECTED DECADES

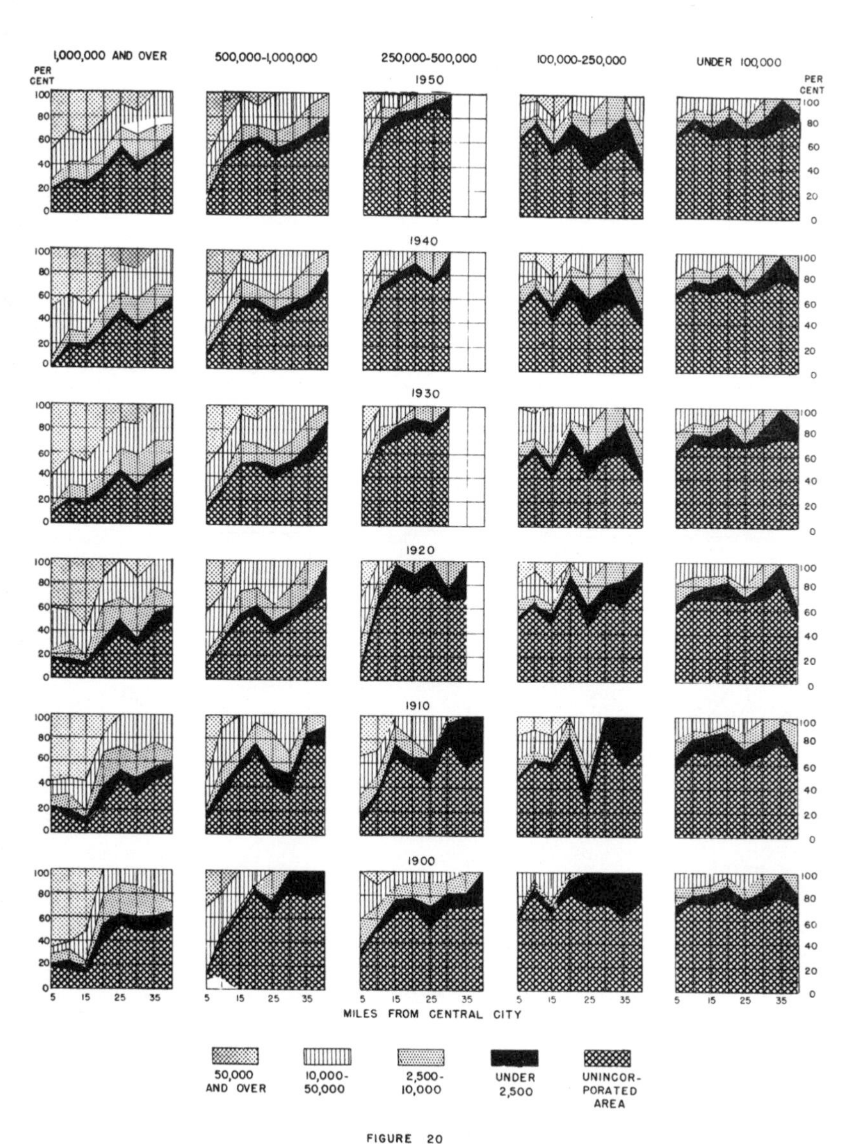


FIGURE 20

PER CENT DISTRIBUTION OF POPULATION IN DISTANCE ZONES OF STANDARD METROPOLITAN AREAS, BY SIZE AND TYPE OF SATELLITE PLACE AND BY SIZE OF CENTRAL CITY, 1900-1950

of less than 2,500 population and a rapid increase of the proportions in places over 2,500 population, especially in zones beyond 20 miles from central cities.

The distribution of satellite population shows the least change in the smallest class of metropolitan areas. It is evident, however, that unincorporated areas declined to 1920 and then regained their 1900 proportions by 1950. These shifts concerned the zones within 10 miles and beyond 35 miles of central cities. There was also some increase in proportions contained by satellites of 10,000 population and over.

CHAPTER IV

# AVERAGE ANNUAL GROWTH OF CENTRAL CITY AND POPULATION REDISTRIBUTION

The suggestion was made in the preceding chapter that rate of growth of central city may influence population redistribution. Evidence of this relationship was observed in the ratios of satellite growth to central city growth for successive decades: satellite area growth rates varied inversely with central city growth rates. But whether this association was the result of changing historical circumstances or an effect of central city growth rates remains to be determined. There is also the possibility that the irregularities in the relationship of population redistribution with size of central city observed in Chapter III may be a function of differences in growth rates. If so those irregularities should disappear when the factor of central city growth rate is controlled. The present chapter will attempt to answer both of these questions.

For the purposes of the following analysis, central city growth rate is defined as the 50-year average annual rate of increase. Central cities were ranked on this basis, and the rank array was divided into three approximately equal parts to provide high, medium, and low classes of central city growth rates. The ranges for each class are:

| | |
|---|---|
| High | 6.14 and over |
| Medium | 2.28 - 6.13 |
| Low | 2.27 and under |

Table 20 indicates the number of metropolitan areas in each central city growth rate class.[1]

## Central Cities and Satellite Areas

That the rate of inter-censal growth of the total metropolitan population is associated with the long-run growth experience of central cities is clearly indicated in Table 21. Areas whose central cities have had the lowest average annual increase have grown more slowly in every decade than have metropolitan areas with more rapidly growing central cities. This direct relationship is not, as might reasonably have been expected, entirely a function of central city rates of increase. Growth rates in satellite areas, after 1910, also varied directly with central city growth trends. The tendency toward an inverse relationship in 1900-10 is a departure from the pattern established during succeeding decades.

### TABLE 20. NUMBER OF STANDARD METROPOLITAN AREAS BY AVERAGE ANNUAL RATE OF CENTRAL CITY CHANGE, SIZE OF CENTRAL CITY, AND DECADE, 1900 - 1950

| *Average annual rate of change and size of central city* | *1940-50* | *1930-40* | *1920-30* | *1910-20* | *1900-10* |
|---|---|---|---|---|---|
| Total | 143 | 157 | 155 | 153 | 148 |
| High | 43 | 51 | 50 | 48 | 44 |
| 1,000,000 and over | 2 | 2 | 1 | - | - |
| 500,000 - 1,000,000 | - | - | - | - | - |
| 250,000 - 500,000 | 2 | 4 | - | 1 | 1 |
| 100,000 - 250,000 | 11 | 10 | 7 | 1 | - |
| Under 100,000 | 28 | 35 | 42 | 46 | 43 |
| Medium | 51 | 54 | 54 | 54 | 54 |
| 1,000,000 and over | 1 | 1 | 1 | 1 | 1 |
| 500,000 - 1,000,000 | 6 | 5 | 3 | 2 | - |
| 250,000 - 500,000 | 5 | 6 | 4 | 4 | 6 |
| 100,000 - 250,000 | 14 | 15 | 14 | 10 | 5 |
| Under 100,000 | 25 | 27 | 32 | 37 | 42 |
| Low | 49 | 52 | 51 | 51 | 50 |
| 1,000,000 and over | 2 | 2 | 2 | 2 | 2 |
| 500,000 - 1,000,000 | 4 | 5 | 5 | 4 | 3 |
| 250,000 - 500,000 | 4 | 5 | 3 | 3 | 4 |
| 100,000 - 250,000 | 16 | 16 | 16 | 13 | 10 |
| Under 100,000 | 23 | 24 | 25 | 29 | 31 |

TABLE 21. PER CENT CHANGE OF POPULATION IN STANDARD METROPOLITAN AREAS, BY TYPE OF PLACE, AVERAGE ANNUAL RATE OF CENTRAL CITY CHANGE, AND DECADE, 1900-1950

| *Type of place and average annual rate of change* | *1940-50* | *1930-40* | *1920-30* | *1910-20* | *1900-10* |
|---|---|---|---|---|---|
| Actual | | | | | |
| Total | | | | | |
| High | 37.1 | 16.7 | 46.6 | 55.2 | 42.0 |
| Medium | 18.9 | 8.2 | 25.7 | 24.3 | 34.7 |
| Low | 12.0 | 3.9 | 17.8 | 18.1 | 22.9 |
| Central cities | | | | | |
| High | 27.9 | 11.5 | 53.4 | 73.8 | 72.9 |
| Medium | 9.9 | 6.2 | 21.6 | 24.8 | 37.6 |
| Low | 5.6 | 0.8 | 11.7 | 17.5 | 20.9 |
| Satellite areas | | | | | |
| High | 50.5 | 25.5 | 35.2 | 32.1 | 17.0 |
| Medium | 35.4 | 11.9 | 34.3 | 23.1 | 29.3 |
| Low | 19.8 | 8.0 | 27.3 | 19.0 | 25.9 |
| Adjusted[a] | | | | | |
| Total | | | | | |
| High | 30.1 | 13.3 | 39.4 | 33.8 | 17.9 |
| Medium | 19.8 | 8.5 | 26.3 | 26.3 | 30.3 |
| Low | 12.7 | 3.9 | 18.4 | 18.6 | 23.3 |
| Central cities | | | | | |
| High | 22.2 | 9.0 | 39.4 | 33.8 | 30.0 |
| Medium | 10.1 | 6.2 | 21.6 | 26.2 | 34.1 |
| Low | 5.7 | 0.8 | 12.0 | 17.6 | 22.4 |
| Satellite areas | | | | | |
| High | 41.6 | 20.5 | 39.7 | 22.9 | 7.8 |
| Medium | 37.4 | 13.0 | 36.2 | 26.3 | 23.2 |
| Low | 21.2 | 8.6 | 28.5 | 20.1 | 24.7 |

[a]Adjusted for size of central city. Size distribution of all areas used as the standard.

An examination of the adjusted rates in Table 21 reveals that the association observed in the unadjusted rates is independent of variations in the size of central city population. The adjustment of rates in each growth class to a standard distribution of central city sizes introduces a number of minor changes, however. For example, the amount of difference in rates is reduced in almost every type of place and decade series. The most striking change of this kind occurs in the central city rates for the first three decades of the period. Evidently the very large proportion of metropolitan areas with small central cities that fell into the high growth class (see Table 20) exaggerated the unadjusted rates for that class. The direct relationship of population change with average annual growth rate of central city observable in the unadjusted rates for all metropolitan areas in 1900-10 disappears when rates are adjusted. That seems to be due to the widened spread of rates for satellite areas. In view of the failure of the adjustment of rates to have added any important correction of the observed relationship, no further adjustment of the data seems necessary.

Growth rates of total populations have declined more or less steadily through the 50-year period regardless of the trends that prevailed in central cities. It is to be noted, furthermore, that the unevenness of decline, which has been attributed to the unique historical events of the 1910-20 and the 1930-40 decades, has not been eliminated by controlling the rate of central city growth. In satellite areas the trend of decline is evident only in the low class and the trend there is irregular.

The direct relationship between average annual rate of central city growth and the growth of population in satellite areas is shown in Fig. 21 and appears to hold in most distance zones after 1910. The relationship is reversed in the 1900-10 decade. Areas with slowly growing central cities started the 50-year period with comparatively high rates in all zones and ended the half century with relatively low rates of increase. Growth rates moved in an opposite direction in the satellite zones of areas with rapidly growing central cities, not, however, without some unevenness. In the medium class the trend has corresponded fairly closely with that of the high areas.

It is only in the 1900-1910 decade that Fig. 21 lends even partial support to the hypothesis that central cities grow at the expense of satellite areas; the record of the following decades appears to contradict the hypothesis. Yet, although the expected effect of central city growth on satellite growth is not perceptible in comparisons of absolute rates, it may emerge when those rates are reduced to relative values.

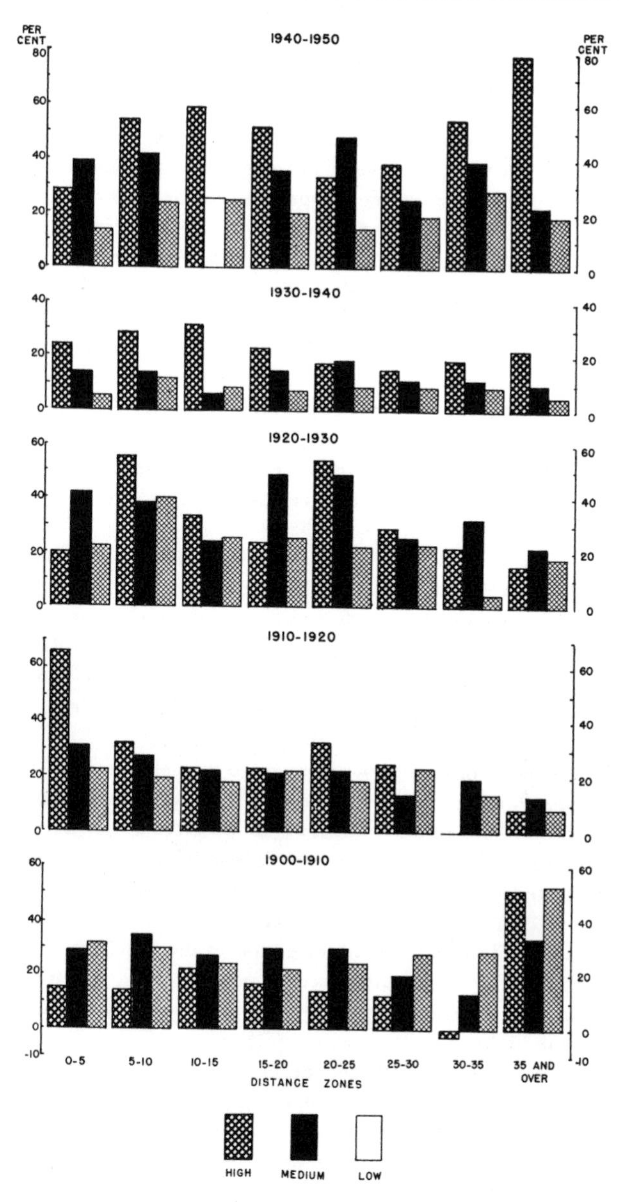


FIGURE 21
PER CENT CHANGE OF POPULATION IN DISTANCE ZONES OF STANDARD METROPOLITAN AREAS, BY AVERAGE ANNUAL RATE OF CHANGE OF CENTRAL CITY POPULATION AND BY DECADE, 1900-1950

The ratios of satellite rates to central city rates of change reveal a clear inverse relationship between the relative growth of satellite population and the average annual increase of central city population. Table 22 reveals exceptions only in the last two decades of the period under study. In other words, deconcentration has proceeded most rapidly where the central city has grown most slowly. It seems quite probable, therefore, that satellite growth is an inverse function of central city growth; as one increases the other tends to decrease or to grow at a reduced rate. The figures support the assumption that metropolitan growth is a unitary phenomenon rather than an arithmetic summation of two or more growth tendencies.

The ratios for distance zones, described in Fig. 22, conform to the pattern observed in Table 22, despite many overlappings of the curves. Not until after 1930 do the ratios for areas with the most rapidly growing central cities rise above unity in any zone. On the other hand, in the areas with the slowest growing central cities ratios fall below unity only in zones beyond 30 miles from metropolitan centers in the early decades. A conspicuous feature of Fig. 22 is the lack of clear cut gradients in the distributions of ratios. Even the comparatively flat gradients observed in Fig. 6 appear to have been vitiated by the subdivision of all Standard Metropolitan Areas into classes based on average annual rate of central city change.

A comparison of the distributions of the amounts of population increase in each decennial period reveals a marked centrifugal tendency in all classes of areas. As may be observed in Table 23, 78 per cent of all increase in high areas accrued to central cities in 1900-10, while in medium areas the proportion was 71 per cent and in low areas it was 56 per cent.

TABLE 22. RATIO OF RATE OF POPULATION CHANGE IN SATELLITE AREAS TO RATE OF CHANGE IN CENTRAL CITIES OF STANDARD METROPOLITAN AREAS, BY AVERAGE ANNUAL RATE OF CENTRAL CITY CHANGE AND BY DECADE, 1900 - 1950

| *Average annual rate of central city change* | *1940-50* | *1930-40* | *1920-30* | *1910-20* | *1900-10* |
|---|---|---|---|---|---|
| All areas | 2.7 | 2.5 | 1.4 | 0.9 | 0.8 |
| High | 1.8 | 2.2 | 0.7 | 0.4 | 0.2 |
| Medium | 3.6 | 1.9 | 1.6 | 0.9 | 0.8 |
| Low | 3.5 | 10.0 | 2.3 | 1.1 | 1.2 |

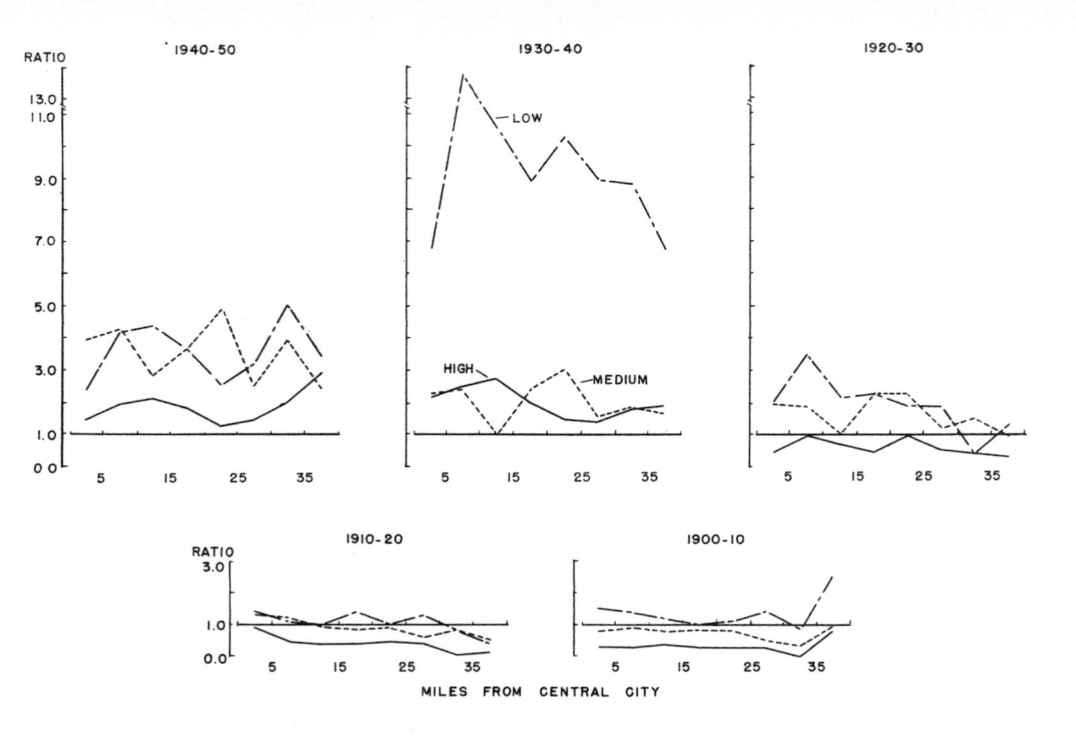


FIGURE 22
RATIO OF RATE OF POPULATION CHANGE IN DISTANCE ZONES TO CENTRAL CITY RATE OF CHANGE IN STANDARD METROPOLITAN AREAS, BY AVERAGE ANNUAL RATE OF CHANGE OF CENTRAL CITY POPULATION AND BY DECADE, 1900-1950

In 1940-50 these proportions had declined to 44, 34, and 26, respectively. But in 1940-50 a radius of more than 10 miles was required to contain the proportion of the increment claimed by central cities of both high and medium areas in 1900-10. In low areas a radius of less than 10 miles contained in 1940-50 the proportion of the increase that went to central cities in the first decade. Thus while the core parts of metropolitan areas with slowly growing central cities received relatively small shares of the gains, the dispersion of the increases to population at least within a 15-mile ra radius proceeded more rapidly in areas with rapidly growing central cities. Actually, however, dispersion over the total metropolitan area moved at a faster pace in low than in either medium or high areas. In spite of the centrifugal tendencies of growth, the fact remains that the more rapid the rate of central city growth the smaller is the proportion of all growth attracted to satellite areas. Needless to say, this adds further confirmation to the inferences that central city growth detracts from satellite area growth.

Despite the uninterrupted dispersion of population increase there has been a concentration of population through part of the 50-year period at least in each class of metropolitan areas. In the high areas, Table 24 shows, concentration continued to 1930, after which deconcentration set in. Concentration in the medium areas gave way to deconcentration after 1920. And in the low areas concentration within a radius of 15 miles ended in 1910, but in the more distant zones the centripetal trend persisted to 1920. The rates of redistribution are more clearly visible in Fig. 23. It will be observed that each of the three classes of areas began the study period with declining rates of redistribution. In each case the decline ended in the decade in which concentration yielded to deconcentration. Thereafter the rate of redistribution increased as deconcentration progressed. Steeper rises for low and medium than for high areas are apparent.

## Size and Type of Satellite Places

In general, all sizes and types of satellite places have grown at rates which vary directly with the average annual rate of central city growth. As Table 25 shows, that association is repeated in the data for every decade. Frequently, however, rates of change are higher in the medium than in the high class of metropolitan areas, especially in the 20-30 mile zones.

A more or less consistent pattern of change in the rates of change is observable in each of the three classes of metropolitan areas. Unincorporated area rates increased over the 50 years and the rates of change in

## TABLE 23. CUMULATIVE PERCENTAGE DISTRIBUTION OF POPULATION INCREASE IN STANDARD METROPOLITAN AREAS, BY AVERAGE ANNUAL RATE OF CENTRAL CITY CHANGE, DISTANCE FROM CENTRAL CITY, AND DECADE, 1900 - 1950

| *Average annual rate of central city change and distance from central city* | *1940-50* | *1930-40* | *1920-30* | *1910-20* | *1900-10* |
|---|---|---|---|---|---|
| High | | | | | |
| Central cities | 44.5 | 43.3 | 71.5 | 74.0 | 77.7 |
| 0 - 5 miles | 50.3 | 51.2 | 74.8 | 82.2 | 80.8 |
| 5 - 10 " | 68.7 | 69.4 | 84.9 | 88.8 | 85.6 |
| 10 - 15 " | 84.1 | 85.4 | 91.7 | 93.9 | 92.9 |
| 15 - 20 " | 92.5 | 93.9 | 94.9 | 97.4 | 96.5 |
| 20 - 25 " | 95.7 | 97.2 | 98.8 | 99.1 | 97.7 |
| 25 - 30 " | 97.0 | 98.3 | 99.5 | 99.8 | 98.3 |
| 30 - 35 " | 98.1 | 99.0 | 99.7 | 99.8 | 98.3 |
| 35 miles and over | 100.0 | 100.0 | 100.0 | 100.0 | 100.0 |
| Medium | | | | | |
| Central cities | 33.7 | 49.7 | 56.9 | 68.7 | 70.7 |
| 0 - 5 miles | 41.2 | 55.7 | 61.9 | 72.7 | 73.6 |
| 5 - 10 " | 66.1 | 74.5 | 76.6 | 83.6 | 83.7 |
| 10 - 15 " | 78.2 | 81.4 | 84.9 | 92.0 | 91.5 |
| 15 - 20 " | 86.8 | 89.2 | 91.7 | 95.2 | 94.8 |
| 20 - 25 " | 93.9 | 95.0 | 96.0 | 97.4 | 96.9 |
| 25 - 30 " | 96.1 | 96.8 | 97.6 | 98.3 | 98.0 |
| 30 - 35 " | 98.2 | 98.2 | 98.8 | 99.1 | 98.4 |
| 35 miles and over | 100.0 | 100.0 | 100.0 | 100.0 | 100.0 |
| Low | | | | | |
| Central cities | 25.8 | 12.1 | 39.9 | 58.7 | 56.1 |
| 0 - 5 miles | 35.8 | 24.5 | 50.9 | 69.1 | 66.8 |
| 5 - 10 " | 61.1 | 58.9 | 75.1 | 80.3 | 80.1 |
| 10 - 15 " | 78.4 | 75.6 | 85.4 | 87.4 | 87.9 |
| 15 - 20 " | 87.3 | 84.7 | 92.1 | 93.0 | 92.2 |
| 20 - 25 " | 91.3 | 91.5 | 95.7 | 96.0 | 95.3 |
| 25 - 30 " | 94.9 | 95.9 | 98.3 | 98.5 | 97.7 |
| 30 - 35 " | 97.3 | 97.8 | 98.6 | 99.3 | 98.6 |
| 35 miles and over | 100.0 | 100.0 | 100.0 | 100.0 | 100.0 |

## TABLE 24. CUMULATIVE PERCENTAGE DISTRIBUTION OF POPULATION IN STANDARD METROPOLITAN AREAS, BY AVERAGE ANNUAL RATE OF CENTRAL CITY CHANGE, DISTANCE ZONE, AND CENSUS YEAR, 1900 - 1950

| *Average annual rate of central city change, and distance zone* | *1950* | *1940* | *1930* | *1920* | *1910* | *1900* |
|---|---|---|---|---|---|---|
| High | | | | | | |
| Central cities | 55.3 | 59.3 | 62.9 | 62.3 | 55.3 | 44.8 |
| 0 - 5 miles | 61.0 | 65.0 | 68.3 | 69.7 | 62.1 | 53.7 |
| 5 - 10 " | 75.2 | 77.7 | 79.0 | 78.3 | 73.3 | 67.9 |
| 10 - 15 " | 86.5 | 87.5 | 87.7 | 87.7 | 85.4 | 82.7 |
| 15 - 20 " | 93.3 | 93.6 | 94.0 | 94.0 | 93.7 | 92.3 |
| 20 - 25 " | 96.8 | 97.2 | 97.3 | 97.4 | 96.6 | 96.0 |
| 25 - 30 " | 98.0 | 98.4 | 98.6 | 98.6 | 98.1 | 97.9 |
| 30 - 35 " | 98.8 | 99.1 | 99.2 | 99.0 | 98.6 | 98.6 |
| 35 miles and over | 100.0 | 100.0 | 100.0 | 100.0 | 100.0 | 100.0 |
| Medium | | | | | | |
| Central cities | 59.6 | 64.5 | 65.5 | 67.7 | 67.2 | 65.3 |
| 0 - 5 miles | 63.9 | 68.2 | 69.1 | 70.9 | 70.4 | 69.0 |
| 5 - 10 " | 77.4 | 79.6 | 80.0 | 80.8 | 80.3 | 79.1 |
| 10 - 15 " | 86.7 | 88.4 | 89.1 | 90.1 | 89.6 | 89.1 |
| 15 - 20 " | 92.0 | 93.0 | 93.4 | 93.7 | 93.3 | 92.9 |
| 20 - 25 " | 95.5 | 95.8 | 96.0 | 96.0 | 95.6 | 95.3 |
| 25 - 30 " | 97.3 | 97.5 | 97.6 | 97.6 | 97.3 | 97.2 |
| 30 - 35 " | 98.5 | 98.5 | 98.6 | 98.5 | 98.3 | 98.3 |
| 35 miles and over | 100.0 | 100.0 | 100.0 | 100.0 | 100.0 | 100.0 |
| Low | | | | | | |
| Central cities | 52.0 | 55.1 | 57.7 | 60.8 | 60.8 | 61.3 |
| 0 - 5 miles | 61.4 | 64.4 | 66.6 | 69.3 | 69.2 | 69.3 |
| 5 - 10 " | 75.8 | 77.5 | 79.2 | 79.9 | 80.0 | 79.7 |
| 10 - 15 " | 85.3 | 86.1 | 87.0 | 87.3 | 87.3 | 87.0 |
| 15 - 20 " | 91.0 | 91.4 | 92.0 | 92.0 | 91.9 | 91.7 |
| 20 - 25 " | 94.5 | 94.8 | 95.2 | 95.1 | 95.0 | 94.8 |
| 25 - 30 " | 97.0 | 97.2 | 97.4 | 97.2 | 97.1 | 96.8 |
| 30 - 35 " | 98.2 | 98.2 | 98.4 | 98.3 | 98.2 | 98.0 |
| 35 miles and over | 100.0 | 100.0 | 100.0 | 100.0 | 100.0 | 100.0 |

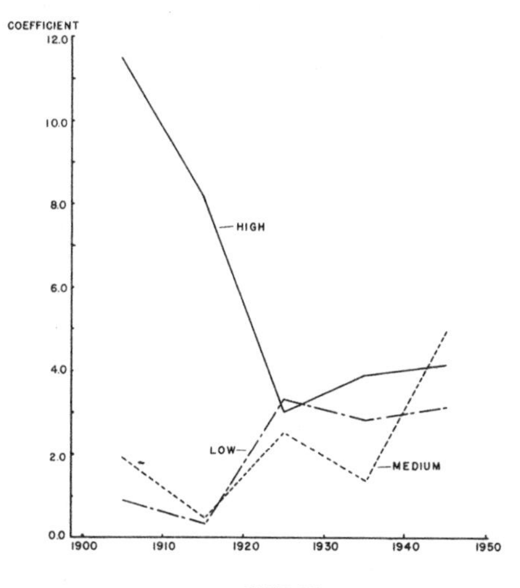


FIGURE 23
COEFFICIENTS OF POPULATION REDISTRIBUTION IN STANDARD METROPOLITAN AREAS, BY AVERAGE ANNUAL RATE OF CHANGE OF CENTRAL CITY POPULATION, 1900-1950

in incorporated places decreased. The largest declines occurred in the biggest satellite incorporated places. In areas with slow growing central cities incorporated places of 10,000 or more population lost population with increasing frequency in the later decades. Changes in the rates of change appear to have been most extreme where the average rate of central city growth has been highest. That appears with greatest clarity at the extremes of the satellite size range, that is, in the rates of unincorporated area and of the largest incorporated places.

But, as previously observed, when rates of change are expressed as ratios to central city rates the direct relationship with average annual rate of central city growth becomes an inverse relationship (Table 26). A notable exception, though not an entirely consistent one, is supplied by the incorporated places of 10,000 or more population. Ratios for such places tend to increase with the rate of central city growth.

In metropolitan areas with low rates of central city growth the highest ratios moved from incorporated places of less than 10,000 population to unincorporated area. This shift seems to have been completed in 1930-40. A similar change occurred in areas with central cities that had medium growth rates, but it was not until 1940-50 that unincorporated area emerged as, in relative terms, the most rapidly growing type of satellite place. Likewise, in areas with central cities that had the highest average annual rates of change such a change was in the making, though it had not been consumated by 1940-50.

Table 25. Per Cent Change of Satellite Population in Standard Metropolitan Areas, by Size and Type of Satellite Place, Distance Zone, Average Annual Rate of Central City Change, and Decade, 1900-1950

| Size and type of place and distance zone | High | | | | | Medium | | | | | Low | | | | |
|---|---|---|---|---|---|---|---|---|---|---|---|---|---|---|---|
| | 1940-1950 | 1930-1940 | 1920-1930 | 1910-1920 | 1900-1910 | 1940-1950 | 1930-1940 | 1920-1930 | 1910-1920 | 1900-1910 | 1940-1950 | 1930-1940 | 1920-1930 | 1910-1920 | 1900-1910 |
| 50,000 and over | | | | | | | | | | | | | | | |
| 0-10 miles | 21.5[a] | 10.1 | ----- | ----- | ----- | 13.2 | -1.3 | 13.9 | 21.2[a] | 46.7[a] | 5.2 | -0.3 | 7.3[a] | 11.9[a] | 23.5 |
| 10-20 miles | 48.0[a] | 15.7[a] | ----- | ----- | ----- | 4.2 | 0.2 | 13.7 | 19.0 | 35.5 | 4.7[a] | -1.6[a] | 5.5[a] | 21.8[a] | ----- |
| 20-30 miles | 10.6[a] | 2.6[a] | ----- | ----- | ----- | ----- | ----- | ----- | ----- | ----- | 18.2[a] | 10.3[a] | 81.3[a] | ----- | ----- |
| 30 miles and over | ----- | ----- | ----- | ----- | ----- | ----- | ----- | ----- | ----- | ----- | ----- | ----- | ----- | ----- | ----- |
| 10,000 - 50,000 | | | | | | | | | | | | | | | |
| 0-10 miles | 35.7 | 17.1 | 41.2 | 63.9[a] | 90.5[a] | 14.4 | 26.2 | 44.7 | 24.1 | 41.3[a] | 0.5 | -10.7 | 25.1 | 22.7 | 23.0 |
| 10-20 miles | 50.4[a] | 17.8[a] | 41.1[a] | 36.1[a] | 10.8[a] | 19.7 | 7.9 | 44.9 | 307.2 | 206.3[a] | 31.6 | 3.4 | 24.2 | -16.5 | 37.3 |
| 20-30 miles | 42.0[a] | 5.5[a] | 89.4[a] | ----- | ----- | 13.8 | 12.0 | 21.7 | 35.2[a] | 26.2[a] | -0.5 | -0.3 | 21.6 | 38.5 | 46.4[a] |
| 30 miles and over | 42.6[a] | 5.3[a] | ----- | ----- | ----- | 30.4 | 0.2 | 2.0[a] | 27.6[a] | 27.2[a] | 12.5 | 1.9 | 25.8 | 15.2 | 18.3[a] |
| 2,500 - 10,000 | | | | | | | | | | | | | | | |
| 0-10 miles | 84.8 | 13.6 | 65.9 | 167.7 | 29.8 | 43.2 | 18.1 | 54.6 | 47.2 | 62.3 | 7.2 | 3.0 | 29.2 | 20.7 | 39.8 |
| 10-20 miles | 90.4 | 29.0 | 54.7 | 41.5 | 35.1[a] | 42.6 | 14.2 | 67.2 | 29.5 | -49.1 | 21.3 | 6.4 | 45.4 | 32.0 | 42.5 |
| 20-30 miles | 6.9 | 7.8[a] | 40.3[a] | ----- | 48.8[a] | 30.3 | 7.3 | 24.4 | 15.6 | 2.2 | 12.1 | 6.0 | 37.5 | 18.2 | 42.1 |
| 30 miles and over | 61.0 | 76.3[a] | -2.8[a] | -28.6[a] | ----- | 18.5 | 4.4 | 34.7 | 23.0 | 47.4 | 17.3 | 3.6 | 15.0 | 10.9 | 39.0 |
| Under 2,500 | | | | | | | | | | | | | | | |
| 0-10 miles | 49.8 | 26.4 | 170.7 | 22.1 | 38.2 | 52.9 | 25.7 | 104.6 | 44.1 | 64.0 | 23.1 | 13.6 | 41.2 | 34.7 | 51.6 |
| 10-20 miles | 38.7 | 20.2 | 25.7 | 34.1 | 20.8 | 36.7 | 16.5 | 54.8 | 26.0 | 33.2 | 27.1 | 7.6 | 35.5 | 27.4 | 21.1 |
| 20-30 miles | 24.3 | 15.8 | 12.6 | 19.3 | 16.8 | 37.3 | 12.3 | 30.2 | 28.9 | 28.5 | 18.3 | 10.2 | 25.0 | 21.0 | 38.2 |
| 30 miles and over | 24.5 | 17.5 | 17.7 | -15.1 | 5.4 | 19.5 | 6.2 | 14.1 | 27.2 | 35.5 | 20.6 | 5.3 | 16.0 | 5.5 | 21.6 |
| Unincorporated area | | | | | | | | | | | | | | | |
| 0-10 miles | 54.6 | 38.3 | 23.9 | 30.2 | 9.3 | 73.4 | 16.7 | 42.8 | 26.4 | 18.3 | 38.4 | 25.6 | 50.1 | 20.5 | 30.5 |
| 10-20 miles | 53.4 | 31.7 | 24.8 | 20.1 | 17.8 | 70.1 | 18.4 | 25.3 | -15.1 | 31.8 | 22.9 | 12.3 | 19.9 | 34.8 | 10.1 |
| 20-30 miles | 43.2 | 21.6 | 44.5 | 32.1 | 10.5 | 58.4 | 20.7 | 58.6 | 8.3 | 38.7 | 25.8 | 13.4 | 5.6 | 8.9 | 12.9 |
| 30 miles and over | 87.6 | 24.4 | 17.6 | 18.1 | 41.4 | 34.7 | 17.7 | 31.0 | 7.4 | 17.0 | 30.5 | 10.4 | 0.7 | 7.5 | 10.4 |

[a] Based on less than five incorporated places.

Table 26. Ratio of Rate of Change of Satellite Population to Central City Rate of Change in Standard Metropolitan Areas, by Size and Type of Satellite Place, Distance Zone, Average Annual Rate of Central City Change, and Decade, 1900-1950

| Size and type of satellite place and distance zone | High | | | | | Medium | | | | | Low | | | | |
|---|---|---|---|---|---|---|---|---|---|---|---|---|---|---|---|
| | 1940-1950 | 1930-1940 | 1920-1930 | 1910-1920 | 1900-1910 | 1940-1950 | 1930-1940 | 1920-1930 | 1910-1920 | 1900-1910 | 1940-1950 | 1930-1940 | 1920-1930 | 1910-1920 | 1900-1910 |
| 50,000 and over | | | | | | | | | | | | | | | |
| 0-10 miles | 0.8 | 0.9 | ---- | ---- | ---- | 1.3 | -0.2 | 0.6 | 0.9 | 1.2 | 0.9 | -0.4 | 0.6 | 0.7 | 1.1 |
| 10-20 miles | 1.7 | 1.4 | ---- | ---- | ---- | 0.4 | 0.0 | 0.6 | 0.8 | 0.9 | 0.8 | -2.0 | 0.5 | 1.2 | ---- |
| 20-30 miles | 0.4 | 0.2 | ---- | ---- | ---- | ---- | ---- | ---- | ---- | ---- | 3.2 | 12.9 | 6.9 | ---- | ---- |
| 30 miles and over | ---- | ---- | ---- | ---- | ---- | ---- | ---- | ---- | ---- | ---- | ---- | ---- | ---- | ---- | ---- |
| 10,000 - 50,000 | | | | | | | | | | | | | | | |
| 0-10 miles | 1.3 | 1.5 | 0.8 | 0.9 | 1.2 | 1.5 | 4.2 | 2.1 | 1.0 | 1.1 | 0.1 | -13.4 | 2.1 | 1.3 | 1.1 |
| 10-20 miles | 1.8 | 1.5 | 0.8 | 0.5 | 0.1 | 2.0 | 1.3 | 2.1 | 12.4 | 5.5 | 5.6 | 4.2 | 2.1 | -0.9 | 1.8 |
| 20-30 miles | 1.5 | 0.5 | 1.7 | ---- | ---- | 1.4 | 1.9 | 1.0 | 1.4 | 0.7 | -0.1 | -0.4 | 1.8 | 2.2 | 2.2 |
| 30 miles and over | 1.5 | 0.5 | ---- | ---- | ---- | 3.1 | 0.0 | 0.1 | 1.1 | 0.7 | 2.2 | 2.4 | 2.2 | 0.9 | 0.9 |
| 2,500 - 10,000 | | | | | | | | | | | | | | | |
| 0-10 miles | 3.0 | 1.2 | 1.2 | 2.3 | 0.4 | 4.4 | 2.9 | 2.5 | 1.9 | 1.7 | 1.3 | 3.8 | 2.5 | 1.2 | 1.9 |
| 10-20 miles | 3.2 | 2.5 | 1.0 | 0.6 | 0.5 | 4.3 | 2.3 | 3.1 | 1.2 | -1.3 | 3.8 | 8.0 | 3.9 | 1.8 | 2.0 |
| 20-30 miles | 0.2 | 0.7 | 0.8 | ---- | 0.7 | 3.1 | 1.2 | 1.1 | 0.6 | 0.1 | 2.2 | 7.5 | 3.2 | 1.0 | 2.0 |
| 30 miles and over | 2.2 | 6.6 | -0.1 | 0.4 | ---- | 1.9 | 0.7 | 1.6 | 0.9 | 1.3 | 3.1 | 4.5 | 1.3 | 0.6 | 1.9 |
| Under 2,500 | | | | | | | | | | | | | | | |
| 0-10 miles | 1.8 | 2.3 | 3.2 | 0.3 | 0.5 | 5.3 | 4.1 | 4.8 | 1.8 | 1.7 | 4.1 | 17.0 | 3.5 | 2.0 | 2.5 |
| 10-20 miles | 1.4 | 1.8 | 0.5 | 0.5 | 0.3 | 3.7 | 2.7 | 2.4 | 1.0 | 0.9 | 4.8 | 9.5 | 3.0 | 1.6 | 1.0 |
| 20-30 miles | 0.9 | 1.4 | 0.2 | 0.3 | 0.2 | 3.8 | 2.0 | 1.4 | 1.2 | 0.8 | 3.3 | 12.8 | 2.1 | 1.2 | 1.8 |
| 30 miles and over | 0.9 | 1.5 | 0.3 | -0.2 | 0.1 | 2.0 | 1.0 | 0.7 | 1.1 | 0.9 | 3.7 | 6.6 | 1.4 | 0.3 | 1.0 |
| Unincorporated area | | | | | | | | | | | | | | | |
| 0-10 miles | 2.0 | 3.3 | 0.4 | 0.4 | 0.1 | 7.4 | 2.7 | 2.0 | 1.1 | 0.5 | 6.9 | 32.0 | 4.3 | 1.2 | 1.5 |
| 10-20 miles | 1.9 | 2.8 | 0.5 | 0.3 | 0.2 | 7.1 | 3.0 | 1.2 | -0.6 | 0.8 | 4.1 | 15.4 | 1.7 | 2.0 | 0.5 |
| 20-30 miles | 1.5 | 1.9 | 0.8 | 0.4 | 0.1 | 5.9 | 3.3 | 2.7 | 0.3 | 1.0 | 4.6 | 16.8 | 0.5 | 0.5 | 0.6 |
| 30 miles and over | 3.1 | 2.1 | 0.3 | 0.2 | 0.6 | 3.5 | 2.9 | 1.4 | 0.3 | 0.5 | 5.4 | 13.0 | 0.1 | 0.4 | 0.5 |

It is apparent, therefore, that deconcentration has progressed most rapidly in areas with slow growing central cities and that it has been directed mainly toward the small incorporated places and unincorporated area. The trends in areas with higher rates of central city growth, however, indicate an accelerating deconcentration and with similar results.

In view of the differentials in rates of deconcentration that have been described, the percentage distributions by size and type of satellite place within each distance zone, as shown in Table 27, contain a number of points of interest. For example, the concentration of population in large incorporated places, i.e., 10,000 or more population, has been highest where the average annual rate of central city change has been lowest. On the other hand, the proportion of population in unincorporated area has varied directly with the rate of central city change. In this connection it should be noted that in all classes of metropolitan areas the proportions in unincorporated areas declined from 1900 to 1930 and then increased through the following census years. These facts, together with the growing tendency for unincorporated area to increase more rapidly than other types of satellite places, make it seem doubtful that the proportion of all population in unincorporated areas will ever drop to as low a figure in the high class of metropolitan areas as it has been in the class of areas with low rates of central city change. This depends somewhat on the observed tendency of large satellite places to continue the relatively high growth rates in metropolitan areas with high average annual rates of central city change.

Table 27. Per Cent Distribution of Satellite Population in Standard Metropolitan Areas, by Size and Type of Satellite Place, Census Year, Average Annual Rate of Central City Change, and Distance Zone, 1900-1950

| Census year and size and type of satellite place | High | | | | Medium | | | | Low | | | |
|---|---|---|---|---|---|---|---|---|---|---|---|---|
| | Miles from central city | | | | Miles from central city | | | | Miles from central city | | | |
| | 0-10 miles | 10-20 miles | 20-30 miles | 30 miles and over | 0-10 miles | 10-20 miles | 20-30 miles | 30 miles and over | 0-10 miles | 10-20 miles | 20-30 miles | 30 miles and over |
| **1950** | | | | | | | | | | | | |
| Total | 100.0 | 100.0 | 100.0 | 100.0 | 100.0 | 100.0 | 100.0 | 100.0 | 100.0 | 100.0 | 100.0 | 100.0 |
| 50,000 and over | 10.4 | 10.9 | 9.5 | ----- | 21.3 | 27.9 | ----- | ----- | 16.8 | 8.2 | 13.6 | ----- |
| 10,000 - 50,000 | 18.6 | 15.0 | 8.3 | 13.9 | 17.6 | 23.4 | 22.9 | 15.3 | 19.6 | 17.3 | 20.9 | 28.5 |
| 2,500 - 10,000 | 10.0 | 13.3 | 8.5 | 9.7 | 10.9 | 12.4 | 16.9 | 20.9 | 11.2 | 12.7 | 17.8 | 12.4 |
| Under 2,500 | 2.9 | 4.8 | 4.8 | 10.4 | 4.1 | 6.5 | 7.6 | 7.3 | 3.5 | 7.9 | 9.3 | 10.9 |
| Unincorporated area | 58.1 | 56.0 | 68.9 | 66.0 | 46.1 | 29.8 | 52.6 | 56.5 | 48.9 | 53.9 | 38.4 | 48.2 |
| **1940** | | | | | | | | | | | | |
| Total | 100.0 | 100.0 | 100.0 | 100.0 | 100.0 | 100.0 | 100.0 | 100.0 | 100.0 | 100.0 | 100.0 | 100.0 |
| 50,000 and over | 12.7 | 11.4 | 11.6 | ----- | 26.5 | 34.6 | ----- | ----- | 19.0 | 9.6 | 13.0 | ----- |
| 10,000 - 50,000 | 20.4 | 15.5 | 7.8 | 16.5 | 21.7 | 25.3 | 28.1 | 15.2 | 23.2 | 16.1 | 24.3 | 31.0 |
| 2,500 - 10,000 | 8.1 | 10.8 | 10.7 | 10.2 | 10.7 | 11.3 | 18.1 | 22.8 | 12.4 | 12.8 | 18.3 | 13.0 |
| Under 2,500 | 2.8 | 5.4 | 5.2 | 14.0 | 3.7 | 6.2 | 7.6 | 7.9 | 3.4 | 7.7 | 9.1 | 11.0 |
| Unincorporated area | 56.0 | 56.9 | 64.7 | 59.3 | 37.4 | 22.6 | 46.2 | 54.1 | 42.0 | 53.8 | 35.3 | 45.0 |
| **1930** | | | | | | | | | | | | |
| Total | 100.0 | 100.0 | 100.0 | 100.0 | 100.0 | 100.0 | 100.0 | 100.0 | 100.0 | 100.0 | 100.0 | 100.0 |
| 50,000 and over | 16.2 | 8.3 | 12.5 | ----- | 28.5 | 36.6 | ----- | ----- | 20.5 | 10.1 | 12.1 | ----- |
| 10,000 - 50,000 | 18.7 | 14.5 | 8.2 | 18.8 | 21.5 | 21.4 | 26.2 | 16.7 | 23.8 | 21.9 | 24.4 | 31.4 |
| 2,500 - 10,000 | 9.7 | 11.1 | 10.6 | 1.8 | 10.4 | 10.4 | 21.3 | 23.4 | 12.4 | 13.4 | 17.5 | 12.9 |
| Under 2,500 | 3.8 | 6.5 | 5.6 | 22.1 | 3.2 | 6.6 | 8.3 | 8.6 | 3.6 | 8.0 | 9.5 | 11.9 |
| Unincorporated area | 51.6 | 59.6 | 63.1 | 57.3 | 36.4 | 25.0 | 44.2 | 51.3 | 39.7 | 46.6 | 36.5 | 43.8 |
| **1920** | | | | | | | | | | | | |
| Total | 100.0 | 100.0 | 100.0 | 100.0 | 100.0 | 100.0 | 100.0 | 100.0 | 100.0 | 100.0 | 100.0 | 100.0 |
| 50,000 and over | ----- | ----- | ----- | ----- | 30.0 | 36.1 | ----- | ----- | 16.5 | 5.7 | 4.9 | ----- |
| 10,000 - 50,000 | 17.2 | 17.5 | 12.1 | ----- | 17.0 | 14.1 | 23.8 | 16.1 | 27.3 | 20.7 | 26.5 | 26.1 |
| 2,500 - 10,000 | 9.8 | 6.7 | 4.6 | 3.5 | 10.1 | 9.8 | 23.3 | 20.7 | 14.6 | 14.8 | 16.4 | 12.7 |
| Under 2,500 | 5.3 | 10.4 | 7.7 | 23.4 | 4.9 | 8.2 | 9.9 | 10.3 | 4.7 | 9.3 | 11.5 | 12.4 |
| Unincorporated area | 67.7 | 65.4 | 75.6 | 73.1 | 38.0 | 31.8 | 43.0 | 52.9 | 36.9 | 49.5 | 40.7 | 48.8 |
| **1910** | | | | | | | | | | | | |
| Total | 100.0 | 100.0 | 100.0 | 100.0 | 100.0 | 100.0 | 100.0 | 100.0 | 100.0 | 100.0 | 100.0 | 100.0 |
| 50,000 and over | ----- | ----- | ----- | ----- | 26.3 | 33.2 | ----- | ----- | 17.4 | 3.4 | ----- | ----- |
| 10,000 - 50,000 | 4.7 | 3.0 | ----- | ----- | 15.1 | 5.5 | 23.8 | 11.7 | 23.7 | 28.3 | 23.4 | 24.9 |
| 2,500 - 10,000 | 10.2 | 5.2 | ----- | 5.7 | 9.9 | 8.8 | 18.6 | 20.0 | 13.8 | 13.7 | 17.8 | 10.4 |
| Under 2,500 | 6.3 | 10.6 | 13.4 | 27.5 | 5.6 | 8.9 | 13.0 | 11.7 | 5.7 | 11.3 | 14.3 | 12.9 |
| Unincorporated area | 78.8 | 81.2 | 86.6 | 66.8 | 43.1 | 43.6 | 44.6 | 56.6 | 39.4 | 43.3 | 44.5 | 51.8 |
| **1900** | | | | | | | | | | | | |
| Total | 100.0 | 100.0 | 100.0 | 100.0 | 100.0 | 100.0 | 100.0 | 100.0 | 100.0 | 100.0 | 100.0 | 100.0 |
| 50,000 and over | ----- | ----- | ----- | ----- | 20.7 | 24.9 | ----- | ----- | 13.3 | ----- | ----- | ----- |
| 10,000 - 50,000 | 2.8 | 1.8 | ----- | ----- | 13.8 | .9 | 17.1 | 9.3 | 25.6 | 29.3 | 9.1 | 19.6 |
| 2,500 - 10,000 | 5.9 | 5.1 | 6.6 | ----- | 6.4 | 8.0 | 27.1 | 14.2 | 10.7 | 11.2 | 16.7 | 11.6 |
| Under 2,500 | 5.5 | 8.2 | 10.3 | 21.9 | 5.6 | 8.6 | 10.9 | 14.7 | 5.7 | 10.9 | 16.1 | 12.1 |
| Unincorporated area | 85.8 | 84.9 | 83.1 | 78.1 | 53.5 | 57.6 | 44.9 | 61.8 | 44.7 | 48.6 | 58.1 | 56.7 |

CHAPTER V

# DISTANCE BETWEEN CENTRAL CITIES AND POPULATION REDISTRIBUTION

It is possible that some of the variation in patterns of population redistribution within metropolitan areas may be affected by the distances between areas. Where areas are located in close proximity to one another the advantages of accessibility to two or more centers rather than to one only may be manifested in a more pronounced tendency to deconcentration than occurs where areas are widely spaced. The presence of two or more metropolitan areas within short distances of one another suggests, too, that the extent of metropolitan development in that locality may have advanced further than where areas are located far apart. If so, the tendency of population to settle in satellite zones is apt to be stronger.

Proximity is measured by air-line distances between central cities.[1] The range of distances is subdivided into three classes and all metropolitan areas are sorted accordingly. The three classes are: (1) centers within 50 miles; (2) centers more than 50 miles but less than 100 miles apart; and (3) centers 100 or more miles apart. Table 28 reports the num- of areas in each class. It would have been desirable also to control the size of central city from which distance is measured. Unfortunately, the number of metropolitan areas is too small to permit so extensive a subdivision of the data.

## Central Cities and Satellite Areas

Except for the years between 1910 and 1930 the highest growth rates occurred in the most remotely located Standard Metropolitan areas, i.e., those 100 or more miles from other metropolitan areas measured from their centers. And, as may be observed in Table 29, the lowest actual rates of change were had in areas situated within 50 miles of other metropolitan areas. A trend of decline is evident in the data for areas within 100 miles of other areas, but the most distantly located areas show no clear trend

TABLE 28. NUMBER OF STANDARD METROPOLITAN AREAS, BY DISTANCE BETWEEN CENTRAL CITIES, SIZE OF CENTRAL CITY, AND DECADE, 1900 - 1950

| *Distance between and size of central city* | *1940-50* | *1930-40* | *1920-30* | *1910-20* | *1900-10* |
|---|---|---|---|---|---|
| Total | 143 | 157 | 155 | 153 | 148 |
| Centers within 50 miles | 74 | 75 | 75 | 75 | 75 |
| 1,000,000 and over | 1 | 1 | 1 | 1 | 1 |
| 500,000 - 1,000,000 | 8 | 7 | 5 | 4 | 2 |
| 250,000 - 500,000 | 4 | 7 | 4 | 5 | 7 |
| 100,000 - 250,000 | 25 | 22 | 24 | 12 | 9 |
| Under 100,000 | 36 | 38 | 41 | 53 | 56 |
| Centers more than 50 but less than 100 miles | 52 | 59 | 58 | 58 | 56 |
| 1,000,000 and over | 4 | 4 | 3 | 2 | 2 |
| 500,000 - 1,000,000 | 1 | 2 | 2 | 1 | 1 |
| 250,000 - 500,000 | 6 | 7 | 3 | 3 | 3 |
| 100,000 - 250,000 | 13 | 15 | 10 | 9 | 5 |
| Under 100,000 | 28 | 31 | 40 | 43 | 45 |
| Centers 100 miles or more | 17 | 23 | 22 | 20 | 17 |
| 250,000 and over[a] | 2 | 2 | 1 | 1 | 1 |
| 100,000 - 250,000 | 3 | 4 | 3 | 3 | 1 |
| Under 100,000 | 12 | 17 | 18 | 16 | 15 |

[a]Includes one metropolitan area with a central city of 500,000 - 1,000,000 population.

toward declining rates. Moreover, the last named class was least affected by the retarding influences on growth incident to the 1930-1940 decade. The growth rates of central cities in the three proximity classes maintained the same relative positions observed in the data for total populations. In this respect, however, the tendency of rates of increase to decline operated in all classes, though the decline was least in the areas farthest removed from other areas.

The adjustment of rates leaves the described relationship of growth with distance between central cities undisturbed in the first three decades of the fifty-year period. But contrary to the findings based on unadjusted

rates, the same pattern extends into the 1930-1940 decade. In the 1940-1950 decade growth rates tended to vary inversely with distance between centers. Thus the expectation of higher growth rates where the distances between metropolitan centers are least finds greater support in the adjusted than in the unadjusted rates. Even so, however, the relationship is not as definite as was anticipated.

Growth in satellite areas presents several interesting departures from the patterns in total and in central city populations. While the size of the growth rate has been directly related to the distance separating areas in three of the five decades, that relationship was sustained by rather diverse trends. For example, in areas with centers within 50 miles of other centers the growth rates of satellite populations were comparatively stable, at least the amount of increase was very slight. In areas with central cities 50 to 100 miles from other metropolitan centers satellite population reached its highest rate of growth in 1920-30 after which the rate subsided. Finally, in the most isolated areas satellite growth rates declined to 1930 and then accelerated rapidly in the last two decades.

Fig. 24 indicates that the effect of distance between metropolitan centers on rates of change in satellite areas has not penetrated far from centers. In 1930-40 and 1940-50 the direct relationship is apparent in the 0-5 mile and the 5-10 mile zones; in 1910-20 and 1920-30 the assocition seems to have been confined mainly to the 0-5 mile zone; and the 1900-10 decade rates tend to be inversely related to proximity between centers. No clear relationship is evident in most zones beyond 10 miles from centers, except in the 35 mile and over zone where the direct relationship appears in the first two and the last decades. If, however, attention is directed only to the within 50 miles and the 50 to 100 mile classes, growth rates are found to be directly related to proximity in virtually all satellite zones after 1910. It seems quite possible, therefore, that the diffusion of metropolitan influence as reflected in high rates of growth is of recent origin in the most isolated metropolitan areas and consequently has not reached far into hinterlands. The passing of another decade or two may produce a consistent relationship in all satellite zones.

There were negligible differences in the relative growth rates of satellite areas in 1900-10 and 1910-20. Differentiation set in, the unstandardized ratios in Table 30 show, in the 1920-30 decade and persisted to 1950. Beginning in 1920, ratios have varied inversely with distance between central cities. That relationship was somewhat indefinite, however, in the most recent inter-censal period. Thus it

## TABLE 29. PER CENT CHANGE OF POPULATION IN STANDARD METROPOLITAN AREAS, BY TYPE OF PLACE, DISTANCE BETWEEN CENTRAL CITIES, AND DECADE, 1900-1950

| *Type of place and distance between central cities* | 1940-50 | *1930-40* | *1920-30* | *1910-20* | *1900-10* |
|---|---|---|---|---|---|
| Actual | | | | | |
| Total | | | | | |
| Central cities within 50 miles | 18.7 | 6.4 | 20.2 | 23.4 | 26.9 |
| " " 50 to 100 " | 19.6 | 8.6 | 29.1 | 25.9 | 31.3 |
| " " 100 or more " | 29.0 | 14.8 | 27.3 | 22.3 | 35.7 |
| Central cities | | | | | |
| Central cities within 50 miles | 10.6 | 2.9 | 15.2 | 25.3 | 27.6 |
| " " 50 to 100 " | 11.4 | 6.0 | 25.4 | 26.7 | 34.2 |
| " " 100 or more " | 23.0 | 11.6 | 32.2 | 23.4 | 40.4 |
| Satellite Areas | | | | | |
| Central cities within 50 miles | 28.5 | 10.9 | 27.3 | 20.8 | 26.0 |
| " " 50 to 100 " | 34.1 | 13.5 | 37.3 | 24.3 | 25.7 |
| " " 100 or more " | 41.1 | 21.6 | 18.0 | 20.1 | 28.0 |
| Adjusted[a] | | | | | |
| Total | | | | | |
| Central cities within 50 miles | 22.1 | 4.5 | 19.3 | 22.5 | 25.4 |
| " " 50 to 100 " | 19.2 | 8.3 | 26.5 | 26.1 | 29.2 |
| " " 100 or more " | 11.2 | 5.8 | 12.9 | 12.1 | 23.0 |
| Central cities | | | | | |
| Central cities within 50 miles | 18.0 | 2.0 | 13.3 | 23.5 | 26.2 |
| " " 50 to 100 " | 11.2 | 5.3 | 23.2 | 28.5 | 33.5 |
| " " 100 or more " | 8.7 | 4.5 | 15.6 | 12.1 | 21.4 |
| Satellite areas | | | | | |
| Central cities within 50 miles | 27.1 | 10.1 | 28.0 | 21.2 | 24.4 |
| " " 50 to 100 " | 33.3 | 14.0 | 33.7 | 21.1 | 20.8 |
| " " 100 or more " | 16.4 | 8.7 | 8.0 | 12.1 | 25.7 |

[a]Adjusted for size of central city. Size distribution of all areas used as the standard.

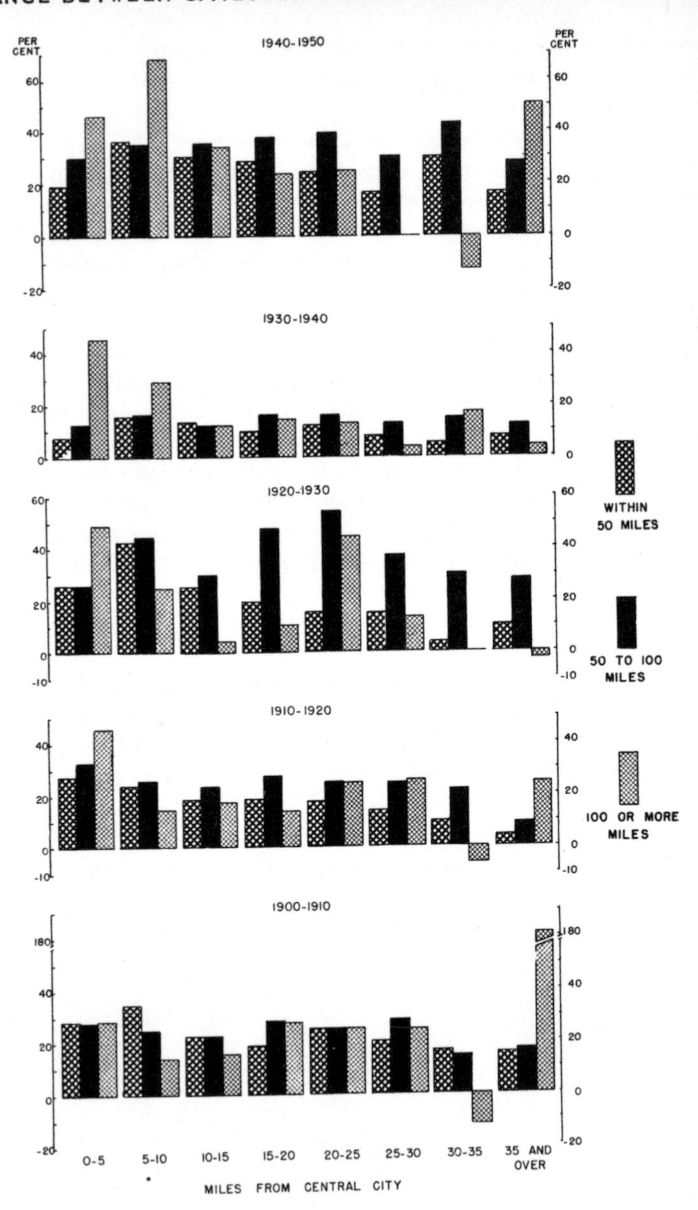


FIGURE 24
PER CENT CHANGE OF POPULATION IN DISTANCE ZONES OF STANDARD METROPOLITAN AREAS, BY DISTANCE BETWEEN CENTRAL CITIES, AND BY DECADES, 1900-1950

appears that, at least during the last 30 years, satellite areas tended to have the highest relative growth rates where the distance between central cities are least.

The absence of consistent differences between relative growth rates during the first two decades of the 50-year period applies to all distance zones, as may be noted in Fig. 25. Barring occasional deviations, zonal rates of those decades were less than the rates of their respective central cities in all proximity classes. After 1920 the relative growth of satellite population in metropolitan areas 100 or more miles from other areas lagged behind comparable rates in less isolated areas, and the lag grew larger with distance away from central cities. Nevertheless, between 1920 and 1950 the satellite area over which rates exceeded central city rates in that proximity class was greatly enlarged. The variations of ratios with distance in metropolitan areas located within 100 miles or less of one another are particularly noteworthy. Evidently the high ratios in satellite territories of areas 50 miles or less from other areas, observed in Table 30, were due mainly to high relative growth rates within 15 miles of central cities. At greater distances dnring most of the period after 1920 ratios were highest in metropolitan areas located 50 to 100 miles from the nearest competing areas.

TABLE 30. RATIO OF RATES OF CHANGE IN SATELLITE AREAS TO RATES OF CHANGE IN CENTRAL CITIES OF STANDARD METROPOLITAN AREAS, BY DISTANCE BETWEEN CENTRAL CITIES AND BY DECADE, 1900 - 1950

| *Distance between central cities* | *1940-50* | *1930-40* | *1920-30* | *1910-20* | *1900-10* |
|---|---|---|---|---|---|
| All areas | 2.7 | 2.5 | 1.4 | 0.9 | 0.8 |
| Within 50 miles | 2.7 | 3.8 | 1.8 | 0.8 | 0.9 |
| 50 to 100 " | 3.0 | 2.2 | 1.5 | 0.9 | 0.8 |
| 100 or more miles | 1.8 | 1.9 | 0.6 | 0.8 | 0.7 |

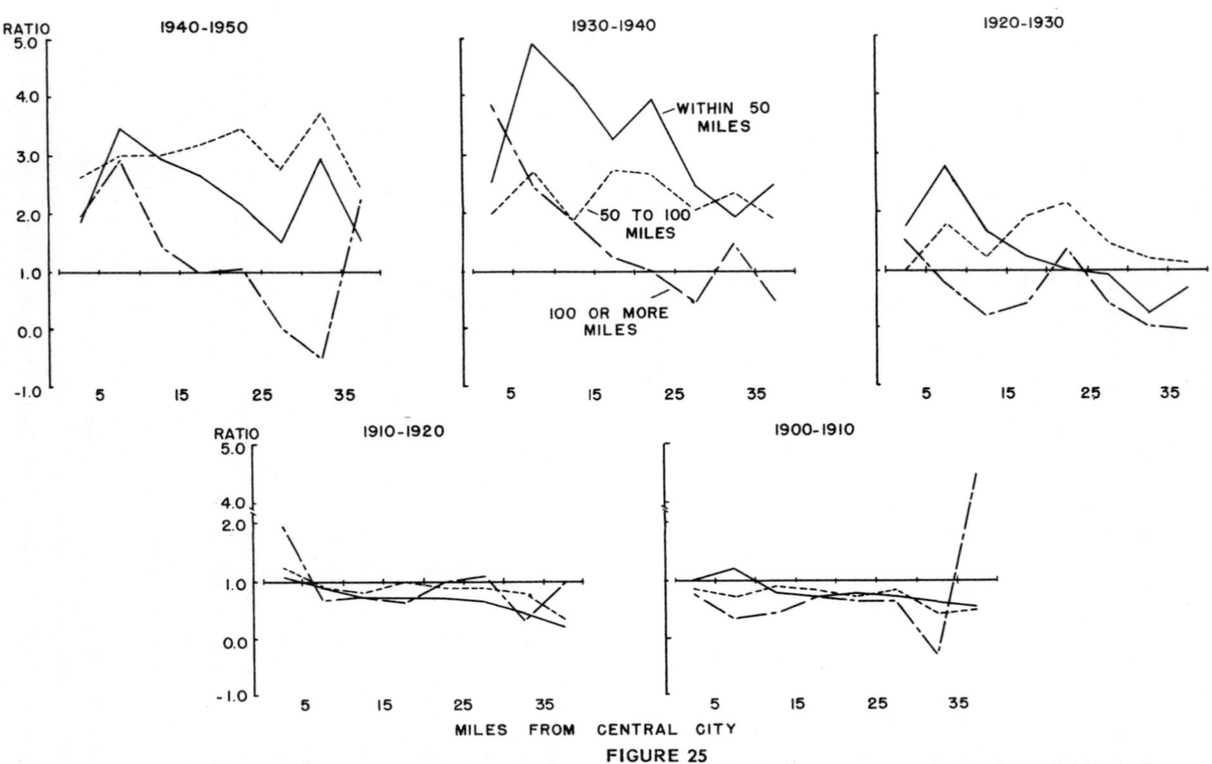


FIGURE 25
RATIO OF RATE OF POPULATION CHANGE IN DISTANCE ZONES TO CENTRAL CITY RATE OF CHANGE IN STANDARD METROPOLITAN AREAS, BY DISTANCE BETWEEN CENTRAL CITIES, AND BY DECADES, 1900-1950

Additional light is shed on the relationship between population redistribution and the distance separating metropolitan centers by an analysis of the distribution of decennial increments as presented in Table 31. Conspicuous in the data is the fact that, since 1920, the closer are central cities to one another the smaller was the proportion of all increase gained by central cities and, conversely, the larger was the proportion absorbed by satellite areas. This was, at best, but a tendency prior to 1920. The dispersion of population growth, however, has been widest and has proceeded with fewest interruptions in areas with central cities 50 to 100 miles from other central cities. In that class a radius of almost 15 miles was required in 1950 to embrace the proportion of increase received by central cities alone in 1900. But in the other proximity classes the 1900 proportion of increase received by central cities had, by 1950, dispersed over an area with a radius of less than 10 miles.

Smaller changes have occurred in the distributions of the total populations. Table 32 indicates, however, that in each proximity class a slightly different pattern of change has been followed. In areas located within 50 miles of other areas concentration was the prevailing trend down to 1930 after which deconcentration set in. In areas 50 to 100 miles from other areas the concentration phase ended in 1920. But in the most distant areas deconcentration characterized redistribution from 1900 to 1920, following which was a decade of concentration, with a return to deconcentration characterizing the last decade. The most important shifts in all proximity classes were from central cities to satellite zones within 10 miles of central cities. For example, in areas nearest to other areas the proportion in central cities declined by 6 percentage points, or about 12 per cent; but this loss was almost entirely absorbed by the 0-5 and 5-10 mile zones. A similar shift took place in the most remotely located areas. Metropolitan areas 50 to 100 miles from other areas are distinguished by the fact that central city losses were spread over a larger part of the satellite area, to a distance of approximately 20 miles.

The coefficients of redistribution, shown in Fig. 26, display considerable irregularity in metropolitan areas whose central cities are 50 to 100 miles and 100 or more miles from other central cities. In both cases redistribution slowed appreciably between 1910 and 1920 and again between 1930 and 1940, both of which were decades of reduced metropolitan growth. Of the two classes only that comprising areas with central cities 50 to 100 miles from other metropolitan centers shows any tendency toward an increasing rate of redistribution over the entire 50-year period. Increase is even more pronounced, however, in areas having

## TABLE 31. CUMULATIVE PERCENTAGE DISTRIBUTION OF POPULATION CHANGE IN STANDARD METROPOLITAN AREAS, BY DISTANCE BETWEEN CENTRAL CITIES, DISTANCE FROM CENTRAL CITY, AND DECADE, 1900 - 1950

| *Distance between central cities, and satellite distance zone* | *1940-50* | *1930-40* | *1920-30* | *1910-20* | *1900-10* |
|---|---|---|---|---|---|
| Within 50 miles | | | | | |
| Central cities | 30.7 | 25.4 | 44.4 | 62.2 | 58.2 |
| 0 - 5 miles | 40.0 | 35.8 | 55.4 | 72.4 | 67.3 |
| 5 - 10 " | 71.2 | 68.5 | 81.5 | 85.6 | 83.5 |
| 10 - 15 " | 86.6 | 85.4 | 91.9 | 92.6 | 91.1 |
| 15 - 20 " | 93.2 | 91.7 | 96.0 | 96.1 | 94.5 |
| 20 - 25 " | 96.6 | 96.6 | 98.2 | 98.2 | 97.2 |
| 25 - 30 " | 98.1 | 98.5 | 99.5 | 99.4 | 98.8 |
| 30 - 35 " | 99.3 | 99.2 | 99.6 | 99.8 | 99.4 |
| 35 miles and over | 100.0 | 100.0 | 100.0 | 100.0 | 100.0 |
| 50 - 100 miles | | | | | |
| Central cities | 37.3 | 45.9 | 59.6 | 69.9 | 72.1 |
| 0 - 5 miles | 43.0 | 51.3 | 63.1 | 74.6 | 75.6 |
| 5 - 10 " | 59.0 | 67.6 | 74.6 | 82.2 | 82.1 |
| 10 - 15 " | 74.1 | 77.8 | 82.8 | 89.6 | 90.4 |
| 15 - 20 " | 85.3 | 88.3 | 90.3 | 94.3 | 94.4 |
| 20 - 25 " | 91.7 | 93.6 | 95.2 | 96.8 | 96.6 |
| 25 - 30 " | 94.8 | 96.1 | 97.2 | 98.4 | 98.2 |
| 30 - 35 " | 97.4 | 97.9 | 98.3 | 99.3 | 98.8 |
| 35 miles and over | 100.0 | 100.0 | 100.0 | 100.0 | 100.0 |
| 100 or more miles | | | | | |
| Central cities | 52.8 | 53.3 | 77.1 | 68.9 | 70.7 |
| 0 - 5 miles | 62.2 | 67.4 | 84.0 | 75.7 | 74.1 |
| 5 - 10 " | 81.3 | 81.5 | 90.2 | 80.8 | 77.5 |
| 10 - 15 " | 87.7 | 90.5 | 91.1 | 87.2 | 81.4 |
| 15 - 20 " | 90.6 | 94.3 | 92.9 | 90.7 | 85.9 |
| 20 - 25 " | 94.7 | 98.2 | 99.8 | 93.4 | 87.6 |
| 25 - 30 " | 94.7 | 98.7 | 100.6 | 95.5 | 89.0 |
| 30 - 35 " | 94.5 | 99.1 | 100.6 | 95.4 | 88.8 |
| 35 miles and over | 100.0 | 100.0 | 100.0 | 100.0 | 100.0 |

# TABLE 32. CUMULATIVE PERCENTAGE DISTRIBUTION OF POPULATION IN STANDARD METROPOLITAN AREAS, BY DISTANCE BETWEEN CENTRAL CITIES, DISTANCE ZONE, AND CENSUS YEAR, 1900 - 1950

| *Distance between central cities, and distance zone* | *1950* | *1940* | *1930* | *1920* | *1910* | *1900* |
|---|---|---|---|---|---|---|
| Within 50 miles | | | | | | |
| Central cities | 50.7 | 54.4 | 56.5 | 58.9 | 57.5 | 56.7 |
| 0 - 5 miles | 59.9 | 63.6 | 65.6 | 67.6 | 66.2 | 65.4 |
| 5 - 10 " | 78.4 | 79.7 | 80.6 | 80.5 | 79.4 | 78.2 |
| 10 - 15 " | 88.8 | 89.2 | 89.6 | 89.2 | 88.4 | 87.8 |
| 15 - 20 " | 93.6 | 93.7 | 93.9 | 93.6 | 93.0 | 92.7 |
| 20 - 25 " | 96.6 | 96.6 | 96.7 | 96.5 | 96.0 | 95.8 |
| 25 - 30 " | 98.4 | 98.4 | 98.4 | 98.3 | 98.0 | 97.9 |
| 30 - 35 " | 99.2 | 99.2 | 99.2 | 99.2 | 99.0 | 98.9 |
| 35 miles and over | 100.0 | 100.0 | 100.0 | 100.0 | 100.0 | 100.0 |
| 50 to 100 miles | | | | | | |
| Central cities | 59.6 | 64.0 | 65.5 | 68.4 | 67.9 | 66.1 |
| 0 - 5 miles | 63.6 | 67.7 | 69.3 | 72.4 | 71.6 | 70.2 |
| 5 - 10 " | 74.0 | 77.1 | 78.4 | 80.1 | 79.6 | 78.7 |
| 10 - 15 " | 83.8 | 85.8 | 86.8 | 88.3 | 88.0 | 87.2 |
| 15 - 20 " | 90.6 | 91.7 | 92.4 | 92.8 | 92.5 | 91.7 |
| 20 - 25 " | 94.4 | 94.9 | 95.4 | 95.4 | 95.1 | 94.5 |
| 25 - 30 " | 96.6 | 96.9 | 97.2 | 97.1 | 96.8 | 96.3 |
| 30 - 35 " | 98.0 | 98.1 | 98.3 | 98.1 | 97.9 | 97.5 |
| 35 miles and over | 100.0 | 100.0 | 100.0 | 100.0 | 100.0 | 100.0 |
| 100 or more miles | | | | | | |
| Central cities | 63.6 | 66.7 | 68.0 | 65.4 | 65.5 | 62.6 |
| 0 - 5 miles | 70.3 | 72.7 | 72.7 | 69.3 | 68.9 | 66.9 |
| 5 - 10 " | 81.0 | 81.0 | 80.1 | 76.6 | 76.8 | 76.7 |
| 10 - 15 " | 86.9 | 86.7 | 86.4 | 84.5 | 85.2 | 86.6 |
| 11 - 20 " | 90.3 | 90.3 | 90.3 | 89.3 | 91.2 | 92.6 |
| 20 - 25 " | 95.1 | 95.3 | 95.0 | 93.7 | 93.6 | 95.1 |
| 25 - 30 " | 96.0 | 96.4 | 96.5 | 95.4 | 95.4 | 97.2 |
| 30 - 35 " | 96.3 | 96.8 | 96.9 | 95.9 | 95.8 | 97.8 |
| 35 miles and over | 100.0 | 100.0 | 100.0 | 100.0 | 100.0 | 100.0 |

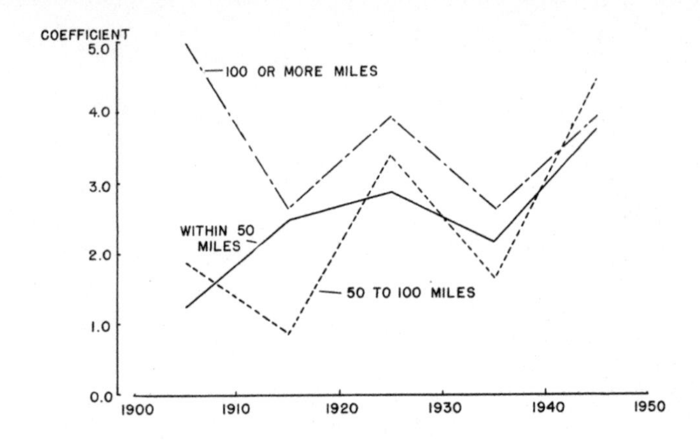


FIGURE 26
COEFFICIENTS OF POPULATION REDISTRIBUTION IN STANDARD METROPOLITAN AREAS, BY DISTANCE BETWEEN CENTRAL CITIES, 1900-1950

central cities within 50 miles of their own centers. The increase is reversed in only one decade, 1930-40, and the decline is comparatively small. Although the rates of redistribution in the most distantly located metropolitan areas exhibit no trend of increase, they have been the highest rates down to the last decade.

## Size and Type of Satellite Place

Growth rates of satellite places of different sizes and types, described in Table 33, have changed over the five decade period showing a relationship to the distances between central cities. Although rates for satellite places of 10,000 or more population have declined, the numbers of places represented by the rates are so small that no reliable conclusion regarding the effect of distance can be drawn. Rates for satellite incorporated places of 2,500 to 10,000 population have declined rapidly in metropolitan areas whose centers are within 50 miles of other centers, and relatively slowly in areas whose centers are 50 to 100 miles from other centers. But in the most isolated metropolitan areas the rates of population growth in satellites of 2,500-10,000 population, within 20 miles of central cities, have increased strikingly. Beyond 20 miles, however, declining trends have prevailed.

Table 33. Per Cent Change of Satellite Population in Standard Metropolitan Areas, by Size and Type of Satellite Place, Distance Zone, Distance Between Central Cities, and Decades, 1900-1950

| Size and type of place and distance zone | Within 50 miles | | | | | 50 to 100 miles | | | | | 100 or more miles | | | | |
|---|---|---|---|---|---|---|---|---|---|---|---|---|---|---|---|
| | 1940-1950 | 1930-1940 | 1920-1930 | 1910-1920 | 1900-1910 | 1940-1950 | 1930-1940 | 1920-1930 | 1910-1920 | 1900-1910 | 1940-1950 | 1930-1940 | 1920-1930 | 1910-1920 | 1900-1910 |
| 50,000 and over | | | | | | | | | | | | | | | |
| 0-10 miles | 19.0 | 1.6 | 16.7 | 21.7 | 41.4[a] | -0.3 | 0.7 | 3.4 | 10.0 | 27.1[a] | ---- | ---- | ---- | ---- | ---- |
| 10-20 miles | 2.5[a] | 0.7[a] | 2.0[a] | ---- | ---- | 10.3 | 1.2 | 13.2 | 19.2 | 35.5[a] | ---- | ---- | ---- | ---- | ---- |
| 20-30 miles | 10.6[a] | 2.6[a] | ---- | ---- | ---- | 21.8[a] | 10.3[a] | 81.3[a] | ---- | ---- | ---- | ---- | ---- | ---- | ---- |
| 30 miles and over | ---- | ---- | ---- | ---- | ---- | ---- | ---- | ---- | ---- | ---- | ---- | ---- | ---- | ---- | ---- |
| 10,000 - 50,000 | | | | | | | | | | | | | | | |
| 0-10 miles | 14.9 | 0.2 | 27.8 | 18.3 | 29.2 | 5.2 | 11.3 | 37.2 | 29.6 | 27.2 | 40.0[a] | 3.9[a] | 64.3[a] | 27.0[a] | ---- |
| 10-20 miles | 23.0 | 4.2 | 20.5 | 26.2 | 22.2 | 34.3 | 10.7 | 50.7 | 47.8 | 63.7 | ---- | ---- | ---- | ---- | ---- |
| 20-30 miles | 4.1 | 3.6 | 11.0 | 18.1 | 28.8 | 13.2 | 6.9 | 41.9 | 55.2 | 42.0 | ---- | ---- | ---- | ---- | ---- |
| 30 miles and over | 6.0[a] | 1.6[a] | 1.0[a] | 23.7[a] | 13.9[a] | 25.3 | 1.5 | 23.8 | 17.2 | 21.4 | 0.4[a] | 3.7[a] | ---- | ---- | ---- |
| 2,500 - 10,000 | | | | | | | | | | | | | | | |
| 0-10 miles | 22.2 | 6.2 | 29.5 | 51.4 | 46.9 | 40.1 | 13.2 | 60.6 | 69.7 | 39.5 | 87.3 | 22.4 | 35.6 | -73.5 | 10.9[a] |
| 10-20 miles | 25.1 | 6.3 | 40.6 | 29.1 | 34.2 | 57.7 | 18.6 | 73.5 | 36.6 | 59.4 | 60.3 | 26.5 | 0.1 | 11.4[a] | -24.4[a] |
| 20-30 miles | 6.8 | 6.2 | 19.6 | 19.8 | 33.6 | 29.8 | 7.7 | 44.4 | 13.4 | 48.5 | 4.0[a] | -5.8[a] | -41.5[a] | ---- | ---- |
| 30 miles and over | 23.3 | 4.6 | 15.0 | 5.4 | 47.3 | 25.2 | 5.7 | 41.1 | 18.4 | 28.6 | -6.7 | 2.3 | -4.7 | 25.0 | 123.5[a] |
| Under 2,500 | | | | | | | | | | | | | | | |
| 0-10 miles | 37.7 | 18.3 | 64.2 | 33.1 | 44.1 | 33.8 | 20.9 | 130.5 | 42.6 | 72.5 | 77.4 | 30.5 | 42.6 | 37.0 | 65.2 |
| 10-20 miles | 18.5 | 8.7 | 20.7 | 21.1 | 21.5 | 49.4 | 18.1 | 64.6 | 37.7 | 31.0 | 54.5 | 19.0 | 37.1 | 37.0 | 65.2 |
| 20-30 miles | 16.0 | 8.3 | 9.5 | 23.4 | 41.6 | 39.1 | 15.6 | 43.2 | 20.1 | 23.1 | -5.6 | 4.7 | 4.0 | 55.7 | 35.5 |
| 30 miles and over | 14.6 | 1.8 | 10.9 | 2.3 | 16.4 | 52.9 | 21.5 | 47.8 | 13.5 | 16.9 | 1.9 | 5.5 | -9.1 | 32.9 | 92.0 |
| Unincorporated area | | | | | | | | | | | | | | | |
| 0-10 miles | 42.4 | 22.5 | 43.9 | 21.5 | 26.4 | 73.6 | 28.0 | 42.3 | 20.3 | 16.5 | 55.2 | 44.9 | 26.0 | 107.7 | 13.7 |
| 10-20 miles | 36.3 | 16.3 | 20.0 | 12.6 | 17.4 | 54.8 | 25.3 | 33.4 | 12.8 | 9.5 | 22.0 | 17.5 | 3.6 | 15.3 | 20.7 |
| 20-30 miles | 37.2 | 16.2 | 16.5 | 10.9 | 11.8 | 52.9 | 21.5 | 47.8 | 13.5 | 16.9 | 22.0 | 11.6 | 37.8 | 19.8 | 23.6 |
| 30 miles and over | 28.0 | 8.4 | 4.0 | 5.7 | 10.8 | 41.2 | 20.9 | 27.3 | 8.9 | 7.3 | 102.4 | 8.7 | -2.1 | 16.9 | 159.9 |

[a] Based on less than five incorporated places.

In the next smaller size class of satellite places, those with less than 2,500 population, rates have also declined within areas the centers of which are not more than 50 miles from other centers. But in areas comprising the 50 to 100 mile class, rates for the small incorporated places declined only in the 0-10 mile zone. Elsewhere their rates increased quite rapidly. And in the most remote metropolitan areas the smallest incorporated satellites within 20 miles of central cities grew with increasing rates. In distance zones beyond 20 miles from central cities their rates of change fell off sharply between 1900 and 1950.

Unincorporated area population grew at progressively higher rates in the within 50 mile and the 50-100 mile classes, the greatest changes occurring in the latter group of metropolitan areas. In the areas that are 100 or more miles distant from other areas increasing rates occurred in the 0-10 mile zone, while in the outlying zones the trends were erratic.

In summary, areas within 50 miles of other areas experienced increasing rates of change in unincorporated population, and those were rather moderate. Areas 50 to 100 miles of other areas had, by comparison, rapid increases of growth rates in incorporated places of less than 2,500 population and in unincorporated area. The largest increases of rates of change in the satellite population of areas 100 or more miles removed from other areas occurred in incorporated places of less than 10,000 population located within 20 miles of central cities. In this class of areas, in other words, there appears to have been a marked centripetal movement of satellite population directed mainly to incorporated places.

The ratios of satellite rates of change to central city rates, presented in Table 34, indicate that change has accelerated from 1900 to 1950 in all satellite places with less than 10,000 population. In the two least isolated groups of metropolitan areas the amount of change in ratios increased with distance from central city. It is also to be noted that the highest relative rates of growth passed from incorporated places to unincorporated areas. Metropolitan areas 100 or more miles removed from other areas are unique in two respects. There has been no tendency for relative growth rates to accelerate more rapidly in outer than in inner distance zones: in fact, the contrary is true. Nor have ratios for unincorporated areas exceeded those for incorporated places.

Metropolitan areas 100 or more miles distant from other centers have had, in all decades, larger proportions of their populations in unincorporated areas than have any other class of areas, as indicated in Table 35. The 30 mile and over zone, however, is an exception to that rule. It is not unlikely that in such areas that zone has not been subject to the influence of central cities. Population concentration has declined in

Table 34. Ratio of Rate of Change of Satellite Population to Central City Rate of Change in Standard Metropolitan Areas, by Size and Type of Satellite Place, Distance Zone, Distance Between Central Cities, and Decades, 1900-1950

| Size and type of place and distance zone | Within 50 miles | | | | | 50 to 100 miles | | | | | 100 or more miles | | | | |
|---|---|---|---|---|---|---|---|---|---|---|---|---|---|---|---|
| | 1940-1950 | 1930-1940 | 1920-1930 | 1910-1920 | 1900-1910 | 1940-1950 | 1930-1940 | 1920-1930 | 1910-1920 | 1900-1910 | 1940-1950 | 1930-1940 | 1920-1930 | 1910-1920 | 1900-1910 |
| 50,000 and over | 10.6 | 2.9 | 15.2 | 25.3 | 27.6 | 11.4 | 6.0 | 25.4 | 26.7 | 34.2 | 23.0 | 11.6 | 32.2 | 23.4 | 40.4 |
| 0-10 miles | 1.8 | 0.6 | 1.1 | 0.9 | 1.5 | 0.0 | -0.1 | 0.1 | 0.4 | 0.8 | ---- | ---- | ---- | ---- | ---- |
| 10-20 miles | 0.2 | 0.2 | 0.1 | ---- | ---- | 0.9 | 0.2 | 0.5 | 0.7 | 1.0 | ---- | ---- | ---- | ---- | ---- |
| 20-30 miles | 1.0 | 0.9 | ---- | ---- | ---- | 1.9 | 1.7 | 3.2 | ---- | ---- | ---- | ---- | ---- | ---- | ---- |
| 30 miles and over | ---- | ---- | ---- | ---- | ---- | ---- | ---- | ---- | ---- | ---- | ---- | ---- | ---- | ---- | ---- |
| 10,000 - 50,000 | | | | | | | | | | | | | | | |
| 0-10 miles | 1.4 | 0.1 | 1.8 | 0.7 | 1.1 | 0.5 | 1.8 | 1.5 | 1.5 | 0.8 | 1.7 | 0.3 | 2.0 | 1.2 | ---- |
| 10-20 miles | 2.2 | 1.4 | 1.3 | 1.0 | 0.8 | 3.0 | 1.8 | 2.0 | 1.8 | 1.9 | ---- | ---- | ---- | ---- | ---- |
| 20-30 miles | 0.4 | 1.2 | 0.7 | 0.7 | 1.0 | 1.2 | 1.1 | 1.6 | 2.1 | 1.2 | ---- | ---- | ---- | ---- | ---- |
| 30 miles and over | 0.6 | 0.6 | 0.1 | 0.9 | 0.5 | 2.2 | 0.2 | 0.9 | 0.6 | 0.6 | 0.0 | 0.3 | ---- | ---- | ---- |
| 2,500 - 10,000 | | | | | | | | | | | | | | | |
| 0-10 miles | 2.1 | 2.1 | 1.9 | 2.0 | 1.7 | 3.5 | 2.2 | 2.4 | 2.6 | 1.2 | 3.8 | 1.9 | 1.1 | -3.1 | 0.3 |
| 10-20 miles | 2.4 | 2.2 | 2.7 | 1.2 | 1.2 | 5.1 | 3.1 | 2.9 | 1.4 | 1.7 | 2.6 | 2.3 | 0.0 | 0.5 | -0.6 |
| 20-30 miles | 0.6 | 2.1 | 1.3 | 0.8 | 1.2 | 2.6 | 1.3 | 1.7 | 0.5 | 1.4 | 0.2 | -0.5 | 1.3 | ---- | ---- |
| 30 miles and over | 2.2 | 1.6 | 1.0 | 0.2 | 1.7 | 2.2 | 0.9 | 1.6 | 0.7 | 0.8 | -0.3 | 0.2 | -0.1 | 1.1 | 3.1 |
| Under 2,500 | | | | | | | | | | | | | | | |
| 0-10 miles | 3.6 | 6.3 | 4.2 | 1.3 | 1.6 | 3.0 | 3.5 | 5.1 | 1.6 | 2.1 | 3.4 | 2.6 | 1.3 | 1.6 | 1.6 |
| 10-20 miles | 1.7 | 3.0 | 1.4 | 0.8 | 0.8 | 4.3 | 3.0 | 2.5 | 1.4 | 0.9 | 2.4 | 1.6 | 1.2 | 0.8 | 0.7 |
| 20-30 miles | 1.5 | 2.9 | 0.6 | 0.9 | 1.5 | 3.4 | 2.6 | 1.7 | 0.8 | 0.7 | -0.2 | 0.4 | 0.1 | 2.4 | 0.9 |
| 30 miles and over | 1.4 | 0.6 | 0.7 | 0.1 | 0.6 | 2.5 | 2.1 | 0.9 | 0.5 | 0.7 | 0.1 | 0.5 | -0.3 | 1.4 | 2.3 |
| Unincorporated area | | | | | | | | | | | | | | | |
| 0-10 miles | 4.0 | 7.8 | 2.9 | 2.8 | 1.0 | 6.5 | 4.7 | 1.7 | 0.8 | 0.5 | 2.4 | 3.9 | 0.8 | 4.6 | 0.3 |
| 10-20 miles | 3.4 | 5.6 | 1.3 | 0.5 | 0.6 | 4.8 | 4.2 | 1.3 | 0.5 | 0.3 | 1.0 | 1.5 | 0.1 | 0.7 | 0.5 |
| 20-30 miles | 3.5 | 5.6 | 1.1 | 0.4 | 0.4 | 4.6 | 3.6 | 1.9 | 0.5 | 0.5 | 1.0 | 1.0 | 1.2 | 0.8 | 0.6 |
| 30 miles and over | 2.6 | 2.9 | 0.3 | 0.2 | 0.4 | 3.6 | 3.5 | 1.1 | 0.3 | 0.2 | 4.5 | 0.7 | -0.1 | 0.7 | 4.0 |

Table 35. Per Cent Distribution of Satellite Population in Standard Metropolitan Areas, by Census Year, Size and Type of Satellite Place, Distance Between Central Cities, and Distance Zone, 1900-1950

| Census year and size and type of place | Within 50 miles: Miles from central city | | | | 50 to 100 miles: Miles from central city | | | | 100 or more miles: Miles from central city | | | |
|---|---|---|---|---|---|---|---|---|---|---|---|---|
| | 0-10 miles | 10-20 miles | 20-30 miles | 30 miles and over | 0-10 miles | 10-20 miles | 20-30 miles | 30 miles and over | 0-10 miles | 10-20 miles | 20-30 miles | 30 miles and over |
| 1950 | 100.0 | 100.0 | 100.0 | 100.0 | 100.0 | 100.0 | 100.0 | 100.0 | 100.0 | 100.0 | 100.0 | 100.0 |
| 50,000 and over | 17.6 | 2.4 | 4.7 | ----- | 18.6 | 29.0 | 9.9 | ----- | ----- | ----- | ----- | ----- |
| 10,000 - 50,000 | 17.1 | 21.1 | 23.2 | 9.4 | 22.0 | 18.7 | 18.8 | 25.6 | 12.5 | ----- | ----- | 16.4 |
| 2,500 - 10,000 | 12.0 | 11.5 | 16.8 | 14.6 | 8.4 | 13.7 | 16.2 | 16.1 | 15.4 | 12.8 | 3.7 | 14.9 |
| Under 2,500 | 4.1 | 7.5 | 8.4 | 12.1 | 2.6 | 5.6 | 7.5 | 8.3 | 4.3 | 11.2 | 5.4 | 8.0 |
| Unincorporated area | 49.2 | 57.5 | 46.9 | 63.9 | 48.4 | 33.0 | 47.6 | 50.0 | 67.8 | 76.0 | 90.9 | 60.7 |
| 1940 | 100.0 | 100.0 | 100.0 | 100.0 | 100.0 | 100.0 | 100.0 | 100.0 | 100.0 | 100.0 | 100.0 | 100.0 |
| 50,000 and over | 19.2 | 3.0 | 5.1 | ----- | 24.8 | 35.6 | 11.0 | ----- | ----- | ----- | ----- | ----- |
| 10,000 - 50,000 | 19.3 | 22.2 | 26.6 | 10.9 | 27.7 | 18.8 | 22.5 | 27.1 | 14.2 | ----- | ----- | 23.4 |
| 2,500 - 10,000 | 12.7 | 11.9 | 18.8 | 14.6 | 7.9 | 11.7 | 16.9 | 17.1 | 13.0 | 10.3 | 4.2 | 22.7 |
| Under 2,500 | 3.9 | 8.2 | 8.7 | 13.0 | 2.6 | 5.1 | 7.3 | 8.6 | 3.8 | 9.3 | 6.8 | 11.2 |
| Unincorporated area | 44.9 | 54.7 | 40.6 | 61.5 | 37.0 | 28.8 | 42.3 | 47.2 | 69.0 | 80.4 | 89.0 | 42.7 |
| 1930 | 100.0 | 100.0 | 100.0 | 100.0 | 100.0 | 100.0 | 100.0 | 100.0 | 100.0 | 100.0 | 100.0 | 100.0 |
| 50,000 and over | 20.8 | 3.3 | 5.4 | ----- | 27.0 | 35.5 | 10.9 | ----- | ----- | ----- | ----- | ----- |
| 10,000 - 50,000 | 20.7 | 23.7 | 26.2 | 11.4 | 25.1 | 18.9 | 22.1 | 29.3 | 15.9 | ----- | ----- | 23.4 |
| 2,500 - 10,000 | 12.5 | 11.9 | 19.5 | 14.0 | 9.2 | 11.7 | 18.0 | 16.1 | 14.2 | 9.7 | 4.4 | 23.0 |
| Under 2,500 | 4.1 | 8.7 | 9.3 | 14.3 | 2.7 | 5.8 | 7.8 | 10.6 | 3.9 | 7.9 | 7.1 | 10.8 |
| Unincorporated area | 41.9 | 52.4 | 39.6 | 60.3 | 36.0 | 28.1 | 41.2 | 44.0 | 66.0 | 82.4 | 88.5 | 42.8 |
| 1920 | 100.0 | 100.0 | 100.0 | 100.0 | 100.0 | 100.0 | 100.0 | 100.0 | 100.0 | 100.0 | 100.0 | 100.0 |
| 50,000 and over | 17.2 | 2.0 | ----- | ----- | 24.1 | 34.6 | 5.7 | ----- | ----- | ----- | ----- | ----- |
| 10,000 - 50,000 | 23.3 | 20.6 | 25.3 | 16.1 | 22.5 | 16.3 | 26.0 | 26.1 | 10.0 | ----- | ----- | ----- |
| 2,500 - 10,000 | 13.0 | 12.6 | 18.8 | 13.3 | 11.8 | 10.8 | 12.9 | 14.8 | 9.4 | 6.9 | 2.9 | 25.0 |
| Under 2,500 | 5.2 | 10.3 | 9.5 | 14.7 | 3.9 | 8.0 | 11.4 | 11.6 | 8.5 | 7.6 | 10.9 | 8.7 |
| Unincorporated area | 41.3 | 54.5 | 46.4 | 55.9 | 37.7 | 30.3 | 39.0 | 47.5 | 72.1 | 85.5 | 86.2 | 66.3 |
| 1910 | 100.0 | 100.0 | 100.0 | 100.0 | 100.0 | 100.0 | 100.0 | 100.0 | 100.0 | 100.0 | 100.0 | 100.0 |
| 50,000 and over | 15.9 | ----- | ----- | ----- | 25.0 | 32.5 | ----- | ----- | ----- | ----- | ----- | ----- |
| 10,000 - 50,000 | 21.3 | 17.3 | 20.4 | 10.5 | 14.9 | 14.3 | 24.6 | 25.1 | 9.9 | ----- | ----- | ----- |
| 2,500 - 10,000 | 11.1 | 12.4 | 18.7 | 9.5 | 11.0 | 9.2 | 15.3 | 13.6 | 39.6 | 2.7 | ----- | 32.8 |
| Under 2,500 | 6.0 | 11.7 | 13.0 | 14.9 | 5.1 | 9.3 | 14.5 | 13.0 | 6.1 | 5.9 | 15.1 | 11.0 |
| Unincorporated area | 45.7 | 58.6 | 47.9 | 65.1 | 44.0 | 34.7 | 45.6 | 48.3 | 44.4 | 91.4 | 84.9 | 56.2 |
| 1900 | 100.0 | 100.0 | 100.0 | 100.0 | 100.0 | 100.0 | 100.0 | 100.0 | 100.0 | 100.0 | 100.0 | 100.0 |
| 50,000 and over | 12.2 | ----- | ----- | ----- | 19.0 | 22.7 | ----- | ----- | ----- | ----- | ----- | ----- |
| 10,000 - 50,000 | 21.2 | 13.3 | 11.3 | 4.6 | 17.0 | 15.4 | 11.8 | 21.2 | ----- | ----- | ----- | ----- |
| 2,500 - 10,000 | 9.9 | 10.4 | 18.4 | 9.5 | 7.3 | 7.8 | 16.9 | 12.3 | 2.1 | 4.7 | ----- | 23.9 |
| Under 2,500 | 5.9 | 11.0 | 14.7 | 13.7 | 5.0 | 8.6 | 13.0 | 13.5 | 7.1 | 3.5 | 7.7 | 18.5 |
| Unincorporated | 50.8 | 65.3 | 55.6 | 72.2 | 51.7 | 45.5 | 58.3 | 53.0 | 90.8 | 91.8 | 92.3 | 57.6 |

unincorporated areas, while the proportion of population in incorporated places of 2,500 or more people have increased more or less steadily. Thus it appears that the distribution of satellite population among the various sizes and types of places in the most isolated areas has been undergoing a radical change since 1900.

The smallest proportions of unincorporated population existed in metropolitan areas located 50 to 100 miles from other areas. Unincorporated area in the 0-10 mile zone had the smallest share of the zone's total population,partly because of the relatively large concentration in places of 50,000 or more population. Places of 10,000-50,000 size gained at the expense of all other types of satellite places from 1900 to 1940 in the 0-10 mile zone and from 1900 to 1920 in the two outermost zones. In later years the resurgence of unincorporated areas in those zones brought declines in the proportions in all incorporated places.

Likewise in metropolitan areas within 50 miles of other areas the proportions of unincorporated population in each distance zone declined from 1900 to about 1930, and then increased once more to the 1910 level. Incorporated places of less than 2,500 population sustained declining proportions throughout the 50 years, except in the 30 mile and over zone. Conversely, incorporated places of 2,500 or more population gained increased proportions until 1930 in inner zones and 1920 in the outer zones, after which their proportions were reduced through the remaining decades. These movements, as well as those in the more distant proximity classes, parallel the concentration and deconcentration phases of the distribution of total metropolitan area population. Concentration appears to deplete unincorporated areas in all distance zones. Deconcentration, on the other hand, seems to affect satellite incorporated places as well as central cities.

CHAPTER VI

# SELECTED GEOGRAPHIC FEATURES AND POPULATION REDISTRIBUTION

The distribution of metropolitan population as well as changes in the distribution pattern doubtlessly are affected by the presence or absence of of certain limiting factors in the geographic environment. For example, the location of a central city on a sea or lake coast confines its satellite area to, at most, three of its sides. Under such conditions the density of satellite population is probably greater and the growth rates in outlying distance zones are probably higher than where the central city is completely surrounded by habitable area. A river is also a barrier. But a river impedes rather than prevents the spread of metropolitan influence in all directions from a center. Hence it seems likely that distributional tendencies in areas with centers located on river banks may reflect the retarding influence of the river barrier. Still another type of central city location is that lacking any kind of water barrier. Presumably such a location would permit a more or less uniform spread of population about the central city. The greater abundance of satellite space or of easily accessible space may result in a lower density and perhaps a lower rate of change of satellite population.

Three types of locations relative to geographic features are recognized therefore. These are: (1) sea or lake coast; (2) river; and (3) other. The sea or lake coast locations present no serious problem of identification. International boundary lines, however, are treated as analogous to coastal lines. Accordingly Laredo and Detroit are included in the sea or lake coast location class. A river location is more difficult to define unequivocally. Any sized stream, even though it may be dry through part of each year, constitutes a barrier in some degree. But if no restrictions were put on the size of the river virtually all metropolitan areas would be included in the river location class. To avoid such inclusiveness and to distinguish only those areas in which a river represents a

a major barrier, a river location is arbitrarily defined as a site on a navigable stream.[1] The third location class, i.e., all other, is accurately described by its designation. It does not comprise only areas with central cities situated on plains as may have been implied in the preceding paragraph. A few central cities are located at the bases of mountain ranges, such as Atlanta and Pueblo, which are no less effective as barriers than are navigable streams. But these are too few to treat separately, hence they are combined with all land-locked locations. The number of metropolitan areas having each type of central city location is shown in Table 36.

TABLE 36. NUMBER OF METROPOLITAN AREAS, BY TYPE OF LOCATION OF CENTRAL CITY, BY SIZE OF CENTRAL CITY, AND BY DECADE, 1900 - 1950

| *Type of location and size of central city* | *1940-50* | *1930-40* | *1920-30* | *1910-20* | *1900-10* |
|---|---|---|---|---|---|
| Total | 143 | 157 | 155 | 153 | 148 |
| Sea or lake coast | 34 | 37 | 36 | 35 | 35 |
| 1,000,000 and over | 4 | 4 | 3 | 2 | 2 |
| 500,000 - 1,000,000 | 6 | 6 | 5 | 3 | 2 |
| 250,000 - 500,000 | 4 | 5 | 3 | 5 | 6 |
| 100,000 - 250,000 | 8 | 7 | 8 | 6 | 5 |
| Under 100,000 | 12 | 15 | 17 | 19 | 20 |
| River | 36 | 40 | 40 | 40 | 40 |
| 500,000 and over[a] | 5 | 5 | 4 | 4 | 2 |
| 250,000 - 500,000 | 3 | 4 | 3 | 3 | 5 |
| 100,000 - 250,000 | 13 | 14 | 13 | 8 | 5 |
| Under 100,000 | 15 | 17 | 20 | 25 | 28 |
| Other | 73 | 80 | 79 | 78 | 73 |
| 250,000 - 500,000 | 4 | 6 | 1 | – | – |
| 100,000 - 250,000 | 20 | 20 | 16 | 10 | 5 |
| Under 100,000 | 49 | 54 | 62 | 68 | 68 |

[a] Includes one area with a central city of 1,000,000 or more population (Philadelphia).

While this classification is adopted primarily to test the effects of geographic factors on population redistribution, it also bears a rough correspondence to a transport location classification. Central cities on sea or lake coasts are port cities with immediate access to deep water transport routes. Some port cities, however, such as Philadelphia and New Orleans, are located so far up a river's course that they are classified as having river locations. Most centers at river locations are oriented principally toward intra-continental exchanges. Both types of water locations, of course, are served also by rail and highway transportation. The class of all other locations, however, depend exclusively on railway and highway facilities with which to maintain inter-regional exchanges.[2] A time dimension is also represented in the classification. Many central cities at deep-water sites were among the first to attain large size. River cities flourished in the 19th century until the coming of the railroad. With the development of fast overland transportation made possible by the railroad and the highway river cities lost much of their former importance to a host of new cities that appeared at rail junctions as well as to coastal cities that gained quicker access to interior regions.[3] Thus central cities at other than water locations, are among the youngest of all metropolitan centers. Although most of the changes occasioned by major shifts in the means of inter-regional transportation occurred prior to 1900, many of the effects of those changes may have lingered on to account for some of the variations to be found in the following analysis. That is most probable of the other than water location class.

### Central Cities and Satellite Areas

The lowest actual rates of change in metropolitan areas occurred, in all decades, in those areas having their central cities at river locations, as may be seen in Table 37. Rates for the other two classes were approximately the same. Central cities at river locations also grew slowly, while the highest rates of change were found in centers at other locations. Satellite area growth was most rapid in metropolitan areas at costal locations and slowest in areas at other locations from 1900 to 1930. After 1930 the relationship of satellite growth to type of location is uncertain.

Apparently most of the differences between location classes observed in the actual or unadjusted rates are due to differences in the size composition of the location classes. For when the growth rates are weighted by a standard size of area distribution, a clear and consistent relationship emerges. Total metropolitan area as well as both types of places within metropolitan areas are observed to have had the highest growth rates at costal locations and the lowest rates at other locations.

TABLE 37. PER CENT CHANGE OF POPULATION IN STANDARD METROPOLITAN AREAS, BY TYPE OF LOCATION OF CENTRAL CITY, TYPE OF PLACE, AND DECADE, 1900-1950

| *Type of place and type of location* | *1940-50* | *1930-40* | *1920-30* | *1910-20* | *1900-10* |
|---|---|---|---|---|---|
| Actual | | | | | |
| Total | | | | | |
| Sea or lake coast | 19.7 | 8.0 | 27.8 | 26.3 | 32.8 |
| River | 16.6 | 7.1 | 18.0 | 18.8 | 23.8 |
| Other | 23.7 | 9.2 | 27.6 | 29.2 | 30.5 |
| Central cities | | | | | |
| Sea or lake coast | 10.2 | 5.4 | 22.1 | 25.2 | 31.7 |
| River | 9.7 | 3.7 | 13.1 | 19.3 | 22.9 |
| Other | 18.8 | 6.2 | 31.4 | 38.9 | 49.2 |
| Satellite areas | | | | | |
| Sea or lake coast | 35.4 | 12.6 | 40.1 | 28.6 | 35.0 |
| River | 25.0 | 11.6 | 25.2 | 18.0 | 25.1 |
| Other | 31.2 | 14.3 | 21.8 | 16.9 | 13.2 |
| Adjusted[a] | | | | | |
| Total | | | | | |
| Sea or lake coast | 21.3 | 7.8 | 23.3 | 26.1 | 30.7 |
| River | 17.1 | 6.6 | 18.8 | 18.8 | 22.2 |
| Other | 9.7 | 4.0 | 13.1 | 11.2 | 11.2 |
| Central cities | | | | | |
| Sea or lake coast | 11.3 | 5.3 | 19.9 | 26.8 | 30.2 |
| River | 9.5 | 3.1 | 14.4 | 19.2 | 22.2 |
| Other | 7.1 | 2.6 | 12.9 | 13.7 | 16.3 |
| Satellite areas | | | | | |
| Sea or lake coast | 37.7 | 11.8 | 31.7 | 24.7 | 31.9 |
| River | 26.3 | 11.2 | 25.2 | 18.2 | 22.3 |
| Other | 13.6 | 6.4 | 13.5 | 7.9 | 6.4 |

[a]Adjusted for size of central city. Size distribution of all areas used as the standard.

The declining rates of central cities at coastal and river locations were fairly well compensated by increasing rates in their respective satellite areas. This has not been true of metropolitan areas at other locations. Satellite area in that location class grew at increasing rates, but the increases were not sufficient to overcome the losses in central city rates, doubtlessly because of the relatively small satellite populations in such areas.

Differences in the patterns of growth within satellite areas, i.e., by distance zones, are much less simple. Until 1920, as may be noted in Fig. 27, satellite population in areas with central cities on coastal sites grew most rapidly in all distance zones; next in order of growth rate were areas with central cities on river sites: while the slowest growth rates obtained in the zones about central cities at other locations. In the next decade, 1920-30, that order of differences was reversed in the 0-5 mile zone, but it persisted in all other distance zones. The upsurge of growth of satellite population within 5 miles of central cities at other locations continued through the two following decades. Although growth rates of satellite population in areas with central cities at such locations showed a tendency to increase within a radius of 20 miles of centers, from 1920 to 1930, they lagged behind satellite rates in the two water location classes in all zones beyond 5 miles in 1920-30 and 1930-40, and, in all zones beyond 10 miles in 1940-50. Metropolitan areas with central cities on sea or lake coast retained through the last decades their high growth rates in the zones beyond 10 miles from their centers; in fact, rates in the outer zones increased while those of inner zones declined. In areas with central cities at river locations satellite growth rates increased in the 5-10 mile zone, rising above the rates of corresponding zones of other location classes, after 1930. Meanwhile, rates of change in outer zones declined.

Greater confidence may be placed in the descriptive accuracy of the foregoing observations regarding the shifts of growth patterns within satellite areas if they reappear when satellite rates are expressed as ratios of central city rates. First, however, it is well to note the differences in the relative growth rates of total satellite area. Table 38 shows that until 1930 there was no appreciable difference between the ratios in metropolitan areas with centers on river and coastal locations. But in 1930-40 the growth of population in satellite areas about centers at river locations surged well ahead of growth in satellite areas about centers at coastal locations. The latter attained their peak growth relative to central city growth in 1940-50, the ratio for the former having declined in that decade. Relative growth rates in satellite areas

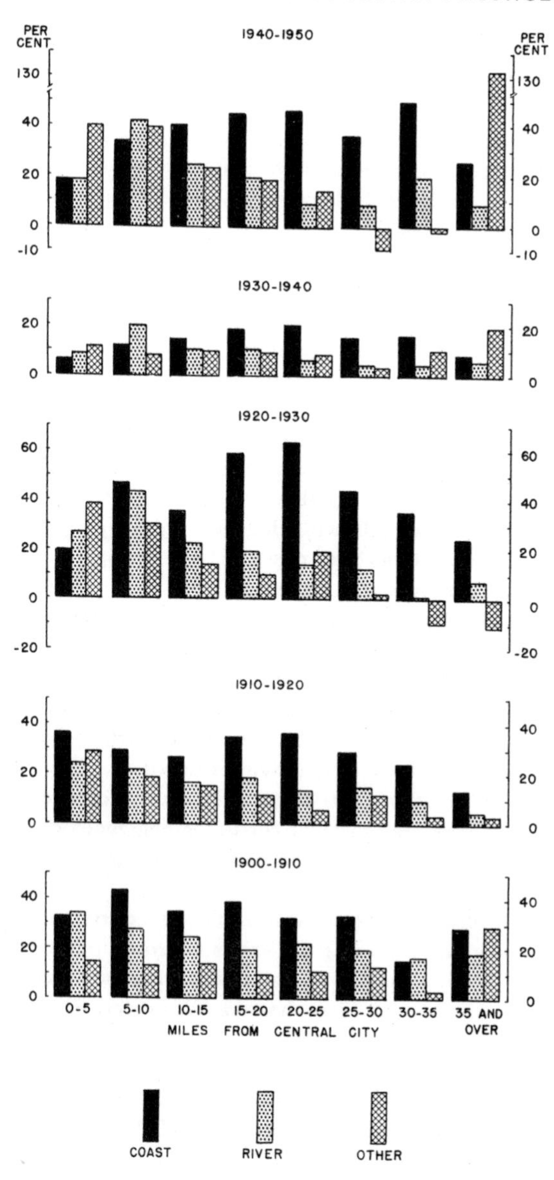


FIGURE 27
PER CENT CHANGE OF POPULATION IN DISTANCE ZONES OF STANDARD METROPOLITAN AREAS, BY TYPE OF LOCATION, AND BY DECADES, 1900-1950

TABLE 38. RATIO OF RATE OF CHANGE IN POPULATION IN SATELLITE AREAS TO RATE OF CHANGE IN CENTRAL CITIES IN STANDARD METROPOLITAN AREAS, BY TYPE OF LOCATION, AND DECADE, 1900 - 1950

| *Type of Location* | *1940-50* | *1930-40* | *1920-30* | *1910-20* | *1900-10* |
|---|---|---|---|---|---|
| Total | 2.7 | 2.5 | 1.4 | 0.9 | 0.8 |
| Sea or lake coast | 3.5 | 2.3 | 1.8 | 1.1 | 1.1 |
| River | 2.6 | 3.1 | 1.9 | 0.9 | 1.1 |
| Other | 1.7 | 2.3 | 0.7 | 0.4 | 0.3 |

surrounding centers at other locations increased slowly until 1930, rose abruptly to their maximum in 1930-40, and then subsided somewhat in the 1940-50 decade. Needless to say, ratios for total satellite area conceal zonal differences.

Ratios by distance zones are shown in Fig. 28. It will be observed that in 1900-10 and 1910-20 the three location classes stood in the same positions relative to one another on the basis of ratios of zonal rates to central city rates that they held on the basis of rates of change. During those decades population deconcentration beyond the 15-mile radius took place only in metropolitan areas with centers at coastal locations. Not until the 1920-30 decade did satellite rates in areas at other than water locations rise above central city rates, and that was limited to the 0-5 mile zone.

Three features of the trends through the last three decades of the 50-year period are noteworthy. First is the rapid rise of ratios in the other location class, particularly in the inner zones. Even so, the ratios for this class surpassed those of metropolitan areas with centers at water locations in just two zones: the 0-5 mile and the 35 mile and over zones. The ratios for the latter were so extreme as to appear to have been chance occurrences. Secondly, large increases occurred in the relative growth rates of zones beyond 10 miles from centers at coastal locations. Population deconcentration advanced farthest and most rapidly in those areas. Finally, the highest ratios of satellite growth in 5-10 mile zones was found in areas at river locations. To what extent that is an effect of river location cannot be inferred from the data presented thus far.

The distributions of the amounts of population change over metropolitan areas, by type of location, are shown in Table 39. In areas with

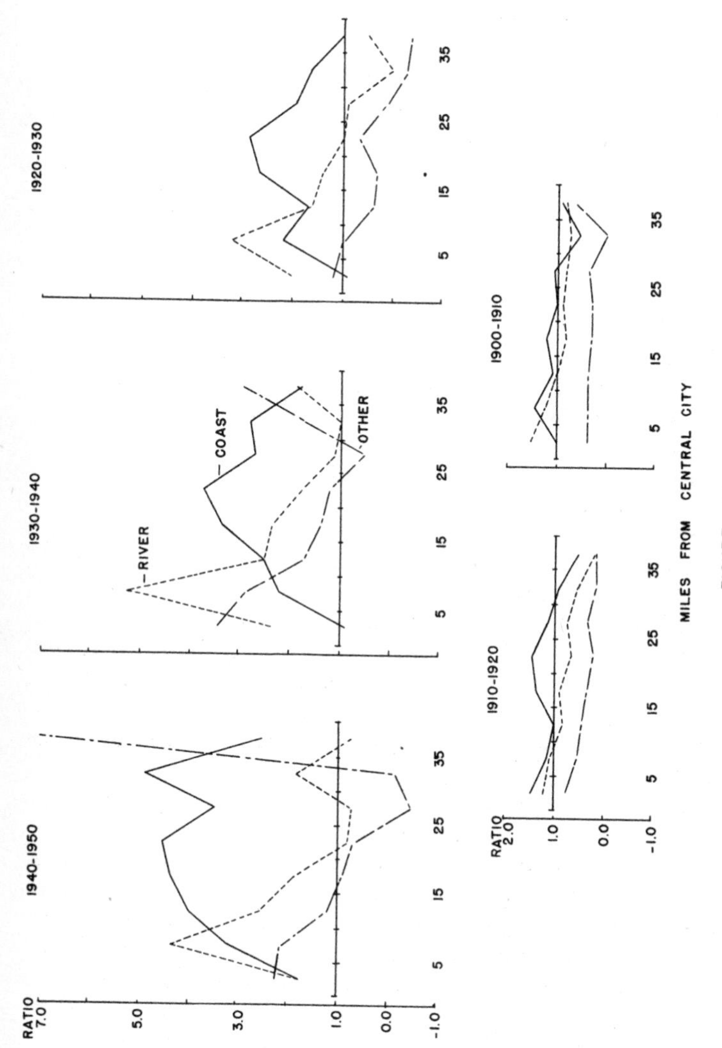


FIGURE 28
RATIO OF RATE OF POPULATION CHANGE IN DISTANCE ZONES TO CENTRAL CITY RATE OF CHANGE IN STANDARD METROPOLITAN AREAS, BY TYPE OF LOCATION, AND BY DECADES, 1900-1950

TABLE 39. CUMULATIVE PERCENTAGE DISTRIBUTION OF POPULATION INCREASE IN STANDARD METROPOLITAN AREAS, BY TYPE OF LOCATION, DISTANCE ZONE, AND DECADE, 1900 - 1950

| *Type of location and distance zone* | *1940-50* | *1930-40* | *1920-30* | *1910-20* | *1900-10* |
|---|---|---|---|---|---|
| Sea or lake coast | | | | | |
| Central cities | 32.1 | 43.2 | 53.9 | 65.7 | 66.6 |
| 0 - 5 miles | 36.0 | 45.9 | 57.5 | 71.9 | 71.1 |
| 5 - 10 " | 53.8 | 60.5 | 72.1 | 81.5 | 81.9 |
| 10 - 15 " | 71.1 | 74.1 | 81.5 | 88.9 | 89.7 |
| 15 - 20 " | 83.3 | 85.2 | 89.2 | 93.3 | 93.5 |
| 20 - 25 " | 91.0 | 92.5 | 94.6 | 96.4 | 95.7 |
| 25 - 30 " | 94.5 | 95.7 | 97.0 | 98.0 | 97.3 |
| 30 - 35 " | 97.3 | 97.7 | 98.2 | 98.9 | 97.8 |
| 35 miles and over | 100.0 | 100.0 | 100.0 | 100.0 | 100.0 |
| River | | | | | |
| Central cities | 32.0 | 29.7 | 43.1 | 60.1 | 55.8 |
| 0 - 5 miles | 40.5 | 39.1 | 53.6 | 69.6 | 65.9 |
| 5 - 10 " | 77.1 | 76.7 | 80.6 | 82.5 | 79.3 |
| 10 - 15 " | 90.2 | 87.9 | 90.2 | 89.6 | 87.8 |
| 15 - 20 " | 95.7 | 94.2 | 95.6 | 94.6 | 92.3 |
| 20 - 25 " | 97.4 | 97.3 | 98.2 | 97.2 | 96.0 |
| 25 - 30 " | 98.4 | 98.6 | 99.7 | 99.0 | 98.1 |
| 30 - 35 " | 99.6 | 99.2 | 99.7 | 99.7 | 99.1 |
| 35 miles and over | 100.0 | 100.0 | 100.0 | 100.0 | 100.0 |
| Other | | | | | |
| Central cities | 47.8 | 42.1 | 68.8 | 74.5 | 77.5 |
| 0 - 5 miles | 62.8 | 60.6 | 78.9 | 81.8 | 82.0 |
| 5 - 10 " | 83.9 | 81.6 | 90.8 | 89.7 | 88.6 |
| 10 - 15 " | 93.3 | 92.6 | 96.5 | 96.5 | 95.3 |
| 15 - 20 " | 96.2 | 96.9 | 98.5 | 98.9 | 97.7 |
| 20 - 25 " | 97.8 | 98.8 | 100.2 | 99.4 | 98.7 |
| 25 - 30 " | 97.9 | 99.1 | 100.3 | 100.0 | 99.4 |
| 30 - 35 " | 97.9 | 99.4 | 100.2 | 100.0 | 99.5 |
| 35 miles and over | 100.0 | 100.0 | 100.0 | 100.0 | 100.0 |

coastal locations there has been an uninterrupted dispersion of growth through successive decades. Whereas almost 67 per cent of all increase gathered in central cities in 1900-10, that proportion of the total increase was spread over an area reaching to almost 15 miles of central cities in 1940-50. The dispersion of increase was more erratic in metropolitan areas with river locations: dispersion was offset by centripetal tendencies in 1910-20 and again in 1940-50. Of particular interest, however, is the 5-10 mile zone; its share of increase advanced from 13 per cent in 1900-10 to 37 per cent in 1930-40 and 1940-50. In neither of the other location classes did the 5-10 mile zone attract more than 21 per cent of the total increase. It is quite possible that the sharp rise of growth in the 5-10 mile zone may have resulted from a recent overcoming of the river barrier through the construction of additional bridges and the elimination of tolls. Dispersion of increase has been the trend also in metropolitan areas at other than water locations, though that trend was reversed in the 1940-50 decade. Central cities, however, have claimed larger shares of the increase than has been true in either of the other location classes. It is largely for this reason that the extent of dispersion has been least in that location class.

Despite the dispersion of population increase that has taken place in metropolitan areas at coastal locations, the central cities of such areas have held larger proportions of the total area populations than have central cities at any other location. Nevertheless, a centrifugal drift has operated throughout the five decades, as may be seen in Table 40. Although most of the decline in the proportions within central cities has been taken up by the 5-10 mile zone -- the proportion in the 0-5 mile zone has remained unchanged, all zones beyond the 5-10 mile zone have steadily increased their shares of the total population. In areas at river locations the prevailing direction of population redistribution down to 1920 was toward concentration, after 1920 deconcentration set in and continued to 1950. In the concentration phase losses were incurred in all zones beyond 5 miles from central cities. On the other hand, deconcentration was largely a matter of shifting proportions from central cities to the 5-10 mile zone. All zones beyond the 15 mile radius have had progressively smaller proportions since 1900. Metropolitan areas situated at other than water locations experienced population concentration from 1900 to 1930 and deconcentration in the remaining two decades. Again the principal shifts involved central cities and 5-10 mile zones. The more distant zones had declining proportions throughout the period under study.

The coefficients shown graphically in Fig. 29 describes the rates at which redistribution occurred. Population in metropolitan areas at coastal

## TABLE 40. CUMULATIVE PERCENTAGE DISTRIBUTION OF POPULATION IN STANDARD METROPOLITAN AREAS, BY TYPE OF LOCATION, DISTANCE ZONE, AND CENSUS YEAR, 1900 - 1950

| *Type of location and distance zone* | *1950* | *1940* | *1930* | *1920* | *1910* | *1900* |
|---|---|---|---|---|---|---|
| Sea or lake coast | | | | | | |
| Central cities | 57.2 | 62.1 | 64.1 | 68.0 | 68.5 | 68.8 |
| 0 - 5 miles | 61.5 | 66.5 | 68.6 | 72.9 | 73.0 | 73.5 |
| 5 - 10 " | 73.6 | 77.5 | 79.1 | 81.7 | 81.8 | 81.6 |
| 10 - 15 " | 83.5 | 85.9 | 87.1 | 89.2 | 89.2 | 89.0 |
| 15 - 20 " | 90.2 | 91.5 | 92.1 | 92.9 | 92.7 | 92.4 |
| 20 - 25 " | 94.2 | 94.8 | 95.0 | 95.3 | 95.0 | 94.7 |
| 25 - 30 " | 96.4 | 96.8 | 96.9 | 96.9 | 96.5 | 96.3 |
| 30 - 35 " | 97.8 | 97.9 | 98.0 | 97.8 | 97.5 | 97.4 |
| 35 miles and over | 100.0 | 100.0 | 100.0 | 100.0 | 100.0 | 100.0 |
| River | | | | | | |
| Central cities | 51.5 | 54.7 | 56.8 | 59.3 | 58.4 | 58.1 |
| 0 - 5 miles | 59.9 | 63.1 | 64.8 | 66.7 | 65.8 | 65.1 |
| 5 - 10 " | 77.8 | 77.8 | 78.6 | 78.2 | 77.3 | 76.8 |
| 10 - 15 " | 87.4 | 86.8 | 87.0 | 86.4 | 85.7 | 85.2 |
| 15 - 20 " | 92.6 | 92.0 | 92.1 | 91.6 | 91.0 | 90.8 |
| 20 - 25 " | 95.9 | 95.6 | 95.7 | 95.3 | 94.9 | 94.7 |
| 25 - 30 " | 98.0 | 97.9 | 98.0 | 97.7 | 97.4 | 97.3 |
| 30 - 35 " | 99.1 | 99.0 | 99.1 | 99.0 | 98.8 | 98.8 |
| 35 miles and over | 100.0 | 100.0 | 100.0 | 100.0 | 100.0 | 100.0 |
| Other | | | | | | |
| Central cities | 57.9 | 60.3 | 62.4 | 60.4 | 56.0 | 48.1 |
| 0 - 5 miles | 67.9 | 69.1 | 70.4 | 67.8 | 63.7 | 57.6 |
| 5 - 10 " | 82.3 | 81.9 | 81.6 | 78.9 | 76.7 | 72.8 |
| 10 - 15 " | 92.2 | 91.9 | 91.5 | 90.1 | 89.1 | 87.5 |
| 15 - 20 " | 96.1 | 96.0 | 96.1 | 95.5 | 95.3 | 94.6 |
| 20 - 25 " | 98.4 | 98.4 | 98.4 | 98.0 | 97.6 | 97.2 |
| 25 - 30 " | 99.1 | 99.3 | 99.4 | 99.2 | 99.0 | 98.9 |
| 30 - 35 " | 99.3 | 99.6 | 99.7 | 99.6 | 99.4 | 99.4 |
| 35 miles and over | 100.0 | 100.0 | 100.0 | 100.0 | 100.0 | 100.0 |

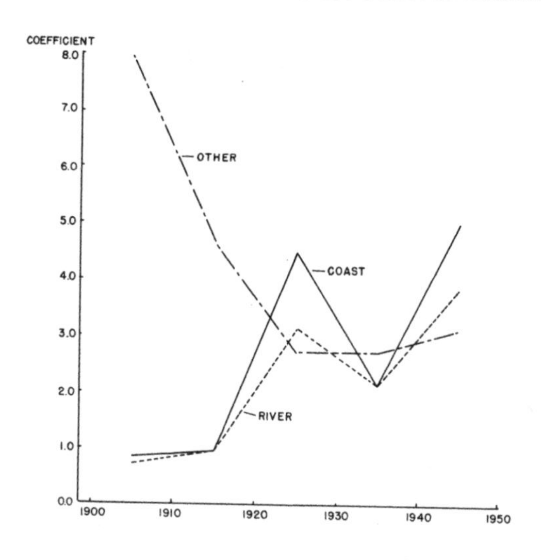


FIGURE 29
COEFFICIENTS OF POPULATION REDISTRIBUTION IN STANDARD METROPOLITAN AREAS, BY TYPE OF LOCATION, 1900-1950

locations deconcentrated at an increasing rate. The 1920-30 and 1940-50 decades were periods of unusually rapid scatter, or, speaking more accurately, of high relative growth rates in outlying zones. This was noted in Fig. 28. Redistribution in metropolitan areas at river locations followed a similar pattern of variation, with the highest rates also in the 1920-30 and the 1940-50 decades. In this class of areas, however, 1920 marked the beginning of deconcentration. The most rapid redistribution occurred in metropolitan areas at other than water locations and during the period of population concentration. That period ended in 1930 and was followed by a comparatively slow deconcentration movement.

## Satellite Area and River Locations

The effect of a river location on the changing distribution of population in metropolitan areas may be explored in another way, that is, by comparing growth tendencies in the parts of areas lying on the two sides of the rivers flowing through them. If the river is a barrier, higher growth rates should be found on the side on which the central city is situated than on the opposite side. Such a comparison obviously requires that the analysis be restricted to Standard Metropolitan areas which lie athwart rivers. The number satisfying that condition, shown in Table 41, is smaller than that of all areas with centers at river locations.

TABLE 41. NUMBER OF STANDARD METROPOLITAN AREAS AT RIVER LOCATIONS WITH PARTS ON OPPOSITE SIDES OF RIVERS, BY SIZE OF CENTRAL CITY, AND DECADE, 1900 - 1950

| *Size of Central city* | *1940-50* | *1930-40* | *1920-30* | *1910-20* | *1900-10* |
|---|---|---|---|---|---|
| 500,000 and over | 5 | 5 | 4 | 4 | 2 |
| 250,000 - 500,000 | 2 | 3 | 3 | 3 | 5 |
| 100,000 - 250,000 | 11 | 12 | 11 | 7 | 3 |
| Under 100,000 | 12 | 12 | 14 | 18 | 22 |

For the most part, since 1920, rates of change have been highest in the parts of metropolitan areas lying on the central city sides of rivers. That has been true of most distance zones as well as of total area, as shown in Table 42. The small differences between growth rates on the two sides of rivers in 1900-10 and 1910-20 may have been due to the early growth of twin cities immediately opposite metropolitan centers. If so, the influences of such rival centers did not last, for the barrier effect of rivers became prominent after 1920 despite the increases in the numbers and sizes of bridges and the eliminations of tolls. The irregularities in the data for zones beyond 25 miles of central cities are very likely a result of the small populations involved, particularly on the sides opposite central cities. For example, the 110.9 per cent growth of population in the 30-35 mile zone on the opposite river side, in the 1940-50 decade, was due almost entirely to the growth in one incorporated place in the Philadelphia metropolitan area. Excluding that one place, the average growth for the fragment of the zone was 2.5 per cent. Similar deviations occurred in other zones and decades where small populations existed.

In Table 43 it is apparent that satellite area on the central city sides of rivers commanded the largest share of the additions to population in all decades. The proportion increased steadily from 1900 to 1940, after which it declined slightly. In the 0-5 mile zone the largest proportion of increase frequently occurred on the sides opposite central cities. Still the proportion accruing to the central city side in that zone is noteworthy in view of the fact that a large part of the 0-5 mile zone is contained in central cities and is not therefore satellite area. The striking feature in Table 43, however, is the evidence of a gravitation of population increase to the 5-10 mile zone and especially to that part on the central city side. That trend

TABLE 42. PER CENT CHANGE OF SATELLITE POPULATION IN STANDARD METROPOLITAN AREAS AT RIVER LOCATIONS, BY DISTANCE ZONE, SIDE OF RIVER AND DECADE, 1900-1950

| *Distance zone and side of river* | *1940-50* | *1940-40* | *1920-30* | *1910-20* | *1900-10* |
|---|---|---|---|---|---|
| All satellite area | | | | | |
| On central city side | 40.1 | 11.3 | 27.8 | 18.6 | 23.5 |
| On opposite side | 22.1 | 5.5 | 13.2 | 17.5 | 24.4 |
| 0-5 mile zone | | | | | |
| On central city side | 20.2 | 11.7 | 38.6 | 28.7 | 33.9 |
| On opposite side | 14.5 | 3.4 | 17.0 | 22.0 | 32.6 |
| 5-10 mile zone | | | | | |
| On central city side | 87.6 | 19.3 | 40.4 | 20.6 | 26.0 |
| On opposite side | 37.2 | 13.8 | 22.6 | 19.8 | 23.1 |
| 10-15 mile zone | | | | | |
| On central city side | 21.1 | 8.0 | 24.1 | 18.9 | 22.5 |
| On opposite side | 23.9 | 7.0 | 19.4 | 14.6 | 19.6 |
| 15-20 mile zone | | | | | |
| On central city side | 16.9 | 8.3 | 16.4 | 18.7 | 12.1 |
| On opposite side | 7.6 | 7.8 | 9.1 | 12.8 | 20.7 |
| 20-25 mile zone | | | | | |
| On central city side | 10.8 | 4.0 | 34.7 | 10.3 | 25.1 |
| On opposite side | 3.8 | -12.7 | 8.3 | 17.9 | 24.4 |
| 25-30 mile zone | | | | | |
| On central city side | 6.7 | 3.4 | 13.3 | 19.8 | 25.8 |
| On opposite side | 10.2 | 5.5 | 8.7 | -4.7 | 13.7 |
| 30-35 mile zone | | | | | |
| On central city zone | 8.9 | 4.3 | 3.6 | 8.1 | 21.0 |
| On opposite side | 110.9 | -10.6 | -12.9 | 22.5 | -0.4 |
| 35 mile and over zone | | | | | |
| On central city side | 8.8 | 6.8 | 4.6 | 4.5 | 12.5 |
| On opposite side | 20.7 | -7.8 | 17.6 | 6.9 | 43.7 |

TABLE 43. PER CENT DISTRIBUTION OF POPULATION INCREASE IN SATELLITE AREA OF STANDARD METROPOLITAN AREAS AT RIVER LOCATIONS, BY DISTANCE ZONE, SIDE OF RIVER AND DECADE, 1900-1950

| *Distance zone and side of river* | *1940-50* | *1930-40* | *1920-30* | *1910-20* | *1900-10* |
|---|---|---|---|---|---|
| All satellite areas | 100.0 | 100.0 | 100.0 | 100.0 | 100.0 |
| On central city side | 73.1 | 74.5 | 69.5 | 59.3 | 58.0 |
| On opposite side | 26.9 | 25.5 | 30.5 | 40.7 | 42.0 |
| 0-5 mile zone | | | | | |
| On central city side | 4.4 | 9.1 | 10.4 | 10.0 | 9.4 |
| On opposite side | 4.9 | 4.5 | 9.2 | 14.3 | 14.3 |
| 5-10 mile zone | | | | | |
| On central city side | 53.1 | 41.4 | 29.9 | 18.8 | 18.7 |
| On opposite side | 14.6 | 19.2 | 11.8 | 13.1 | 11.6 |
| 10-15 mile zone | | | | | |
| On central city side | 8.9 | 11.9 | 13.9 | 13.6 | 12.2 |
| On opposite side | 4.2 | 4.6 | 5.2 | 5.0 | 5.2 |
| 15-20 mile zone | | | | | |
| On central city side | 3.4 | 6.2 | 5.0 | 7.0 | 3.6 |
| On opposite side | 1.1 | 4.0 | 2.0 | 3.6 | 4.5 |
| 20-25 mile zone | | | | | |
| On central city side | 1.5 | 2.0 | 6.7 | 3.0 | 5.5 |
| On opposite side | 0.4 | -6.6 | 1.6 | 4.2 | 4.1 |
| 25-30 mile zone | | | | | |
| On central city side | 0.8 | 1.7 | 2.8 | 5.1 | 4.9 |
| On opposite side | 0.4 | 0.7 | 0.5 | -0.4 | 1.0 |
| 30-35 mile zone | | | | | |
| On central city side | 0.6 | 1.1 | 0.4 | 1.3 | 2.6 |
| On opposite side | 1.0 | -0.4 | -0.3 | 0.6 | 0.0 |
| 35 mile and over zone | | | | | |
| On central city side | 0.4 | 1.2 | 0.4 | 0.5 | 1.2 |
| On opposite side | 0.4 | -0.6 | 0.5 | 0.3 | 1.2 |

reached its highest point in 1940-50 when 53 per cent of all satellite increase concentrated in the part of the 5-10 mile zone on the central city side of rivers. Nevertheless, the effect of rivers on the distributions of growth has extended 30 miles or more from central cities.

## Size and Type of Satellite Place

It is not surprising in view of earlier findings to discover that the growth rates of all sizes and types of satellite places located in metropolitan areas at coastal locations exceeded those of similar places in other locations (Table 44). Moreover, high growth rates extended further into outlying zones about centers at coastal locations than in other location classes. Growth rates in satellite places at both river and other than water locations fell off abruptly beyond 20 miles from centers. But metropolitan areas at all types of locations had in common the tendency for rates of change to decline in incorporated places of 2,500 or more population. Although there was some tendency in incorporated places of less than 2,500 for the rates of change to increase, especially within 20 miles, the largest increases of growth rates occurred in unincorporated area. The most rapid increase of this kind took place within areas at other than water locations.

These comparisons stand out more sharply when rates of change are expressed as ratios to central city rates, as in Table 45. The highest relative rates of change occurred in areas at coastal locations and the lowest developed at other than water locations. All types of satellite places gained in the deconcentration of population within areas at coastal locations; in fact, deconcentration accelerated over the years since 1900 in all types of places except those of 50,000 or more population. In the two other location classes deconcentration affected all unincorporated areas and incorporated places of less than 10,000 population which are within 20 miles of central cities. In the zones beyond 20 miles from centers the effect of differential growth was to increase concentration at the centers or within the 20 mile zones about centers.

Although unincorporated population in areas at coastal locations enjoyed the highest growth rates, both absolute and relative, the proportion unincorporated was of the total population in each zone never grew as large as that in areas at river and other than water locations. The largest proportions, Table 46 shows, consistently occurred in the satellite areas of land-locked centers. This variation finds a parallel in incorporated places of less than 2,500 population. Low proportions of population in unincorporated areas and in small incorporated places are a function of large proportions in large incorporated places, and, conversely, large

Table 44. Per Cent Change of Satellite Population in Standard Metropolitan Areas, by Size and Type of Satellite Place, Distance Zone, Type of Location, and Decade, 1900-1950

| Size and type of satellite place and distance zone | Sea or lake coast | | | | | River | | | | | Other | | | | |
|---|---|---|---|---|---|---|---|---|---|---|---|---|---|---|---|
| | 1940-1950 | 1930-1940 | 1920-1930 | 1910-1920 | 1900-1910 | 1940-1950 | 1930-1940 | 1920-1930 | 1910-1920 | 1900-1910 | 1940-1950 | 1930-1940 | 1920-1930 | 1910-1920 | 1900-1910 |
| 50,000 and over | | | | | | | | | | | | | | | |
| 0-10 miles | 11.4 | 0.9 | 12.1 | 19.7 | 36.9 | 4.6 | -1.7 | 6.0 | 6.5 | 25.5[a] | ---- | ---- | ---- | ---- | ---- |
| 10-20 miles | 10.6 | 1.8 | 13.7 | 19.0 | 35.5 | 3.6 | -3.5 | 5.5 | 21.8[a] | ---- | ---- | ---- | ---- | ---- | ---- |
| 20-30 miles | 18.8 | 8.1 | 81.3 | ---- | ---- | ---- | ---- | ---- | ---- | ---- | ---- | ---- | ---- | ---- | ---- |
| 30 miles and over | ---- | ---- | ---- | ---- | ---- | ---- | ---- | ---- | ---- | ---- | ---- | ---- | ---- | ---- | ---- |
| 10,000 - 50,000 | | | | | | | | | | | | | | | |
| 0-10 miles | 13.5 | 7.7 | 40.1 | 34.6 | 35.0 | 7.2 | 3.2 | 14.9 | 11.9 | 22.5 | 13.2 | -1.1 | 41.9 | 15.4 | 17.5[a] |
| 10-20 miles | 40.6 | 11.0 | 44.3 | 39.9 | 59.6 | 4.9 | 2.4 | 21.5 | 22.5 | 37.3 | 12.9 | 2.6 | 24.6 | 41.2 | -54.7[a] |
| 20-30 miles | 14.3 | 6.9 | 32.2 | 46.3 | 38.4 | 9.8 | 2.3 | 15.6 | 17.4 | 41.7 | -31.8 | 3.4 | 15.3 | 26.8 | 23.5[a] |
| 30 miles and over | 22.9 | 1.7 | 19.6 | 18.4 | 21.4 | 6.0 | 1.6 | 6.5 | 19.7 | 13.9 | ---- | ---- | ---- | ---- | ---- |
| 2,500 - 10,000 | | | | | | | | | | | | | | | |
| 0-10 miles | 53.7 | 23.0 | 75.7 | 96.5 | 60.9 | 19.0 | 9.0 | 31.7 | 22.2 | 57.6 | 27.2 | -3.1 | 21.6 | 26.1 | 5.9 |
| 10-20 miles | 60.7 | 119.4 | 88.5 | 39.0 | 56.8 | 13.7 | 6.7 | 34.9 | 27.8 | 33.1 | 32.6 | -58.1[a] | 11.2 | 24.7 | 35.0[a] |
| 20-30 miles | 30.8 | 9.4 | 48.5 | 18.6 | 43.8 | 0.1 | 3.4 | 17.2 | 16.0 | 37.1 | 5.8 | 2.5 | 10.0[a] | 16.6[a] | 30.3[a] |
| 30 miles and over | 24.3 | 4.5 | 33.6 | 22.2 | 41.2 | 9.6 | 4.0 | 7.9 | 85.6[a] | 50.0[a] | 4.8[a] | 25.6[a] | -11.0[a] | -67.9[a] | 23.7[a] |
| Under 2,500 | | | | | | | | | | | | | | | |
| 0-10 miles | 75.7 | 37.4 | 214.1 | 76.1 | 77.0 | 36.5 | 18.2 | 62.1 | 39.0 | 57.2 | 26.9 | 14.3 | 41.4 | 17.2[a] | 38.8[a] |
| 10-20 miles | 64.4 | 29.1 | 110.0 | 53.3 | 47.5 | 23.1 | 8.1 | 20.0 | 24.4 | 20.8 | 18.2 | 6.3 | 12.1 | 14.7 | 16.1[a] |
| 20-30 miles | 54.7 | 25.0 | 63.3 | 32.0 | 27.1 | 4.1 | 3.1 | 8.0 | 18.7 | 37.3[a] | 14.1 | 4.5 | 1.5 | 19.6[a] | 34.4[a] |
| 30 miles and over | 29.5 | 12.4 | 25.6 | 18.6 | 31.2[a] | 14.5 | 1.8 | 3.3 | -4.6[a] | 18.1[a] | -59.2[a] | 2.9[a] | -2.5[a] | 6.8[a] | 11.8[a] |
| Unincorporated | | | | | | | | | | | | | | | |
| 0-10 miles | 59.2 | 20.8 | 42.9 | 21.9 | 37.5 | 54.1 | 28.0 | 52.9 | 29.5 | 23.7 | 46.7 | 27.2 | 32.7 | 21.6 | 12.2 |
| 10-20 miles | 66.0 | 9.4 | 45.7 | 22.6 | 14.0 | 31.2 | 14.6 | 18.0 | 11.3 | 17.7 | 21.8 | 42.1 | 10.7 | 8.3 | 12.7 |
| 20-30 miles | 73.2 | 33.3 | 73.4 | 26.0 | 26.8 | 10.1 | 7.7 | 10.2 | 9.2 | 11.3 | 26.5 | 7.9 | 16.5 | 1.3 | 2.7 |
| 30 miles and over | 44.3 | 19.6 | 28.2 | 9.5 | 18.0 | 14.6 | 6.9 | 1.9 | 1.4 | 12.2 | 92.3 | 14.7 | -12.8 | 36.6 | 16.4 |

[a] Based on less than 5 incorporated places.

Table 45. Ratio of Rate of Change of Satellite Population to Central City Rate of Change in Standard Metropolitan Areas, by Size and Type of Satellite Place, Distance Zone, Type of Location, and Decade, 1900-1950

| Size and type of satellite place and distance zone | Sea or lake coast | | | | | River | | | | | Other | | | | |
|---|---|---|---|---|---|---|---|---|---|---|---|---|---|---|---|
| | 1940-1950 | 1930-1940 | 1920-1930 | 1910-1920 | 1900-1910 | 1940-1950 | 1930-1940 | 1920-1930 | 1910-1920 | 1900-1910 | 1940-1950 | 1930-1940 | 1920-1930 | 1910-1920 | 1900-1910 |
| 50,000 and over | | | | | | | | | | | | | | | |
| 0-10 miles | 1.1 | 0.2 | 0.6 | 0.8 | 1.2 | 0.5 | -0.5 | 0.5 | 0.3 | 1.1 | ---- | ---- | ---- | ---- | ---- |
| 10-20 miles | 1.0 | 0.3 | 0.6 | 0.8 | 1.1 | 0.4 | -1.0 | 0.4 | 1.1 | ---- | ---- | ---- | ---- | ---- | ---- |
| 20-30 miles | 1.8 | 1.5 | 3.7 | ---- | ---- | ---- | ---- | ---- | ---- | ---- | ---- | ---- | ---- | ---- | ---- |
| 30 miles and over | ---- | ---- | ---- | ---- | ---- | ---- | ---- | ---- | ---- | ---- | ---- | ---- | ---- | ---- | ---- |
| 10,000 - 50,000 | | | | | | | | | | | | | | | |
| 0-10 miles | 1.3 | 1.4 | 1.8 | 1.4 | 1.1 | 0.7 | 0.9 | 1.1 | 0.6 | 1.0 | 0.7 | 0.2 | 1.3 | 0.4 | 0.4 |
| 10-20 miles | 4.0 | 2.0 | 2.0 | 1.6 | 1.9 | 0.5 | 0.6 | 1.6 | 1.2 | 1.6 | 0.7 | 0.4 | 0.8 | 1.1 | -1.1 |
| 20-30 miles | 1.4 | 1.3 | 1.5 | 1.8 | 1.2 | 1.0 | 0.6 | 1.2 | 0.9 | 1.8 | -1.7 | 0.6 | 0.5 | 0.7 | 0.5 |
| 30 miles and over | 2.2 | 0.3 | 0.9 | 0.7 | 0.7 | 0.6 | 0.4 | 0.5 | 1.0 | 0.6 | ---- | ---- | ---- | ---- | ---- |
| 2,500 - 10,000 | | | | | | | | | | | | | | | |
| 0-10 miles | 5.3 | 4.3 | 3.4 | 3.8 | 1.9 | 2.0 | 2.4 | 2.4 | 1.2 | 2.5 | 1.4 | -0.5 | 0.7 | 0.7 | 0.1 |
| 10-20 miles | 6.0 | 22.1 | 4.0 | 1.6 | 1.8 | 1.4 | 1.8 | 2.7 | 1.4 | 1.4 | 1.7 | -9.4 | 0.4 | 0.6 | 0.7 |
| 20-30 miles | 3.0 | 1.7 | 2.2 | 0.7 | 1.4 | 0.0 | 0.9 | 1.3 | 0.8 | 1.6 | 0.3 | 0.4 | 0.3 | 0.4 | 0.6 |
| 30 miles and over | 2.4 | 0.8 | 1.5 | 0.9 | 1.3 | 1.0 | 1.1 | 0.6 | 4.4 | 2.2 | 0.3 | 4.1 | -0.4 | -1.8 | 0.5 |
| Under 2,500 | | | | | | | | | | | | | | | |
| 0-10 miles | 7.4 | 6.9 | 9.7 | 3.0 | 2.4 | 3.8 | 4.9 | 4.7 | 2.0 | 2.5 | 1.4 | 2.3 | 1.3 | 0.4 | 0.8 |
| 10-20 miles | 6.3 | 5.4 | 5.0 | 2.1 | 1.5 | 2.4 | 2.2 | 1.5 | 1.3 | 0.9 | 1.0 | 1.0 | 4.0 | 0.4 | 0.3 |
| 20-30 miles | 5.4 | 4.6 | 2.9 | 1.3 | 0.8 | 0.4 | 0.8 | 0.6 | 1.0 | 1.6 | 0.8 | 0.7 | 0.0 | 0.5 | 0.7 |
| 30 miles and over | 2.9 | 2.3 | 1.2 | 0.7 | 1.0 | 1.5 | 0.5 | 0.2 | -0.2 | 0.8 | -3.2 | 0.5 | 0.0 | 0.2 | 0.2 |
| Unincorporated | | | | | | | | | | | | | | | |
| 0-10 miles | 5.8 | 3.8 | 1.9 | 0.9 | 1.2 | 5.6 | 7.6 | 4.0 | 1.5 | 1.0 | 2.5 | 4.4 | 1.0 | 0.6 | 0.2 |
| 10-20 miles | 6.5 | 1.7 | 2.1 | 0.9 | 0.4 | 3.2 | 4.0 | 1.4 | 0.6 | 0.8 | 1.2 | 6.8 | 0.3 | 0.2 | 0.3 |
| 20-30 miles | 7.2 | 6.2 | 3.3 | 1.0 | 0.8 | 1.0 | 2.1 | 0.8 | 0.5 | 0.5 | 1.4 | 1.3 | 0.5 | 0.0 | 0.0 |
| 30 miles and over | 4.3 | 3.6 | 1.3 | 0.4 | 0.6 | 1.5 | 1.9 | 0.2 | 0.1 | 0.5 | 4.9 | 2.4 | -0.4 | 0.9 | 0.3 |

Table 46. Per Cent Distribution of Satellite Population in Standard Metropolitan Areas, by Census Year, Size and Type of Satellite Place, Type of Location, and Distance Zone, 1900-1950

| Census year and size and type of satellite place | Sea or lake coast | | | | River | | | | Other | | | |
|---|---|---|---|---|---|---|---|---|---|---|---|---|
| | 0-10 miles | 10-20 miles | 20-30 miles | 30 miles and over | 0-10 miles | 10-20 miles | 20-30 miles | 30 miles and over | 0-10 miles | 10-20 miles | 20-30 miles | 30 miles and over |
| **1950** | | | | | | | | | | | | |
| Total | 100.0 | 100.0 | 100.0 | 100.0 | 100.0 | 100.0 | 100.0 | 100.0 | 100.0 | 100.0 | 100.0 | 100.0 |
| 50,000 and over | 34.8 | 25.2 | 11.5 | 0.0 | 5.4 | 7.7 | 0.0 | 0.0 | 0.0 | 0.0 | 0.0 | 0.0 |
| 10,000 - 50,000 | 23.6 | 22.3 | 21.1 | 24.4 | 19.7 | 13.1 | 18.7 | 13.1 | 8.3 | 16.2 | 10.4 | 0.0 |
| 2,500 - 10,000 | 7.4 | 13.8 | 16.0 | 17.4 | 15.3 | 11.9 | 16.1 | 12.0 | 11.4 | 10.2 | 12.9 | 6.2 |
| Under 2,500 | 1.5 | 4.0 | 6.0 | 8.5 | 4.9 | 8.3 | 11.1 | 14.9 | 5.5 | 13.1 | 10.1 | 1.9 |
| Unincorporated area | 32.7 | 34.7 | 45.4 | 49.7 | 54.7 | 59.0 | 54.1 | 60.0 | 74.8 | 60.5 | 66.6 | 91.9 |
| **1940** | | | | | | | | | | | | |
| Total | 100.0 | 100.0 | 100.0 | 100.0 | 100.0 | 100.0 | 100.0 | 100.0 | 100.0 | 100.0 | 100.0 | 100.0 |
| 50,000 and over | 40.0 | 32.3 | 13.7 | 0.0 | 6.8 | 9.0 | 0.0 | 0.0 | 0.0 | 0.0 | 0.0 | 0.0 |
| 10,000 - 50,000 | 26.5 | 22.5 | 26.2 | 26.5 | 24.3 | 15.3 | 18.4 | 13.9 | 10.3 | 17.3 | 17.1 | 0.0 |
| 2,500 - 10,000 | 6.1 | 12.2 | 17.4 | 18.7 | 17.0 | 12.8 | 17.3 | 12.4 | 12.5 | 9.3 | 13.7 | 10.1 |
| Under 2,500 | 1.1 | 3.4 | 5.5 | 8.8 | 4.8 | 8.2 | 11.4 | 14.7 | 6.0 | 13.4 | 10.0 | 8.0 |
| Unincorporated area | 26.3 | 29.6 | 37.2 | 46.0 | 47.1 | 54.7 | 52.9 | 59.0 | 71.2 | 60.0 | 59.2 | 81.9 |
| **1930** | | | | | | | | | | | | |
| Total | 100.0 | 100.0 | 100.0 | 100.0 | 100.0 | 100.0 | 100.0 | 100.0 | 100.0 | 100.0 | 100.0 | 100.0 |
| 50,000 and over | 43.1 | 34.7 | 14.8 | 0.0 | 9.2 | 9.3 | 0.0 | 0.0 | 0.0 | 0.0 | 0.0 | 0.0 |
| 10,000 - 50,000 | 25.4 | 23.1 | 26.4 | 28.8 | 24.8 | 17.4 | 20.8 | 13.7 | 11.7 | 16.8 | 9.2 | 0.0 |
| 2,500 - 10,000 | 5.9 | 6.5 | 19.2 | 9.9 | 5.2 | 8.2 | 11.5 | 17.6 | 5.9 | 13.4 | 10.0 | 8.9 |
| Under 2,500 | 1.1 | 3.9 | 6.0 | 9.9 | 5.2 | 8.2 | 11.5 | 17.6 | 5.9 | 13.4 | 10.0 | 8.9 |
| Unincorporated area | 24.5 | 31.8 | 33.6 | 43.0 | 43.7 | 50.8 | 51.3 | 57.8 | 68.9 | 49.0 | 66.4 | 81.9 |
| **1920** | | | | | | | | | | | | |
| Total | 100.0 | 100.0 | 100.0 | 100.0 | 100.0 | 100.0 | 100.0 | 100.0 | 100.0 | 100.0 | 100.0 | 100.0 |
| 50,000 and over | 35.3 | 34.8 | 5.8 | 0.0 | 11.7 | 7.8 | 0.0 | 0.0 | 0.0 | 0.0 | 0.0 | 0.0 |
| 10,000 - 50,000 | 29.8 | 20.7 | 34.4 | 26.6 | 22.2 | 15.9 | 17.9 | 9.8 | 10.0 | 13.8 | 9.0 | 0.0 |
| 2,500 - 10,000 | 7.1 | 11.6 | 19.1 | 17.2 | 18.7 | 14.2 | 16.9 | 12.9 | 12.8 | 7.9 | 13.4 | 8.4 |
| Under 2,500 | 1.9 | 5.4 | 8.1 | 10.9 | 7.0 | 8.8 | 12.7 | 14.8 | 6.9 | 15.2 | 11.4 | 15.4 |
| Unincorporated area | 25.9 | 27.5 | 32.6 | 45.3 | 40.4 | 53.3 | 52.5 | 62.5 | 70.3 | 63.1 | 66.2 | 76.2 |
| **1910** | | | | | | | | | | | | |
| Total | 100.0 | 100.0 | 100.0 | 100.0 | 100.0 | 100.0 | 100.0 | 100.0 | 100.0 | 100.0 | 100.0 | 100.0 |
| 50,000 and over | 34.6 | 33.6 | 0.0 | 0.0 | 13.1 | 4.5 | 0.0 | 0.0 | 0.0 | 0.0 | 0.0 | 0.0 |
| 10,000 - 50,000 | 25.1 | 19.3 | 34.5 | 23.8 | 20.9 | 11.8 | 13.2 | 8.8 | 5.1 | 12.2 | 9.2 | 0.0 |
| 2,500 - 10,000 | 7.7 | 10.6 | 16.6 | 16.2 | 16.7 | 12.8 | 18.2 | 5.6 | 12.7 | 7.0 | 10.4 | 28.7 |
| Under 2,500 | 2.1 | 6.7 | 12.0 | 12.7 | 7.6 | 10.1 | 14.5 | 14.7 | 8.8 | 15.6 | 16.1 | 14.9 |
| Unincorporated area | 30.5 | 29.8 | 36.9 | 47.3 | 41.7 | 60.8 | 54.1 | 70.9 | 73.4 | 65.2 | 64.3 | 56.4 |
| **1900** | | | | | | | | | | | | |
| Total | 100.0 | 100.0 | 100.0 | 100.0 | 100.0 | 100.0 | 100.0 | 100.0 | 100.0 | 100.0 | 100.0 | 100.0 |
| 50,000 and over | 30.9 | 26.5 | 0.0 | 0.0 | 7.7 | 0.0 | 0.0 | 0.0 | 0.0 | 0.0 | 0.0 | 0.0 |
| 10,000 - 50,000 | 26.3 | 20.9 | 16.6 | 20.4 | 23.0 | 13.8 | 3.9 | 5.3 | 3.5 | 3.6 | 17.0 | 0.0 |
| 2,500 - 10,000 | 6.0 | 8.5 | 22.0 | 13.7 | 11.4 | 9.3 | 17.3 | 9.9 | 8.7 | 9.0 | 4.3 | 4.9 |
| Under 2,500 | 2.6 | 6.3 | 10.7 | 13.8 | 7.4 | 9.5 | 15.8 | 13.5 | 7.3 | 13.8 | 14.5 | 14.8 |
| Unincorporated area | 34.2 | 37.8 | 50.7 | 52.1 | 50.5 | 67.4 | 63.0 | 71.3 | 80.5 | 73.6 | 64.2 | 80.3 |

proportions in the smallest or least densely settled places are made possible by a lack of development, if not an absence, of large incorporated satellites. Thus areas at coastal locations have had a comparatively full complement of satellite places, while areas at other than water locations have stood at the other extreme in this respect. The proportions of zonal populations contained within satellites of over 10,000 population have declined since 1930, however, particularly in the inner zones.

### Transportation Access to Central City

An implicit assumption in much of the preceding discussion is that some of the variation in the territorial extent and the rate of population redistribution among differenc classes of metropolitan areas is due to differences in the development of transportation access from satellite zones to central cities. This factor has been referred to as an element in the concept of metropolitan maturity, which in turn has been associated with the "age" of metropolitan areas. It seems appropriate at this point to bring the matter out of the realm of speculation and into that of observation.

To test the influence of intramural transportation access a thirty-three per cent sample of minor civil divisions was drawn from thirteen metropolitan areas with central cities of 250,000 or more population in 1940.[4] These were sorted into four types of transportation classes; namely, highway and railway, highway only, railway only, and neither highway nor railway. A highway location was identified as a location on a hard-surfaced national or state highway leading directly to the central city. This is exclusive of locations on lateral roads and township and county roads. Where the minor civil division was not an incorporated place the unit was classed as having a highway location when the route passed through or near its geometric center. A rail location was defined also as a location on a direct rail route to the central city. A township was identified as having such a location when an incorporated place near its geometric center was located on a direct rail route to the center. Needless to say, this classification by type of transportation access, based as it is on 1940 maps, is not entirely satisfactory. No allowance is made for the length of time a given type of access has been in existence. Nor is there any control over the frequency and quality of railway service. The difficulties involved in standardizing such variables are probably too obvious to require mention. While it may be possible to find ways of discounting the deficiencies, it seems better to turn directly to the data to see what they indicate.

It is evident in Table 47 that from 1900 to 1930 the most rapidly growing satellite places were those served by both highways and railways.

TABLE 47. PER CENT CHANGE OF POPULATION IN A SAMPLE OF SATELLITE PLACES IN STANDARD METROPOLITAN AREAS WITH CENTRAL CITIES OF 250,000 OR MORE POPULATION, BY TYPE OF TRANSPORTATION ACCESS, DISTANCE ZONE, AND DECADE, 1900 - 1950

| *Type of transportation access and distance zone* | *1940-50* | *1930-40* | *1920-30* | *1910-20* | *1900-10* |
|---|---|---|---|---|---|
| Highway and railway | | | | | |
| 5 - 10 miles | 37.9 | 17.4 | 57.2 | 22.3 | 38.9 |
| 10 - 15 " | 59.6 | 17.8 | 62.1 | 27.5 | 16.5 |
| 15 - 20 " | 23.4 | 14.7 | 39.3 | 28.2 | 24.3 |
| 20 - 25 " | 50.4 | 7.3 | 36.4 | 35.3 | 13.2 |
| 25 - 30 " | 24.8 | 12.2 | 37.1 | 44.8 | 46.5 |
| 30 - 35 " | 24.5 | 7.3 | 5.1 | 18.9 | 29.8 |
| 35 miles and over | 45.3 | 6.4 | 13.1 | 14.4 | 6.7 |
| Highway only | | | | | |
| 5 - 10 miles | 68.9 | 46.7 | 21.3 | 12.2 | 36.4 |
| 10 - 15 " | 74.9 | 34.8 | 57.1 | 15.9 | -5.0 |
| 15 - 20 " | 68.1 | 26.8 | 53.3 | 12.2 | 9.8 |
| 20 - 25 " | 69.6 | 18.7 | 14.9 | 28.2 | 14.6 |
| 25 - 30 " | 21.8 | 4.0 | -3.5 | -3.3 | -4.4 |
| 30 - 35 " | 19.4 | -0.8 | 3.7 | 3.5 | 0.4 |
| 35 miles and over | 31.8 | 20.1 | 2.1 | -5.7 | 6.0 |
| Railway only | | | | | |
| 5 - 10 miles | — | — | — | — | — |
| 10 - 15 " | — | — | — | — | — |
| 15 - 20 " | — | — | — | — | — |
| 20 - 25 " | 31.4 | 7.9 | -5.0 | -8.6 | 8.6 |
| 25 - 30 " | 2.4 | -8.1 | 3.0 | 7.5 | -18.0 |
| 30 - 35 " | 8.5 | -4.3 | -20.8 | -8.3 | 5.9 |
| 35 miles and over | 4.3 | -9.3 | -1.0 | 3.6 | -9.4 |
| Neither highway nor railway | | | | | |
| 5 - 10 miles | — | — | — | — | — |
| 10 - 15 " | 26.8 | 15.2 | -1.9 | -11.2 | 5.3 |
| 15 - 20 " | 20.0 | 8.9 | 30.5 | -6.1 | -0.7 |
| 20 - 25 " | 14.1 | 12.1 | -4.2 | -3.7 | -5.4 |
| 25 - 30 " | 0.8 | 1.9 | -4.7 | -5.1 | -7.1 |
| 30 - 35 " | 10.7 | 9.9 | 12.6 | 6.0 | -0.3 |
| 35 miles and over | -2.6 | 5.2 | -7.8 | -10.4 | -1.8 |

After 1930 the highest rates of change occurred in places served exclusively by highways. The differential as between highway and railway, and highway only, favored the latter, however, just within 25 miles of central cities. Beyond that distance places with both highway and railway excess maintained higher growth rates. Thus it appears that large-scale metropolitan expansion based primarily on the motor vehicle began with 1930, though there were evidences of beginnings in the preceding decade. Of interest is the fact that as early as 1900-10 satellite places dependent exclusively on the railway for direct contact with central cities were losing population. Losses in such places continued down to 1940. Even the gains in the 1940-50 decade were small. But the highest incidence of population loss occurred between 1900 and 1930 in places without either direct highway or railway access to metropolitan centers. Losses ceased after 1930 and in 1940-50 substantial gains were recorded. If the facts were known, it probably would be discovered that growth after 1930 in places with neither highway nor railway access was a consequence of the development of lateral roads serving the interstices between radial thoroughfares.

In Table 48 growth rates are reduced to ratios to the average growth rates for corresponding zones of the thirteen metropolitan areas from which the sample was drawn. On this basis, it is apparent that satellite places with both rail and highway contacts maintained, in 1900-10, a near average rate of growth. They attained their peak rates of increase in 1910 to 1920, after which decline set in returning them to average growth rates in 1940-50. Places with only highway access began the 50 years with considerably less than average growth. Growth rose above average within 10 to 20 miles of centers in 1920-1930, and since then higher than average rates spread over all area within 25 miles of centers. Despite the upsurge of growth in places with neither highway nor railway access after 1930, rates in such places tended to remain well below the averages for their respective zones.

There seems little doubt, in view of these data, that the kind of transportation access to the central city has important bearing on the relative growth of satellite population. It does not follow, of course, that locations on direct routes must necessarily dominate satellite growth. A more refined classification of location doubtlessly would show that places on hard-surfaced lateral roads have also grown rapidly. They may grow even more rapidly in the future. In any event, the inference from this analysis would seem to be: the more developed is the highway network of a metropolitan area the more rapid will be the growth of its satellite population.

TABLE 48. RATIO OF RATE OF POPULATION CHANGE IN A SAMPLE OF SATELLITE PLACES TO RATE OF CHANGE OF ALL POPULATION IN CORRESPONDING DISTANCE ZONE IN STANDARD METROPOLITAN AREAS WITH CENTRAL CITIES OF 250,000 OR MORE POPULATION, BY TYPE OF TRANSPORTATION ACCESS, DISTANCE ZONE, AND DECADE, 1900 - 1950

| *Type of transportation access and distance zone* | *1940-50* | *1930-40* | *1920-30* | *1910-20* | *1900-10* |
|---|---|---|---|---|---|
| Highway and railway | | | | | |
| 5 - 10 miles | 1.0 | 1.2 | 1.1 | 0.7 | 0.9 |
| 10 - 15 " | 1.6 | 1.4 | 2.0 | 1.2 | 0.5 |
| 15 - 20 " | 0.6 | 1.0 | 1.0 | 1.1 | 0.9 |
| 20 - 25 " | 1.6 | 0.6 | 1.2 | 2.0 | 0.7 |
| 25 - 30 " | 1.1 | 1.0 | 2.3 | 4.0 | 3.1 |
| 30 - 35 " | 1.0 | 0.9 | 0.5 | 2.2 | 2.6 |
| 35 miles and over | 2.7 | 0.8 | 1.2 | 3.6 | 0.8 |
| Highway only[a] | | | | | |
| 5 - 10 miles | 1.8 | 3.2 | 0.4 | 0.4 | 0.8 |
| 10 - 15 " | 2.0 | 2.7 | 1.8 | 0.7 | -0.2 |
| 15 - 20 " | 1.8 | 1.8 | 1.3 | 0.5 | 0.4 |
| 20 - 25 " | 2.2 | 1.4 | 0.5 | 1.6 | 0.8 |
| 25 - 30 " | 1.0 | 0.3 | -0.2 | -0.3 | -0.3 |
| 30 - 35 " | 0.8 | -0.1 | -0.3 | 0.4 | 0.0 |
| 35 miles and over | 1.9 | 2.6 | 0.2 | -1.4 | 0.7 |
| Railway only[a] | | | | | |
| 5 - 10 miles | — | — | — | — | — |
| 10 - 15 " | — | — | — | — | — |
| 15 - 20 " | — | — | — | — | — |
| 20 - 25 " | 1.0 | 0.6 | -0.2 | -0.5 | 0.5 |
| 25 - 30 " | 0.1 | -0.6 | 0.2 | 0.7 | -1.2 |
| 30 - 35 " | 0.3 | -0.5 | -1.9 | -1.0 | 0.5 |
| 35 miles and over | 0.3 | -1.2 | -0.1 | 0.9 | -1.1 |
| Neither highway nor railway[a] | | | | | |
| 5 - 10 miles | — | — | — | — | — |
| 10 - 15 " | 0.7 | 1.2 | -0.1 | -0.5 | 0.2 |
| 15 - 20 " | 0.5 | 0.6 | 0.8 | -0.2 | 0.0 |
| 20 - 25 " | 0.4 | 0.9 | -0.1 | -0.2 | -0.3 |
| 25 - 30 " | 0.0 | 0.2 | -0.3 | -0.5 | -0.5 |
| 30 - 35 " | 0.4 | 1.2 | 1.2 | 0.7 | 0.0 |
| 35 miles and over | -0.2 | 0.7 | -0.7 | -1.2 | -0.2 |

[a]Minus value indicates that one rate is negative.

CHAPTER VII

# MANUFACTURING INDUSTRY AND POPULATION REDISTRIBUTION

In part because of its orientation to an interregional more than to a local market and in part because of its relatively extensive use of land, manufacturing industry tends to scatter over the satellite areas about metropolitan centers.[1] This tendency has been greatly abetted by the electrification of power, the enhanced mobility of labor afforded by the automobile, and the separation of central office functions from producing functions, to mention only a few of the more salient factors that have enlarged the range of choice of sites for the location of manufacturing plants. By contrast, service industry is subject to a much stronger centripetal force. Since it is adapted primarily to local market conditions, the location of service industry is governed to a much greater extent by the need to maximize accessibility within the locality. In other words, service industry seeks locations at points where intra-mural transportation and communication lines converge. Thus, so far as population is attracted to places of employment, the extent to which the labor force of a metropolitan area is engaged in manufacturing employment should be associated with the rate and the direction of population redistribution. More specifically, the higher frequency of employment in manufacturing industry the higher should be the rate of population deconcentration.

The classification of Standard Metropolitan Areas by amount of manufacturing industry is based on the ratio of production workers in manufacturing, as reported in the Census of Manufactures, of 1948, to total population. Areas whose proportion of manufacturing workers exceeded the mean for all areas by more than one-half standard unit are classed as high or manufacturing areas. Those in which the proportions fell short of the mean by more than one-half standard unit are identified as areas of low proportions employed in manufacturing. These may also be characterized as non-manufacturing or service industry areas. The terms high and manufacturing will be used interchangeably, as will also the terms low and

non-manufacturing. An intervening class, termed average areas, contains all areas the proportions of manufacturing workers in which deviated from the mean by not more than one-half standard unit. The use of one-half standard unit as the class limit was expedient; a wider spread of the class limits would have yielded too few areas in the high and low, or manufacturing, classes.

It will be noted, in Table 49, that the total number of metropolitan areas comprised in the three classes is less than that dealt with in earlier chapters. The reduction of the number for the purposes of this chapter results largely from the Census Bureau's practice of withholding information for any political unit in which the number of establishments is three or less. Some of the loss also results from the fact that detailed data are not reported for minor civil divisions of less than 10,000 population. This excludes many of the New England Standard Metropolitan Areas, for they are defined in terms of towns rather than counties and towns frequently had less than the minimum population.

The use of 1948 data for the classification by proportion of workers engaged in manufacturing employment is defensible when the question to be answered is: what have been the patterns of population change in metropolitan areas that, in 1948, had varying proportions of manufacturing workers residing in them. This is the question the present chapter seeks to answer. A classification based on the data for a single year is not entirely satisfactory, however, if the primary intention is to measure the correlation of population redistribution and the frequency of manufacturing employment. Metropolitan areas may shift classes from year to year. A perusal of census data will reveal that such shifts do in fact take place. Still, as the following analysis demonstrates, the sorting of areas as of a single year is serviceable in the measurement of that correlation, though the results are not as refined as they might have been.

## Central Cities and Satellite Areas

Although metropolitan areas with average proportions of employment in manufacturing industry began the 50-year period with higher growth rates than did those classified as high or manufacturing areas, the two classes maintained comparable rates of change in the decades following 1920. Non-manufacturing areas, according to Table 50, had rates similar to those of the other two classes until 1930, after which date their rates became twice as high as the rates in manufacturing and average areas. The rates of population change in the central cities of the three classes were more sharply differentiated. All groups of central cities increased at

## TABLE 49. NUMBER OF STANDARD METROPOLITAN AREAS, BY PROPORTION OF POPULATION EMPLOYED IN MANUFACTURING, SIZE OF CENTRAL CITY, AND DECADE, 1900 - 1950

| *Proportion of population in manufacturing and size of central city* | *1940-50* | *1930-40* | *1920-30* | *1910-20* | *1900-10* |
|---|---|---|---|---|---|
| Total | 122 | 134 | 132 | 130 | 127 |
| High | 45 | 46 | 46 | 46 | 46 |
| 500,000 and over | 7[a] | 7[a] | 6[a] | 4[b] | 3[b] |
| 250,000 - 500,000 | 1 | 2 | 2 | 3 | 4 |
| 100,000 - 250,000 | 14 | 14 | 9 | 4 | 2 |
| Under 100,000 | 23 | 23 | 29 | 35 | 37 |
| Average | 35 | 39 | 38 | 38 | 38 |
| 500,000 and over | 5[c] | 6[c] | 5[c] | 4[c] | 2[c] |
| 250,000 - 500,000 | 8 | 8 | 3 | 3 | 5 |
| 100,000 - 250,000 | 6 | 7 | 9 | 10 | 6 |
| Under 100,000 | 16 | 18 | 21 | 21 | 25 |
| Low | 42 | 49 | 48 | 46 | 43 |
| 250,000 and over | 3[d] | 5[e] | 2 | 2 | 2 |
| 100,000 - 250,000 | 11 | 11 | 9 | 3 | 2 |
| Under 100,000 | 28 | 33 | 37 | 41 | 39 |

[a] Includes three areas with central cities of 1,000,000 or more population (Chicago, Philadelphia, and Detroit).

[b] Includes two areas with central cities of 1,000,000 or more population (Chicago and Philadelphia).

[c] Includes one area with a central city of 1,000,000 or more population (New York).

[d] Includes one area with a central city of 1,000,000 or more population (Los Angeles), and one area with a central city of 500,000-1,000,000 population (Washington, D. C.).

[e] Includes one area with a central city of 1,000,000 or more population (Los Angeles).

decreasing rates, but the central cities of manufacturing areas began and ended the period with the lowest rates. In average areas central city rates of change paralleled rather closely the rates for all central cities as reported in Table 4 (p. 16). The central cities of non-manufacturing areas had the highest growth rates and the smallest decline of growth rates. It was only in this latter class, too, that satellite population increased at progressively higher rates. In both of the other two classes rates reached their highest points in 1920-30, and then declined. Special note should be taken of the fact that the retardation of metropolitan growth during the 1930's was most pronounced in areas with the largest proportions employed in manufacturing industry. Although the effect of the depression years was greatest in central cities, it was also felt in satellite areas. But in the 1940-50 decade growth rates in both central cities and satellite zones of manufacturing areas made the largest recovery.

The principal effect of the adjustment of rates for size differences, as shown in the lower panel of Table 50, is to alter the pattern of change for the so-called non-manufacturing areas. The central cities of areas in that class began the period with the lowest rates of change, rather than the highest, and gained the highest rates after 1930. No retardation of growth in the 1930's is observable in the adjusted rates of areas with relatively small proportions employed in manufacturing. Stated differently, a low proportion of manufacturing employment seems to be associated with stability of growth.

The differences between satellite rates of change in corresponding distance zones of the three classes of areas are similar to those for all satellite areas, as may be seen in Fig. 30. Average areas had the highest rates in all zones within 35 miles of central cities, in 1900-10, and by 1940-50 their zonal rates with a few exceptions had fallen to the lowest position. The least change occurred in the 15-20 and the 20-25 mile zones. On the other hand, non-manufacturing areas had low zonal rates at the outset, particularly in 1910-20, and by 1940-50 their zonal rates were higher than those of either of the two classes. Most of the increase in rate of growth developed between 5 and 20 miles from central cities. In manufacturing areas growth rate increases took place mainly in the 10-15 and 15-20 mile zones. though there is evidence that such a tendency operated in most of the area beyond 20 miles from central cities.

When growth rates are stated as ratios, as in Table 51, the relationship of growth to frequency of manufacturing employment assumes a different aspect. There is no clear relationship between the two variables from 1900 to 1920. Beginning in 1920, however, a direct correlation emerged and continued through the remainder of the period. Deconcentration

TABLE 50. PER CENT CHANGE OF POPULATION IN STANDARD METROPOLITAN AREAS, BY TYPE OF PLACE, PROPORTION OF POPULATION EMPLOYED IN MANUFACTURING, AND DECADE, 1900-1950

| *Type of place and proportion of population in manufacturing* | *1940-50* | *1930-40* | *1920-30* | *1910-20* | *1900-10* |
|---|---|---|---|---|---|
| Actual | | | | | |
| Total | | | | | |
| High | 17.2 | 5.1 | 27.5 | 30.9 | 26.2 |
| Average | 17.1 | 7.3 | 25.2 | 20.1 | 32.2 |
| Low | 34.3 | 18.1 | 26.2 | 25.2 | 32.4 |
| Central cities | | | | | |
| High | 8.5 | 1.1 | 22.0 | 33.2 | 29.4 |
| Average | 9.7 | 5.3 | 21.4 | 19.6 | 32.9 |
| Low | 26.2 | 15.4 | 31.3 | 31.7 | 37.4 |
| Satellite areas | | | | | |
| High | 31.8 | 12.5 | 39.3 | 26.4 | 20.3 |
| Average | 28.5 | 10.4 | 31.8 | 20.9 | 31.1 |
| Low | 44.9 | 22.3 | 18.5 | 16.6 | 26.7 |
| Adjusted[a] | | | | | |
| Total | | | | | |
| High | 18.0 | 5.4 | 33.8 | 30.6 | 27.7 |
| Average | 16.1 | 9.4 | 24.8 | 19.8 | 27.8 |
| Low | 31.3 | 17.0 | 12.5 | 11.3 | 16.8 |
| Central cities | | | | | |
| High | 8.4 | 0.8 | 21.9 | 33.3 | 32.3 |
| Average | 9.1 | 6.7 | 22.1 | 21.4 | 29.5 |
| Low | 23.1 | 14.6 | 14.3 | 13.2 | 17.9 |
| Satellite areas | | | | | |
| High | 36.4 | 14.0 | 40.1 | 25.4 | 19.3 |
| Average | 26.9 | 13.9 | 29.3 | 17.0 | 26.5 |
| Low | 42.0 | 20.6 | 9.8 | 8.8 | 15.6 |

[a]Adjusted for size of central city. Size distribution of all areas used as the standard.

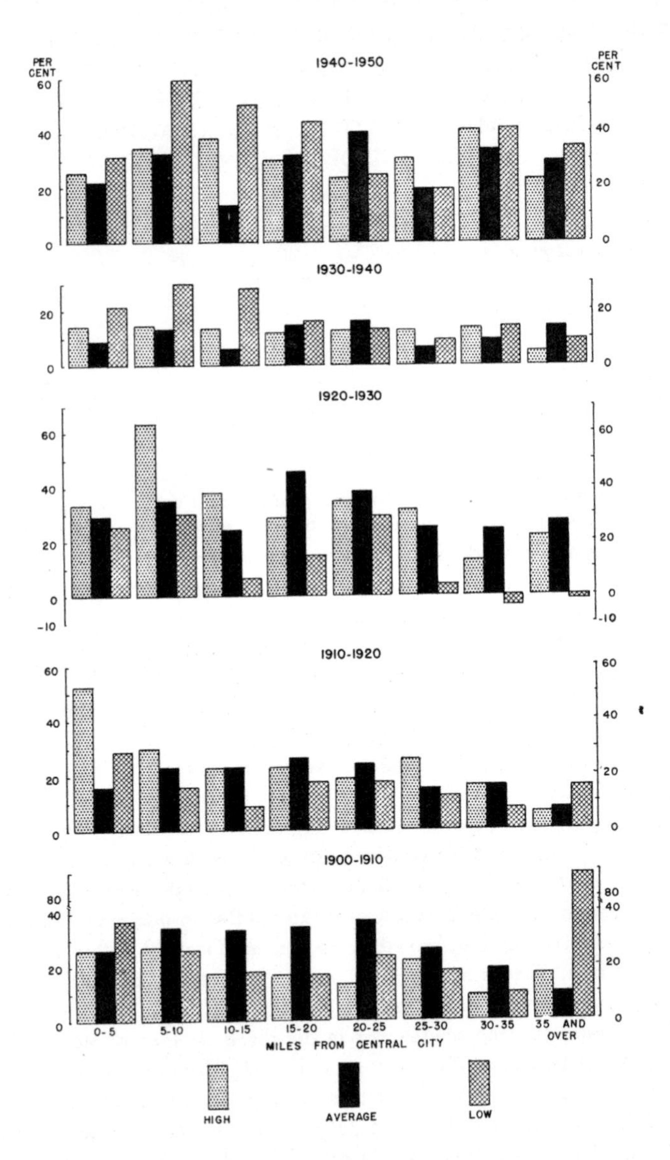


FIGURE 30
PER CENT CHANGE OF SATELLITE POPULATION IN STANDARD METROPOLITAN AREAS, BY PROPORTION OF POPULATION EMPLOYED IN MANUFACTURING, DISTANCE ZONE, AND DECADE, 1900-1950

TABLE 51. RATIO OF RATE OF POPULATION CHANGE IN SATELLITE AREAS TO CENTRAL CITY RATE OF CHANGE IN STANDARD METROPOLITAN AREAS, BY PROPORTION OF POPULATION EMPLOYED IN MANUFACTURING INDUSTRY, AND DECADE, 1900 - 1950

| *Proportion of population in manufacturing* | *1940-50* | *1930-40* | *1920-30* | *1910-20* | *1900-10* |
|---|---|---|---|---|---|
| All areas | 2.7 | 2.5 | 1.4 | 0.9 | 0.8 |
| High | 3.7 | 11.4 | 1.8 | 0.8 | 0.7 |
| Average | 2.9 | 2.0 | 1.5 | 1.1 | 1.0 |
| Low | 1.7 | 1.4 | 0.6 | 0.5 | 0.7 |

progressed most rapidly in manufacturing areas and most slowly in non-manufacturing areas. It is noteworthy that the ratios for average areas were in no decade less than 1.0, and that their satellite rates began to exceed central city rates as early as 1910-20. Again the similarity between ratios in average areas and all areas is apparent. It seems clear that metropolitan areas with average amounts of manufacturing employment are more representative of all metropolitan areas in respect to population redistribution than is any other class of areas observed thus far.

The progressive spread of relatively high rates of growth over the satellite areas of all metropolitan classes is observable in Fig. 31. Although dispersion in this sense began earlier in average areas, it has moved much more rapidly in manufacturing areas. Not until 1930-40, however, were all zones in the satellite portions of high areas growing more rapidly than central cities -- a decade after the growth rates of all zones in average areas exceeded central city rates. But in non-manufacturing areas high relative rates of growth were confined mainly within 20 miles of central cities. Rates in the 30-35 and 35 mile and over zones, in 1940-50, remain as unexplained exceptions.

The deconcentration tendencies in the three classes of metropolitan areas are described in another way in Table 52. The proportion of all increase that accrued to the central cities of manufacturing areas declined from a high of 72 per cent, in 1900-10, to 31 per cent, in 1940-50. Most of the central cities' loss was absorbed in the 5-10 and 10-15 mile zones, though all distance zones gained at the expense of central cities. A less radical change in the distribution of population increase occurred in average areas.

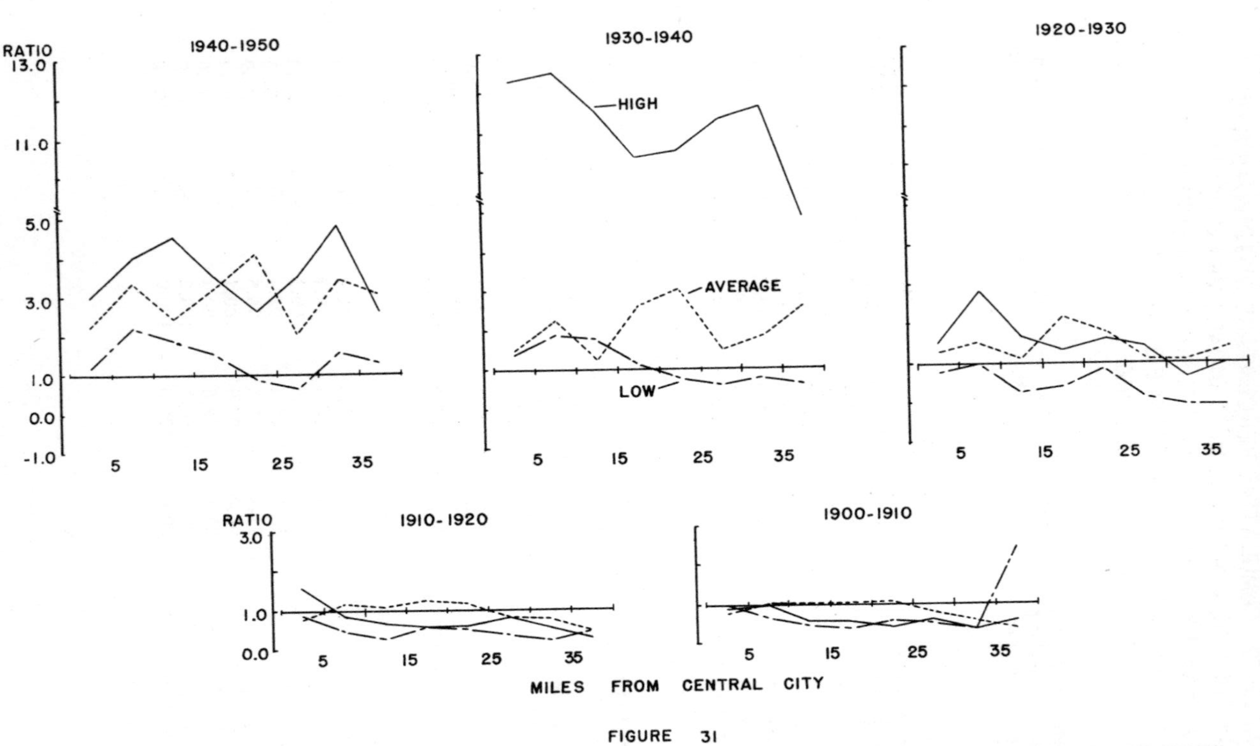


FIGURE 31

RATIO OF RATE OF SATELLITE POPULATION CHANGE TO RATE OF CENTRAL CITY CHANGE IN STANDARD METROPOLITAN AREAS, BY PROPORTION OF POPULATION EMPLOYED IN MANUFACTURING, DISTANCE ZONE, AND DECADE, 1900-1950

## TABLE 52. CUMULATIVE PERCENTAGE DISTRIBUTION OF POPULATION INCREASE IN STANDARD METROPOLITAN AREAS, BY PROPORTION OF POPULATION EMPLOYED IN MANUFACTURING, DISTANCE ZONE, AND DECADE, 1900 - 1950

| *Proportion of population in manufacturing and distance zone* | *1940-50* | *1930-40* | *1920-30* | *1910-20* | *1900-10* |
|---|---|---|---|---|---|
| High | | | | | |
| Central cities | 31.2 | 14.1 | 54.4 | 71.5 | 72.5 |
| 0 - 5 miles | 39.1 | 27.0 | 60.0 | 78.4 | 76.8 |
| 5 - 10 " | 60.6 | 54.7 | 77.8 | 86.2 | 85.4 |
| 10 - 15 " | 79.8 | 74.6 | 87.9 | 92.0 | 91.2 |
| 15 - 20 " | 87.8 | 84.5 | 92.5 | 95.4 | 94.6 |
| 20 - 25 " | 91.9 | 91.2 | 96.0 | 97.2 | 96.3 |
| 25 - 30 " | 95.6 | 96.0 | 98.2 | 98.9 | 98.0 |
| 30 - 35 " | 97.8 | 98.1 | 99.6 | 99.5 | 98.4 |
| 35 miles and over | 100.0 | 100.0 | 100.0 | 100.0 | 100.0 |
| Average | | | | | |
| Central cities | 34.1 | 44.7 | 53.6 | 61.7 | 63.9 |
| 0 - 5 miles | 39.2 | 49.3 | 58.3 | 65.4 | 67.8 |
| 5 - 10 " | 60.1 | 67.7 | 73.1 | 77.1 | 78.8 |
| 10 - 15 " | 73.6 | 76.1 | 82.5 | 87.5 | 88.9 |
| 15 - 20 " | 84.2 | 86.6 | 90.8 | 93.0 | 93.4 |
| 20 - 25 " | 92.7 | 93.9 | 95.5 | 96.7 | 96.7 |
| 25 - 30 " | 95.1 | 96.1 | 97.5 | 98.3 | 98.6 |
| 30 - 35 " | 97.6 | 97.7 | 98.7 | 99.4 | 99.5 |
| 35 miles and over | 100.0 | 100.0 | 100.0 | 100.0 | 100.0 |
| Low | | | | | |
| Central cities | 43.5 | 51.6 | 71.9 | 71.7 | 61.3 |
| 0 - 5 miles | 49.0 | 58.3 | 78.1 | 79.4 | 69.6 |
| 5 - 10 " | 73.7 | 77.6 | 90.3 | 87.3 | 80.8 |
| 10 - 15 " | 85.6 | 89.4 | 92.4 | 90.3 | 86.3 |
| 15 - 20 " | 93.4 | 95.3 | 95.5 | 94.7 | 89.9 |
| 20 - 25 " | 96.2 | 97.9 | 100.1 | 97.1 | 92.4 |
| 25 - 30 " | 97.1 | 98.6 | 100.3 | 97.9 | 93.6 |
| 30 - 35 " | 98.1 | 99.1 | 100.2 | 98.1 | 93.8 |
| 35 miles and over | 100.0 | 100.0 | 100.0 | 100.0 | 100.0 |

Furthermore, the increased share acquired by satellite area was not so highly concentrated as in manufacturing areas. In non-manufacturing areas the proportion of all increase attracted to central cities increased from 1900 to 1930, and then declined rapidly but not to as low a figure as that of either of the other classes. As with manufacturing areas the major part of the gain in satellite areas was taken up in the 5-10 and 10-15 mile zones. The changes in zones beyond 20 miles from central cities were comparatively small.

The high rates of population deconcentration in manufacturing areas become more understandable when it is observed, in Table 53, that such areas had the greatest concentration of population of any class of areas. Population in low or non-manufacturing areas, on the other hand, has been least concentrated. Evidently the rate of deconcentration is a function of the extent of concentration, as well as of other factors.

All classes of areas passed through a phase of increasing concentration. That phase lasted until 1920 in manufacturing and in average areas, and until 1930 in non-manufacturing areas. But if, instead of the proportion of the population in central cities, the proportion within 10 miles of central cities is taken as the measure of concentration, then average areas ended their concentration phase in 1910. Although non-manufacturing areas experienced both concentration and deconcentration phases, they ended the 50-year period with a more concentrated population than they had at the beginning.

Periods of population concentration were in general marked by declining rates of redistribution. This is shown to be true of all classes of metropolitan areas in Fig. 32. The changes in rates of redistribution from 1900-10 to 1910-20 were of small consequence, however, in manufacturing and in average areas. Contrasting with these changes is the rapid decline in rate of redistribution which occurred in non-manufacturing areas from 1900 to 1930. As the trends swung from concentration to deconcentration rates of redistribution accelerated, attaining their maximum in manufacturing areas between 1940 and 1950.

### Size and Type of Satellite Place

The growth rates of almost all sizes of incorporated places in high and in average areas tended to decline, though, as may be seen in Table 54, the decline frequently occurred after 1930 following a period of rate increases. In areas with low proportions of population employed in manufacturing rates of change in incorporated places declined from 1900 to 1930 and then increased through the last two decades. Unincorporated population, on the

# TABLE 53. CUMULATIVE PERCENTAGE DISTRIBUTION OF POPULATION IN STANDARD METROPOLITAN AREAS, BY PROPORTION OF POPULATION EMPLOYED IN MANUFACTURING, DISTANCE ZONE, AND CENSUS YEAR, 1900 - 1950

| *Proportion of population in manufacturing and distance zone* | *1950* | *1940* | *1930* | *1920* | *1910* | *1900* |
|---|---|---|---|---|---|---|
| High | | | | | | |
| Central cities | 58.1 | 62.8 | 65.2 | 68.1 | 66.7 | 64.6 |
| 0 - 5 miles | 63.8 | 68.1 | 70.1 | 72.8 | 70.8 | 68.8 |
| 5 - 10 " | 76.2 | 79.0 | 80.1 | 80.6 | 78.7 | 76.8 |
| 10 - 15 " | 86.4 | 87.6 | 88.1 | 88.0 | 86.8 | 85.6 |
| 15 - 20 " | 91.5 | 92.2 | 92.5 | 92.5 | 91.7 | 90.9 |
| 20 - 25 " | 94.7 | 95.3 | 95.4 | 95.3 | 94.7 | 94.3 |
| 25 - 30 " | 97.1 | 97.4 | 97.4 | 97.2 | 96.7 | 96.4 |
| 30 - 35 " | 98.2 | 98.3 | 98.3 | 98.2 | 97.8 | 97.6 |
| 35 miles and over | 100.0 | 100.0 | 100.0 | 100.0 | 100.0 | 100.0 |
| Average | | | | | | |
| Central cities | 56.6 | 60.4 | 61.3 | 63.2 | 63.1 | 62.5 |
| 0 - 5 miles | 60.8 | 64.4 | 65.6 | 67.3 | 67.5 | 67.1 |
| 5 - 10 " | 73.5 | 75.7 | 77.0 | 77.8 | 78.0 | 77.6 |
| 10 - 15 " | 83.9 | 85.6 | 86.8 | 87.7 | 87.8 | 87.4 |
| 15 - 20 " | 90.4 | 91.4 | 92.2 | 92.3 | 92.1 | 91.7 |
| 20 - 25 " | 94.8 | 95.1 | 95.5 | 95.4 | 95.2 | 94.7 |
| 25 - 30 " | 97.0 | 97.3 | 97.6 | 97.5 | 97.4 | 97.0 |
| 30 - 35 " | 98.5 | 98.6 | 98.8 | 98.8 | 98.7 | 98.4 |
| 35 miles and over | 100.0 | 100.0 | 100.0 | 100.0 | 100.0 | 100.0 |
| Low | | | | | | |
| Central cities | 53.4 | 56.9 | 60.6 | 60.2 | 57.0 | 53.1 |
| 0 - 5 miles | 59.3 | 62.9 | 66.4 | 66.8 | 63.7 | 60.3 |
| 5 - 10 " | 76.3 | 77.3 | 78.2 | 77.3 | 76.5 | 74.3 |
| 10 - 15 " | 85.4 | 85.4 | 85.7 | 85.1 | 85.0 | 84.4 |
| 15 - 20 " | 92.1 | 91.7 | 92.1 | 90.9 | 91.2 | 91.3 |
| 20 - 25 " | 95.8 | 95.7 | 95.8 | 95.0 | 94.6 | 95.0 |
| 25 - 30 " | 97.2 | 97.2 | 97.3 | 96.6 | 96.4 | 97.1 |
| 30 - 35 " | 98.1 | 98.0 | 98.1 | 97.2 | 97.0 | 97.8 |
| 35 miles and over | 100.0 | 100.0 | 100.0 | 100.0 | 100.0 | 100.0 |

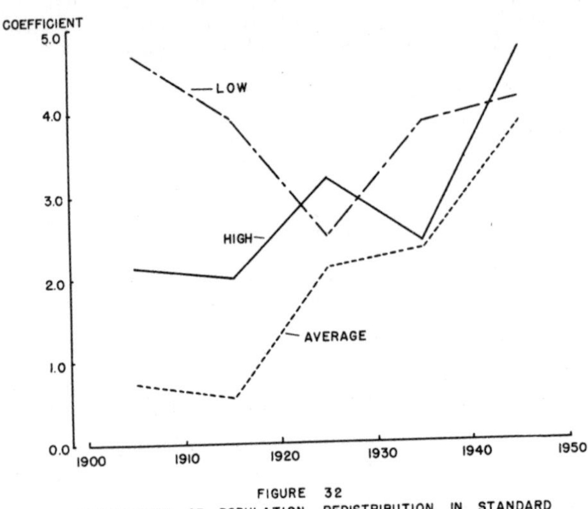


FIGURE 32
COEFFICIENTS OF POPULATION REDISTRIBUTION IN STANDARD METROPOLITAN AREAS, BY PROPORTION OF POPULATION EMPLOYED IN MANUFACTURING, 1900-1950

other hand, increased at progressively higher rates in succeeding decades in most zones of each metropolitan area class. The largest changes between 1900 and 1950 occurred in the high or manufacturing areas.

These changes are made more intelligible in Table 55. The ratios of incorporated places of 10,000 or more population which are located within 20 miles of central cities increased in all classes of areas. In distance zones beyond 20 miles of centers the prevalent tendency was toward decline, especially in non-manufacturing areas. As a matter of fact, all sizes of incorporated places 20 or more miles from the centers of non-manufacturing areas had declining ratios. Incorporated places of less than 10,000 population in all distance zones of manufacturing and average areas had increasing relative growth rates. The largest changes occurred in unincorporated areas.

Although in general the ratios of all sizes and types of places in manufacturing areas exceeded those in average areas after 1920, the 1930-40 decade is exceptional in this respect. Accelerated growth, due largely to an acutely depressed central city growth, occurred in even the largest satellite places. The small places and unincorporated areas, however, received the greatest relative gains.

Table 54. Per Cent Change of Satellite Population in Standard Metropolitan Areas, by Size and Type of Place, Distance Zone, Proportion of Population Employed in Manufacturing, and Decade, 1900-1950

| Size and type of place and distance zone | High | | | | | Average | | | | | Low | | | | |
|---|---|---|---|---|---|---|---|---|---|---|---|---|---|---|---|
| | 1940-1950 | 1930-1940 | 1920-1930 | 1910-1920 | 1900-1910 | 1940-1950 | 1930-1940 | 1920-1930 | 1910-1920 | 1900-1910 | 1940-1950 | 1930-1940 | 1920-1930 | 1910-1920 | 1900-1910 |
| 50,000 and over | | | | | | | | | | | | | | | |
| 0-10 miles | 35.4 | 8.9 | 8.4 | 23.5 | 24.4 | 11.0 | 3.2 | 14.5 | 16.8 | 43.6 | 30.3 | 18.4 | -16.0 | ---- | ---- |
| 10-20 miles | 8.3 | 6.8 | 23.7 | ---- | ---- | 42.2 | -0.6 | 11.3 | 19.3 | 35.5 | 48.0 | 15.6 | 155.5 | ---- | ---- |
| 20-30 miles | 16.0 | 8.1 | 81.3 | ---- | ---- | ---- | ---- | ---- | ---- | ---- | ---- | ---- | ---- | ---- | ---- |
| 30 miles and over | ---- | ---- | ---- | ---- | ---- | ---- | ---- | ---- | ---- | ---- | ---- | ---- | ---- | ---- | ---- |
| 10,000 - 50,000 | | | | | | | | | | | | | | | |
| 0-10 miles | 14.3 | 5.7 | 49.7 | 31.5 | 27.4 | -1.4 | 2.3 | 25.7 | 18.2 | 30.4 | 28.3 | 12.1 | 9.9 | 11.7 | 22.0 |
| 10-20 miles | 23.8 | 3.9 | 30.4 | 46.3 | 26.8 | 30.5 | 8.8 | 42.9 | 37.1 | 59.3 | 69.0 | 28.9 | 7.6 | 9.4 | 25.9 |
| 20-30 miles | 3.4 | 6.3 | 42.8 | 67.6 | 41.5 | 9.1 | 5.8 | 19.2 | 27.0 | 42.2 | 19.4 | 4.5 | 13.9 | 26.8 | 78.6 |
| 30 miles and over | 7.9 | 1.7 | 25.8 | 15.2 | 18.3 | 36.8 | 0.0 | 6.2 | 25.9 | 27.2 | 22.6 | 4.5 | -5.1 | 33.8 | ---- |
| 2,500 - 10,000 | | | | | | | | | | | | | | | |
| 0-10 miles | 27.8 | 7.6 | 58.4 | 100.4 | 44.2 | 30.4 | 10.6 | 45.5 | 21.5 | 48.1 | 33.9 | 10.9 | 15.0 | 13.8 | 42.7 |
| 10-20 miles | 42.2 | 10.4 | 56.2 | 26.9 | 43.7 | 35.2 | 13.2 | 65.0 | 40.1 | 47.1 | 62.8 | 22.6 | 8.4 | 19.8 | 7.4 |
| 20-30 miles | 17.9 | 6.9 | 36.8 | 19.9 | 29.0 | 25.5 | 6.9 | 31.0 | 20.3 | 47.4 | 0.0 | 8.4 | 6.2 | -12.8 | 50.9 |
| 30 miles and over | 21.8 | 4.2 | 20.9 | 14.7 | 40.2 | 21.1 | 6.2 | 39.0 | 15.2 | 31.6 | 21.3 | 1.7 | -6.0 | 22.3 | 99.2 |
| Under 2,500 | | | | | | | | | | | | | | | |
| 0-10 miles | 34.6 | 19.4 | 108.5 | 47.7 | 40.7 | 38.7 | 19.5 | 72.2 | 37.0 | 67.3 | 46.8 | 23.6 | 39.9 | 10.4 | 54.9 |
| 10-20 miles | 34.5 | 14.0 | 43.8 | 28.5 | 18.3 | 34.1 | 15.5 | 55.4 | 31.7 | 36.8 | 31.8 | 8.4 | 7.9 | 19.4 | 23.0 |
| 20-30 miles | 30.0 | 16.3 | 39.3 | 20.6 | 25.3 | 27.5 | 9.0 | 22.6 | 22.6 | 41.3 | 12.3 | 9.4 | 0.0 | 8.9 | 30.9 |
| 30 miles and over | 26.8 | 6.6 | 22.4 | 7.2 | 16.7 | 24.5 | 7.9 | 18.0 | 20.4 | 27.4 | 4.5 | 9.2 | -0.3 | 0.0 | 45.7 |
| Unincorporated area | | | | | | | | | | | | | | | |
| 0-10 miles | 39.1 | 21.5 | 49.1 | 22.5 | 23.4 | 62.4 | 22.1 | 45.2 | 22.6 | 18.4 | 71.2 | 40.1 | 45.7 | 26.5 | 27.1 |
| 10-20 miles | 45.0 | 18.8 | 26.7 | 32.7 | 9.1 | 9.3 | 18.8 | 27.3 | 12.3 | 19.7 | 41.7 | 25.4 | -2.4 | 11.1 | 16.8 |
| 20-30 miles | 43.4 | 18.0 | 16.1 | 3.4 | 7.0 | 50.4 | 20.4 | 43.4 | 15.8 | 22.5 | 28.8 | 13.7 | 27.1 | 19.4 | 12.0 |
| 30 miles and over | 70.4 | 14.6 | 10.0 | 5.9 | 7.3 | 34.6 | 17.2 | 25.0 | 8.3 | 6.3 | 52.1 | 14.0 | -0.8 | 14.8 | 70.3 |

Table 55. Ratio of Rate of Change of Satellite Population to Central City Rate of Change in Standard Metropolitan Areas, by Size and Type of Place, Distance Zone, Proportion of Population Employed in Manufacturing, and Decade, 1900-1950

| Size and type of place and distance zone | High | | | | | Average | | | | | Low | | | | |
|---|---|---|---|---|---|---|---|---|---|---|---|---|---|---|---|
| | 1940-1950 | 1930-1940 | 1920-1930 | 1910-1920 | 1900-1910 | 1940-1950 | 1930-1940 | 1920-1930 | 1910-1920 | 1900-1910 | 1940-1950 | 1930-1940 | 1920-1930 | 1910-1920 | 1900-1910 |
| 50,000 and over | | | | | | | | | | | | | | | |
| 0-10 miles | 4.1 | 8.1 | 0.4 | 0.7 | 0.8 | 1.1 | 0.6 | 0.7 | 0.9 | 1.3 | 1.2 | 1.2 | -0.5 | ---- | ---- |
| 10-20 miles | 1.0 | 6.2 | 1.1 | ---- | ---- | 4.3 | 0.0 | 0.5 | 1.0 | 1.1 | 1.8 | 1.0 | 5.0 | ---- | ---- |
| 20-30 miles | 1.9 | 7.4 | 3.7 | ---- | ---- | ---- | ---- | ---- | ---- | ---- | ---- | ---- | ---- | ---- | ---- |
| 30 miles and over | ---- | ---- | ---- | ---- | ---- | ---- | ---- | ---- | ---- | ---- | ---- | ---- | ---- | ---- | ---- |
| 10,000 - 50,000 | | | | | | | | | | | | | | | |
| 0-10 miles | 1.7 | 5.2 | 2.3 | 0.9 | 0.9 | -0.1 | 0.4 | 1.2 | 0.9 | 0.9 | 1.1 | 0.8 | 0.3 | 0.4 | 0.6 |
| 10-20 miles | 2.8 | 3.5 | 1.4 | 1.4 | 0.9 | 3.1 | 1.7 | 2.0 | 1.9 | 1.8 | 2.6 | 1.9 | 0.2 | 0.3 | 0.7 |
| 20-30 miles | 0.4 | 5.7 | 1.9 | 2.0 | 1.4 | 0.9 | 1.1 | 0.9 | 1.4 | 1.3 | 0.7 | 0.3 | 0.4 | 0.8 | 2.1 |
| 30 miles and over | 0.9 | 1.5 | 1.2 | 0.5 | 0.6 | 3.8 | 0.0 | 0.3 | 1.3 | 0.8 | 0.9 | 0.3 | -0.2 | 1.1 | ---- |
| 2,500 - 10,000 | | | | | | | | | | | | | | | |
| 0-10 miles | 3.2 | 6.9 | 2.7 | 3.0 | 1.5 | 3.1 | 2.0 | 2.1 | 1.1 | 1.5 | 1.3 | 0.7 | 0.5 | 0.4 | 1.1 |
| 10-20 miles | 4.9 | 9.5 | 2.6 | 0.8 | 1.5 | 3.6 | 2.5 | 3.0 | 2.0 | 1.4 | 2.4 | 1.5 | 0.3 | 0.6 | 0.2 |
| 20-30 miles | 2.1 | 6.3 | 1.7 | 0.6 | 1.0 | 2.6 | 1.3 | 1.4 | 1.0 | 1.4 | 0.0 | 0.5 | 0.2 | -0.4 | 1.4 |
| 30 miles and over | 2.6 | 3.8 | 0.9 | 0.4 | 1.4 | 2.2 | 1.2 | 1.8 | 0.8 | 1.0 | 0.8 | 0.1 | -0.2 | 0.7 | 2.6 |
| Under 2,500 | | | | | | | | | | | | | | | |
| 0-10 miles | 4.0 | 17.6 | 4.9 | 1.4 | 1.4 | 4.0 | 3.7 | 3.4 | 1.9 | 2.0 | 1.8 | 1.5 | 1.3 | 0.3 | 1.5 |
| 10-20 miles | 4.0 | 12.7 | 2.0 | 0.9 | 0.6 | 3.5 | 2.9 | 2.6 | 1.6 | 1.1 | 1.2 | 0.5 | 0.3 | 0.6 | 0.6 |
| 20-30 miles | 3.5 | 14.8 | 1.8 | 0.6 | 0.9 | 2.8 | 1.7 | 1.1 | 1.4 | 1.3 | 0.5 | 0.6 | 0.0 | 0.3 | 0.8 |
| 30 miles and over | 3.0 | 6.0 | 1.0 | 0.2 | 0.6 | 2.5 | 1.5 | 0.8 | 1.0 | 0.8 | 0.2 | 0.6 | 0.0 | 0.0 | 1.2 |
| Unincorporated area | | | | | | | | | | | | | | | |
| 0-10 miles | 4.6 | 19.5 | 2.2 | 0.7 | 0.8 | 6.4 | 4.2 | 2.1 | 1.2 | 0.6 | 2.7 | 2.6 | 1.5 | 0.8 | 0.7 |
| 10-20 miles | 5.3 | 17.1 | 1.2 | 1.0 | 0.3 | 1.0 | 3.5 | 1.3 | 0.6 | 0.6 | 1.6 | 1.6 | -0.1 | 0.4 | 0.4 |
| 20-30 miles | 5.1 | 16.4 | 0.7 | 0.1 | 0.2 | 5.2 | 3.8 | 2.0 | 0.8 | 0.7 | 1.1 | 0.9 | 0.9 | 0.6 | 0.3 |
| 30 miles and over | 8.2 | 13.3 | 0.4 | 0.2 | 0.2 | 3.6 | 3.2 | 1.2 | 0.4 | 0.2 | 2.0 | 0.9 | 0.0 | 0.5 | 1.9 |

Table 56. Per Cent Distribution of Satellite Population in Standard Metropolitan Areas, by Census Year, Size and Type of Place, Proportion of Population Employed in Manufacturing, and Distance Zone, 1900-1950

| Census year and size and type of place | High | | | | Average | | | | Low | | | |
|---|---|---|---|---|---|---|---|---|---|---|---|---|
| | Miles from central city | | | | Miles from central city | | | | Miles from central city | | | |
| | 0-10 miles | 10-20 miles | 20-30 miles | 30 miles and over | 0-10 miles | 10-20 miles | 20-30 miles | 30 miles and over | 0-10 miles | 10-20 miles | 20-30 miles | 30 miles and over |
| 1950 | | | | | | | | | | | | |
| Total | 100.0 | 100.0 | 100.0 | 100.0 | 100.0 | 100.0 | 100.0 | 100.0 | 100.0 | 100.0 | 100.0 | 100.0 |
| 50,000 and over | 13.1 | 7.3 | 20.1 | 0.0 | 23.5 | 37.4 | 0.0 | 0.0 | 8.5 | 14.2 | 0.0 | 0.0 |
| 10,000 - 50,000 | 20.8 | 20.8 | 11.0 | 27.2 | 16.4 | 21.2 | 24.9 | 13.6 | 19.3 | 9.6 | 15.3 | 18.2 |
| 2,500 - 10,000 | 11.6 | 15.9 | 17.7 | 10.4 | 14.5 | 11.4 | 16.5 | 20.7 | 12.8 | 13.0 | 9.6 | 12.8 |
| Under 2,500 | 4.6 | 9.2 | 8.8 | 11.4 | 3.8 | 5.3 | 7.6 | 6.5 | 4.5 | 6.6 | 6.2 | 9.2 |
| Unincorporated area | 49.9 | 46.8 | 42.4 | 51.0 | 41.8 | 24.7 | 51.0 | 59.2 | 54.9 | 56.6 | 68.9 | 59.8 |
| 1940 | | | | | | | | | | | | |
| Total | 100.0 | 100.0 | 100.0 | 100.0 | 100.0 | 100.0 | 100.0 | 100.0 | 100.0 | 100.0 | 100.0 | 100.0 |
| 50,000 and over | 17.2 | 9.3 | 21.7 | 0.0 | 27.3 | 33.9 | 0.0 | 0.0 | 9.9 | 14.0 | 0.0 | 0.0 |
| 10,000 - 50,000 | 21.7 | 23.0 | 13.1 | 33.7 | 21.7 | 21.0 | 30.1 | 13.0 | 22.8 | 8.4 | 15.7 | 20.2 |
| 2,500 - 10,000 | 11.3 | 14.6 | 18.1 | 11.5 | 14.4 | 10.9 | 17.3 | 22.4 | 14.5 | 11.7 | 11.8 | 14.1 |
| Under 2,500 | 5.2 | 10.4 | 8.8 | 12.9 | 3.6 | 5.1 | 7.9 | 6.9 | 4.6 | 7.3 | 6.8 | 12.0 |
| Unincorporated area | 44.6 | 42.7 | 38.3 | 41.9 | 33.0 | 29.1 | 44.7 | 57.7 | 48.2 | 58.6 | 65.7 | 53.7 |
| 1930 | | | | | | | | | | | | |
| Total | 100.0 | 100.0 | 100.0 | 100.0 | 100.0 | 100.0 | 100.0 | 100.0 | 100.0 | 100.0 | 100.0 | 100.0 |
| 50,000 and over | 6.3 | 5.2 | 9.8 | 0.0 | 29.1 | 35.1 | 0.0 | 0.0 | 7.5 | 9.8 | 0.0 | 0.0 |
| 10,000 - 50,000 | 26.8 | 21.2 | 24.2 | 35.6 | 20.8 | 20.8 | 28.6 | 14.2 | 22.8 | 7.9 | 14.5 | 21.1 |
| 2,500 - 10,000 | 14.4 | 17.0 | 17.3 | 10.0 | 14.0 | 11.2 | 19.3 | 22.3 | 16.6 | 11.5 | 10.8 | 11.2 |
| Under 2,500 | 10.6 | 12.4 | 11.8 | 14.3 | 3.4 | 5.2 | 8.8 | 8.6 | 5.0 | 8.6 | 7.5 | 15.7 |
| Unincorporated area | 41.9 | 44.2 | 36.9 | 40.1 | 32.7 | 27.7 | 43.3 | 54.9 | 48.1 | 62.2 | 67.2 | 52.0 |
| 1920 | | | | | | | | | | | | |
| Total | 100.0 | 100.0 | 100.0 | 100.0 | 100.0 | 100.0 | 100.0 | 100.0 | 100.0 | 100.0 | 100.0 | 100.0 |
| 50,000 and over | 8.7 | 0.0 | 0.0 | 0.0 | 32.3 | 34.2 | 0.0 | 0.0 | 4.9 | 6.3 | 0.0 | 0.0 |
| 10,000 - 50,000 | 14.1 | 21.7 | 28.3 | 33.5 | 16.4 | 17.8 | 26.3 | 10.2 | 19.9 | 2.1 | 8.8 | 13.5 |
| 2,500 - 10,000 | 21.3 | 14.4 | 14.5 | 9.2 | 13.3 | 11.7 | 21.1 | 20.5 | 22.4 | 8.0 | 7.1 | 15.8 |
| Under 2,500 | 10.7 | 14.8 | 14.1 | 13.9 | 5.0 | 6.9 | 10.4 | 10.3 | 6.5 | 14.3 | 9.3 | 13.7 |
| Unincorporated area | 45.2 | 49.1 | 43.1 | 43.4 | 33.0 | 29.4 | 42.2 | 59.0 | 46.3 | 69.3 | 74.8 | 57.0 |
| 1910 | | | | | | | | | | | | |
| Total | 100.0 | 100.0 | 100.0 | 100.0 | 100.0 | 100.0 | 100.0 | 100.0 | 100.0 | 100.0 | 100.0 | 100.0 |
| 50,000 and over | 6.1 | 0.0 | 0.0 | 0.0 | 30.6 | 33.3 | 0.0 | 0.0 | 0.0 | 0.0 | 0.0 | 0.0 |
| 10,000 - 50,000 | 8.7 | 12.0 | 9.7 | 25.5 | 15.8 | 14.2 | 20.4 | 9.0 | 18.0 | 2.3 | 9.7 | 5.7 |
| 2,500 - 10,000 | 13.2 | 17.6 | 19.4 | 11.2 | 12.4 | 10.8 | 19.6 | 16.9 | 19.5 | 5.0 | 10.0 | 19.2 |
| Under 2,500 | 9.0 | 13.7 | 15.1 | 14.4 | 5.5 | 7.9 | 14.0 | 11.4 | 7.4 | 14.2 | 12.4 | 16.8 |
| Unincorporated area | 63.0 | 56.7 | 55.8 | 48.9 | 35.7 | 33.8 | 46.0 | 62.7 | 55.1 | 78.5 | 67.9 | 58.3 |
| 1900 | | | | | | | | | | | | |
| Total | 100.0 | 100.0 | 100.0 | 100.0 | 100.0 | 100.0 | 100.0 | 100.0 | 100.0 | 100.0 | 100.0 | 100.0 |
| 50,000 and over | 6.3 | 0.0 | 0.0 | 0.0 | 21.5 | 23.6 | 0.0 | 0.0 | 0.0 | 0.0 | 0.0 | 0.0 |
| 10,000 - 50,000 | 8.7 | 11.1 | 7.9 | 24.7 | 18.4 | 16.4 | 8.6 | 8.3 | 19.3 | 2.2 | 6.7 | 0.0 |
| 2,500 - 10,000 | 11.7 | 14.0 | 17.4 | 9.2 | 10.4 | 7.7 | 20.5 | 14.8 | 8.2 | 3.8 | 5.3 | 11.6 |
| Under 2,500 | 8.2 | 13.5 | 14.0 | 14.1 | 5.7 | 7.7 | 14.3 | 12.5 | 8.8 | 10.3 | 11.0 | 17.0 |
| Unincorporated area | 65.1 | 61.4 | 60.7 | 52.0 | 44.0 | 44.6 | 56.6 | 64.4 | 63.7 | 83.7 | 77.0 | 70.8 |

The percentage distribution of population by size and type of satel-place within each zone, shown in Table 56, indicates that average areas have had the greatest concentrations in large satellites and the smallest proportions in unincorporated area. Non-manufacturing areas have had the largest proportions of their zonal populations in unincorporated area. In all classes of areas the proportions in unincorporated areas declined to 1930 and then increased once more. Conversely, the proportions in large satellites increased to 1930 and declined thereafter. This pattern of change occurred in all distance zones.

CHAPTER VIII

# INDUSTRIAL RELOCATION AND POPULATION REDISTRIBUTION

It has been shown that deconcentration has been most characteristic of metropolitan areas with the largest proportions of manufacturing workers. That was anticipated on the assumption that manufacturing establishments are more inclined to locate outside of central cities than are other kinds of industries. But it remains to be determined whether the high rates of deconcentration are a function of the centrifugal movement of industry or are characteristic of manufacturing areas independently of the direction taken by industrial relocations. The first of these alternatives is treated in this chapter. A comparison of the findings here with those of Chapter VII will provide at least a partial answer to the second.

By industrial relocation is meant changes in the percentage distribution of place of employment of production workers in manufacturing[1] as between central city and satellite area. Where the central city proportion of the metropolitan area's total number of workers in manufacturing increased through four of the five decades between 1900 and 1950 the trend was toward industrial concentration and the area is placed in a class with that designation. This definition of industrial concentration is altered for areas that are included in the study for only a part of the period. In that event it is required that the central city's proportion should show an increase in every decade. Industrial deconcentration occurred when the central city's proportion of all workers in manufacturing declined through four of the five decades, or if the area is included in the study for but a part of the period, through all decades. A third class is comprised of metropolitan areas in which the changing proportion of manufacturing workers contained in central cities followed no clear trend. The number of areas in each class is shown in Table 57. Perhaps it is unnecessary to point out that industrial relocation is used in a relative sense. Changes in proportions may be produced either by actual plant relocations or by a more rapid expansion of employment in one part of an area than in another.

TABLE 57. NUMBER OF STANDARD METROPOLITAN AREAS, BY DIRECTION OF INDUSTRIAL RELOCATION, SIZE OF CENTRAL CITY, AND DECADE, 1900 - 1950

| *Direction of industrial relocation and size of central city* | *1940-50* | *1930-40* | *1920-30* | *1910-20* | *1900-10* |
|---|---|---|---|---|---|
| Total | 122 | 134 | 132 | 130 | 127 |
| Concentrating | 13 | 13 | 13 | 13 | 13 |
| 100,000 and over | 6[a] | 6[a] | 4 | 3 | 2 |
| Under 100,000 | 7 | 7 | 9 | 10 | 11 |
| No clear trend | 53 | 60 | 59 | 57 | 54 |
| 250,000 and over | 6[b] | 7[c] | 4[c] | 4[d] | 4[d] |
| 100,000 - 250,000 | 11 | 14 | 9 | 7 | 5 |
| Under 100,000 | 36 | 39 | 46 | 46 | 45 |
| Deconcentrating | 56 | 61 | 60 | 60 | 60 |
| 500,000 and over | 11[e] | 11[e] | 8[f] | 6[f] | 3[f] |
| 250,000 - 500,000 | 6 | 9 | 5 | 6 | 9 |
| 100,000 - 250,000 | 15 | 13 | 15 | 7 | 3 |
| Under 100,000 | 24 | 28 | 32 | 41 | 45 |

[a] Includes one area with a central city of 250,000-500,000 population (Rochester).

[b] Includes two areas with central cities of 1,000,000 or more population (Philadelphia and Detroit), and one with a central city of 500,000-1,000,000 population (Washington, D. C.).

[c] Includes two areas with central cities of 1,000,000 or more population (Philadelphia and Detroit), and one with a central city of 500,000-1,000,000 population (St. Louis).

[d] Includes one area with a central city of 1,000,000 or more population (Philadelphia), and one with a central city of 500,000-1,000,000 population (St. Louis).

[e] Includes three areas with central cities of 1,000,000 or more population (New York, Chicago, and Los Angeles).

[f] Includes one area with a central city of 1,000,000 or more population (Chicago).

TABLE 58. PER CENT CHANGE OF POPULATION IN STANDARD METROPOLITAN AREAS, BY TYPE OF PLACE, DIRECTION OF INDUSTRIAL RELOCATION, AND DECADE, 1900-1950

| *Type of place and direction of industrial relocation* | *1940-50* | *1930-40* | *1920-30* | *1910-20* | *1900-10* |
|---|---|---|---|---|---|
| Actual | | | | | |
| Total | | | | | |
| Concentrating | 18.5 | 6.7 | 18.0 | 25.8 | 36.4 |
| No clear trend | 23.5 | 8.9 | 27.0 | 26.1 | 23.3 |
| Deconcentrating | 19.4 | 8.5 | 26.5 | 24.3 | 32.5 |
| Central cities | | | | | |
| Concentrating | 15.1 | 4.3 | 22.0 | 34.2 | 45.2 |
| No clear trend | 15.9 | 5.2 | 25.4 | 31.2 | 27.9 |
| Deconcentrating | 10.5 | 5.7 | 22.1 | 24.2 | 33.0 |
| Satellite areas | | | | | |
| Concentrating | 23.3 | 10.2 | 12.4 | 15.9 | 27.9 |
| No clear trend | 35.0 | 14.8 | 29.7 | 18.5 | 17.2 |
| Deconcentrating | 33.1 | 13.2 | 35.2 | 24.4 | 31.5 |
| Adjusted[a] | | | | | |
| Total | | | | | |
| Concentrating | 7.2 | 2.9 | 7.4 | 10.3 | 15.3 |
| No clear trend | 24.3 | 9.5 | 27.6 | 27.5 | 23.4 |
| Deconcentrating | 19.5 | 11.2 | 26.5 | 27.2 | 32.5 |
| Central cities | | | | | |
| Concentrating | 5.8 | 1.9 | 8.1 | 12.9 | 16.8 |
| No clear trend | 15.1 | 4.9 | 23.4 | 31.1 | 27.1 |
| Deconcentrating | 11.2 | 9.8 | 23.1 | 29.4 | 35.2 |
| Satellite areas | | | | | |
| Concentrating | 9.3 | 4.4 | 6.4 | 7.3 | 13.4 |
| No clear trend | 38.4 | 15.3 | 34.7 | 22.2 | 18.6 |
| Deconcentrating | 32.4 | 13.6 | 33.3 | 22.8 | 27.4 |

[a] Adjusted for size of central city. Size distribution of all areas used as the standard.

In either case the effect is to reduce the relative importance as a manufacturing site of one part and to increase the importance of the other part.

### Central City and Satellite Area

Standard Metropolitan Areas in which industrial concentration was the prevailing trend, though they had the highest rates of change in 1900-10, had the lowest rates of change from 1920 to 1950, as Table 58 indicates. Areas in which there was no clear trend of industrial relocation came into ascendancy in 1910-20 and continued to grow more rapidly than the other classes through the remaining decades. The differences between rates of change in that class and rates of change in areas of industrial deconcentration, however, were very small in the years from 1910 to 1950. Rates of change of central city populations parallel rather closely those of total populations. Departures from similarity of pattern occurred in 1910-20 and 1940-50 in which central city rates of deconcentrating areas fell well below those in the other classes of areas. The satellite populations of deconcentrating metropolitan areas increased most rapidly from 1900 to 1930. Thereafter the highest rates of satellite growth occurred in areas of the no clear trend class. The trends of change are more revealing of the influence of industrial movement than are the rates at any point in time. In concentrating areas the rates of satellite growth declined for 40 years and then increased abruptly in the last decade. The trend in areas with no clear direction evident in industrial relocation was for satellite rates to double during the five decades. And in deconcentrating areas rates of change of satellite population tended to remain at a high level, though they fell away from it in 1910-20 and 1930-40. It would appear that the deconcentrating areas have been more effected by the ebb and flow of migration than have areas in which there was no trend of industrial deconcentration.

The adjustment of growth rates to a standard size of area distribution, the results of which are shown in the lower panel of Table 58, depresses the rates of concentrating areas and expands the rates in areas with no clear trend of industrial movement, especially in their satellite territories. The ascendancy of satellite growth in the no clear trend class began a decade earlier when adjusted rates are used. Barring these slight modifications, the differences in growth tendencies seem not to have been a function of variations in size distribution.

Population changes in satellite areas are shown by distance zones in Fig. 33. The pattern of differential changes among distance zones in concentrating areas shifted radically between 1900 and 1950. In 1900-10 growth was fairly even in most zones. But in succeeding decades growth

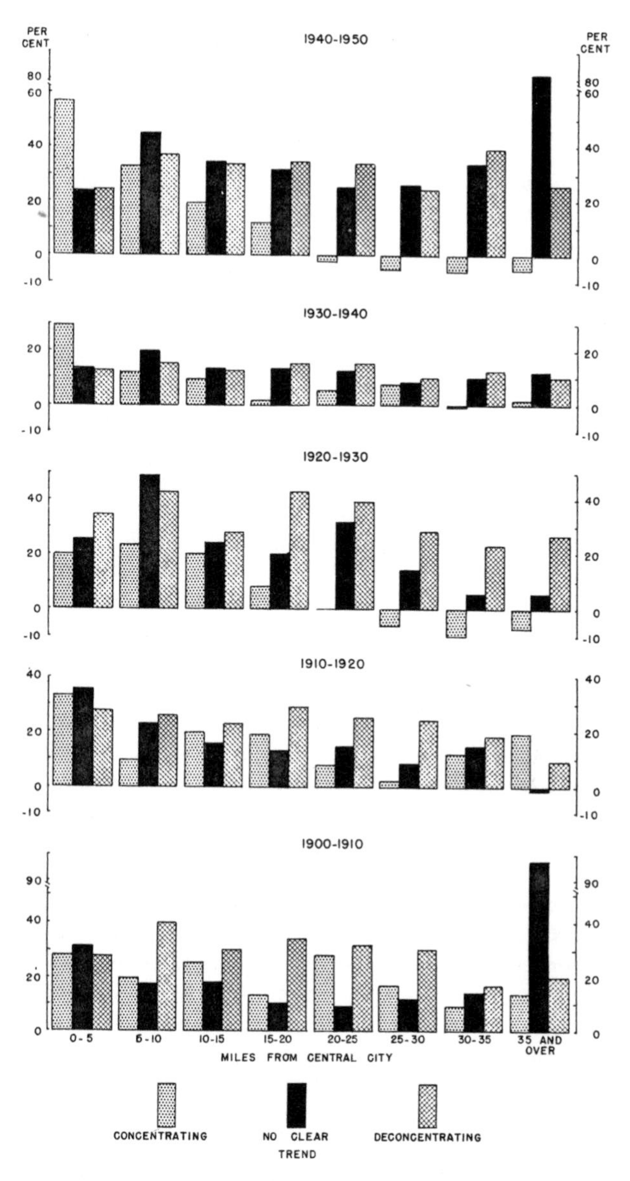


FIGURE 33

PER CENT CHANGE OF SATELLITE POPULATION IN STANDARD METROPOLITAN AREAS, BY DIRECTION OF INDUSTRIAL RELOCATION, DISTANCE ZONE, AND DECADE, 1900-1950

concentrated more and more in the inner zones. Rates increased in the 0-5 and 5-10 mile zones, and declined in all other zones. And beyond 20 miles from central cities population losses were prevalent after 1920. In areas with no clear trend all zones beyond 5 miles from central cities had higher rates in 1940-50 than in 1900-10, though in many of them most of the change occurred after 1940. If the 35 mile and over zone is excluded from consideration, growth was more concentrated in the no clear trend areas than in areas of industrial deconcentration. That is, the zones of most rapid growth were further from central cities in the latter than in the former in almost every decade. Whereas high rates in zones beyond 10 miles from centers came late to areas with no clear trend, they must have operated in deconcentrating areas from the beginning.

The more rapid dispersion of population in areas of industrial deconcentration is shown in Table 59. In no decade, as measured by actual rates, did the satellite population of such areas fail to grow as rapidly as central cities. Dispersion did not affect concentrating areas until after 1930. The sudden increase in 1930-40 was more a consequence of low central city rates than of high satellite rates, as reference to Table 58 will indicate. This cannot be said, however, of the high 1930-40 ratio in areas with no clear trend of industrial relocation. Clearly in that one decade dispersion was greatest in areas with no clear trend.

TABLE 59. RATIO OF RATE OF POPULATION CHANGE IN SATELLITE AREAS TO CENTRAL CITY RATE OF CHANGE IN STANDARD METROPOLITAN AREAS, BY DIRECTION OF INDUSTRIAL RELOCATION, AND DECADE, 1900 - 1950

| *Direction of industrial relocation* | *1940-50* | *1930-40* | *1920-30* | *1910-20* | *1900-10* |
|---|---|---|---|---|---|
| All areas | 2.7 | 2.5 | 1.4 | 0.9 | 0.8 |
| Concentrating | 1.5 | 2.4 | 0.6 | 0.5 | 0.6 |
| No clear trend | 2.2 | 2.8 | 1.2 | 0.6 | 0.6 |
| Deconcentrating | 3.2 | 2.3 | 1.6 | 1.0 | 1.0 |

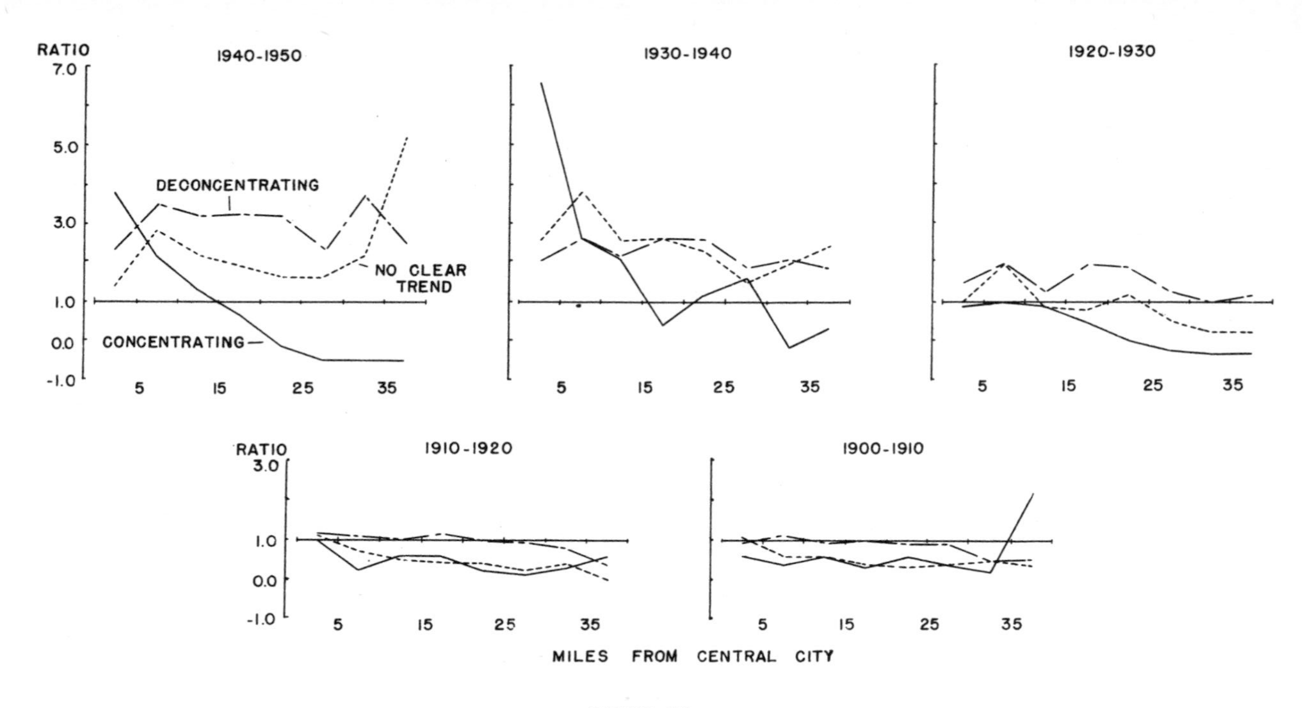


FIGURE 34

RATIO OF RATE OF SATELLITE POPULATION CHANGE TO RATE OF CENTRAL CITY CHANGE IN STANDARD METROPOLITAN AREAS, BY DIRECTION OF INDUSTRIAL RELOCATION, DISTANCE ZONE, AND DECADE, 1900-1950

The reduction of zonal rates to ratios eliminates many of the irregularities observed in Fig. 33. In concentrating areas increases in relative rates of change, shown in Fig. 34, extended over all zones within 20 miles of centers, though only within a 15-mile radius of centers did satellite rates rise above central city rates. In zones beyond 20 miles decline was the rule. Industrial concentration, in other words, exerted a strong centripetal pull on satellite population.

Dispersion accelerated rapidly in 1930-40 in areas within which there was no clear trend of industrial movement. In the next decade population deconcentration subsided in zones 0 to 25 miles from centers, while in outer zones the rates continued their rise. In areas of industrial deconcentration consistent increases occurred in all zones. The centrifugal effect of industrial deconcentration on population growth began early and proceeded without interruption.

These patterns of change are repeated in the cumulative percentage distributions of the amounts of population change of Table 60. The delayed beginnings of dispersion followed by an extraordinary impetus in that direction within areas of industrial concentration is marked by the decline of the central cities' share of population increase from 71 per cent, in 1920-30, to 39 per cent, in 1930-40. During the same period the proportion of increase attracted to satellite areas within 10 miles of central cities doubled, changing from 22 per cent to 45 per cent.

In areas of the no clear trend class the scatter of population increments was a more even process. But as in areas of industrial concentration central cities regained some of their losses in 1940-50. The major increases in the distribution of population increments occurred in the 5-10 and 10-15 mile zones; together these zones received 18 per cent in 1900-10, and 39 per cent in 1940-50.

As has been observed in other connections, the most consistent trend of change in the distribution of population gains took place in areas of industrial deconcentration. Beginning with a relatively high proportion of gain, amounting to 66 per cent in 1900-10, the central cities' share declined without interruption to 33 per cent in 1940-50. That loss was compensated by substantial gains in satellite areas 5 to 20 miles from central cities.

It seems quite probable, after an inspection of Table 61, that the high rates of satellite growth in areas of industrial deconcentration were due partly to the greater degree of population concentration in those areas. The central cities of deconcentrating areas held a larger proportion of their total area populations than did the central cities of the other classes in every census year down to 1950. This was not true, however, of the

## TABLE 60. CUMULATIVE PERCENTAGE DISTRIBUTION OF POPULATION INCREASE IN STANDARD METROPOLITAN AREAS, BY DIRECTION OF INDUSTRIAL RELOCATION, DISTANCE ZONE, AND DECADE, 1900 - 1950

| *Direction of industrial relocation and distance zone* | *1940-50* | *1930-40* | *1920-30* | *1910-20* | *1900-10* |
|---|---|---|---|---|---|
| Concentrating | | | | | |
| Central cities | 48.2 | 39.1 | 71.3 | 72.0 | 61.1 |
| 0 - 5 miles | 68.7 | 62.8 | 77.4 | 78.8 | 66.8 |
| 5 - 10 " | 91.4 | 84.6 | 92.7 | 83.6 | 75.6 |
| 10 - 15 " | 100.4 | 95.6 | 102.0 | 90.3 | 82.7 |
| 15 - 20 " | 102.8 | 96.4 | 104.0 | 94.0 | 84.9 |
| 20 - 25 " | 102.5 | 98.0 | 104.0 | 94.9 | 87.1 |
| 25 - 30 " | 102.0 | 99.3 | 103.3 | 95.1 | 88.3 |
| 30 - 35 " | 101.7 | 99.2 | 102.8 | 95.5 | 88.6 |
| 35 miles and over | 100.0 | 100.0 | 100.0 | 100.0 | 100.0 |
| No clear trend | | | | | |
| Central cities | 41.0 | 36.7 | 59.0 | 71.7 | 68.4 |
| 0 - 5 miles | 47.2 | 45.6 | 64.8 | 79.8 | 76.4 |
| 5 - 10 " | 71.0 | 72.6 | 83.4 | 88.6 | 84.9 |
| 10 - 15 " | 86.1 | 86.4 | 92.0 | 94.9 | 94.1 |
| 15 - 20 " | 92.0 | 93.2 | 95.5 | 97.6 | 96.7 |
| 20 - 25 " | 95.4 | 97.2 | 98.9 | 99.0 | 98.0 |
| 25 - 30 " | 96.8 | 98.4 | 99.7 | 99.5 | 98.9 |
| 30 - 35 " | 97.9 | 99.2 | 99.9 | 100.0 | 99.5 |
| 35 miles and over | 100.0 | 100.0 | 100.0 | 100.0 | 100.0 |
| Deconcentrating | | | | | |
| Central cities | 33.1 | 42.4 | 54.9 | 65.5 | 66.2 |
| 0 - 5 miles | 38.2 | 48.1 | 59.9 | 70.1 | 69.8 |
| 5 - 10 " | 59.7 | 66.2 | 74.2 | 80.0 | 80.7 |
| 10 - 15 " | 74.8 | 77.9 | 82.8 | 87.6 | 88.3 |
| 15 - 20 " | 85.4 | 87.6 | 90.1 | 92.8 | 92.9 |
| 20 - 25 " | 92.0 | 93.6 | 94.9 | 96.2 | 96.0 |
| 25 - 30 " | 95.0 | 96.3 | 97.2 | 98.3 | 98.1 |
| 30 - 35 " | 97.5 | 97.9 | 98.2 | 99.2 | 98.7 |
| 35 miles and over | 100.0 | 100.0 | 100.0 | 100.0 | 100.0 |

spaces within 10 mile radii of metropolitan centers. And that, of course, is because population deconcentration began earlier in areas of industrial deconcentration.

Expressed as coefficients of redistribution, shown in Fig. 35, the rates of distribution changes show three fairly distinct patterns. In concentrating areas the rate of redistribution declined precipitously from 1900 to 1940, and then increased once more. It is noteworthy that in even the period in which the relative rate of satellite growth increased sharply -- 1930-40, the rate of redistribution continued its decline. In contrast to concentrating areas, the rates of redistribution in areas of deconcentration have followed a trend of increase. A third pattern, if it may be called that, occurred in areas with no clear trend of industrial relocation. In those areas redistribution rates fluctuated widely with only a suggestion of a long-run tendency to increase.

## Size and Type of Satellite Place

While all sizes and types of satellite places in concentrating areas had relatively high rates of change, in 1900-10, as shown in Table 62, the rates of all places and in all zones declined rapidly during the following 40 years. Population losses developed after 1920 in places located 20 or more miles from central cities, some of the largest among which occurred in unincorporated areas. Thus all satellite places shared in the low rates of concentrating areas. But rates of change in incorporated places of less than 2,500 population and of unincorporated area within 10 miles of centers remained comparatively high. This together with losses in outer zones is in keeping with the expected effects of industrial concentration.

The highest rates of change occurred in deconcentrating areas after 1910. Rates declined, however, in all incorporated places, particularly in those located within 30 miles of central cities. Industrial deconcentration appears to have stimulated satellite population growth only in unincorporated areas. Rates of change of unincorporated population increased in all zones.

The high rates of satellite population growth in metropolitan areas with no clear trend of industrial relocation were due largely to rapid and increasing rates of growth in unincorporated areas and in the smallest class of incorporated places. Elsewhere trends of declining rates prevailed.

Measures of relative growth, presented in Table 63, were low in all sizes and types of satellite places in concentrating areas. A tendency

## TABLE 61. CUMULATIVE PERCENTAGE DISTRIBUTION OF POPULATION IN STANDARD METROPOLITAN AREAS, BY DIRECTION OF INDUSTRIAL RELOCATION, DISTANCE ZONE, AND CENSUS YEAR, 1900 - 1950

| *Direction of industrial relocation and distance zone* | *1950* | *1940* | *1930* | *1920* | *1910* | *1900* |
|---|---|---|---|---|---|---|
| Concentrating | | | | | | |
| Central cities | 57.3 | 58.9 | 60.3 | 58.3 | 54.4 | 49.2 |
| 0 - 5 miles | 66.1 | 65.6 | 65.8 | 63.7 | 59.8 | 56.6 |
| 5 - 10 " | 80.8 | 78.8 | 78.5 | 75.9 | 74.1 | 72.8 |
| 10 - 15 " | 89.5 | 87.5 | 87.0 | 84.3 | 83.0 | 83.0 |
| 15 - 20 " | 93.4 | 91.7 | 91.4 | 89.1 | 88.0 | 89.0 |
| 20 - 25 " | 95.1 | 93.8 | 93.5 | 91.6 | 90.8 | 91.9 |
| 25 - 30 " | 96.1 | 95.1 | 94.8 | 93.3 | 92.8 | 94.4 |
| 30 - 35 " | 96.6 | 95.7 | 95.5 | 94.2 | 93.9 | 95.7 |
| 35 miles and over | 100.0 | 100.0 | 100.0 | 100.0 | 100.0 | 100.0 |
| No clear trend | | | | | | |
| Central cities | 56.8 | 60.5 | 62.0 | 62.6 | 60.0 | 57.2 |
| 0 - 5 miles | 63.1 | 66.8 | 68.2 | 68.9 | 66.1 | 63.3 |
| 5 - 10 " | 77.8 | 79.3 | 80.3 | 79.1 | 76.8 | 74.6 |
| 10 - 15 " | 89.0 | 89.7 | 89.9 | 89.0 | 87.8 | 86.4 |
| 15 - 20 " | 93.8 | 94.2 | 94.4 | 93.9 | 93.6 | 92.7 |
| 20 - 25 " | 97.0 | 97.4 | 97.4 | 96.9 | 96.4 | 96.0 |
| 25 - 30 " | 98.3 | 98.6 | 98.7 | 98.4 | 98.2 | 98.0 |
| 30 - 35 " | 99.1 | 99.4 | 99.4 | 99.3 | 99.1 | 99.0 |
| 35 miles and over | 100.0 | 100.0 | 100.0 | 100.0 | 100.0 | 100.0 |
| Deconcentrating | | | | | | |
| Central cities | 56.4 | 60.9 | 63.1 | 66.1 | 65.6 | 65.2 |
| 0 - 5 miles | 60.8 | 65.1 | 67.2 | 70.1 | 69.6 | 69.3 |
| 5 - 10 " | 73.8 | 76.4 | 77.6 | 79.0 | 78.7 | 78.2 |
| 10 - 15 " | 83.4 | 85.0 | 85.9 | 87.0 | 86.7 | 86.5 |
| 15 - 20 " | 90.0 | 90.9 | 91.4 | 91.6 | 91.1 | 90.9 |
| 20 - 25 " | 94.2 | 94.6 | 94.8 | 94.9 | 94.4 | 94.1 |
| 25 - 30 " | 96.7 | 97.0 | 97.1 | 97.1 | 96.6 | 96.4 |
| 30 - 35 " | 98.1 | 98.2 | 98.2 | 98.2 | 97.8 | 97.7 |
| 35 miles and over | 100.0 | 100.0 | 100.0 | 100.0 | 100.0 | 100.0 |

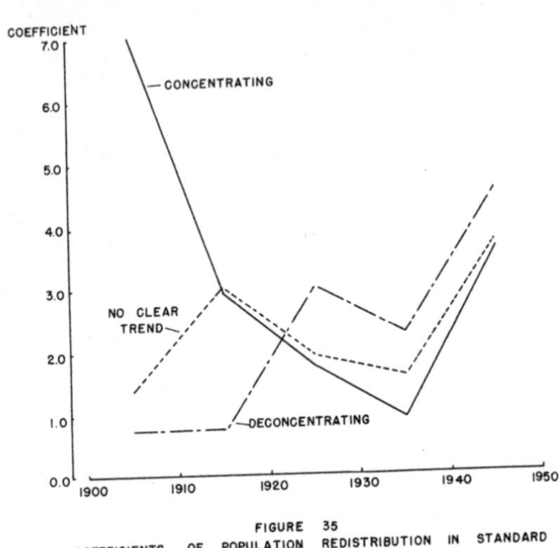


FIGURE 35
COEFFICIENTS OF POPULATION REDISTRIBUTION IN STANDARD METROPOLITAN AREAS, BY DIRECTION OF INDUSTRIAL RELOCATION, 1900-1950

for ratios to increase is evident in most places of less than 10,000 population located within 20 miles of central cities. But the increases were small and were limited to the years between 1910 and 1940. Much larger increases in the relative growth rates of satellite places occurred in areas of industrial deconcentration. Accelerating growth took place in all classes of places with less than 10,000 population regardless of location. There were increases, too, in incorporated places of 10,000-50,000 population located in the 10-20 and the 30 and over mile zones. Metropolitan areas in which there was no clear direction to the relocation of industry had increasing ratios in satellites of 2,500 to 50,000 population within 20 miles of centers and in smaller places in all distance zones. Unlike the deconcentrating areas, in which the increase of ratios was more or less continuous through the five decades, increase in the no clear trend areas reached its height in 1930-40.

Differential growth within concentrating areas has shifted the pattern of distribution not only as between zones but also as between types of satellite places. Table 64 indicates that in the 0-10 mile zone unincorporated area gained a steadily larger proportion of the population at the expense of most classes of incorporated places. In all other zones unincorporated areas had declining proportions, while incorporated places acquired increased proportions. Within deconcentrating areas unincorporated population in all zones declined proportionally until 1930 and

Table 62. Per Cent Change of Satellite Population in Standard Metropolitan Areas, by Size and Type of Place, Distance Zone, Direction of Industrial Relocation and Decade, 1900-1950

| Size and type of place and distance zone | Concentrating | | | | | No clear trend | | | | | Deconcentrating | | | | |
|---|---|---|---|---|---|---|---|---|---|---|---|---|---|---|---|
| | 1940-1950 | 1930-1940 | 1920-1930 | 1910-1920 | 1900-1910 | 1940-1950 | 1930-1940 | 1920-1930 | 1910-1920 | 1900-1910 | 1940-1950 | 1930-1940 | 1920-1930 | 1910-1920 | 1900-1910 |
| 50,000 and over | | | | | | | | | | | | | | | |
| 0-10 miles | ---- | ---- | ---- | ---- | ---- | 10.9 | 0.5 | 4.2 | 11.0 | 25.5 | 10.9 | 0.7 | 16.0 | 20.0[a] | 46.7 |
| 10-20 miles | ---- | ---- | ---- | ---- | ---- | 7.6 | -5.2 | 5.5 | 21.8 | ---- | 10.0 | 0.2 | 13.7 | 19.0[a] | 35.5[a] |
| 20-30 miles | ---- | ---- | ---- | ---- | ---- | 10.6[a] | 2.6[a] | ---- | ---- | ---- | 21.8[a] | 10.3[a] | 81.3[a] | ---- | ---- |
| 30 miles and over | ---- | ---- | ---- | ---- | ---- | ---- | ---- | ---- | ---- | ---- | ---- | ---- | ---- | ---- | ---- |
| 10,000 - 50,000 | | | | | | | | | | | | | | | |
| 0-10 miles | 4.7[a] | -1.3 | 12.1 | 11.6 | 15.8 | 21.9 | 4.4 | 20.2 | -2.4 | 9.0 | 9.1 | 6.8 | 41.7 | 30.2 | 41.8 |
| 10-20 miles | 10.5[a] | 2.4 | 66.5[a] | 43.2 | ---- | 17.9 | 3.2 | 18.9 | 31.6 | 38.9 | 35.9 | 10.3 | 42.2 | 45.0 | 52.4 |
| 20-30 miles | 16.8 | ---- | ---- | ---- | ---- | 9.9 | 4.4 | 58.1 | 52.5 | ---- | 9.1 | 5.8 | 23.3 | 41.9 | 46.6 |
| 30 miles and over | 0.4 | 3.7[a] | -5.1 | 33.9[a] | ---- | 6.5 | 0.6 | 6.5 | 19.7 | 13.9 | 24.4 | 1.6 | 23.8 | 17.2 | 21.4 |
| 2,500 - 10,000 | | | | | | | | | | | | | | | |
| 0-10 miles | 12.9 | 4.3 | 8.4 | 10.1 | 16.6 | 23.1 | 5.7 | 46.6 | 55.7 | 35.3 | 35.6 | 12.6 | 40.6 | 39.4 | 51.5 |
| 10-20 miles | 18.5 | 8.0 | 11.0 | 26.0 | 46.2 | 43.5 | 13.6 | 36.1 | 18.5 | 30.4 | 43.7 | 14.0 | 66.5 | 39.9 | 47.8 |
| 20-30 miles | -2.7 | 12.0 | -2.5 | 5.7 | 37.0 | 12.6 | 5.0 | 20.2 | -2.8 | 24.0 | 21.5 | 7.4 | 36.6 | 24.0 | 48.0 |
| 30 miles and over | -9.6 | -5.9 | -6.4 | 29.4 | 99.3 | 12.1 | 18.8 | 2.0 | -3.3 | 70.4 | 26.2 | 5.5 | 35.6 | 15.5 | 31.0 |
| Under 2,500 | | | | | | | | | | | | | | | |
| 0-10 miles | 23.0 | 25.8 | 39.9 | 25.9 | 64.5 | 34.3 | 14.8 | 20.2 | 39.6 | 52.2 | 46.6 | 25.5 | 77.6 | 34.9 | 55.1 |
| 10-20 miles | 5.4 | 4.6 | 9.2 | 19.2 | 20.4 | 30.5 | 12.3 | 18.9 | 22.8 | 20.7 | 40.5 | 15.3 | 57.2 | 31.9 | 29.1 |
| 20-30 miles | 4.9 | 5.5 | -1.9 | 7.0 | 28.4 | 19.8 | 7.5 | 58.1 | 18.5 | 20.5 | 29.7 | 13.8 | 36.4 | 24.9 | 39.3 |
| 30 miles and over | -9.5 | 2.9 | -7.4 | 20.6 | 46.1 | 19.5 | 7.7 | 6.5 | 10.9 | 17.7 | 28.0 | 9.5 | 22.5 | 7.5 | 24.1 |
| Unincorporated area | | | | | | | | | | | | | | | |
| 0-10 miles | 57.8 | 25.0 | 26.3 | 16.0 | 109.5 | 52.0 | 31.3 | 45.5 | 25.9 | 18.3 | 63.4 | 28.5 | 47.2 | 23.2 | 25.3 |
| 10-20 miles | 21.1 | 7.8 | 7.0 | 16.2 | 16.2 | 38.4 | 18.1 | 22.7 | 7.7 | 8.4 | 50.9 | 25.3 | 24.6 | 14.3 | 20.7 |
| 20-30 miles | 14.1 | 3.7 | -3.5 | 5.3 | 19.3 | 31.5 | 13.8 | 24.3 | 7.5 | 4.1 | 49.2 | 20.9 | 37.0 | 15.1 | 19.8 |
| 30 miles and over | -9.6 | 2.3 | -12.0 | 7.9 | 82.1 | 86.3 | 14.0 | 2.8 | 3.5 | 6.2 | 36.8 | 17.6 | 22.1 | 10.2 | 12.0 |

[a] Based on less than 5 incorporated places.

Table 63. Ratio of Rate of Change of Satellite Population to Central City Rate of Change in Standard Metropolitan Areas, by Size and Type of Place, Distance Zone, Direction of Industrial Relocation, and Decade, 1900-1950

| Size and type of place and distance zone | Concentrating | | | | | No clear trend | | | | | Deconcentrating | | | | |
|---|---|---|---|---|---|---|---|---|---|---|---|---|---|---|---|
| | 1940-1950 | 1930-1940 | 1920-1930 | 1910-1920 | 1900-1910 | 1940-1950 | 1930-1940 | 1920-1930 | 1910-1920 | 1900-1910 | 1940-1950 | 1930-1940 | 1920-1930 | 1910-1920 | 1900-1910 |
| 50,000 and over | | | | | | | | | | | | | | | |
| 0-10 miles | ---- | ---- | ---- | ---- | ---- | 0.7 | 0.1 | 0.2 | 0.4 | 0.9 | 1.0 | 0.1 | 0.7 | 0.8 | 1.4 |
| 10-20 miles | ---- | ---- | ---- | ---- | ---- | 0.5 | -1.0 | 0.2 | 0.7 | ---- | 1.0 | 0.0 | 0.6 | 0.8 | 1.1 |
| 20-30 miles | ---- | ---- | ---- | ---- | ---- | 0.7 | 0.5 | ---- | ---- | ---- | 2.1 | 1.8 | 3.7 | ---- | ---- |
| 30 miles and over | ---- | ---- | ---- | ---- | ---- | ---- | ---- | ---- | ---- | ---- | ---- | ---- | ---- | ---- | ---- |
| 10,000 - 50,000 | | | | | | | | | | | | | | | |
| 0-10 miles | 0.3 | -0.3 | 0.6 | 0.3 | 0.3 | 1.4 | 0.8 | 0.8 | -0.1 | 0.3 | 0.9 | 1.2 | 1.9 | 1.2 | 1.3 |
| 10-20 miles | 0.7 | 0.6 | 3.0 | 1.3 | ---- | 1.1 | 0.6 | 0.7 | 1.0 | 1.4 | 3.4 | 1.8 | 1.9 | 1.9 | 1.6 |
| 20-30 miles | 1.1 | ---- | ---- | ---- | ---- | 0.6 | 0.8 | 2.3 | 1.7 | ---- | 0.9 | 1.0 | 1.1 | 1.7 | 1.4 |
| 30 miles and over | 0.0 | 0.9 | -0.2 | 1.0 | ---- | 0.4 | 0.1 | 0.3 | 0.6 | 0.5 | 2.3 | 0.3 | 1.1 | 0.7 | 0.6 |
| 2,500 - 10,000 | | | | | | | | | | | | | | | |
| 0-10 miles | 0.9 | 1.0 | 0.4 | 0.3 | 0.4 | 1.5 | 1.1 | 1.8 | 1.8 | 1.3 | 3.4 | 2.2 | 1.8 | 1.6 | 1.6 |
| 10-20 miles | 1.2 | 1.9 | 0.5 | 0.8 | 1.0 | 2.7 | 2.6 | 1.4 | 0.6 | 1.1 | 4.2 | 2.5 | 3.0 | 1.6 | 1.4 |
| 20-30 miles | -0.2 | 2.8 | -0.1 | 0.2 | 0.8 | 0.8 | 1.0 | 0.8 | -0.1 | 0.9 | 2.0 | 1.3 | 1.7 | 1.0 | 1.5 |
| 30 miles and over | -0.6 | -1.4 | -0.3 | 0.9 | 2.2 | 0.8 | 3.6 | 0.1 | -0.1 | 2.5 | 2.5 | 1.0 | 1.6 | 0.6 | 0.9 |
| Under 2,500 | | | | | | | | | | | | | | | |
| 0-10 miles | 1.5 | 6.0 | 1.8 | 0.8 | 1.4 | 2.2 | 2.8 | 0.8 | 1.3 | 1.9 | 4.4 | 4.5 | 3.5 | 1.4 | 1.7 |
| 10-20 miles | 0.4 | 1.1 | 0.4 | 0.6 | 0.5 | 1.9 | 2.4 | 0.7 | 0.7 | 0.7 | 3.9 | 2.7 | 2.6 | 1.3 | 0.9 |
| 20-30 miles | 0.3 | 1.3 | -0.1 | 0.2 | 0.6 | 1.2 | 1.4 | 2.3 | 0.6 | 0.7 | 2.8 | 2.4 | 1.6 | 1.0 | 1.2 |
| 30 miles and over | -0.6 | 0.7 | -0.3 | 0.6 | 1.0 | 1.2 | 1.5 | 0.3 | 0.3 | 0.6 | 2.7 | 1.7 | 1.0 | 0.3 | 0.7 |
| Unincorporated area | | | | | | | | | | | | | | | |
| 0-10 miles | 3.8 | 5.8 | 1.2 | 0.5 | 2.4 | 3.3 | 6.0 | 1.8 | 0.8 | 0.7 | 6.0 | 5.0 | 2.1 | 1.0 | 0.8 |
| 10-20 miles | 1.4 | 1.8 | 0.3 | 0.5 | 0.4 | 2.4 | 3.5 | 0.9 | 0.2 | 0.3 | 4.8 | 4.4 | 1.1 | 0.6 | 0.6 |
| 20-30 miles | -0.9 | 0.9 | -0.2 | 0.2 | 0.4 | 2.0 | 2.7 | 1.0 | 0.2 | 0.1 | 4.7 | 3.7 | 1.7 | 0.6 | 0.0 |
| 30 miles and over | -0.6 | 0.5 | -0.5 | 0.2 | 1.8 | 5.4 | 2.7 | 0.1 | 0.1 | 0.2 | 3.5 | 3.1 | 1.0 | 0.4 | 0.4 |

Table 64. Per Cent Distribution of Satellite Population in Standard Metropolitan Areas, by Census Year, Size and Type of Place, Direction of Industrial Relocation, and Distance Zone, 1900-1950

| Census year and size and type of place | Concentrating: Miles from central city | | | | No clear trend: Miles from central city | | | | Deconcentrating: Miles from central city | | | |
|---|---|---|---|---|---|---|---|---|---|---|---|---|
| | 0-10 miles | 10-20 miles | 20-30 miles | 30 miles and over | 0-10 miles | 10-20 miles | 20-30 miles | 30 miles and over | 0 -10 miles | 10-20 miles | 20-30 miles | 30 miles and over |
| **1950** | | | | | | | | | | | | |
| Total | 100.0 | 100.0 | 100.0 | 100.0 | 100.0 | 100.0 | 100.0 | 100.0 | 100.0 | 100.0 | 100.0 | 100.0 |
| 50,000 and over | 0.0 | 0.0 | 0.0 | 0.0 | 8.6 | 5.3 | 8.9 | 0.0 | 18.7 | 23.4 | 7.1 | 0.0 |
| 10,000 - 50,000 | 14.5 | 19.7 | 13.6 | 23.5 | 14.8 | 13.3 | 3.4 | 11.4 | 21.2 | 21.0 | 22.4 | 22.2 |
| 2,500 - 10,000 | 9.4 | 7.2 | 21.7 | 19.3 | 13.0 | 11.7 | 12.3 | 7.8 | 13.4 | 14.4 | 16.3 | 16.9 |
| Under 2,500 | 5.6 | 13.3 | 21.7 | 15.9 | 5.9 | 8.6 | 6.8 | 12.3 | 3.4 | 6.1 | 7.6 | 8.1 |
| Unincorporated area | 70.5 | 59.8 | 43.0 | 41.3 | 57.7 | 61.1 | 68.6 | 68.5 | 43.3 | 35.1 | 46.6 | 52.8 |
| **1940** | | | | | | | | | | | | |
| Total | 100.0 | 100.0 | 100.0 | 100.0 | 100.0 | 100.0 | 100.0 | 100.0 | 100.0 | 100.0 | 100.0 | 100.0 |
| 50,000 and over | 0.0 | 0.0 | 0.0 | 0.0 | 10.7 | 6.6 | 10.0 | 0.0 | 22.5 | 28.6 | 7.6 | 0.0 |
| 10,000 - 50,000 | 19.4 | 20.8 | 11.1 | 21.7 | 16.7 | 15.0 | 3.8 | 16.6 | 25.9 | 20.8 | 26.6 | 23.4 |
| 2,500 - 10,000 | 11.7 | 7.1 | 21.2 | 19.7 | 14.5 | 10.9 | 13.7 | 10.8 | 13.2 | 13.5 | 17.5 | 17.6 |
| Under 2,500 | 6.4 | 14.6 | 19.8 | 16.3 | 6.0 | 8.8 | 7.2 | 15.8 | 3.1 | 5.8 | 7.7 | 8.3 |
| Unincorporated area | 62.5 | 57.5 | 47.9 | 42.3 | 52.1 | 58.7 | 65.3 | 56.8 | 35.3 | 31.3 | 40.6 | 50.7 |
| **1930** | | | | | | | | | | | | |
| Total | 100.0 | 100.0 | 100.0 | 100.0 | 100.0 | 100.0 | 100.0 | 100.0 | 100.0 | 100.0 | 100.0 | 100.0 |
| 50,000 and over | 0.0 | 0.0 | 0.0 | 0.0 | 14.7 | 6.9 | 9.4 | 0.0 | 25.0 | 29.6 | 7.8 | 0.0 |
| 10,000 - 50,000 | 22.8 | 21.8 | 0.0 | 21.1 | 16.7 | 16.1 | 5.0 | 16.8 | 25.0 | 21.2 | 26.7 | 25.4 |
| 2,500 - 10,000 | 11.9 | 6.3 | 20.1 | 21.2 | 14.8 | 13.0 | 13.1 | 8.1 | 13.5 | 12.6 | 18.9 | 17.0 |
| Under 2,500 | 6.7 | 15.6 | 19.8 | 15.8 | 6.1 | 9.0 | 8.8 | 19.8 | 3.1 | 6.4 | 7.8 | 9.7 |
| Unincorporated area | 58.6 | 56.3 | 60.1 | 41.9 | 47.7 | 55.0 | 63.7 | 55.3 | 33.4 | 30.2 | 38.8 | 47.9 |
| **1920** | | | | | | | | | | | | |
| Total | 100.0 | 100.0 | 100.0 | 100.0 | 100.0 | 100.0 | 100.0 | 100.0 | 100.0 | 100.0 | 100.0 | 100.0 |
| 50,000 and over | 0.0 | 0.0 | 0.0 | 0.0 | 12.5 | 7.9 | 0.0 | 0.0 | 21.8 | 26.2 | 3.7 | 0.0 |
| 10,000 - 50,000 | 24.9 | 12.7 | 0.0 | 20.3 | 16.4 | 12.6 | 10.2 | 16.7 | 22.8 | 19.1 | 27.6 | 20.9 |
| 2,500 - 10,000 | 10.5 | 8.9 | 20.0 | 21.7 | 15.3 | 11.1 | 13.9 | 6.7 | 15.6 | 12.9 | 18.2 | 16.3 |
| Under 2,500 | 7.7 | 17.3 | 19.6 | 14.4 | 7.8 | 10.3 | 10.5 | 18.4 | 5.1 | 8.7 | 10.0 | 10.5 |
| Unincorporated area | 56.9 | 61.1 | 60.4 | 43.6 | 48.0 | 58.1 | 65.4 | 58.2 | 34.7 | 33.1 | 40.5 | 52.3 |
| **1910** | | | | | | | | | | | | |
| Total | 100.0 | 100.0 | 100.0 | 100.0 | 100.0 | 100.0 | 100.0 | 100.0 | 100.0 | 100.0 | 100.0 | 100.0 |
| 50,000 and over | 0.0 | 0.0 | 0.0 | 0.0 | 14.0 | 4.4 | 0.0 | 0.0 | 20.6 | 24.7 | 0.0 | 0.0 |
| 10,000 - 50,000 | 25.1 | 6.4 | 0.0 | 8.6 | 11.2 | 12.3 | 8.2 | 15.3 | 17.6 | 15.1 | 24.0 | 19.1 |
| 2,500 - 10,000 | 8.1 | 10.6 | 16.7 | 25.3 | 15.2 | 8.9 | 14.2 | 7.6 | 14.9 | 12.2 | 17.1 | 13.1 |
| Under 2,500 | 8.6 | 17.3 | 22.5 | 16.5 | 8.7 | 10.7 | 12.8 | 17.6 | 6.2 | 10.7 | 13.5 | 11.6 |
| Unincorporated area | 58.2 | 65.7 | 60.8 | 49.6 | 50.9 | 63.7 | 64.8 | 59.5 | 40.6 | 37.3 | 45.4 | 56.2 |
| **1900** | | | | | | | | | | | | |
| Total | 100.0 | 100.0 | 100.0 | 100.0 | 100.0 | 100.0 | 100.0 | 100.0 | 100.0 | 100.0 | 100.0 | 100.0 |
| 50,000 and over | 0.0 | 0.0 | 0.0 | 0.0 | 10.2 | 0.0 | 0.0 | 0.0 | 15.3 | 19.1 | 0.0 | 0.0 |
| 10,000 - 50,000 | 42.6 | 0.0 | 0.0 | 0.0 | 13.2 | 12.9 | 0.0 | 8.9 | 14.6 | 12.7 | 12.2 | 17.4 |
| 2,500 - 10,000 | 5.3 | 12.5 | 8.1 | 18.1 | 8.3 | 7.4 | 18.3 | 5.7 | 12.4 | 10.5 | 17.1 | 12.8 |
| Under 2,500 | 8.8 | 14.3 | 27.4 | 23.6 | 8.5 | 9.7 | 11.5 | 17.8 | 6.4 | 10.3 | 13.7 | 11.8 |
| Unincorporated area | 43.3 | 73.2 | 64.5 | 58.3 | 59.8 | 70.0 | 70.2 | 67.6 | 51.3 | 47.4 | 57.0 | 58.0 |

afterwards recovered some of its loss. Incorporated population, particularly in the larger places, expanded from 1900 to 1930 and then contracted. In every census year after 1900 the satellite population of deconcentrating areas has occupied incorporated places to a much greater extent than in the other classes of metropolitan areas. The trends of changing distribution in areas of no clear industrial relocation have been similar to those in deconcentrating areas. But the former has had a considerably greater concentration of its satellite population in small incorporated places and in unincorporated area.

In conclusion, the dispersion of metropolitan population is closely associated with industrial deconcentration, though it is not entirely dependent on the outward movement of manufacturing industry. Actually, dispersion moved more rapidly, at least after 1920, in areas with high proportions of their populations engaged in manufacturing industry (Table 51) than in areas of deconcentration (Table 59). Parenthetically, manufacturing areas are almost evenly distributed over the three industrial relocation classes, as may be determined from Appendix Table 1. Hence, it appears that there are factors associated with large proportion of manufacturing employment that encourage the centrifugal movement of population over and above that produced by industrial deconcentration itself.

CHAPTER IX

# REGIONAL LOCATION AND POPULATION REDISTRIBUTION

The effect of regional location on many population and urban phenomena has been often demonstrated. Hence, it is to be expected that such a variation will appear in distribution tendencies within metropolitan areas. But what makes for regional differentials has not been determined. That is, whether there is any residual effect that may be attributed to regional location remaining after the characteristics of the units under study are standarized or controlled has not been ascertained. So far as population redistribution in metropolitan areas is concerned, it seems unlikely that regional variations can be anything other than the composite effects of variables such as those treated in Chapters III to VIII. Unfortunately, the number of metropolitan units available for study is too small to permit the simultaneous control of all those factors. This chapter, then, will analyze crude regional differences refined only for differences in size of central city.

The number of metropolitan areas in each of the three major regions -- North, South, and West -- is shown in Table 65. The North includes all states north of the Mason-Dixon line and of an arbitrary extension of that line to the western boundary of Kansas. All states south of the line comprise the South. The West, then, is made up of Rocky Mountain and Pacific Coastal states.[1] A disporportionate number of the metropolitan areas excluded from the study are located in the West. In consequence, the number of areas in that region available for study is almost too small for purposes of generalization. Their size distribution, however, compares favorably with that of the North.

## Central Cities and Satellite Areas

Metropolitan areas in the West have maintained the highest actual growth rates in every decade since 1900. The lowest rates, as is to be seen in Table 66, occurred in the North in every decade since 1910. Very

TABLE 65. NUMBER OF STANDARD METROPOLITAN AREAS, BY REGION, SIZE OF CENTRAL CITY, AND DECADE, 1900 - 1950

| *Region and size of central city* | *1940-50* | *1930-40* | *1920-30* | *1910-20* | *1900-10* |
|---|---|---|---|---|---|
| Total | 143 | 157 | 155 | 153 | 148 |
| North | 90 | 91 | 91 | 91 | 91 |
| 1,000,000 and over | 4 | 4 | 4 | 3 | 3 |
| 500,000 - 1,000,000 | 7 | 8 | 6 | 5 | 2 |
| 250,000 - 500,000 | 6 | 7 | 5 | 5 | 8 |
| 100,000 - 250,000 | 30 | 28 | 23 | 17 | 13 |
| Under 100,000 | 43 | 44 | 53 | 61 | 65 |
| South | 43 | 54 | 54 | 53 | 49 |
| 500,000 - 1,000,000 | 2 | 1 | 1 | 1 | 1 |
| 250,000 - 500,000 | 5 | 8 | 2 | 2 | 2 |
| 100,000 - 250,000 | 8 | 11 | 12 | 6 | 2 |
| Under 100,000 | 28 | 34 | 39 | 44 | 44 |
| West | 10 | 12 | 10 | 9 | 8 |
| 1,000,000 and over | 1 | 1 | - | - | - |
| 500,000 - 1,000,000 | 1 | 1 | 1 | - | - |
| 250,000 - 500,000 | - | - | - | 1 | 1 |
| 100,000 - 250,000 | 3 | 2 | 2 | 1 | - |
| Under 100,000 | 5 | 8 | 7 | 7 | 7 |

much the same variation by region applies to central city rates, though central cities in Southern metropolitan areas grew most rapidly in 1910-20 and 1920-30. The very sharp decline of the central city rate in Northern areas during 1930-40 should be noted: the rate fell to one-seventh of what it had been in the preceding decade, while in neither of the other regions did central cities fall to as low as one-third of their former levels. The highest rates of satellite population change also occurred in metropolitan areas in the West. Those declined from an exceptionally high figure of 62 per cent, in 1900-10, to a low of 25 per cent, in 1930-40, and in the last decade the satellite rate in Western areas increased abruptly to 73 per cent. In the South satellite rates of change increased slowly until 1940, exceeding the satellite rate in Northern areas for the first time in 1930-40. After 1940 the rate in Southern areas almost doubled. Although satellite population in the North grew at the lowest rates following 1930, the change of rate that took place between 1930-40 and 1940-50 was comparable to that in Western Areas.

TABLE 66. PER CENT CHANGE OF POPULATION IN STANDARD METROPOLITAN AREAS, BY TYPE OF PLACE, REGION, AND DECADE, 1900-1950

| *Type of place and region* | *1940-50* | *1930-40* | *1920-30* | *1910-20* | *1900-10* |
|---|---|---|---|---|---|
| Actual | | | | | |
| Total | | | | | |
| North | 13.5 | 4.9 | 23.4 | 23.8 | 29.6 |
| South | 31.6 | 16.7 | 30.0 | 27.1 | 25.5 |
| West | 51.4 | 19.0 | 32.1 | 29.1 | 45.4 |
| Central cities | | | | | |
| North | 7.2 | 2.5 | 18.6 | 24.2 | 31.3 |
| South | 24.6 | 13.0 | 33.9 | 34.6 | 32.4 |
| West | 29.9 | 13.5 | 25.6 | 25.0 | 33.7 |
| Satellite areas | | | | | |
| North | 23.0 | 8.7 | 32.1 | 22.9 | 26.8 |
| South | 43.4 | 24.0 | 23.1 | 15.9 | 16.5 |
| West | 72.6 | 25.0 | 39.7 | 34.4 | 61.9 |
| Adjusted[a] | | | | | |
| Total | | | | | |
| North | 13.3 | 4.7 | 22.0 | 26.7 | 28.9 |
| South | 22.8 | 15.6 | 20.1 | 15.2 | 18.3 |
| West | 46.8 | 18.3 | 17.7 | 11.9 | 23.0 |
| Central cities | | | | | |
| North | 7.3 | 2.2 | 17.6 | 25.5 | 31.6 |
| South | 13.4 | 15.5 | 18.9 | 21.1 | 18.3 |
| West | 27.6 | 15.0 | 13.3 | 11.8 | 18.6 |
| Satellite areas | | | | | |
| North | 22.5 | 8.8 | 29.8 | 28.6 | 24.4 |
| South | 38.5 | 15.8 | 22.3 | 6.4 | 12.5 |
| West | 66.9 | 22.1 | 22.7 | 12.1 | 29.2 |

[a]Adjusted for size of central city. Size distribution of all areas used as the standard.

Apparently some of the variation of metropolitan change with regional location, observed in the actual rates, was due to irregularities in the size distribution of metropolitan areas among the regions. For when the comparisons are standardized for size of area distribution, as in the lower panel of Table 66, certain alterations of the observed relationships occurs. Particularly noteworthy is the fact that metropolitan areas in the North maintained the highest adjusted rates until 1930, instead of 1910 as the actual rates indicate, after which their growth rates receded to the lowest position. It is also of interest that metropolitan areas in the South and West sustained relatively slight reduction of growth in the depression decade of 1930-40. In other respects the patterns found in the adjusted rates are similar to those revealed in the actual rates.

Fig. 36 indicates that the high rates of satellite growth in metropolitan areas of the West were shared by most distance zones. In only a few instances did zonal rates fall below those in the North or South. Western areas were also distinguished by a rapid diffusion of metropolitan influence as suggested by the large increases in rates of change within zones beyond 10 miles from central cities. Evidence of an outward movement of high growth rates is likewise present in the data for Northern areas. But in the South the rising rates of satellite growth were brought about largely by increases in zones within 20 miles of central cities. At greater distances declining rates were the rule.

It is interesting to note that a centrifugal tendency in the redistribution of population within Western areas has operated since the beginning of the century. In no decade did actual satellite rates fail to exceed central city rates by at least 40 per cent, as may be observed in Table 67. But while in Northern areas satellite growth just kept pace with central

TABLE 67. RATIO OF RATE OF CHANGE OF SATELLITE POPULATION TO CENTRAL CITY RATE OF CHANGE IN STANDARD METROPOLITAN AREAS, BY REGION, AND DECADE, 1900 - 1950

| *Region* | *1940-50* | *1930-40* | *1920-30* | *1910-20* | *1900-10* |
|---|---|---|---|---|---|
| All areas | 2.7 | 2.5 | 1.4 | 0.9 | 0.8 |
| North | 3.2 | 3.5 | 1.7 | 1.0 | 0.9 |
| South | 1.8 | 1.8 | 0.7 | 0.5 | 0.5 |
| West | 2.4 | 1.8 | 1.6 | 1.4 | 1.8 |

city growth from 1900 to 1920, it surged far above central city growth in following decades. After 1920 the highest rates of dispersion occurred in Northern rather than in Western metropolitan areas. In the South the growth of satellite population lagged well behind central city growth until 1930. In 1930-40 a sudden acceleration in the relative growth of satellite population occurred. In that decade the ratio for the South equalled the ratio for the West. No further increase followed, however.

The ratios by distance zones, shown in Fig. 37, reveal that the satellite territory in areas of the West over which growth rates exceeded central city rates extended to 30 miles from central cities in 1900-10. The area was enlarged to a 35 mile radius in 1910-20, and to the entire satellite area in 1920-30. A more dramatic change occurred in Northern metropolitan areas. In 1900-10 only the 0-5 mile zones had a growth rate as high as that of central cities. That radius was enlarged by 5 miles in the next decade, and was extended to 35 miles in 1920-30. In 1930-40 all distance zones in Northern areas had higher ratios than comparable zones in Western areas. The tardy development of satellite growth in Southern areas is clearly indicated. As late as 1920-30 only in one zone did satellite growth surpass central city growth. Substantial gains were made in the following 10-year interval; satellite ratios rose above unity over all zones within 25 miles of centers. That radius was reduced to 20 miles, however, in 1940-50.

The differences of growth rate as between central cities and satellite areas are reflected again in the distributions of decennial population increases. These are shown in Table 68. The share of all increase received by central cities of metropolitan areas in the North declined from two-thirds, in 1900-10, to one-third, in 1940-50. The proportions attracted to all zones beyond 5 miles from centers doubled during the 50-year period. Hence while an area with a 15 mile radius contained 90 per cent of the total increase in 1900-10, that proportion, in 1940-50, was spread over an area with a radius of almost 25 miles. In metropolitan areas of the South central cities increased their share of growth from 1900-10 to 1910-20. The proportion declined thereafter from 77 per cent, in 1910-20, to 49 per cent, in 1940-50. Most of the decline in central cities was acquired by the 0-5 and the 5-10 mile zones. In fact, the proportion that accumulated within a 15-mile radius increased from 92 per cent at the beginning of the period under study to 95 per cent, in 1940-50. Central cities of metropolitan areas in the West also attracted larger shares of the increases in 1910-20 than they received in 1900-10. At the same time, however, all distance zones with the exception of the 5-10 and the 35 and over mile zones increased their shares of growth. Virtually all of the increases occurred

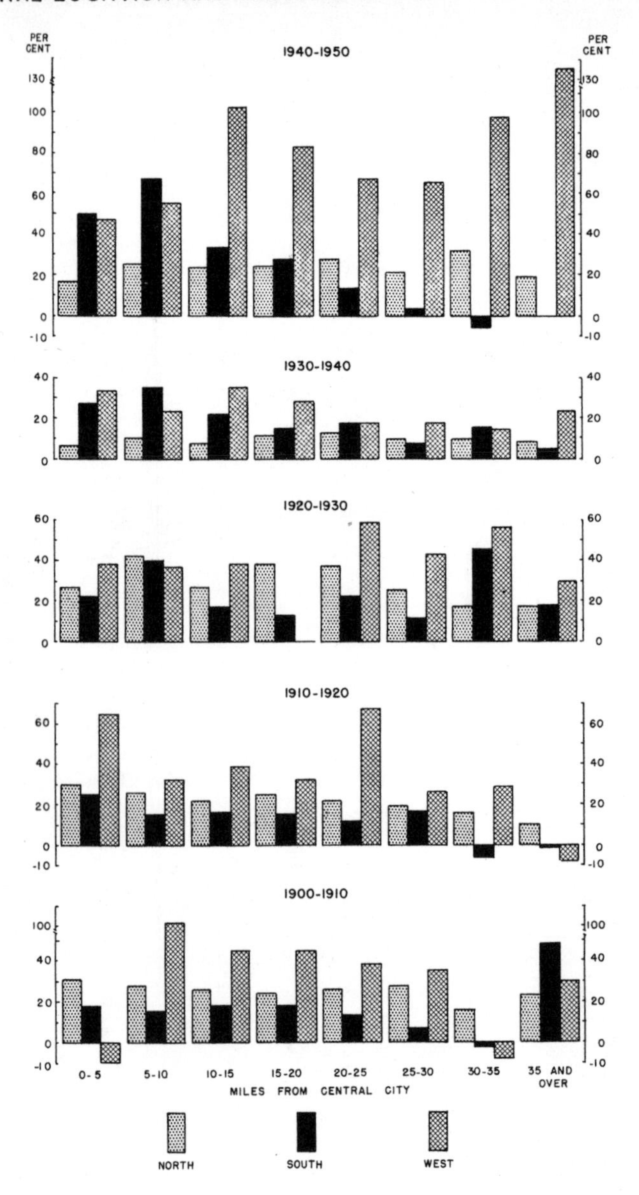


FIGURE 36.
PER CENT CHANGE OF SATELLITE POPULATION IN STANDARD METROPOLITAN AREAS, BY REGION, DISTANCE ZONE, AND DECADE, 1900 - 1950

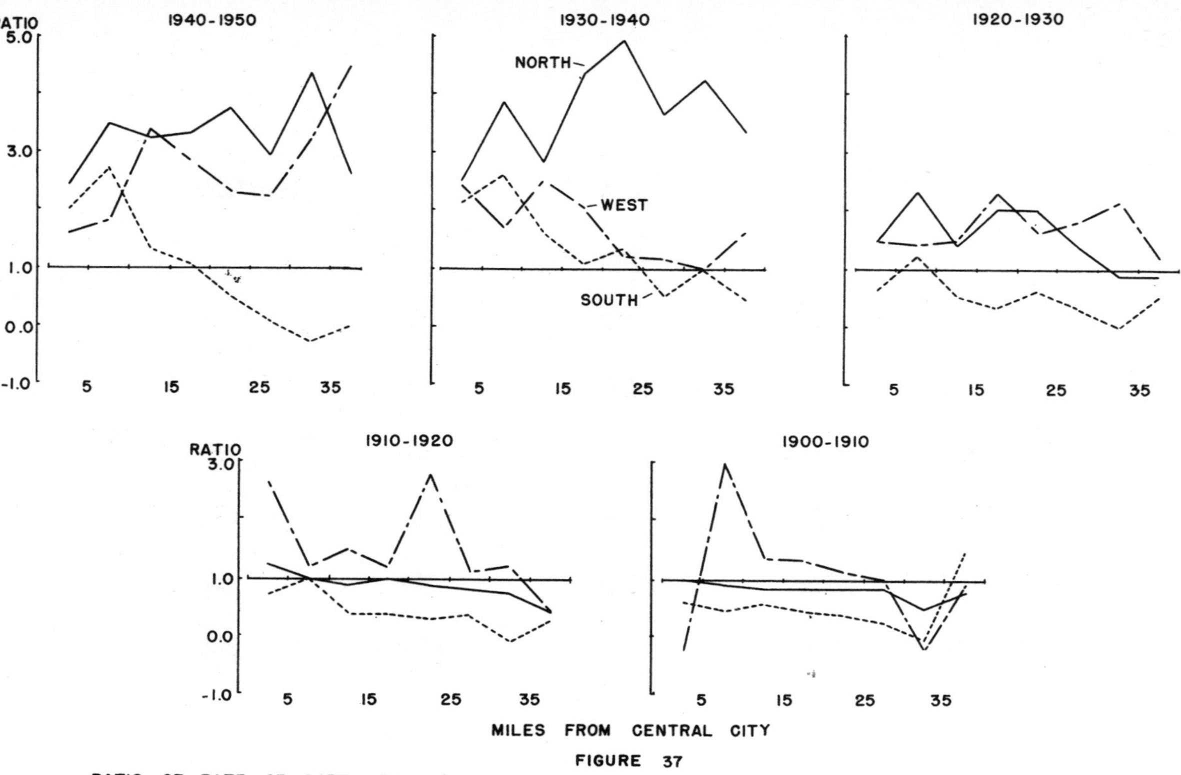


FIGURE 37

RATIO OF RATE OF SATELLITE POPULATION CHANGE TO RATE OF CENTRAL CITY CHANGE IN STANDARD METROPOLITAN AREAS, BY REGION, DISTANCE ZONE, AND DECADE, 1900-1950

## TABLE 68. CUMULATIVE PERCENTAGE DISTRIBUTION OF POPULATION INCREASE IN STANDARD METROPOLITAN AREAS, BY REGION, DISTANCE ZONE, AND DECADE, 1900 - 1950

| *Region and distance zone* | *1940-50* | *1930-40* | *1920-30* | *1910-20* | *1900-10* |
|---|---|---|---|---|---|
| North | | | | | |
| Central cities | 32.6 | 31.6 | 51.0 | 65.0 | 66.1 |
| 0 - 5 miles | 41.2 | 40.1 | 58.4 | 72.9 | 72.7 |
| 5 - 10 " | 62.1 | 61.8 | 75.5 | 82.9 | 82.2 |
| 10 - 15 " | 77.0 | 74.0 | 85.0 | 90.3 | 90.0 |
| 15 - 20 " | 85.8 | 84.4 | 91.8 | 94.5 | 93.6 |
| 20 - 25 " | 92.1 | 91.8 | 96.1 | 96.9 | 96.1 |
| 25 - 30 " | 95.2 | 95.2 | 98.0 | 98.4 | 97.8 |
| 30 - 35 " | 97.7 | 97.4 | 98.8 | 99.2 | 98.5 |
| 35 miles and over | 100.0 | 100.0 | 100.0 | 100.0 | 100.0 |
| South | | | | | |
| Central cities | 48.7 | 51.5 | 72.5 | 76.7 | 71.7 |
| 0 - 5 miles | 58.8 | 60.9 | 76.8 | 82.0 | 76.5 |
| 5 - 10 " | 86.1 | 82.2 | 89.9 | 88.4 | 84.3 |
| 10 - 15 " | 95.2 | 92.5 | 95.0 | 94.1 | 92.0 |
| 15 - 20 " | 98.9 | 96.6 | 97.2 | 97.7 | 96.7 |
| 20 - 25 " | 99.9 | 99.1 | 99.0 | 98.9 | 98.2 |
| 25 - 30 " | 100.0 | 99.6 | 99.6 | 99.8 | 98.8 |
| 30 - 35 " | 100.0 | 99.8 | 99.6 | 99.7 | 98.7 |
| 35 miles and over | 100.0 | 100.0 | 100.0 | 100.0 | 100.0 |
| West | | | | | |
| Central cities | 28.9 | 37.4 | 42.5 | 48.4 | 42.6 |
| 0 - 5 miles | 31.1 | 41.6 | 44.8 | 51.9 | 43.4 |
| 5 - 10 " | 52.4 | 63.7 | 69.1 | 76.7 | 83.2 |
| 10 - 15 " | 71.9 | 80.4 | 78.9 | 85.8 | 90.9 |
| 15 - 20 " | 85.3 | 91.6 | 86.4 | 90.2 | 94.5 |
| 20 - 25 " | 91.6 | 95.8 | 95.0 | 96.8 | 96.7 |
| 25 - 30 " | 94.1 | 97.6 | 97.3 | 98.6 | 98.3 |
| 30 - 35 " | 97.6 | 98.5 | 98.2 | 99.3 | 98.2 |
| 35 miles and over | 100.0 | 100.0 | 100.0 | 100.0 | 100.0 |

at the expense of the 5-10 mile zone which had received 41 per cent of the population increment in 1900-10. Dispersion continued to 1950. The proportion contained by a 15-mile radius, in 1900-10, was spread over an area with a 25-mile radius in 1940-50.

The distributions of the total populations changed much more slowly. In Northern metropolitan areas, as Table 69 indicates, population was increasingly concentrated between 1900 and 1920. Deconcentration followed 1920 and continued through the next 30 years. The 5-10 mile zones absorbed most of the losses from central cities. Southern metropolitan areas entered the 20th century with the lowest degree of population concentration and by 1950 they had the most highly concentrated populations. Their period of increasing concentration ended in 1930, however; but while the subsequent deconcentration was comparatively rapid, it did not reach far into satellite areas. All zones beyond 10 miles from central cities experienced declining proportions of total populations. The association of rapid growth with concentration noted in an earlier chapter does not apply to metropolitan areas in the West. Deconcentration has been continuous in the West since 1900. The proportions in all zones within 35 miles of centers increased more or less steadily after 1910. In every census year since 1910 Western metropolitan areas have had the most widely scattered populations.

Rates of redistribution, shown graphically in Fig. 38, have tended to increase in all regions. The rates of both the North and the West varied inversely with those of the South. That is to say, low rates in Northern and Western areas coincide with high rates in Southern areas, and to a lesser extent high rates in the North and West coincide with low rates in the South. These variations do not correspond to phases of concentration and deconcentration: rates fluctuated rather widely regardless of the direction taken by population redistribution. Thus the inverse correlation of Southern with Northern and Western redistribution rates poses an interesting question for speculation.

## Size and Type of Satellite Place

Regional differences likewise appeared in the growth trends in satellite places of various sizes and types. Table 70 reveals that in Northern areas all incorporated satellites had declining rates of change from 1900 to 1940. After 1940 rates increased, though in few instances did they return to levels that obtained prior to 1930-40. The largest declines occurred in incorporated places located within 10 miles of central cities.

# TABLE 69. CUMULATIVE PERCENTAGE DISTRIBUTION OF POPULATION IN STANDARD METROPOLITAN AREAS, BY REGION, DISTANCE ZONE, AND CENSUS YEAR, 1900 - 1950

| *Region and distance zone* | *1950* | *1940* | *1930* | *1920* | *1910* | *1900* |
|---|---|---|---|---|---|---|
| North | | | | | | |
| Central cities | 57.2 | 60.5 | 61.8 | 64.3 | 63.7 | 62.5 |
| 0 - 5 miles | 64.1 | 67.2 | 68.4 | 70.7 | 70.7 | 68.8 |
| 5 - 10 " | 76.5 | 78.4 | 79.4 | 80.2 | 79.6 | 78.7 |
| 10 - 15 " | 86.0 | 87.2 | 87.9 | 88.5 | 88.1 | 87.5 |
| 15 - 20 " | 91.4 | 92.1 | 92.6 | 92.7 | 92.3 | 91.9 |
| 20 - 25 " | 94.9 | 95.3 | 95.5 | 95.4 | 95.1 | 94.8 |
| 25 - 30 " | 97.0 | 97.2 | 97.4 | 97.2 | 97.0 | 96.7 |
| 30 - 35 " | 98.3 | 98.3 | 98.4 | 98.3 | 98.1 | 98.0 |
| 35 miles and over | 100.0 | 100.0 | 100.0 | 100.0 | 100.0 | 100.0 |
| South | | | | | | |
| Central cities | 59.3 | 62.6 | 66.2 | 64.2 | 60.2 | 56.4 |
| 0 - 5 miles | 66.6 | 69.0 | 72.0 | 70.3 | 66.2 | 63.1 |
| 5 - 10 " | 83.0 | 81.9 | 82.6 | 80.1 | 77.9 | 76.1 |
| 10 - 15 " | 91.9 | 90.8 | 90.6 | 89.1 | 87.8 | 87.0 |
| 15 - 20 " | 96.1 | 95.1 | 95.4 | 94.9 | 94.3 | 93.8 |
| 20 - 25 " | 98.2 | 97.6 | 97.8 | 97.4 | 97.1 | 96.9 |
| 25 - 30 " | 99.3 | 99.0 | 99.1 | 99.0 | 98.8 | 98.9 |
| 30 - 35 " | 99.5 | 99.3 | 99.4 | 99.3 | 99.2 | 99.3 |
| 35 miles and over | 100.0 | 100.0 | 100.0 | 100.0 | 100.0 | 100.0 |
| West | | | | | | |
| Central cities | 42.6 | 49.7 | 52.4 | 53.4 | 56.3 | 58.5 |
| 0 - 5 miles | 45.0 | 52.1 | 54.9 | 55.3 | 57.9 | 62.3 |
| 5 - 10 " | 65.6 | 72.3 | 73.7 | 76.6 | 81.0 | 80.5 |
| 10 - 15 " | 78.8 | 82.2 | 83.0 | 85.0 | 88.0 | 88.4 |
| 15 - 20 " | 88.9 | 90.6 | 90.7 | 89.2 | 92.1 | 92.1 |
| 20 - 25 " | 94.2 | 95.4 | 95.3 | 95.8 | 95.0 | 94.7 |
| 25 - 30 " | 96.3 | 97.4 | 97.4 | 97.5 | 97.0 | 96.9 |
| 30 - 35 " | 97.9 | 98.6 | 98.7 | 98.1 | 97.7 | 97.2 |
| 35 miles and over | 100.0 | 100.0 | 100.0 | 100.0 | 100.0 | 100.0 |

Table 70. Per Cent Change of Satellite Population in Standard Metropolitan Areas, by Size and Type of Satellite Place, Distance Zone, Region, and Decade, 1900-1950

| Size and type of place and distance zone | North | | | | | South | | | | | West | | | | |
|---|---|---|---|---|---|---|---|---|---|---|---|---|---|---|---|
| | 1940-1950 | 1930-1940 | 1920-1930 | 1910-1920 | 1900-1910 | 1940-1950 | 1930-1940 | 1920-1930 | 1910-1920 | 1900-1910 | 1940-1950 | 1930-1940 | 1920-1930 | 1910-1920 | 1900-1910 |
| 50,000 and over | | | | | | | | | | | | | | | |
| 0-10 miles | -1.3 | -1.7 | 6.4 | 12.2 | 25.1 | 57.7[a] | ---- | -16.0[a] | ---- | ---- | 26.5 | 9.3 | 34.5 | 44.0[a] | 124.3[a] |
| 10-20 miles | 4.3 | -32.8 | 12.6 | 19.2 | 35.5[a] | ---- | ---- | ---- | ---- | ---- | 48.0[a] | 15.7 | ---- | ---- | ---- |
| 20-30 miles | 21.8[a] | 10.3[a] | 81.3[a] | ---- | ---- | ---- | ---- | ---- | ---- | ---- | 10.6[a] | 2.6[a] | ---- | ---- | ---- |
| 30 miles and over | ---- | ---- | ---- | ---- | ---- | ---- | ---- | ---- | ---- | ---- | ---- | ---- | ---- | ---- | ---- |
| 10,000 - 50,000 | | | | | | | | | | | | | | | |
| 0-10 miles | 2.6 | 2.4 | 32.6 | 25.9 | 30.8 | 45.6 | 11.1 | 18.8 | 7.1 | 34.8[a] | 61.4 | 31.8 | 21.6 | 32.9 | 115.0 |
| 10-20 miles | 19.1 | 4.9 | 31.6 | 36.3 | 43.8 | 8.1 | 3.2 | 80.3[a] | 6.5[a] | 10.8 | 107.9[a] | 31.4 | 19.3 | ---- | ---- |
| 20-30 miles | 5.1 | 4.7 | 29.0 | 35.7 | 32.9 | -9.5 | 5.8 | 20.7 | 27.3 | 56.0[a] | 49.0 | 10.8 | -23.9[a] | 109.7[a] | ---- |
| 30 miles and over | 18.3 | 1.3 | 17.8 | 18.6 | 20.6 | ---- | ---- | ---- | ---- | ---- | 42.6 | 5.3 | ---- | ---- | ---- |
| 2,500 - 10,000 | | | | | | | | | | | | | | | |
| 0-10 miles | 19.1 | 5.1 | 40.5 | 46.4 | 47.8 | 66.0 | 22.7 | 35.5 | -5.9 | 16.6 | 95.3 | 30.2 | 39.6 | 12.9 | 19.1 |
| 10-20 miles | 33.8 | -20.3 | 56.1 | 30.9 | 42.7 | 46.1 | 4.8 | 8.8 | 27.2 | 47.3 | 89.0 | 32.3 | 86.5 | 53.7 | -13.1 |
| 20-30 miles | 18.5 | 6.0 | 34.6 | 17.1 | 42.4 | -43.7 | 10.5 | 28.4 | 21.3 | 8.5 | 72.2 | 11.3 | 66.1 | -7.1 | 42.0 |
| 30 miles and over | 14.9 | 3.9 | 24.4 | 18.5 | 42.9 | 17.9 | 2.8 | 12.7 | 3.1 | ---- | 67.0 | 17.7 | 62.9 | -30.1 | ---- |
| Under 2,500 | | | | | | | | | | | | | | | |
| 0-10 miles | 33.5 | 17.8 | 88.0 | 42.1 | 57.4 | 51.8 | 26.1 | 51.5 | 12.5 | 24.5 | 87.8 | 17.0 | 25.0 | 16.4 | 54.4 |
| 10-20 miles | 28.7 | 12.0 | 43.2 | 28.1 | 23.8 | 39.1 | 12.8 | 24.3 | 26.4 | 25.3 | 77.7 | 35.4 | 43.5 | 32.1 | 74.3 |
| 20-30 miles | 24.7 | 10.3 | 27.3 | 22.1 | 35.3 | 7.9 | 11.2 | 18.5 | 25.5 | 12.6 | 121.1 | 29.7 | 3.5 | 48.0 | 44.1 |
| 30 miles and over | 17.7 | 5.5 | 14.2 | 8.1 | 25.7 | -11.7 | 0.4 | -4.9 | 20.3 | 65.4 | 61.1 | 32.3 | 39.5 | 31.2 | 20.7 |
| Unincorporated area | | | | | | | | | | | | | | | |
| 0-10 miles | 49.8 | 19.6 | 45.0 | 25.6 | 22.4 | 63.6 | 36.1 | 35.5 | 21.5 | 13.9 | 76.3 | 42.8 | 47.8 | 22.5 | 40.2 |
| 10-20 miles | 33.8 | 102.6 | 28.7 | 11.5 | 13.0 | 31.3 | 22.5 | 10.7 | 13.6 | 15.7 | 109.7 | 36.4 | 31.9 | 30.2 | 44.9 |
| 20-30 miles | 40.0 | 17.5 | 30.9 | 12.0 | 16.7 | 20.6 | 15.6 | 16.0 | 9.0 | 6.9 | 90.0 | 26.5 | 53.7 | 41.0 | 33.8 |
| 30 miles and over | 30.8 | 16.2 | 15.0 | 8.8 | 13.5 | -3.2 | 8.1 | 12.5 | 3.7 | 28.4 | 182.7 | 20.0 | 26.3 | 13.1 | 27.3 |

[a] Based on less than 5 incorporated places.

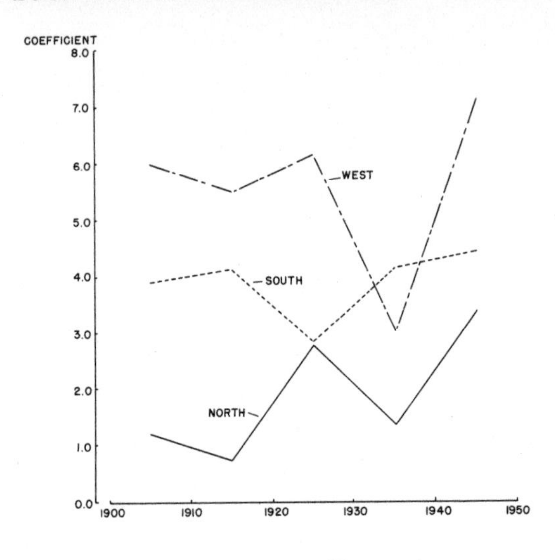


FIGURE 38.
COEFFICIENTS OF POPULATION REDISTRIBUTION IN STANDARD METROPOLITAN AREAS, BY REGION, 1900-1950

Thus most of the increases in the rates of satellite growth observed in Table 66 and Fig. 36 were a function of accelerating growth in unincorporated areas.

In the South, on the other hand, most incorporated places within 20 miles of metropolitan centers experienced increasing rates of growth, while those 20 or more miles distant had declining rates of growth. Substantial increases also occurred in unincorporated rates in zones within 30 miles of centers. Unincorporated population in the outermost zone changed with a declining rate which became a loss of population in the last decade. A centripetal tendency in the growth of population in Southern metropolitan regions is clearly manifested in these data.

A third pattern of satellite change developed in the West. Satellites of 50,000 or more population located within 10 miles of central cities sustained declining rates of change. But large satellites 10 or more miles from centers and all incorporated population of less than 10,000 population regardless of location increased their populations at progressively higher rates. Unincorporated rates followed a similar trend in all distance zones. In all classes of satellite places the largest increases occurred in the most distant zones.

The ratios of satellite rates to central city rates, shown in Table 71, describe a somewhat different pattern of change in Northern metropolitan

Table 71. Ratio of Rate of Change of Satellite Population to Central City Rate of Change in Standard Metropolitan Areas, by Size and Type of Satellite Place, Distance Zone, Region, and Decade, 1900-1950

| Size and type of place and distance zone | North | | | | | South | | | | | West | | | | |
|---|---|---|---|---|---|---|---|---|---|---|---|---|---|---|---|
| | 1940-1950 | 1930-1940 | 1920-1930 | 1910-1920 | 1900-1910 | 1940-1950 | 1930-1940 | 1920-1930 | 1910-1920 | 1900-1910 | 1940-1950 | 1930-1940 | 1920-1930 | 1910-1920 | 1900-1910 |
| 50,000 and over | | | | | | | | | | | | | | | |
| 0-10 miles | -0.2 | -0.7 | 0.3 | 0.5 | 0.8 | 2.3 | ---- | -0.5 | ---- | ---- | 0.9 | 0.7 | 1.3 | 1.8 | 3.7 |
| 10-20 miles | 0.6 | -13.1 | 0.7 | 0.8 | 1.1 | ---- | ---- | ---- | ---- | ---- | 1.6 | 1.2 | ---- | ---- | ---- |
| 20-30 miles | 3.0 | 4.1 | 4.4 | ---- | ---- | ---- | ---- | ---- | ---- | ---- | 0.4 | 0.2 | ---- | ---- | ---- |
| 30 miles and over | ---- | ---- | ---- | ---- | ---- | ---- | ---- | ---- | ---- | ---- | ---- | ---- | ---- | ---- | ---- |
| 10,000 - 50,000 | | | | | | | | | | | | | | | |
| 0-10 miles | 0.4 | 1.0 | 1.8 | 1.1 | 1.0 | 1.9 | 0.9 | 0.6 | 0.2 | 1.1 | 2.1 | 2.4 | 0.8 | 1.3 | 3.4 |
| 10-20 miles | 2.7 | 2.0 | 1.7 | 1.5 | 1.4 | 0.3 | 0.2 | 2.4 | 0.2 | 0.3 | 3.6 | 2.3 | 0.8 | ---- | ---- |
| 20-30 miles | 0.7 | 1.9 | 1.6 | 1.5 | 1.1 | -0.4 | 0.4 | 0.6 | 0.8 | 1.7 | 1.6 | 0.8 | -0.9 | 4.4 | ---- |
| 30 miles and over | 2.5 | 0.5 | 1.0 | 0.8 | 0.7 | ---- | ---- | ---- | ---- | ---- | 1.4 | 0.4 | ---- | ---- | ---- |
| 2,500 - 10,000 | | | | | | | | | | | | | | | |
| 0-10 miles | 2.7 | 2.0 | 2.2 | 1.9 | 1.5 | 2.7 | 1.7 | 1.0 | -0.2 | 0.5 | 3.2 | 2.2 | 1.5 | 0.5 | 0.6 |
| 10-20 miles | 4.7 | -8.1 | 3.0 | 1.3 | 1.4 | 1.9 | 0.4 | 0.3 | 0.8 | 1.5 | 3.0 | 2.4 | 3.4 | 2.1 | -0.4 |
| 20-30 miles | 2.6 | 2.4 | 1.9 | .7 | 1.4 | -1.8 | 0.8 | 0.8 | 0.6 | 0.3 | 2.4 | 0.8 | 2.6 | -0.3 | 1.2 |
| 30 miles and over | 2.1 | 1.6 | 1.3 | .8 | 1.4 | 0.7 | 0.2 | 0.4 | 0.1 | ---- | 2.2 | 1.3 | 2.5 | -1.2 | ---- |
| Under 2,500 | | | | | | | | | | | | | | | |
| 0-10 miles | 4.7 | 7.1 | 4.7 | 1.7 | 1.9 | 2.1 | 2.0 | 1.5 | 0.4 | 0.8 | 2.9 | 1.3 | 1.0 | 0.7 | 1.6 |
| 10-20 miles | 4.0 | 4.8 | 2.3 | 1.2 | 0.8 | 1.6 | 1.0 | 0.7 | 0.8 | 0.8 | 2.6 | 2.6 | 1.7 | 1.3 | 2.2 |
| 20-30 miles | 3.4 | 4.1 | 1.5 | 0.9 | 1.1 | 0.3 | 0.9 | 0.5 | 0.7 | 0.4 | 4.1 | 2.2 | 0.1 | 1.9 | 1.3 |
| 30 miles and over | 2.5 | 2.2 | 0.8 | 0.3 | 0.8 | -0.5 | 0.0 | -0.1 | 0.6 | 2.0 | 2.0 | 2.4 | 1.5 | 1.2 | 0.6 |
| Unincorporated area | | | | | | | | | | | | | | | |
| 0-10 miles | 6.9 | 7.8 | 2.4 | 1.1 | 0.7 | 2.6 | 2.8 | 1.0 | 0.6 | 0.4 | 2.6 | 3.2 | 1.9 | 0.9 | 1.2 |
| 10-20 miles | 4.7 | 41.0 | 1.5 | 0.5 | 0.4 | 1.3 | 1.7 | 0.3 | 0.4 | 0.5 | 3.7 | 2.7 | 1.2 | 1.2 | 1.3 |
| 20-30 miles | 5.6 | 7.0 | 1.7 | 0.5 | 0.5 | 0.8 | 1.2 | 0.5 | 0.3 | 0.2 | 3.0 | 2.0 | 2.1 | 1.6 | 1.0 |
| 30 miles and over | 4.3 | 6.5 | 0.8 | 0.4 | 0.4 | 0.1 | 0.6 | 0.4 | 0.1 | 0.9 | 6.1 | 1.5 | 1.0 | 0.5 | 0.8 |

areas. On this basis declines occurred in all satellites of 50,000 or more population and in satellites of 10,000-50,000 population located in the 0-10 and 20-30 mile zones. All other sizes and types of satellite places in all distance zones had increasing relative rates of growth. The delayed penetration of dispersion into unincorporated areas is noteworthy: not until 1920-30 did unincorporated rates rise significantly above central city rates.

The conversion of rates to ratios does not alter the pattern of change in Southern metropolitan areas observed in Table 70. Despite the high growth rates attained by satellite places in the South, their ratios are, with two exceptions, consistently below those in the North. The two exceptions are places of 10,000-50,000 and of 50,000 or more population located within 10 miles of centers. Similarly in the West the changes in relative rates correspond to the changes in absolute rates. In other words, ratios increased in all size classes and distance zones except in places of 50,000 or more population within the 0-10 mile zone.

As a consequence of differential rates of change in the satellite areas in Northern metropolitan areas, the proportions of the populations within each zone that occupied incorporated places of 2,500 or more population increased to 1920 and then declined to 1950. The proportion in unincorporated area and in the smallest class of incorporated places declined to 1930 and increased in succeeding census years. In no zone did unincorporated population ever exceed 57 per cent. By contrast, unincorporated population in Southern areas was never lower than 68 per cent and in 1900 it comprised 99 per cent of the 30 mile and over zone. As in Northern areas, unincorporated population within 20 miles of Southern metropolitan centers declined to 1930 and increased thereafter. The decline was continuous, however, 30 or more miles from centers. The proportions in incorporated places tended to follow an opposite and complementary trend. In the West the proportion of unincorporated population within 10 miles of central cities has generally been less than that in places of 50,000 or more population, and the proportions in satellites of less than 2,500 population have been negligible. Distributions in zones beyond 10 miles from Southern centers as well as the changes in those distributions have been comparable to those in other parts of the country.

Table 72. Per Cent Distribution of Satellite Population in Standard Metropolitan Areas, by Census Year, Size and Type of Place, Region, and Distance Zone, 1900-1950

| Census year and size and type of place | North | | | | South | | | | West | | | |
|---|---|---|---|---|---|---|---|---|---|---|---|---|
| | Miles from central city | | | | Miles from central city | | | | Miles fron. central city | | | |
| | 0-10 miles | 10-20 miles | 20-30 miles | 30 miles and over | 0-10 miles | 10-20 miles | 20-30 miles | 30 miles and over | 0-10 miles | 10-20 miles | 20-30 miles | 30 miles and over |
| **1950** | | | | | | | | | | | | |
| Total | 100.0 | 100.0 | 100.0 | 100.0 | 100.0 | 100.0 | 100.0 | 100.0 | 100.0 | 100.0 | 100.0 | 100.0 |
| 50,000 and over | 17.8 | 20.2 | 7.4 | 0.0 | 2.6 | 0.0 | 0.0 | 0.0 | 35.6 | 16.2 | 11.6 | 0.0 |
| 10,000 - 50,000 | 21.3 | 21.0 | 20.7 | 23.0 | 8.9 | 7.8 | 11.1 | 0.0 | 19.7 | 21.0 | 18.1 | 14.3 |
| 2,500 - 10,000 | 12.1 | 13.3 | 17.7 | 15.8 | 7.9 | 7.5 | 5.2 | 8.8 | 9.2 | 14.9 | 12.7 | 16.4 |
| Under 2,500 | 3.9 | 7.4 | 8.6 | 10.1 | 4.2 | 7.6 | 8.5 | 3.5 | 0.8 | 2.6 | 3.1 | 6.9 |
| Unincorporated area | 44.9 | 38.1 | 45.6 | 51.1 | 76.4 | 77.1 | 75.2 | 87.7 | 34.7 | 45.3 | 54.5 | 62.4 |
| **1940** | | | | | | | | | | | | |
| Total | 100.0 | 100.0 | 100.0 | 100.0 | 100.0 | 100.0 | 100.0 | 100.0 | 100.0 | 100.0 | 100.0 | 100.0 |
| 50,000 and over | 22.1 | 23.8 | 7.6 | 0.0 | 2.7 | 0.0 | 0.0 | 0.0 | 43.1 | 21.0 | 17.4 | 0.0 |
| 10,000 - 50,000 | 25.3 | 21.8 | 24.5 | 24.0 | 9.9 | 9.3 | 13.4 | 0.0 | 18.8 | 19.4 | 20.3 | 21.6 |
| 2,500 - 10,000 | 12.4 | 12.2 | 18.7 | 17.1 | 7.6 | 6.7 | 10.0 | 7.4 | 7.3 | 15.2 | 12.3 | 21.3 |
| Under 2,500 | 3.6 | 7.1 | 8.6 | 10.6 | 4.4 | 7.2 | 8.6 | 3.8 | 0.6 | 2.8 | 2.3 | 9.3 |
| Unincorporated area | 36.6 | 35.1 | 40.6 | 48.3 | 75.4 | 76.8 | 68.0 | 88.8 | 30.2 | 41.6 | 47.7 | 47.8 |
| **1930** | | | | | | | | | | | | |
| Total | 100.0 | 100.0 | 100.0 | 100.0 | 100.0 | 100.0 | 100.0 | 100.0 | 100.0 | 100.0 | 100.0 | 100.0 |
| 50,000 and over | 23.6 | 37.3 | 7.5 | 0.0 | 0.0 | 0.0 | 0.0 | 0.0 | 48.7 | 17.2 | 19.9 | 0.0 |
| 10,000 - 50,000 | 25.3 | 22.6 | 24.4 | 25.5 | 11.5 | 8.9 | 12.6 | 0.0 | 15.1 | 20.1 | 18.0 | 24.2 |
| 2,500 - 10,000 | 12.1 | 12.2 | 19.8 | 17.1 | 9.4 | 6.9 | 8.2 | 4.0 | 8.3 | 15.9 | 13.8 | 15.3 |
| Under 2,500 | 3.6 | 7.4 | 8.9 | 12.1 | 4.9 | 8.1 | 8.1 | 3.9 | 1.1 | 3.5 | 4.7 | 13.6 |
| Unincorporated area | 35.4 | 20.5 | 39.4 | 45.3 | 74.2 | 76.1 | 71.1 | 92.1 | 26.8 | 43.3 | 43.6 | 46.9 |
| **1920** | | | | | | | | | | | | |
| Total | 100.0 | 100.0 | 100.0 | 100.0 | 100.0 | 100.0 | 100.0 | 100.0 | 100.0 | 100.0 | 100.0 | 100.0 |
| 50,000 and over | 18.8 | 22.6 | 3.3 | 0.0 | 4.3 | 0.0 | 0.0 | 0.0 | 62.5 | 0.0 | 0.0 | 0.0 |
| 10,000 - 50,000 | 26.9 | 21.1 | 26.9 | 22.6 | 7.3 | 4.6 | 12.2 | ----- | 6.6 | 7.2 | 13.6 | 0.0 |
| 2,500 - 10,000 | 13.8 | 12.4 | 17.6 | 16.2 | 8.8 | 5.4 | 4.4 | 4.0 | 5.4 | 21.8 | 8.7 | 16.5 |
| Under 2,500 | 5.2 | 9.0 | 11.3 | 12.5 | 4.2 | 8.5 | 9.4 | 4.1 | 2.5 | 11.8 | 3.6 | 22.4 |
| Unincorporated area | 35.3 | 34.9 | 40.9 | 48.7 | 75.4 | 81.5 | 74.0 | 91.9 | 23.0 | 59.2 | 74.1 | 61.1 |
| **1910** | | | | | | | | | | | | |
| Total | 100.0 | 100.0 | 100.0 | 100.0 | 100.0 | 100.0 | 100.0 | 100.0 | 100.0 | 100.0 | 100.0 | 100.0 |
| 50,000 and over | 20.8 | 19.6 | 0.0 | 0.0 | 0.0 | 0.0 | 0.0 | 0.0 | 44.0 | 0.0 | 0.0 | 0.0 |
| 10,000 - 50,000 | 20.3 | 19.1 | 24.2 | 19.9 | 11.7 | 1.3 | 8.1 | 0.0 | 18.7 | 0.0 | 14.9 | 0.0 |
| 2,500 - 10,000 | 14.3 | 11.1 | 18.9 | 14.9 | 5.2 | 6.0 | 6.1 | 4.3 | 4.2 | 21.6 | 4.3 | 10.0 |
| Under 2,500 | 5.9 | 10.6 | 14.4 | 13.7 | 5.8 | 8.2 | 9.8 | 3.1 | 2.7 | 14.1 | 15.1 | 26.5 |
| Unincorporated area | 38.7 | 39.6 | 42.5 | 51.5 | 77.3 | 84.5 | 76.0 | 92.6 | 30.4 | 64.3 | 65.7 | 63.5 |
| **1900** | | | | | | | | | | | | |
| Total | 100.0 | 100.0 | 100.0 | 100.0 | 100.0 | 100.0 | 100.0 | 100.0 | 100.0 | 100.0 | 100.0 | 100.0 |
| 50,000 and over | 16.5 | 13.1 | 0.0 | 0.0 | 0.0 | 0.0 | 0.0 | 0.0 | 35.6 | 0.0 | 0.0 | 0.0 |
| 10,000 - 50,000 | 20.8 | 17.3 | 12.6 | 15.8 | 8.2 | 1.4 | 5.8 | 0.0 | 15.8 | 0.0 | 0.0 | 0.0 |
| 2,500 - 10,000 | 10.0 | 10.0 | 19.2 | 13.2 | 4.6 | 5.3 | 6.4 | 0.0 | 1.9 | 6.9 | 17.5 | 0.0 |
| Under 2,500 | 6.1 | 10.5 | 15.2 | 14.3 | 4.5 | 5.7 | 6.5 | 1.2 | 2.6 | 11.0 | 11.9 | 24.8 |

CHAPTER X

# SUMMARY

## All Metropolitan Areas

Population growth declined in all metropolitan areas between 1900 and 1950. A larger decline occurred in Standard than in Extended Metropolitan Areas. With the declining rates of change occurred a shift of growth from central cities to satellite areas; that is, the decreasing rates of increase were functions mainly of the slowing growth of central cities, for growth rates in satellite areas increased over the 50-year period. As a consequence of certain historical factors the trend lines were not smooth curves, however.

When growth rates are plotted by distance zones the result for Extended Metropolitan Areas is a fairly uniform gradient, i.e., rates decline with distance from central city. No such gradient appears in the data for Standard Metropolitan Areas. It is to be inferred, therefore, that the definition of the Standard Metropolitan Area is selective of the most rapidly growing parts of satellite areas. In other words that concept of metropolitan area encompasses the parts of outlying area that are most immediately responsive to developments in the central city.

The scope of metropolitan influence, as measured both by the ratios of metropolitan area growth rates to total United States rates and by the ratios of zonal rates to central city rates, was progressively extended in the decades since 1900-10. Approximately 25 to 30 miles were added to the radius of metropolitan influence.

Redistribution of population moved toward concentration from 1900 to 1920, and toward dispersion from 1920 to 1950. A conclusion from this as well as from observation of changes in growth rates in central cities and in distance zones, is that metropolitan development in the first half of the 20th century involved, first, a rapid growth of centers at the expense of satellite areas, and, subsequently, a centrifugal movement to satellite areas to the detriment of growth in central cities. It is probable that the maturation of centers is a requisite to the expansion of settlement in satellite areas.

Indirect support of these inferences is found in the changes of growth rates in different sizes and types of satellite places. Incorporated places of 25,000 or more, most of which are located within 10 miles of central cities, had declining rates of growth from 1900 to 1950. Declining rates appeared in smaller incorporated satellites in later decades. Beginning in 1920 growth rates in unincorporated areas accelerated rapidly. Thus nearly all of the increased growth of total satellite population after 1920 took place in unincorporated area.

## Size of Central City

The absence of a clear relationship of metropolitan growth with size of central city is due partly to the facts that growth of central cities varied inversely with size while the growth of satellite areas varied directly with size of central city. In general, the rates of change in central cities declined during the 50 years, the greatest declines having occurred in the largest and in the smallest size classes. Satellite rates followed a trend of increase in all but the 1,000,000 and over size class. Although growth rates correlate negatively with density, the coefficients are not large enough to have explanatory value.

The larger the size of the central city the more extensive has been the part of the satellite area over which growth rates have exceeded the average growth of the total population of the nation. This is also true of the satellite rates as compared to central city rates. The relationship between size of central city and dispersion is evident again in the spread of decennial population increments.

Growth rates in different sizes and types of satellite places varied more or less directly with size of central city. The relationship was least equivocal where small incorporated places and unincorporated areas were concerned. Rates of change in incorporated places of 25,000 or more population declined, and in unincorporated areas the trend was toward increase. The highest rates of change in incorporated population occurred in zones between 10 and 20 miles from central cities. Ratios of satellite rates to central city rates were more closely related to size of central city than were the rates themselves.

## Average Annual Growth Rate of Central City

Satellite as well as total populations have grown most slowly in areas whose central cities have had the lowest annual rate of growth, and most rapidly where central cities have increased at the highest rates. Relative growth rates, however, reveal an inverse relationship with average annual

rate of central city growth. Ratios for distance zones in areas with slowly growing central cities have been consistently at or above unity. On the other hand, the 1930-40 decade was the first in which the ratio for any distance zone in areas with rapidly growing central cities exceeded unity. The dispersion of population increments was greater as measured both by the distance of the spread and the amounts involved where the average annual rate of central city growth was lowest. Deconcentration began earliest in areas with lowest rates of central city growth and latest in areas of highest rates of growth in central cities. Control of size of central city introduces no qualifications of these observations. The differentials among metropolitan areas distinguished by average annual rate of central city growth also occurred in the growth trends of various sizes and types of satellite places.

Deconcentration was directed mainly toward small incorporated places and unincorporated area. Further, satellite growth has been an inverse function of central city growth.

### Distance between Central Cities

Growth rates varied directly with distance between central cities. That relationship was characteristic of all distance zones after 1910. Until 1920 the differences between relative growth rates of satellite areas were negligible. Following 1920 the highest ratios developed in areas the central cities of which were within 50 miles of other central cities. The more isolated areas had the lowest ratios of satellite growth. The outlying zones of areas 50 to 100 miles from other areas, however, had higher ratios than did similar zones in areas within 50 miles of other areas, in both 1910-20 and 1940-50. The less the distance between central cities the smaller was the proportion of all increase gained by central cities and the larger was the share received by satellite area. Nevertheless, the percentage distributions of population indicate that deconcentration began a decade earlier (1920) in areas 50-100 miles removed from other areas than in those located within 50 miles of other areas.

Some of the irregularities observed in the relationship between redistribution tendencies and proximity of central cities to one another were due to unequal weighting by size of central city. When the rates are standardized for size of central city, deconcentration is found to have been inversely related to distance between central cities. The change in the relative growth rates of satellite places conform to that relationship.

## Selected Geographic Features

The lowest rates of change in all decades occurred in areas at river locations, and the highest rates were experienced in metropolitan areas at other than water locations. While that was true also of central city rates, it did not apply to satellite rates. Areas with central cities located on sea or lake coasts maintained the highest satellite rates in every decade but 1930-40. Relative growth rates have been highest, particularly in zones beyond 15 miles from centers, in coastal areas, and lowest in areas at other than water locations.

The dispersion of growth in coastal locations has proceeded without interruption from 1900 to 1950. In the other location classes dispersion was more limited and was occasionally reversed. Despite continuous deconcentration in areas at coastal locations, the central cities of such areas, in every census year until 1950, contained a larger proportion of their area populations than did central cities at other locations. Although the concentration phase of population redistribution in areas at other than water locations ended in 1930, in 1950 those areas had the most highly concentrated populations. Differences in size of central city were not responsible for the variations in population redistribution among the three location classes.

In areas at river locations deconcentration progressed most rapidly on the central city side, though after 1930 rivers appear to have lost much of their barrier effect on population redistribution.

All satellite places of less than 50,000 population in areas at coastal locations increased their relative growth rates. But in the other location classes increases were confined to the small places within 20 miles of centers.

Until 1930 growth was most rapid in satellite places served by both highways and railways. After 1930 the importance of the railway for intra-area transportation diminished, for the highest rates passed to places located on highways only. Low rates of growth and frequent population losses occurred in areas with only railway and with neither railway nor highway access to central cities.

## Proportion of Population Employed in Manufacturing

The populations of metropolitan areas with low proportions employed in manufacturing in 1948 have grown most rapidly, while those with the largest proportions so employed have grown at the lowest rates. Average areas had the highest satellite rates in 1900-10, manufacturing areas

gained most rapidly in 1910-20 and 1920-30, and in the last two decades the satellite populations of non-manufacturing areas grew at the fastest rates. The relative growth rates of satellite population in manufacturing areas exceeded those of other classes after 1920; the lowest ratios occurred in non-manufacturing areas. Ratios increased, however, in all distance zones of all classes of areas. Decennial increments were distributed more widely in succeeding decades, particularly in manufacturing areas. Areas with high proportions employed in manufacturing had the most concentrated populations in every census year, but the amount of deconcentration after 1920 also exceeded that in other classes of areas. The least concentration of population obtained in non-manufacturing areas. With one or two exceptions the observed association of redistribution with the proportion of population employed in manufacturing was repeated in each size class

### Industrial Relocation

Rates of population change were low in metropolitan areas in which industry has been deconcentrating and high in areas where there has been no clear trend of industrial relocation. The differences, however, were small. Central city rates varied as did rates for the total populations. Satellite rates were highest in areas of industrial deconcentration from 1900 to 1930, and after that the highest rates occurred in areas of no clear industrial relocation trend. In areas of concentration satellite rates declined to 1940 and then increased in the last decade. Growth has been widely dispersed in deconcentrating areas since 1900. On the other hand, growth has concentrated increasingly in concentrating areas. As was expected, the highest ratios of satellite growth to central city growth occurred in deconcentrating areas, while the lowest ratios were found in areas of industrial concentration. The differences in the tendencies to dispersion are reflected also in the changing distributions of population increments. The most concentrated as well as the most rapidly deconcentrating population was that of areas of industrial dispersion. Areas in which industry has been moving centripetally had a more concentrated population at the end than at the beginning of the 50-year period. No significant deviations from these generalizations appeared when size of central city was controlled.

All sizes and types of satellite places experienced declining rates of change in areas of industrial concentration, especially in zones 10 or more miles from centers. Industrial deconcentration accelerated satellite growth only in unincorporated area. The satellite population of

deconcentrating areas has been more concentrated in incorporated places than has that of either of the other industrial relocation classes.

## Regional Location

The most rapidly growing metropolitan areas, since 1900, have been those in the West, while the lowest rates of growth occurred in Northern areas. But while the relative growth of satellite areas was highest in the West, from 1900 to 1920, the North has led in that respect since 1920. Ratios of satellite growth to central city growth have been consistently low in the South.

Whereas decennial increments to metropolitan populations were spread more and more widely in Northern and Western areas, they were concentrated increasingly in the 0-5 and 5-10 mile zones in Southern areas.

In every census year since 1910 metropolitan areas in the West have had the most widely scattered population. Deconcentration has been the dominating trend in population redistribution within Western areas since the beginning of the century. That trend began in Northern areas in 1920 and in Southern areas in 1930.

Regional differences in redistribution tendencies remain when size of central city is controlled. They appear also in the data on rates of change in all sizes and types of satellite places.

## A Comparison of Variables

It has been observed that all variables studied are associated with differences in population redistribution within metropolitan areas. Table 73 provides a partial summary of the findings. The characteristics related to the highest ratios of satellite growth to central city growth are contrasted with the characteristics associated with the lowest ratios of satellite to central city growth. Although the differences between high and low ratios vary from decade to decade, in all but five instances the former exceeds the latter by 50 per cent or more.

In no one metropolitan area are combined all of the characteristics that make for high ratios of satellite growth. And in only two metropolitan areas -- Amarillo and Jackson, Miss. -- do all factors related to low ratios of satellite growth coincide.[1] An approximation of the effect of such a coincidence, however, may be gained by observing the ratios in individual areas in which are combined five or more of the seven high ratio factors or a like number of low ratio factors. Table 74 lists the metropolitan areas that have the given number of characteristics. It is

TABLE 73. RATIO OF RATE OF CHANGE OF SATELLITE POPULATION TO CENTRAL CITY RATE OF CHANGE IN STANDARD METROPOLITAN AREAS, BY RATIO LEVEL, CHARACTERISTIC, AND DECADE, 1900 - 1950

| *Ratio level and characteristics of metropolitan areas* | *1940-50* | *1930-40* | *1920-30* | *1910-20* | *1900-10* |
|---|---|---|---|---|---|
| High ratio | | | | | |
| Central city with 500,000-1,000,000 population | 4.1 | 10.1 | 2.9 | 1.1 | 1.6 |
| Low average annual rate of central city growth | 3.5 | 10.0 | 2.3 | 1.1 | 1.2 |
| Central city within 50 miles of other central cities | 2.7 | 3.8 | 1.8 | 0.8 | 0.9 |
| Central city at sea or lake coast location | 3.5 | 2.3 | 1.8 | 1.1 | 1.1 |
| High proportion employed in manufacturing | 3.7 | 11.4 | 1.8 | 0.8 | 0.7 |
| Industry deconcentrating | 3.2 | 2.3 | 1.6 | 1.0 | 1.0 |
| North | 3.2 | 3.5 | 1.7 | 1.0 | 0.7 |
| Low ratio | | | | | |
| Central city with less than 100,000 population | 1.3 | 1.7 | 0.6 | 0.4 | 0.4 |
| High average annual rate of central city growth | 1.8 | 2.2 | 0.7 | 0.4 | 0.2 |
| Central city 100 or more miles of other central cities | 1.8 | 1.9 | 0.6 | 0.8 | 0.7 |
| Central city at other than water location | 1.7 | 2.3 | 0.7 | 0.4 | 0.3 |
| Low proportion employed in manufacturing | 1.7 | 1.4 | 0.6 | 0.5 | 0.7 |
| Industry concentrating | 1.5 | 2.4 | 0.6 | 0.5 | 0.6 |
| South | 1.8 | 1.8 | 0.7 | 0.5 | 0.5 |

## TABLE 74. RATIOS OF RATE OF CHANGE IN SATELLITE POPULATION TO CENTRAL CITY RATE OF CHANGE IN STANDARD METROPOLITAN AREAS WITH FIVE OR MORE LOW RATIO FACTORS, BY DECADE, 1900-1950

| *Ratio level and metropolitan area* | *1940-50* | *1930-40* | *1920-30* | *1910-20* | *1900-10* |
|---|---|---|---|---|---|
| High ratio | | | | | |
| Baltimore | 6.9 | 3.7 | 5.4 | --[a] | 2.5 |
| Boston | 2.7 | --[b] | 5.5 | 2.3 | 1.2 |
| Buffalo | 47.3 | 25.9 | 2.8 | 1.3 | 1.3 |
| Chicago | 4.7 | 16.6 | 2.4 | 1.9 | 1.5 |
| Cleveland | 9.9 | 5.2 | 8.9 | 2.3 | 0.7 |
| Galveston | 13.7 | 5.1 | 1.5 | 0.9 | --[c] |
| Milwaukee | 3.6 | 13.8 | 3.3 | 1.7 | 1.1 |
| Philadelphia | 3.6 | 69.3 | 4.7 | 1.3 | 1.0 |
| Pittsburgh | 11.1 | 14.3 | 2.7 | 2.5 | 3.3 |
| Reading | --[d] | --[e] | 9.5 | 0.6 | 0.4 |
| San Francisco | 3.5 | --[f] | 1.7 | 1.9 | 3.6 |
| Wheeling | --[g] | --[h] | 1.6 | 1.2 | 5.2 |
| York | 3.1 | 3.2 | 0.9 | 0.9 | 0.3 |
| Low ratio | | | | | |
| Amarillo | 0.7 | 0.1 | 0.6 | 0.3 | 0.6 |
| Corpus Christi | | 0.4 | 0.6 | | |
| Fresno | 1.1 | 1.8 | 0.6 | 0.8 | 1.0 |
| Jackson, Miss. | --[i] | 0.8 | 0.1 | --[j] | 0.0 |
| Lubbock | | 0.1 | 0.4 | 2.9 | |
| Phoenix | 1.4 | 0.5 | 1.1 | | |
| Shreveport | --[k] | 0.3 | 0.5 | 0.5 | 0.1 |
| Sioux Falls | 0.3 | --[l] | 0.1 | 0.1 | 0.4 |

[a] Central city rate 31.4; satellite rate -27.0.
[b] Central city rate -1.3; satellite rate 3.4.
[c] Central city rate -2.1; satellite rate 19.0.
[d] Central city rate -1.1; satellite rate 11.5.
[e] Central city rate -0.5; satellite rate 8.9.
[f] Central city rate 0.0; satellite rate 16.0.
[g] Central city rate -3.7; satellite rate -2.6.
[h] Central city rate -0.9; satellite rate 5.8.
[i] Central city rate 58.2; satellite rate -12.8.
[j] Central city rate 7.3; satellite rate -19.2.
[k] Central city rate 29.6; satellite rate -5.2.
[l] Central city rate 21.0; satellite rate -3.7.

immediately apparent that in all metropolitan areas possessing five or more more high ratio factors, except for York, the ratios are in three or more decades well above those shown for high ratio areas in Table 73. In most of those rapid dispersion to satellite areas began after 1920. On the other hand, ratios for the low ratio areas are considerably below in most instances the ratios shown for the corresponding level in Table 73. The Fresno and Phoenix metropolitan areas alone show any tendency toward the development of population drift to satellite areas.

# APPENDIX

Appendix table 1. Characteristics of Metropolitan Areas

| Metropolitan area | Size of central city | | | | | Growth rate Ave. annual 1900-1950 | Distance between central cities (Miles) | Geographic feature | Proportion of population employed in manufacturing | Direction of industrial relocation | Regional location |
|---|---|---|---|---|---|---|---|---|---|---|---|
| | 1940-[a] 1950 | 1930-[a] 1940 | 1920-[a] 1930 | 1910-[a] 1920 | 1900-[a] 1910 | | | | | | |
| Akron | 4 | 3 | 4 | 5 | 5 | High | Within 50 | Other | High | Deconcentrating | North |
| Albany - Schnectady | 4 | 4 | 4 | 4 | 5 | Low | 50 - 100 | River | Average | Deconcentrating | North |
| Albuquerque | -[b] | 5 | 5 | 5 | 5 | High | 100 or more | Other | Low | Deconcentrating | West |
| Allentown - Bethlehem | 4 | 4 | 4 | 5 | 5 | Med. | Within 50 | River | High | No clear trend | North |
| Altoona | 5 | 5 | 5 | 5 | 5 | Low | Within 50 | Other | Low | ------ | North |
| Amarillo | 5 | 5 | 5 | 5 | 5 | High | 100 or more | Other | Low | Concentrating | South |
| Asheville | 5 | 5 | 5 | 5 | 5 | Med. | 50 - 100 | Other | Average | Deconcentrating | South |
| Atlanta | 3 | 3 | 4 | 4 | 5 | Med. | 50 - 100 | Other | Average | Deconcentrating | South |
| Atlantic City | 5 | 5 | 5 | 5 | 5 | Med. | 50 - 100 | Coast | Low | No clear trend | North |
| Augusta | 5 | 5 | 5 | 5 | 5 | Low | 50 - 100 | Other | Low | Deconcentrating | South |
| Austin | 5 | 5 | 5 | 5 | 5 | High | 50 - 100 | Other | Low | No clear trend | South |
| Baltimore | 2 | 2 | 2 | 2 | 2 | Low | Within 50 | Coast | High | Deconcentrating | South |
| Baton Rouge | - | 5 | 5 | 5 | 5 | High | 50 - 100 | River | Low | No clear trend | South |
| Bay City | 5 | 5 | 5 | 5 | 5 | Low | Within 50 | Coast | Average | No clear trend | North |
| Beaumont - Port Arthur | - | 4 | 5 | 5 | 5 | High | 50 - 100 | River | Average | No clear trend | South |
| Binghamton | 5 | 5 | 5 | 5 | 5 | Low | 50 - 100 | River | High | Deconcentrating | North |
| Birmingham | 3 | 3 | 4 | 4 | 5 | High | 50 - 100 | Other | Average | No clear trend | South |
| Boston | 2 | 2 | 2 | 2 | 2 | Low | Within 50 | Coast | - | - | North |
| Bridgeport | 4 | 4 | 4 | 4 | 5 | Med. | Within 50 | Coast | - | - | North |
| Brockton | 5 | 5 | 5 | 5 | 5 | Low | Within 50 | Other | - | - | North |
| Buffalo | 2 | 2 | 2 | 3 | 3 | Low | 50 - 100 | Coast | High | Deconcentrating | North |
| Canton | 4 | 4 | 5 | 5 | 5 | Med. | Within 50 | Other | High | Concentrating | North |
| Cedar Rapids | 5 | 5 | 5 | 5 | 5 | Med. | Within 50 | Other | Average | Concentrating | North |
| Charleston, S.C. | 5 | 5 | 5 | 5 | 5 | Low | 50 - 100 | Coast | Low | Deconcentrating | South |
| Charleston, W.V. | 5 | 5 | 5 | 5 | 5 | High | Within 50 | River | Low | - | North |
| Charlotte | 4 | 5 | 5 | 5 | 5 | High | 50 - 100 | Other | Average | Deconcentrating | South |
| Chattanooga | - | 4 | 5 | 5 | 5 | High | 100 or more | River | High | No clear trend | South |
| Chicago | 1 | 1 | 1 | 1 | 1 | Low | 50 - 100 | Coast | High | Deconcentrating | North |
| Cincinnati | 3 | 3 | 3 | 3 | 3 | Low | Within 50 | River | Average | Deconcentrating | North |
| Cleveland | 2 | 2 | 2 | 2 | 3 | Med. | Within 50 | Coast | High | Deconcentrating | North |
| Columbia | 5 | 5 | 5 | 5 | 5 | High | 50 - 100 | Other | Low | Deconcentrating | South |
| Columbus, Ga. | 5 | 5 | 5 | 5 | 5 | High | 50 - 100 | Other | Low | Deconcentrating | South |
| Columbus, O. | 3 | 3 | 4 | 4 | 4 | Med. | Within 50 | Other | Average | Deconcentrating | North |
| Corpus Christi | - | 5 | 5 | - | - | High | 100 or more | Coast | Low | | South |

Appendix table 1 (cont'd). Characteristics of Metropolitan Areas

| Metropolitan area | Size of central city | | | | | Growth rate Ave. annual 1900-1950 | Distance between central cities (Miles) | Geographic feature | Proportion of population employed in manufacturing | Direction of industrial relocation | Regional location |
|---|---|---|---|---|---|---|---|---|---|---|---|
| | 1940-[a] 1950 | 1930-[a] 1940 | 1920-[a] 1930 | 1910-[a] 1920 | 1900-[a] 1910 | | | | | | |
| Dallas | - | 3 | 4 | 5 | 5 | High | Within 50 | Other | Low | Concentrating | South |
| Davenport - Rock Island Moline | 5 | 5 | 5 | 5 | 5 | Low | 50 - 100 | River | High | No clear trend | North |
| Dayton | 4 | 4 | 4 | 4 | 5 | Med. | Within 50 | Other | High | No clear trend | North |
| Decatur | 5 | 5 | 5 | 5 | 5 | Med. | Within 50 | Other | Average | No clear trend | North |
| Denver | - | - | - | - | - | -- | --- | --- | --- | ---- | --- |
| Des Moines | 4 | 4 | 4 | 5 | 5 | Med. | 50 - 100 | Other | Low | Concentrating | North |
| Detroit | 1 | 1 | 1 | 3 | 3 | High | 50 - 100 | Coast | High | No clear trend | North |
| Duluth - Superior | 4 | 4 | 5 | 5 | 5 | Med. | 100 or more | Coast | Low | Concentrating | North |
| Durham | 5 | 5 | 5 | 5 | 5 | High | Within 50 | Other | High | Concentrating | South |
| El Paso | - | - | - | - | - | -- | --- | --- | --- | ---- | --- |
| Erie | 4 | 4 | 5 | 5 | 5 | Med. | 50 - 100 | Coast | High | Deconcentrating | North |
| Evansville | 5 | 5 | 5 | 5 | 5 | Low | 100 or more | River | High | Concentrating | North |
| Fall River | 4 | 4 | 4 | 4 | 4 | Low | Within 50 | Coast | --- | ---- | North |
| Flint | 4 | 4 | 5 | 5 | 5 | High | Within 50 | Other | High | Concentrating | North |
| Fort Wayne | 4 | 4 | 5 | 5 | 5 | High | 50 - 100 | Other | Average | No clear trend | North |
| Fort Worth | 4 | 4 | 4 | 5 | 5 | High | Within 50 | Other | Low | No clear trend | South |
| Fresno | 5 | 5 | 5 | 5 | 5 | High | 100 or more | Other | Low | ---- | West |
| Gadsden | 5 | 5 | 5 | 5 | 5 | High | 50 - 100 | Other | High | Concentrating | South |
| Galveston | 5 | 5 | 5 | 5 | 5 | Low | Within 50 | Coast | Low | Deconcentrating | South |
| Grand Rapids | 4 | 4 | 4 | 4 | 5 | Low | 50 - 100 | Other | High | Deconcentrating | North |
| Green Bay | 5 | 5 | 5 | 5 | 5 | Med. | 100 or more | Coast | Average | No clear trend | North |
| Greensboro - High Point | 5 | 5 | 5 | 5 | 5 | High | 50 - 100 | Other | High | Deconcentrating | South |
| Greenville | 5 | 5 | 5 | 5 | 5 | High | 50 - 100 | Other | High | No clear trend | South |
| Hamilton - Middletown | 5 | 5 | 5 | 5 | 5 | Med. | Within 50 | Other | High | No clear trend | North |
| Harrisburg | 5 | 5 | 5 | 5 | 5 | Low | Within 50 | River | Average | Deconcentrating | North |
| Hartford | 4 | 4 | 4 | 5 | 5 | Med. | Within 50 | River | --- | ---- | North |
| Houston | 3 | 3 | 4 | 5 | 5 | High | Within 50 | Coast | Low | Deconcentrating | South |
| Huntington - Ashland | 5 | 5 | 5 | 5 | 5 | High | Within 50 | River | Average | Concentrating | North |
| Indianapolis | 3 | 3 | 3 | 4 | 4 | Med. | 50 - 100 | Other | Average | Deconcentrating | North |
| Jackson, Mich. | 5 | 5 | 5 | 5 | 5 | Low | Within 50 | Other | Average | Deconcentrating | North |
| Jackson, Miss. | 5 | 5 | 5 | 5 | 5 | High | 100 or more | Other | Low | Concentrating | South |
| Jacksonville | - | - | - | - | - | -- | --- | --- | --- | ---- | South |
| Johnstown | 5 | 5 | 5 | 5 | 5 | Low | Within 50 | Other | Low | Concentrating | North |
| Kalamazoo | 5 | 5 | 5 | 5 | 5 | Med. | Within 50 | Other | High | Deconcentrating | North |

Appendix table 1 (cont'd). Characteristics of Metropolitan Areas

| Metropolitan area | Size of central city 1940-1950[a] | 1930-1940[a] | 1920-1930[a] | 1910-1920[a] | 1900-1910[a] | Growth rate Ave. annual 1900-1950 | Distance between central cities (Miles) | Geographic feature | Proportion of population employed in manufacturing | Direction of industrial relocation | Regional location |
|---|---|---|---|---|---|---|---|---|---|---|---|
| Kansas City | 2 | 2 | 3 | 3 | 3 | Med. | Within 50 | River | High | Deconcentrating | North |
| Kenosha | 5 | 5 | 5 | 5 | 5 | High | Within 50 | Coast | High | No clear trend | North |
| Knoxville | - | 4 | 5 | 5 | 5 | Med. | 50 - 100 | Other | Average | Deconcentrating | South |
| Lancaster | 5 | 5 | 5 | 5 | 5 | Low | Within 50 | Other | High | No clear trend | North |
| Lansing | 5 | 5 | 5 | 5 | 5 | High | Within 50 | Other | High | No clear trend | North |
| Laredo | - | 5 | 5 | 5 | 5 | Med. | 100 or more | Coast | -- | ---- | South |
| Lawrence | 5 | 5 | 5 | 5 | 5 | Med. | Within 50 | River | -- | ---- | North |
| Lexington | 5 | 5 | 5 | 5 | 5 | Low | 50 - 100 | Other | Low | No clear trend | South |
| Lima | 5 | 5 | 5 | 5 | 5 | Med. | 50 - 100 | Other | Average | Concentrating | North |
| Lincoln | 5 | 5 | 5 | 5 | 5 | Med. | 50 - 100 | Other | Low | Concentrating | North |
| Little Rock | 5 | 5 | 5 | 5 | 5 | Med. | 100 or more | River | Low | No clear trend | South |
| Lorain - Elyria | 5 | 5 | 5 | 5 | 5 | Med. | Within 50 | Coast | Average | No clear trend | North |
| Los Angeles | 1 | 1 | - | - | - | High | 50 - 100 | Coast | High | Deconcentrating | West |
| Louisville | 3 | 3 | 4 | 4 | 4 | Low | 50 - 100 | River | Average | Deconcentrating | South |
| Lowell | 4 | 4 | 4 | 4 | 5 | Low | Within 50 | River | -- | ---- | North |
| Lubbock | - | 5 | 5 | 5 | - | High | 100 or more | Other | -- | ---- | South |
| Macon | 5 | 5 | 5 | 5 | 5 | Med. | 50 - 100 | Other | Average | Deconcentrating | South |
| Madison | 5 | 5 | 5 | 5 | 5 | High | 50 - 100 | Other | Low | Concentrating | North |
| Manchester | 5 | 5 | 5 | 5 | 5 | Low | Within 50 | River | -- | No clear trend | North |
| Memphis | 3 | 3 | 4 | 4 | 4 | Med. | 100 or more | River | Average | No clear trend | North |
| Miami | - | - | - | - | - | -- | ---- | -- | -- | ---- | --- |
| Milwaukee | 2 | 2 | 3 | 3 | 3 | Med. | Within 50 | Coast | High | Deconcentrating | North |
| Minneapolis - St. Paul | 2 | 2 | 2 | 2 | 3 | Med. | 100 or more | River | Average | Deconcentrating | North |
| Mobile | 5 | 5 | 5 | 5 | 5 | Med. | 100 or more | Coast | Average | No clear trend | South |
| Montgomery | 5 | 5 | 5 | 5 | 5 | Med. | 50 - 100 | Other | Low | ---- | South |
| Muncie | 5 | 5 | 5 | 5 | 5 | High | 50 - 100 | Other | High | Deconcentrating | North |
| Nashville | 4 | 4 | 4 | 4 | 5 | Med. | 100 or more | River | Average | Concentrating | South |
| New Bedford | 4 | 4 | 4 | 5 | 5 | Low | Within 50 | Coast | -- | ---- | North |
| New Britain - Bristol | 5 | 5 | 5 | 5 | 5 | High | Within 50 | Other | -- | ---- | North |
| New Haven | 4 | 4 | 4 | 4 | 4 | Low | Within 50 | Coast | -- | ---- | North |
| New Orleans | - | 3 | 3 | 3 | 3 | Low | 50 - 100 | Coast | Low | No clear trend | South |
| New York | 1 | 1 | 1 | 1 | 1 | Med. | 50 - 100 | Coast | Average | Deconcentrating | North |
| Norfolk - Portsmouth | 4 | 4 | 4 | 5 | 5 | High | 50 - 100 | Coast | Low | No clear trend | South |
| Ogden | 5 | 5 | 5 | 5 | 5 | Med. | Within 50 | Other | Low | Deconcentrating | West |

Appendix table 1 (cont'd). Characteristics of Metropolitan Areas

| Metropolitan area | Size of central city | | | | | Growth rate Ave. annual 1900-1950 | Distance between central cities (Miles) | Geographic feature | Proportion of population employed in manufacturing | Direction of industrial relocation | Regional location |
|---|---|---|---|---|---|---|---|---|---|---|---|
| | 1940-1950[a] | 1930-1940[a] | 1920-1930[a] | 1910-1920[a] | 1900-1910[a] | | | | | | |
| Oklahoma City | 4 | 4 | 5 | 5 | - | High | 50 - 100 | Other | Low | Deconcentrating | South |
| Omaha | 4 | 4 | 4 | 4 | 4 | Med. | 50 - 100 | River | Low | Concentrating | North |
| Orlando | - | - | - | - | - | -- | ---- | --- | -- | ---- | --- |
| Peoria | 4 | 4 | 5 | 5 | 5 | Low | 50 - 100 | River | Average | Deconcentrating | North |
| Philadelphia | 1 | 1 | 1 | 1 | 1 | Low | Within 50 | River | High | No clear trend | North |
| Phoenix | 5 | 5 | 5 | - | - | High | 100 or more | Other | Low | Deconcentrating | West |
| Pittsburgh | 2 | 2 | 2 | 2 | 3 | Low | Within 50 | River | Average | Deconcentrating | North |
| Pittsfield | 5 | 5 | 5 | 5 | 5 | Med. | Within 50 | Other | -- | No clear trend | North |
| Portland, Me. | 5 | 5 | 5 | 5 | 5 | Low | 50 - 100 | Coast | -- | No clear trend | North |
| Portland, Oregon | - | - | - | - | - | -- | ---- | --- | -- | ---- | --- |
| Providence | 3 | 3 | 4 | 4 | 4 | Low | Within 50 | Coast | -- | Concentrating | North |
| Pueblo | - | 5 | - | - | - | Low | 100 or more | Other | Average | ---- | West |
| Racine | 5 | 5 | 5 | 5 | 5 | Med. | Within 50 | Coast | High | No clear trend | North |
| Raleigh | 5 | 5 | 5 | 5 | 5 | High | Within 50 | Other | High | No clear trend | South |
| Reading | 4 | 4 | 4 | 5 | 5 | Low | Within 50 | River | High | Deconcentrating | North |
| Richmond | 4 | 4 | 4 | 4 | 5 | Med. | 50 - 100 | River | Average | No clear trend | South |
| Roanoke | 5 | 5 | 5 | 5 | 5 | High | 50 - 100 | Other | Average | ---- | South |
| Rochester | 3 | 3 | 3 | 4 | 4 | Low | 50 - 100 | Coast | High | No clear trend | North |
| Rockford | 5 | 5 | 5 | 5 | 5 | Med. | 50 - 100 | Other | High | Deconcentrating | North |
| Sacramento | 4 | 5 | 5 | 5 | 5 | High | Within 50 | River | Low | Deconcentrating | West |
| Saginaw | 5 | 5 | 5 | 5 | 5 | Med. | Within 50 | Coast | High | No clear trend | North |
| St. Joseph | 5 | 5 | 5 | 5 | 4 | Low | Within 50 | River | Average | Concentrating | North |
| St. Louis | - | 2 | 2 | 2 | 2 | Low | 50 - 100 | River | Average | No clear trend | North |
| Salt Lake City | 4 | 4 | 4 | 5 | 5 | Med. | Within 50 | Other | Low | Deconcentrating | West |
| San Angelo | 5 | 5 | 5 | 5 | - | High | 100 or more | Other | -- | ---- | South |
| San Antonio | - | 4 | 4 | 5 | 5 | High | 50 - 100 | Other | Low | No clear trend | South |
| San Bernardino | - | - | - | - | - | -- | ---- | --- | -- | ---- | --- |
| San Diego | - | - | - | - | - | -- | ---- | --- | -- | ---- | --- |
| San Francisco - Oakland | 2 | 2 | 2 | 3 | 3 | Med. | Within 50 | Coast | Average | Deconcentrating | West |
| San Jose | 5 | 5 | 5 | 5 | 5 | High | Within 50 | Other | Average | ---- | West |
| Savannah | 5 | 5 | 5 | 5 | 5 | Med. | 50 - 100 | Coast | Average | Deconcentrating | South |
| Scranton | 4 | 4 | 4 | 4 | 4 | Low | 50 - 100 | Other | Low | Deconcentrating | North |
| Seattle | - | - | - | - | - | -- | ---- | --- | -- | ---- | --- |
| Shreveport | 5 | 5 | 5 | 5 | 5 | High | 100 or more | Other | Low | Deconcentrating | South |
| Sioux City | 5 | 5 | 5 | 5 | 5 | Med. | 50 - 111 | River | Low | Concentrating | North |
| Sioux Falls | 5 | 5 | 5 | 5 | 5 | High | 100 or more | Other | Low | Concentrating | West |

Appendix table 1 (cont'd). Characteristics of Metropolitan Areas

| Metropolitan area | Size of central city 1940-1950[a] | 1930-1940[a] | 1920-1910[a] | 1910-1920[a] | 1900-1910[a] | Growth rate Ave. annual 1900-1950 | Distance between central cities (Miles) | Geographic feature | Proportion of population employed in manufacturing | Direction of industrial relocation | Regional location |
|---|---|---|---|---|---|---|---|---|---|---|---|
| South Bend | 4 | 4 | 5 | 5 | 5 | Med. | 50 - 100 | Other | High | No clear trend | North |
| Spokane | 4 | 4 | 4 | 4 | - | Low | 100 or more | Other | Low | No clear trend | West |
| Springfield, Ill. | 5 | 5 | 5 | 5 | 5 | Med. | Within 50 | Other | Low | Deconcentrating | North |
| Springfield, Mo. | 5 | 5 | 5 | 5 | 5 | Med. | 100 or more | Other | Low | No clear trend | North |
| Springfield, O. | 5 | 5 | 5 | 5 | 5 | Low | Within 50 | Other | High | ---- | North |
| Springfield - Holyoke | 4 | 4 | 4 | 4 | 4 | Low | Within 50 | River | -- | No clear trend | North |
| Stamford - Norwalk | 4 | 5 | 5 | 5 | 5 | High | Within 50 | Coast | -- | ---- | North |
| Stockton | 5 | 5 | 5 | 5 | 5 | High | Within 50 | River | Low | Deconcentrating | West |
| Syracuse | 4 | 4 | 4 | 4 | 4 | Low | Within 50 | Other | High | No clear trend | North |
| Tacoma | - | - | - | - | - | -- | --- | --- | --- | ---- | --- |
| Tampa - St. Petersburg | - | - | - | - | - | -- | --- | --- | --- | ---- | --- |
| Terre-Haute | 5 | 5 | 5 | 5 | 5 | Low | 50 - 100 | River | Average | No clear trend | North |
| Toledo | 3 | 3 | 4 | 4 | 4 | Med. | 50 - 100 | Coast | Average | No clear trend | North |
| Topeka | 5 | 5 | 5 | 5 | 5 | Med. | 50 - 100 | Other | Low | Deconcentrating | North |
| Trenton | 4 | 4 | 4 | 5 | 5 | Low | Within 50 | River | High | Deconcentrating | North |
| Tulsa | 4 | 4 | 5 | 5 | 5 | High | 50 - 100 | Other | Low | Concentrating | South |
| Utica - Rome | 4 | 4 | 5 | 5 | 5 | Low | Within 50 | Other | High | Deconcentrating | North |
| Waco | - | 5 | 5 | 5 | 5 | Med. | 50 - 100 | Other | Low | No clear trend | South |
| Washington | 2 | 3 | 3 | 3 | 3 | Med. | Within 50 | River | Low | No clear trend | South |
| Waterbury | 5 | 5 | 5 | 5 | 5 | Med. | Within 50 | Other | --- | ---- | North |
| Waterloo | 5 | 5 | 5 | 5 | 5 | High | Within 50 | Other | High | Concentrating | North |
| Wheeling - Steubenville | 5 | 5 | 5 | 5 | 5 | Low | Within 50 | River | High | Deconcentrating | North |
| Wichita | 4 | 4 | 5 | 5 | 5 | High | 100 or more | Other | Low | No clear trend | North |
| Wichita Falls | 5 | 5 | 5 | 5 | 5 | High | 100 or more | Other | Low | No clear trend | North |
| Wilkes Barre - Hazelton | 5 | 5 | 5 | 5 | 5 | Low | Within 50 | River | Low | No clear trend | South |
| Wilmington | 4 | 4 | 4 | 5 | 5 | Low | Within 50 | River | High | Deconcentrating | South |
| Winston Salem | 5 | 5 | 5 | 5 | 5 | High | 50 - 100 | Other | High | Deconcentrating | South |
| Worcester | 4 | 4 | 4 | 4 | 4 | Low | Within 50 | Other | -- | No clear trend | North |
| York | 5 | 5 | 5 | 5 | 5 | Low | Within 50 | Other | High | Deconcentrating | North |
| Youngstown | 4 | 4 | 4 | 5 | 5 | Med | Within 50 | Other | High | No clear trend | North |

[a] 1. 1,000,000 and over
2. 500,000 - 1,000,000
3. 250,000 - 500,000
4. 100,000 - 250,000
5. Under 100,000

[b] Area not in study

Appendix table 2. Population in Standard and Extended Metropolitan Areas at the Beginning and at the End of Each Decade, by Distance Zones, 1900-1950

| Type of metropolitan area and distance zone | 1950 | 1940 | 1940 | 1930 | 1930 | 1920 | 1920 | 1910 | 1910 | 1900 |
|---|---|---|---|---|---|---|---|---|---|---|
| Standard Metropolitan Areas | | | | | | | | | | |
| Total | 74,752,984 | 62,433,458 | 66,280,931 | 61,376,780 | 58,980,287 | 47,234,553 | 47,120,246 | 37,842,271 | 37,558,718 | 29,025,992 |
| Central cities | 41,786,414 | 37,381,460 | 39,869,502 | 37,923,688 | 36,616,115 | 30,161,635 | 29,955,285 | 23,793,535 | 23,441,484 | 17,819,542 |
| All satellite area | 32,966,570 | 25,051,998 | 26,411,429 | 23,453,092 | 22,364,172 | 17,072,918 | 17,164,961 | 14,048,736 | 14,117,234 | 11,206,450 |
| 0-5 miles | 4,834,191 | 3,911,407 | 4,157,597 | 3,764,929 | 3,680,737 | 2,914,255 | 2,966,248 | 2,293,245 | 2,349,276 | 1,836,809 |
| 5-10 miles | 10,470,630 | 7,683,032 | 8,143,176 | 7,081,167 | 6,707,428 | 4,751,580 | 4,885,371 | 3,957,916 | 3,992,008 | 3,084,990 |
| 10-15 miles | 7,339,531 | 5,550,705 | 5,831,959 | 5,224,188 | 4,990,278 | 3,978,812 | 3,948,248 | 3,283,363 | 3,309,473 | 2,648,812 |
| 15-20 miles | 4,277,616 | 3,218,413 | 3,456,905 | 3,047,519 | 2,803,503 | 2,112,136 | 2,113,413 | 1,734,494 | 1,711,043 | 1,392,778 |
| 20-25 miles | 2,610,197 | 1,998,310 | 2,071,679 | 1,824,863 | 1,802,416 | 1,335,055 | 1,273,736 | 1,053,780 | 1,041,052 | 838,695 |
| 25-30 miles | 1,430,334 | 1,160,967 | 1,198,473 | 1,096,221 | 1,025,840 | 827,762 | 828,844 | 696,234 | 696,550 | 563,232 |
| 30-35 miles | 831,193 | 607,446 | 617,661 | 557,011 | 513,896 | 439,067 | 435,701 | 378,073 | 366,661 | 321,009 |
| 35 miles and over | 1,172,878 | 921,718 | 933,979 | 857,194 | 840,074 | 714,251 | 713,400 | 651,631 | 651,171 | 520,125 |
| Extended Metropolitan Areas | | | | | | | | | | |
| Total | 91,122,250 | 77,437,212 | 82,307,268 | 76,615,719 | 74,222,515 | 61,802,003 | 61,670,397 | 51,802,434 | 51,289,678 | 42,080,553 |
| Central cities | 41,786,414 | 37,381,460 | 39,869,502 | 37,923,688 | 36,616,115 | 30,161,635 | 29,955,285 | 23,793,535 | 23,441,484 | 17,819,542 |
| All satellite area | 49,335,836 | 40,055,752 | 42,437,766 | 38,692,031 | 37,606,400 | 31,640,368 | 31,715,112 | 28,008,899 | 27,848,194 | 24,261,011 |
| 0-5 miles | 4,884,181 | 3,943,641 | 4,193,325 | 3,795,353 | 3,711,162 | 2,933,521 | 2,983,264 | 2,305,724 | 2,360,980 | 1,846,940 |
| 5-10 miles | 10,875,929 | 8,010,261 | 8,483,398 | 7,394,600 | 7,020,950 | 5,034,220 | 5,169,354 | 4,218,397 | 4,255,209 | 3,325,956 |
| 10-15 miles | 8,611,710 | 6,628,280 | 6,948,762 | 6,268,821 | 6,042,476 | 4,969,936 | 4,946,561 | 4,230,105 | 4,230,693 | 3,531,682 |
| 15-20 miles | 6,777,444 | 5,441,637 | 5,789,931 | 5,253,110 | 5,014,591 | 4,176,670 | 4,166,592 | 3,712,300 | 3,661,804 | 3,237,838 |
| 20-25 miles | 5,557,407 | 4,690,548 | 4,929,361 | 4,540,644 | 4,502,060 | 3,943,385 | 3,890,566 | 3,590,040 | 3,551,191 | 3,223,354 |
| 25-30 miles | 4,838,783 | 4,296,974 | 4,529,708 | 4,247,706 | 4,164,739 | 3,849,067 | 3,831,948 | 3,564,917 | 3,506,511 | 3,230,033 |
| 30-35 miles | 3,771,849 | 3,370,229 | 3,627,702 | 3,433,480 | 3,397,176 | 3,174,721 | 3,163,734 | 2,970,855 | 2,930,130 | 2,765,378 |
| 35 miles and over | 4,018,533 | 3,674,182 | 3,935,579 | 3,768,317 | 3,753,246 | 3,558,848 | 3,563,093 | 3,416,561 | 3,351,676 | 3,099,830 |

## CHAPTER 1

1. See R. D. McKenzie, *The Metropolitan Community* (New York: The McGraw-Hill Co., 1933), for an extensive treatment of metropolitan development.

2. The term area, or Standard Metropolitan Area, was first used in 1950, and is defined on pp. 7-9 of this report. In prior census years the term employed was Metropolitan District the definition of which changed from census to census. See W. S. Thompson, *The Growth of Metropolitan Districts in the United States: 1900-1940* (Washington, D. C.: U. S. Government Printing Office, 1947) for a statement of the various definitions used.

3. R. D. McKenzie, *op. cit.;* Amos H. Hawley and Donald J. Bogue, "Recent Shifts in Population: The Drift toward the Metropolitan District," *The Review of Economic Statistics,* XXIV (Aug., 1942), 143-48; W. S. Thompson, *op. cit.;* Donald J. Bogue, *Population Growth in Standard Metropolitan Areas, 1900-1950* (Washington, D. C.: U. S. Government Printing Office, 1953).

4. 1950 Census of Population. *Population of Standard Metropolitan Areas: April 1, 1950* (U. S. Bureau of the Census: Washington, D. C., 1950), Series PC-3, pp. 1 and 3.

5. The number of zones is often less than eight in Standard Metropolitan Areas because of the definition which results in many instances in one county areas.

## CHAPTER II

1. Centrifugal is used here and elsewhere in this report in a relative sense. None of the data employed throw any light on the sources of population growth in metropolitan areas. Centrifugal, then, means simply that the effect of differential growth is to increase the population in the satellite areas relative to that of central cities, regardless of whether the added population originates from the center of from outside the metropolitan area.

2. For other uses of this measure see National Resources Planning Board, *Industrial Location and National Policy* (Wash., D. C.: U. S. Gov. Printing Office), E. M. Hoover, Jr. "Interstate Redistribution of Population, 1850-1940", *The Journal of Economic History,* Vol. I (Nov., 1941), pp. 199-205.

3. It is interesting to note that the number of incorporated satellite places tends to double successively in each smaller size class, especially in Extended Metropolitan Areas. No doubt the rate of progression is a function of the class interval, yet it seems likely that some geometric pattern might appear regardless of class interval size. There is here a suggestion of a tendency to equilibrium in the number and size distribution of service sub-centers such as was proposed by Christaller *(Die Zentralen Orte Suddeutschlands,* Jena, 1933).

## CHAPTER IV

1. Appendix Table 1 lists the metropolitan areas in each class.

## CHAPTER V

1. Measures of distance were obtained from: C. A. Whitten, *Air-Lines Distances Between Cities in the United States,* U. S. Dept. of Commerce, Coast and Geodetic Survey, Special Publication No. 238. (U. S. Gov't Printing Office: Washington, D. C., 1947).

## CHAPTER VI

1. Use was made of the map of "Principal Waterways of the United States" (Army Map Service, Corps of Engineers, Dept. of the Army, 1942) to identify river locations.

2. This is not to over-look air transportation. The major concern here, however, is with surface means of transport.

3. See R. D. McKenzie, *op. cit.,* Chs. X, XI, and XII.

4. These are: Atlanta; Buffalo; Chicago; Columbus, O.; Dallas; Detroit; Indianapolis; Louisville; Milwaukee; Minneapolis; Rochester; St. Louis; and San Francisco.

## CHAPTER VII

1. See D. J. Bogue, *The Structure of the Metropolitan Community,* Ch. XIV.

## CHAPTER VIII

1. As reported in the *Census of Manufacturers,* 1899, 1909, 1929, 1939, 1948.

## CHAPTER IX

1. See Appendix Table 1.

## CHAPTER X

1. See Appendix Table 1.

# BOOKS PUBLISHED BY

# *The Free Press*

LORD ACTON: *Essays on Freedom and Power* $6.00

FRANZ ALEXANDER, M.D., AND HUGO STAUB: *The Criminal, The Judge and The Public* 4.00

ARISTIDES: *To Rome* 1.00

ARISTOTLE: *The Constitution of the Athenians* temporarily out of print

MIKHAIL BAKUNIN: *The Political Philosophy of Bakunin* 6.00

EDWARD C. BANFIELD: *Government Project* 3.50

BERNARD BARBER: *Science and the Social Order* 4.50

KARL BEDNARIK: *The Young Worker of Today: A New Type* 2.50

SALO W. BARON: *Freedom and Reason* 5.00

REINHARD BENDIX AND SEYMOUR MARTIN LIPSET: *Class, Status and Power: A Reader in Social Stratification* 7.50

BERNARD BERELSON: *Content Analysis in Communications Research* 4.00

BERNARD BERELSON AND MORRIS JANOWITZ: *Reader in Public Opinion and Communication* 5.50

BRUNO BETTELHEIM: *Love Is Not Enough* 4.50

BRUNO BETTELHEIM: *Symbolic Wounds* 4.75

BRUNO BETTELHEIM: *Truants from Life: The Rehabilitation of Emotionally Disturbed Children* 6.00

ROBERT BLOOD: *Anticipating Your Marriage* 5.00

HERBERT BUTTERFIELD: *The History of Science* O.P.

RICHARD CHRISTIE AND MARIE JAHODA: *Studies in the Scope and Method of "The Authoritarian Personality"* 4.50

ALBERT K. COHEN: *Delinquent Boys: The Culture of the Gang* 3.50

MORRIS R. COHEN: *American Thought* 5.00

MORRIS R. COHEN: *A Dreamer's Journey* 4.50

MORRIS R. COHEN: *King Saul's Daughter* 3.00

Morris R. Cohen: *Reason and Law* 4.00
Morris R. Cohen: *Reason and Nature* 6.00
Morris R. Cohen: *Reflections of a Wondering Jew* 2.75
Commission on Educational Reconstruction: *Organizing the Teaching Profession* 4.50
Charles H. Cooley: *Two Books by Charles H. Cooley: Human Nature and the Social Order* and *Social Organization* 7.50
Lewis Coser: *The Functions of Social Conflict* 3.50
Donald R. Cressey: *Other People's Money* 3.00
Herbert Dinerstein and Leon Goure: *Two Studies in Soviet Controls* 4.50
Emile Durkheim: *The Division of Labor in Society* 5.00
Emile Durkheim: *Education and Sociology* 3.50
Emile Durkheim: *Elementary Forms of the Religious Life* 5.00
Emile Durkheim: *The Rules of the Sociological Method* 2.75
Emile Durkheim: *Sociology and Philosophy* 2.50
Emile Durkheim: *Suicide* 5.00
Joseph W. Eaton and Robert J. Weil: *Culture and Mental Disorders* 4.00
Joseph W. Eaton and Albert J. Mayer: *Man's Capacity To Reproduce* 2.00
Abraham Edel: *Ethical Judgment: The Use of Science in Ethics* 5.00
Paul Edwards: *The Logic of Moral Discourse* 4.00
S. N. Eisenstadt: *The Absorption of Immigrants* 6.00
S. N. Eisenstadt: *From Generation to Generation: Age Groups and the Social Structure* 6.00
E. E. Evans-Pritchard: *The Institutions of Primitive Society* 2.50
E. E. Evans-Pritchard: *Social Anthropology* 2.50
E. K. Francis: *In Search of Utopia* 6.50
Georges Friedmann: *Industrial Society: The Emergence of the Human Problems of Automation* 6.00
Lawrence Fuchs: *The Political Behavior of American Jews* 4.00
Raymond Garthoff: *Soviet Military Doctrine* 7.50
Harlan W. Gilmore: *Transportation and the Growth of Cities* 3.00
D. V. Glass: *Social Mobility in Britain* O.P.
Max Gluckman: *Custom and Conflict in Africa* 3.50
Max Gluckman: *The Judicial Process Among the Barotse* 6.75
Herbert Goldhamer and Andrew Marshall: *Psychosis and Civilization* 4.00

Walter Goldschmidt: *As You Sow* 3.50
Joseph Goldstein: *The Government of a British Trade Union* 5.00
William J. Goode: *Religion Among the Primitives* 5.00
William J. Goode: *After Divorce* 6.00
Alvin Gouldner: *Patterns of Industrial Bureaucracy* 4.50
Charles M. Hardin: *The Politics of Agriculture* 4.00
Charles Hartshorne: *Reality as Social Process* 4.00
Paul K. Hatt and Albert J. Reiss, Jr.:
*Reader in Urban Sociology* (revised ed., 1956) 6.00
Amos H. Hawley: *The Changing Shape of Metropolitan America: Deconcentration Since 1920* 4.00
Frederick von Hayek: *The Counter-Revolution of Science* 4.00
Andrew F. Henry and James F. Short, Jr.:
*Suicide and Homicide* 4.00
Roger Hilsman: *Strategic Intelligence and National Decisions* 4.00
George Homans and David Schneider: *Marriage, Authority and Final Causes* 2.00
Everett C. Hughes and Helen M. Hughes:
*Where Peoples Meet* 3.50
W. H. Hutt: *The Theory of Collective Bargaining* 3.00
Herbert H. Hyman: *Survey Design and Analysis* 7.50
Morris Janowitz: *The Community Press in an Urban Setting* 3.50
Elihu Katz and Paul F. Lazarsfeld: *Personal Influence* 6.00
Patricia Kendall: *Conflict and Mood* 3.50
Harold D. Lasswell: *The Political Writings of Harold D. Lasswell* 5.00
Harold D. Lasswell, Charles E. Merriam and T. V. Smith:
*A Study of Power* 6.00
Paul F. Lazarsfeld and Morris Rosenberg:
*The Language of Social Research: A Reader in the Methodology of the Social Sciences* 6.75
Paul Lazarsfeld, Ed.: *Mathematical Thinking in the Social Sciences* 10.00
Nathan Leites: *A Study of Bolshevism* 6.50
Nathan Leites and Elsa Bernaut: *Ritual of Liquidation* 6.50
S. M. Lipset, Martin Trow and James Coleman:
*Union Dmocracy: The Inside Politics of the International Typographical Union* 6.50
Charles Loomis and Others: *Turrialba: Social Systems and the Introduction of Change* 3.00

Bronislaw Malinowski: *Magic, Science and Religion* — o.p.
Henri de Man: *Joy in Work* — o.p.
Maurice Mandelbaum: *The Phenomenology of Moral Experience* — 5.00
Karl Marx and Frederick Engels: *The Russian Menace to Europe* — 3.75
Marcel Mauss: *Essay on the Gift* — 2.50
Carl Menger: *Principles of Economics* — 5.00
Robert K. Merton, Marjorie Fiske and Patricia Kendall: *The Focused Interview* — 3.00
Robert K. Merton and Others: *Reader in Bureaucracy* — 5.00
Robert K. Merton: *Social Theory and Social Structure* (revised and enlarged ed., 1956) — 6.00
Robert K. Merton and Paul F. Lazarsfeld: *Studies in the Scope and Method of "The American Soldier"* — 4.00
Martin Meyerson and Edward Banfield: *Politics, Planning and the Public Interest* — 5.00
Robert Michels: *Political Parties* — o.p.
S. F. Nadel: *Foundations of Social Anthropology* — 5.00
S. F. Nadel: *Nupe Religion* — 4.75
Ernest Nagel: *Sovereign Reason* — 5.00
Franz Neumann: *Political Theory and Freedom* — 5.00
James Olds: *The Growth and Structure of Motives: Psychological Studies in the Theory of Action* — 5.00
Robert Owen: *A New View of Society* — o.p.
Robert E. Park: *Human Communities* — 4.50
Robert E. Park: *Race and Culture* — 5.00
Robert E. Park: *Society: Collective Behavior, News and Opinion, Sociology and Modern Society* — 5.00
Talcott Parsons: *Essays in Sociological Theory* — 6.00
Talcott Parsons: *The Social System* — 6.00
Talcott Parsons: *The Structure of Social Action* — 7.50
Talcott Parsons and Robert Bales: *Family, Socialization and Interaction Process* — 6.00
Talcott Parsons, Robert F. Bales and Edward A. Shils: *Working Papers in the Theory of Action* — 3.75
Wilhelm Pauck: *Heritage of the Reformation* — o.p.
Herbert Phillipson: *The Object Relations Technique* (Book & Test Cards) — 10.00
Jean Piaget: *The Moral Judgment of the Child* — 4.50

Henry Quastler, Ed.: *Information Theory in Psychology* 6.00
A. R. Radcliffe-Brown: *The Andaman Islanders* 5.00
A. R. Radcliffe-Brown: *Structure and Function in Primitive Society* 5.00
The Rand Corporation: *A Million Random Digits with 100,000 Normal Deviates* 10.00
Fritz Redl and David Wineman: *Children Who Hate* 3.50
Fritz Redl and David Wineman: *Controls from Within* 4.50
A. Richards: *Hunger and Work in a Savage Tribe* 3.50
David Riesman: *Individualism Reconsidered* 6.00
Natalie Rogoff: *Recent Trends in Occupational Mobility* 4.00
Peter H. Rossi: *Why Families Move* 4.00
Bertrand Russell: *The Scientific Outlook* 3.50
Edward A. Shils: *The Present State of American Sociology* O.P.
Edward A. Shils: *The Torment of Secrecy: The Background and Consequences of American Security Policies* 3.50
Georg Simmel: *Conflict and The Web of Group-Affiliations* 3.50
Georg Simmel: *The Sociology of Georg Simmel* 5.50
Marshall Sklare: *Conservative Judaism* 4.50
Werner Sombart: *Jews and Modern Capitalism* 4.50
Georges Sorel: *Reflections on Violence* 4.00
W. J. H. Sprott: *Science and Social Action* 3.50
Alfred H. Stanton and Stewart E. Perry: *Personality and Political Crisis* 3.75
George Stern, Morris Stein and Benjamin Bloom: *Methods In Personality Assessment* 6.00
Eric Strauss: *Sir William Petty: Portrait of a Genius* 5.00
Leo Strauss: *On Tyranny* 2.50
Leo Strauss: *Persecution and the Art of Writing* 4.00
Adolf Sturmthal: *Unity and Diversity in European Labor* 3.75
Sol Tax: *Heritage of Conquest* 5.00
Dinko Tomasic: *The Impact of Russian Culture on Soviet Communism* 4.50
Ernst Troeltsch: *The Social Teachings of the Christian Churches*, 2 vols. O.P.
Jacob Viner: *International Economics* 5.00
Jacob Viner: *International Trade and Economic Development* 2.75
W. Allen Wallis and Harry V. Roberts: *Statistics: A New Approach* 6.00
Max Weber: *Ancient Judaism* 6.00

**DATE DUE**

| | | | |
|---|---|---|---|
| | | | |
| | | | |
| | | | |
| | | | |
| | | | |
| | | | |
| | | | |
| | | | |
| | | | |
| | | | |
| | | | |

# *Operation Otherworld*

*Also by Poul Anderson*

Alight in the Void
All One Universe
The Armies of Elfland
The Boat of a Million Years
The Dancer from Atlantis
The Day of Their Return
Explorations
The Fleet of Stars
Harvest of Stars
Harvest the Fire
Hoka! *(with Gordon R. Dickson)*
Kinship with the Stars
A Knight of Ghosts and Shadows
The Long Night
The Longest Voyage
Maurai and Kith
A Midsummer Tempest
No Truce with Kings
Past Times
The Saturn Game
The Shield of Time
Starfarers
The Stars Are Also Fire
Tales of the Flying Mountains
The Time Patrol
There Will Be Time
War of the Gods

# Operation Otherworld

Operation Chaos

Operation Luna

**POUL ANDERSON**

Parts of this novel have appeared as separate stories in *The Magazine of Fantasy and Science Fiction* as follows:

"Operation Afreet," September 1956, copyright © 1956 by Fantasy House, Inc.

"Operation Salamander," January 1957, copyright © 1956 by Fantasy House, Inc.

"Operation Incubus," October 1959, copyright © 1959 by Mercury Press, Inc.

"Operation Changeling," May–June 1969, copyright © 1969 by Mercury Press, Inc.



This edition published by arrangement with
Tor Books
Tom Doherty Associates, Inc.
175 Fifth Avenue
New York, NY 10010



ISBN 0-7394-0580-2

Visit The Science Fiction Book Club online at *http://www.sfbc.com*
Visit Tor online at *http://www.tor.com*

First SFBC printing: August 1999

PRINTED IN THE UNITED STATES OF AMERICA

# CONTENTS

# Operation Chaos

*To Robert A. Heinlein—*
*who first incorporated magic—*
*and his own red-haired Virginia*

Hello, out there!

If you exist, hello!

We may well never find out. This is a wild experiment, test of a wilder hypothesis. But it is also a duty.

I lie dream-bound, only half-aware of my world. They are using me to call for them across the time streams because that which happened to me, so many years ago, has left its traces beneath my ordinariness; they believe a message thought by me has a better chance of finding a resonance in you than if it came from almost anyone else.

Not that the chance is good. My ordinariness quite overwhelms what little mana may still drift smokelike within. And in any case, I may well be—I probably am—radiating into nothingness.

It is only a philosophical idea, that time has more than one dimension, that any number of entire universes may coexist, some utterly alien, some whose differences from ours are perhaps too subtle to detect. . . . Why am I dreaming in this language? It isn't my normal speech. The preparations have cast me into a strange state. Damnation, I will be myself, not only myself again when I wake tomorrow but myself now and throughout the night. . . . Earths where Lee won at Gettysburg or Napoleon at Waterloo; Earths where Mithraism won over Christianity in the Roman Empire; Earths where Rome never was; Earths where another animal than man evolved toward a rational soul, or none did; Earths, whole cosmoses where the laws of nature are something else, where it is possible to do what we forever cannot, but they will never accomplish what we do with ease. . . .

Well, I am told that a little more than philosophy supports the hypothesis. There are certain indications in modern physical theory,

too abstruse for me. There are anecdotes, cases of appearance or disappearance or both, which suggest that the body itself can transfer between such time currents—Benjamin Bathurst, Kaspar Hauser. . . . There is what happened to me and mine, though that isn't the same thing. It is, however, the source of our duty.

You see, if parallel worlds exist, they must be linked in a very fundamental way; otherwise the hypothesis is unverifiable in principle and therefore meaningless. Deriving from the same source, embedded in the same matrix, they must in some fashion have a common destiny. Whatever manifold forms it takes, the war of Law and Chaos surely goes on in them all.

We have learned certain things. We ought to broadcast the lesson and the warning.

To you out yonder, this may appear nothing but a dream. It feels that way to me, though I recall matters which truly happened. We doubt if you—any of you whom we may reach—will be able to reply, even if willing. Otherwise we would already have gotten messages from elsewhere. But think over what you receive. Ask yourselves how you could have a simple dream that was quite like this one.

While we have no certain idea what you are like, assuming you are more than a void, we can guess. You probably do not live in worlds radically foreign to ours, or communication would be impossible. How could uncomplicated I resonate with a true alien? No, you too must be human, of technological culture at that. You too must remember Galileo, Newton, Lavoisier, Watt; the chances are that you too are an American. But we have diverged at some point. Have you had an Einstein? And if you did, what did he think about after his early papers on Brownian movement and special relativity? The questions go on without end.

You will have such questions about us, of course. So I'm going to ramble through my story. (That's hard to avoid anyway, in this drowsy twilight they've laid on me.) No doubt I'll often belabor the obvious. If you already know how electric generators work or how the First World War came out—or whatever—bear with me. Better too much information than too little. This is more than vital to you.

If you exist.

Where to begin? I suppose where the affair really began for me, during World War II, though of course the roots run much deeper and further back; the strife is older than creation. . . .

I

It was sheer bad luck, or maybe their Intelligence was better than we knew, but the last raid, breaking past our air defenses, had spattered the Weather Corps tent from here to hell. Supply problems being what they were, we couldn't get replacements for weeks, and meanwhile the enemy had control of the weather. Our only surviving Corpsman, Major Jackson, had to save what was left of his elementals to protect us against thunderbolts; so otherwise we took whatever they chose to throw at us. At the moment, it was rain.

There's nothing so discouraging as a steady week of cold rain. The ground turns liquid and runs up into your boots, which get so heavy you can barely lift them. Your uniform is a drenched rag around your shivering skin, the rations are soggy, the rifles have to have extra care, and always the rain drums down on your helmet till you hear it in dreams. You'll never forget that endless gray washing and beating; ten years later a rainstorm will make you feel depressed.

The one consolation, I thought, was that they couldn't very well attack us from the air while it went on. Doubtless they'd yank the cloud cover away when they were ready to strafe us, but our broomsticks could scramble as fast as their carpets could arrive. Meanwhile, we slogged ahead, a whole division of us with auxiliaries—the 45th, the Lightning Busters, pride of the United States Army, turned into a wet misery of men and dragons hunting through the Oregon hills for the invader.

I made a slow way through the camp. Water ran off tents and gurgled in slit trenches. Our sentries were, of course, wearing Tarnkappen, but I could see their footprints form in the mud and hear the boots squelch and the tired monotonous cursing.

I passed by the Air Force strip; they were bivouacked with us, to give support as needed. A couple of men stood on guard outside the knockdown hangar, not bothering with invisibility. Their blue uniforms were as mucked and bedraggled as my OD's, but they had shaved and their insignia—the winged broomstick and the anti-Evil Eye beads—were polished. They saluted me, and I returned the gesture idly. *Esprit de corps,* wild blue yonder, nuts.

Beyond was the armor. The boys had erected portable shelters for their beasts, so I only saw steam rising out of the cracks and caught the rank reptile smell. Dragons hate rain, and their drivers were having a hell of a time controlling them.

Nearby lay Petrological Warfare, with a pen full of hooded basilisks writhing and hissing and striking out with their crowned heads at the men feeding them. Personally, I doubted the practicality of that whole corps. You have to get a basilisk quite close to a man, and looking straight at him, for petrifaction; and the aluminum-foil suit and helmet you must wear to deflect the influence of your pets is an invitation to snipers. Then, too, when human carbon is turned to silicon, you have a radioactive isotope, and maybe get such a dose of radiation yourself that the medics have to give you St. John's Wort plucked from a graveyard in the dark of the moon.

So, in case you didn't know, cremation hasn't simply died out as a custom; it's become illegal under the National Defense Act. We have to have plenty of old-fashioned cemeteries. Thus does the age of science pare down our liberties.

I went on past the engineers, who were directing a gang of zombies carving another drainage ditch, and on to General Vanbrugh's big tent. When the guard saw my Tetragrammaton insigne, for the Intelligence Corps, and the bars on my shoulders, he saluted and let me in. I came to a halt before the desk and brought my own hand up.

"Captain Matuchek reporting, sir," I said.

Vanbrugh looked at me from beneath shaggy gray brows. He was a large man with a face like weathered rock, 103 percent Regular Army, but we liked him as well as you can like a buck general. "At ease," he said. "Sit down. This'll take a while."

I found a folding chair and lowered myself into it. Two others were already seated whom I didn't know. One was a plump man with a round red face and a fluffy white beard, a major bearing the crystal-ball emblem of the Signal Corps. The other was a young woman. In spite of my weariness, I blinked and looked twice at her. She was worth it—a tall green-eyed redhead with straight high-cheeked features and

a figure too good for the WAC clothes or any other. Captain's bars, Cavalry spider . . . or Sleipnir, if you want to be official about it.

"Major Harrigan," grumfed the general. "Captain Graylock. Captain Matuchek. Let's get down to business."

He spread a map out before us. I leaned over and looked at it. Positions were indicated, ours and the enemy's. They still held the Pacific seaboard from Alaska halfway down through Oregon, though that was considerable improvement from a year ago, when the Battle of the Mississippi had turned the tide.

"Now then," said Vanbrugh, "I'll tell you the overall situation. This is a dangerous mission, you don't have to volunteer, but I want you to know how important it is."

What I knew, just then, was that I'd been told to volunteer or else. That was the Army, at least in a major war like this, and in principle I couldn't object. I'd been a reasonably contented Hollywood actor when the Saracen Caliphate attacked us. I wanted to go back to more of the same, but that meant finishing the war.

"You can see we're driving them back," said the general, "and the occupied countries are primed and cocked to revolt as soon as they get a fighting chance. The British have been organizing the underground and arming them while readying for a cross-Channel jump. The Russians are set to advance from the north. But we have to give the enemy a decisive blow, break this whole front and roll 'em up. That'll be the signal. If we succeed, the war will be over this year. Otherwise, it might drag on for another three."

I knew it. The whole Army knew it. Official word hadn't been passed yet, but somehow you feel when a big push is impending.

His stumpy finger traced along the map. "The 9th Armored Division is here, the 12th Broomborne here, the 14th Cavalry here, the Salamanders here where we know they've concentrated their firebreathers. The Marines are ready to establish a beachhead and retake Seattle, now that the Navy's bred enough Krakens. One good goose, and we'll have 'em running."

Major Harrigan snuffled into his beard and stared gloomily at a crystal ball. It was clouded and vague; the enemy had been jamming our crystals till they were no use whatsoever, though naturally we'd retaliated. Captain Graylock tapped impatiently on the desk with a perfectly manicured nail. She was so clean and crisp and efficient, I decided I didn't like her looks after all. Not while I had three days' beard bristling from my chin.

"But apparently something's gone wrong, sir," I ventured.

"Correct, damn it," said Vanbrugh. "In Trollburg."

I nodded. The Saracens held that town: a key position, sitting as it did on U.S. Highway 20 and guarding the approach to Salem and Portland.

"I take it we're supposed to seize Trollburg, sir," I murmured.

Vanbrugh scowled. "That's the job for the 45th," he grunted. "If we muff it, the enemy can sally out against the 9th, cut them off, and throw the whole operation akilter. But now Major Harrigan and Captain Graylock come from the 14th to tell me the Trollburg garrison has an afreet."

I whistled, and a chill crawled along my spine. The Caliphate had exploited the Powers recklessly—that was one reason why the rest of the Moslem world regarded them as heretics and hated them as much as we did—but I never thought they'd go as far as breaking Solomon's seal. An afreet getting out of hand could destroy more than anybody cared to estimate.

"I hope they haven't but one," I whispered.

"No, they don't," said the Graylock woman. Her voice was low and could have been pleasant if it weren't so brisk. "They've been dredging the Red Sea in hopes of finding another Solly bottle, but this seems to be the last one left."

"Bad enough," I said. The effort to keep my tone steady helped calm me down. "How'd you find out?"

"We're with the 14th," said Graylock unnecessarily. Her Cavalry badge had surprised me, however. Normally, the only recruits the Army can dig up to ride unicorns are pickle-faced schoolteachers and the like.

"I'm simply a liaison officer," said Major Harrigan in haste. "I go by broomstick myself." I grinned at that. No American male, unless he's in holy orders, likes to admit he's qualified to control a unicorn. He saw me and flushed angrily.

Graylock went on, as if dictating. She kept her tone flat, though little else. "We had the luck to capture a bimbashi in a commando attack. I questioned him."

"They're pretty close-mouthed, those noble sons of . . . um . . . the desert," I said. I'd bent the Geneva Convention myself, occasionally, but didn't relish the idea of breaking it completely—even if the enemy had no such scruples.

"Oh, we practiced no brutality," said Graylock. "We housed him and fed him very well. But the moment a bite of food was in his throat,

I'd turn it into pork. He broke pretty fast, and spilled everything he knew."

I had to laugh aloud, and Vanbrugh himself chuckled; but she sat perfectly deadpan. Organic-organic transformation, which merely shuffles molecules around without changing atoms, has no radiation hazards but naturally requires a good knowledge of chemistry. That's the real reason the average dogface hates the technical corps: pure envy of a man who can turn K rations into steak and French fries. The quartermasters have enough trouble conjuring up the rations themselves, without branching into fancy dishes.

"Okay, you learned they have an afreet in Trollburg," said the general. "What about their strength otherwise?"

"A small division, sir. You can take the place handily, if that demon can be immobilized," said Harrigan.

"Yes, I know." Vanbrugh swiveled his eyes around to me. "Well, Captain, are you game? If you can carry the stunt off, it'll mean a Silver Star at least—pardon me, a Bronze."

"Uh—" I paused, fumbling after words. I was more interested in promotion and ultimate discharge, but that might follow too. Nevertheless . . . quite apart from my own neck, there was a practical objection. "Sir, I don't know a damn thing about the job. I nearly flunked Demonology 1 in college."

"That'll be my part," said Graylock.

"You!" I picked my jaw off the floor again, but couldn't find anything else to say.

"I was head witch of the Arcane Agency in New York before the war," she said coldly. Now I knew where she got that personality: the typical big-city career girl. I can't stand them. "I know as much about handling demons as anyone on this coast. Your task will be to escort me safely to the place and back."

"Yeah," I said weakly. "Yeah, that's all."

Vanbrugh cleared his throat. He didn't like sending a woman on such a mission, but time was too short for him to have any choice. "Captain Matuchek is one of the best werewolves in the business," he complimented me.

*Ave, Caesar, morituri te salutant,* I thought. No, that isn't what I mean, but never mind. I can figure out a better phrasing at my leisure after I'm dead.

I wasn't afraid, exactly. Besides the spell laid on me to prevent that, I had reason to believe my personal chances were no worse than those of any infantryman headed into a firefight. Nor would Vanbrugh

sacrifice personnel on a mission he himself considered hopeless. But I did feel less optimistic about the prospects than he.

"I think two adepts can get past their guards," the general proceeded. "From then on, you'll have to improvise. If you can put that monster out of action, we attack at noon tomorrow." Grimly: "If I haven't got word to that effect by dawn, we'll have to regroup, start retreating, and save what we can. Okay, here's a geodetic survey map of the town and approaches—"

He didn't waste time asking me if I had really volunteered.

# II

I guided Captain Graylock back to the tent I shared with two brother officers. Darkness was creeping across the long chill slant of rain. We plodded through the muck in silence until we were under canvas. My tentmates were out on picket duty, so we had the place to ourselves. I lit the saintelmo and sat down on the sodden plank floor.

"Have a chair," I said, pointing to our one camp stool. It was an animated job we'd bought in San Francisco: not especially bright, but it would carry our duffel and come when called. It shifted uneasily at the unfamiliar weight, then went back to sleep.

Graylock took out a pack of Wings and raised her brows. I nodded my thanks, and the cigaret flapped over to my mouth. Personally, I smoke Luckies in the field: self-striking tobacco is convenient when your matches may be wet. When I was a civilian and could afford it, my brand was Philip Morris, because the little red-coated smoke sprite can also mix you a drink.

We puffed for a bit in silence, listening to the rain. "Well," I said at last, "I suppose you have transportation."

"My personal broomstick," she said. "I don't like this GI Willys. Give me a Cadillac anytime. I've souped it up, too."

"And you have your grimoires and powders and whatnot?"

"Just some chalk. No material agency is much use against a powerful demon."

"Yeah? What about the sealing wax on the Solly bottle?"

"It isn't the wax that holds an afreet in, but the seal. The spells are symbolic; in fact, it's believed their effect is purely psychosomatic." She hollowed the flat planes of her cheeks, sucking in

smoke, and I saw what a good bony structure she had. "We may have a chance to test that theory tonight."

"Well, then, you'll want a light pistol loaded with silver slugs; they have weres of their own, you know. I'll take a grease gun and a forty-five and a few grenades."

"How about a squirter?"

I frowned. The notion of using holy water as a weapon has always struck me as blasphemous, though the chaplain said it was permissible against Low World critters. "No good to us," I said. "The Moslems don't have that ritual, so of course they don't use any beings that can be controlled by it. Let's see, I'll want my Polaroid flash too. And that's about it."

Ike Abrams stuck his big nose in the tent flap. "Would you and the lady captain like some eats, sir?" he asked.

"Why, sure," I said. Inwardly, I thought: Hate to spend my last night on Midgard standing in a chow line. When he had gone, I explained to the girl: "Ike's only a private, but we were friends in Hollywood—he was a prop man when I played in *Call of the Wild* and *Silver Chief*—and he's kind of appointed himself my orderly. He'll bring us some food here."

"You know," she remarked, "that's one good thing about the technological age. Did you know there used to be widespread anti-Semitism in this country? Not just among a few Johannine cranks; no, among ordinary respectable citizens."

"Fact?"

"Fact. Especially a false belief that Jews were cowards and never found in the front lines. Now, when religion forbids most of them to originate spells, and the Orthodox don't use goetics at all, the proportion of them who serve as dogfaces and Rangers is simply too high to ignore."

I myself had gotten tired of comic-strip supermen and pulp-magazine heroes having such monotonously Yiddish names—don't Anglo-Saxons belong to our culture too?—but she'd made a good point. And it showed she was a trifle more than a money machine. A bare trifle.

"What'd you do in civilian life?" I asked, chiefly to drown out the incessant noise of the rain.

"I told you," she snapped, irritable again. "I was with the Arcane Agency. Advertising, public relations, and so on."

"Oh, well," I said. "Hollywood is at least as phony, so I shouldn't sneer."

I couldn't help it, however. Those Madison Avenue characters gave

me a pain in the rear end. Using the good Art to puff some self-important nobody, or to sell a product whose main virtue is its total similarity to other brands of the same. The SPCA has cracked down on training nixies to make fountains spell out words, or cramming young salamanders into glass tubes to light up Broadway, but I can still think of better uses for slick paper than trumpeting Ma Chère perfume. Which is actually a love potion anyway, though you know what postal regulations are.

"You don't understand," she said. "It's part of our economy—part of our whole society. Do you think the average backyard warlock is capable of repairing, oh, say a lawn sprinkler? Hell, no! He'd probably let loose the water elementals and flood half a township if it weren't for the inhibitory spells. And we, Arcane, undertook the campaign to convince the Hydros they had to respect our symbols. I told you it's psychosomatic when you're dealing with these really potent beings. For that job, I had to go down in an aqualung!"

I stared at her with more respect. Ever since mankind found how to degauss the ruinous effects of cold iron, and the goetic age began, the world has needed some pretty bold people. Apparently she was one of them.

Abrams brought in two plates of rations. He looked wistful, and I would have invited him to join us except that our mission was secret and we had to thresh out the details.

Captain Graylock chanted the coffee into martinis—not quite dry enough—and the dog food into steaks—a turn too well done; but you can't expect the finer sensibilities in a woman, and it was the best chow I'd had in a month. She relaxed a bit over the brandy, and I learned that her repellent crispness was simply armor against the slick types she dealt with, and we found out that our first names were Steven and Virginia. But then dusk had become dark outside, and we must be going.

You may think it was sheer lunacy, sending two people, one of them a woman, into an enemy division on a task like this. It would seem to call for a Ranger brigade, at least. But present-day science has transformed war as well as industry, medicine, and ordinary life. Our mission was desperate in any event, and we wouldn't have gained enough by numbers to make reinforcements worthwhile.

You see, while practically anyone can learn a few simple cantrips, to operate a presensitized broomstick or vacuum cleaner or turret lathe or whatever, only a small minority of the human race can qualify as adepts. Besides years of study and practice, that takes inborn talent. It's kind of like therianthropy: if you're one of the rare persons with chromosomes for that, you can change into your characteristic animal almost by instinct; otherwise you need a transformation performed on you by powerful outside forces.

My scientific friends tell me that the Art involves regarding the universe as a set of Cantorian infinities. Within any given class, the part is equal to the whole and so on. One good witch could do all the runing we were likely to need; a larger party would simply be more liable to detection, and would risk valuable personnel. So Vanbrugh had very rightly sent us two alone.

The trouble with sound military principles is that sometimes you personally get caught in them.

Virginia and I turned our backs on each other while we changed clothes. She got into an outfit of slacks and combat jacket, I into the elastic knit garment which would fit me as well in wolf-shape. We put on our helmets, hung our equipment around us, and turned about. Even in the baggy green battle garb she looked good.

"Well," I said tonelessly, "shall we go?"

I wasn't afraid, of course. Every recruit is immunized against fear when they put the geas on him. But I didn't like the prospect.

"The sooner the better, I suppose," she answered. Stepping to the entrance, she whistled.

Her stick swooped down and landed just outside. It had been stripped of the fancy chrome, but was still a neat job. The foam-rubber seats had good shock absorbers and well-designed back rests, unlike Army transport. Her familiar was a gigantic tomcat, black as a furry midnight, with two malevolent yellow eyes. He arched his back and spat indignantly. The weatherproofing spell kept rain off him, but he didn't like this damp air.

Virginia chucked him under the chin. "Oh, so, Svartalf," she murmured. "Good cat, rare sprite, prince of darkness, if we outlive this night you shall sleep on cloudy cushions and lap cream from a golden bowl." He cocked his ears and raced his motor.

I climbed into the rear seat, snugged my feet in the stirrups, and leaned back. The woman mounted in front of me and crooned to the stick. It swished upward, the ground fell away and the camp was hidden in gloom. Both of us had been given witch-sight—infrared vision, actually—so we didn't need lights.

When we got above the clouds, we saw a giant vault of stars overhead and a swirling dim whiteness below. I also glimpsed a couple of P-56's circling on patrol, fast jobs with six brooms each to lift their weight of armor and machine guns. We left them behind and streaked northward. I rested the BAR on my lap and sat listening to the air whine past. Underneath us, in the rough-edged murk of the hills, I spied occasional flashes, an artillery duel. So far no one had been able to cast a spell fast enough to turn or implode a shell. I'd heard rumors that General Electric was developing a gadget which could recite the formula in microseconds, but meanwhile the big guns went on talking.

Trollburg was a mere few miles from our position. I saw it as a vague sprawling mass, blacked out against our cannon and bombers. It would have been nice to have an atomic weapon just then, but as long as the Tibetans keep those antinuclear warfare prayer wheels turning, such thoughts must remain merely sciencefictional. I felt my belly muscles tighten. The cat bottled out his tail and swore. Virginia sent the broomstick slanting down.

We landed in a clump of trees and she turned to me. "Their outposts must be somewhere near," she whispered. "I didn't dare try land-

ing on a rooftop; we could have been seen too easily. We'll have to go in from here."

I nodded. "Okay. Gimme a minute."

I turned the flash on myself. How hard to believe that transforming had depended on a bright full moon till only ten years ago! Then Wiener showed that the process was simply one of polarized light of the right wavelengths, triggering the pineal gland, and the Polaroid Corporation made another million dollars or so from its WereWish Lens. It's not easy to keep up with this fearful and wonderful age we live in, but I wouldn't trade.

The usual rippling, twisting sensations, the brief drunken dizziness and half-ecstatic pain, went through me. Atoms reshuffled into whole new molecules, nerves grew some endings and lost others, bone was briefly fluid and muscles like stretched rubber. Then I stabilized, shook myself, stuck my tail out the flap of the skin-tight pants, and nuzzled Virginia's hand.

She stroked my neck, behind the helmet. "Good boy," she whispered. "Go get 'em."

I turned and faded into the brush.

A lot of writers have tried to describe how it feels to be were, and every one of them has failed, because human language doesn't have the words. My vision was no longer acute, the stars were blurred above me and the world took on a colorless flatness. But I heard with a clarity that made the night almost a roar, way into the supersonic; and a universe of smells roiled in my nostrils, wet grass and teeming dirt, the hot sweet little odor of a scampering field mouse, the clean tang of oil and guns, a faint harshness of smoke— Poor stupefied humanity, half-dead to such earthy glories!

The psychological part is the hardest to convey. I was a wolf, with a wolf's nerves and glands and instincts, a wolf's sharp but limited intelligence. I had a man's memories and a man's purposes, but they were unreal, dreamlike. I must make an effort of trained will to hold to them and not go hallooing off after the nearest jackrabbit. No wonder weres had a bad name in the old days, before they themselves understood the mental changes involved and got the right habits drilled into them from babyhood.

I weigh a hundred and eighty pounds, and the conservation of mass holds good like any other law of nature, so I was a pretty big wolf. But it was easy to flow through the bushes and meadows and gullies, another drifting shadow. I was almost inside the town when I caught a near smell of man.

I flattened, the gray fur bristling along my spine, and waited. The sentry came by. He was a tall bearded fellow with gold earrings that glimmered wanly under the stars. The turban wrapped around his helmet bulked monstrous against the Milky Way.

I let him go and followed his path until I saw the next one. They were placed around Trollburg, each pacing a hundred-yard arc and meeting his opposite number at either end of it. No simple task to—

Something murmured in my ears. I crouched. One of their aircraft ghosted overhead. I saw two men and a couple of machine guns squatting on top of the carpet. It circled low and lazily, above the ring of sentries. Trollburg was well guarded.

Somehow, Virginia and I had to get through that picket. I wished the transformation had left me with full human reasoning powers. My wolf-impulse was simply to jump on the nearest man, but that would bring the whole garrison down on my hairy ears.

Wait—maybe that was what was needed!

I loped back to the thicket. The Svartalf cat scratched at me and zoomed up a tree. Virginia Graylock started, her pistol sprang into her hand, then she relaxed and laughed a bit nervously. I could work the flash hung about my neck, even as I was, but it went more quickly with her fingers.

"Well?" she asked when I was human again. "What'd you find out?"

I described the situation, and saw her frown and bite her lip. It was really too shapely a lip for such purposes. "Not so good," she reflected. "I was afraid of something like this."

"Look," I said, "can you locate that afreet in a hurry?"

"Oh, yes. I've studied at Congo U. and did quite well at witch-smelling. What of it?"

"If I attack one of those guards and make a racket doing it, their main attention will be turned that way. You should have an even chance to fly across the line unobserved, and once you're in the town your Tarnkappe—"

She shook her red head. "I didn't bring one. Their detection systems are as good as ours. Invisibility is actually obsolete."

"Mmm—yeah, I suppose you're right. Well, anyhow, you can take advantage of the darkness to get to the afreet house. From there on, you'll have to play by ear."

"I suspected we'd have to do something like this," she replied. With a softness that astonished me: "But Steve, that's a long chance for you to take."

"Not unless they hit me with silver, and most of their cartridges are plain lead. They use a tracer principle like us; every tenth round is argent. I've got a ninety percent probability of getting home free."

"You're a liar," she said. "But a brave liar."

I wasn't brave at all. It's inspiring to think of Valley Forge, or the Alamo, or San Juan Hill, or Casablanca where our outnumbered Army stopped three Panther divisions of von Ogerhaus' Afrika Korps—but only when you're safe and comfortable yourself. Down underneath the antipanic geas, a cold knot was in my guts. Still, I couldn't see any other way to do the job, and failure to attempt it would mean court-martial.

"I'll run their legs off once they start chasing me," I told her. "When I've shaken 'em, I'll try to circle back and join you."

"Okay." Suddenly she rose on tiptoe and kissed me. The impact was explosive.

I stood for a moment, looking at her. "What are you doing Saturday night?" I asked, a mite shakily.

She laughed. "Don't get ideas, Steve. I'm in the Cavalry."

"Yeah, but the war won't last forever." I grinned at her, a reckless fighting grin that made her eyes linger. Acting experience is often useful.

We settled the details as well as we could. She herself had no soft touch: the afreet would be well guarded, and was plenty dangerous in itself. The chances of us both seeing daylight were nothing to feel complacent about.

I turned back to wolf-shape and licked her hand. She rumpled my fur. I slipped off into the darkness.

I had chosen a sentry well off the highway, across which there would surely be barriers. A man could be seen to either side of my victim, tramping slowly back and forth. I glided behind a stump near the middle of his beat and waited for him.

When he came, I sprang. I caught a dark brief vision of eyes and teeth in the bearded face, I heard him yelp and smelled the upward spurt of his fear, then we shocked together. He went down on his back, threshing, and I snapped for the throat. My jaws closed on his arm, and blood was hot and salty on my tongue.

He screamed again. I sensed the call going down the line. The two nearest Saracens ran to help. I tore out the gullet of the first man and bunched myself for a leap at the next.

He fired. The bullet went through me in a jag of pain and the impact sent me staggering. But he didn't know how to deal with a

were. He should have dropped on one knee and fired steadily till he got to the silver bullet; if necessary, he should have fended me off, even pinned me with his bayonet, while he shot. This one kept running toward me, calling on the Allah of his heretical sect.

My tissues knitted as I plunged to meet him. I got past the bayonet and gun muzzle, hitting him hard enough to knock the weapon loose but not to bowl him over. He braced his legs, grabbed my neck, and hung on.

I swung my left hind leg back of his ankle and shoved. He fell with me on top, the position an infighting werewolf always tries for. My head swiveled; I gashed open his arm and broke his grip.

Before I could settle the business, three others had piled on me. Their trench scimitars went up and down, in between my ribs and out again. Lousy training they'd had. I snapped my way free of the heap—half a dozen by then—and broke loose.

Through sweat and blood I caught the faintest whiff of Chanel No. 5, and something in me laughed. Virginia had sped past the confusion, riding her stick a foot above ground, and was inside Trollburg. My next task was to lead a chase and not stop a silver slug while doing so.

I howled, to taunt the men spilling from outlying houses, and let them have a good look at me before making off across the fields. My pace was easy, not to lose them at once; I relied on zigzags to keep me unpunctured. They followed, stumbling and shouting.

As far as they knew, this had been a mere commando raid. Their pickets would have re-formed and the whole garrison been alerted. But surely none except a few chosen officers knew about the afreet, and none of those knew we'd acquired the information. So they had no way of telling what we really planned. Maybe we *would* pull this operation off—

Something swooped overhead, one of their damned carpets. It rushed down on me like a hawk, guns spitting. I made for the nearest patch of woods.

Into the trees! Given half a break, I could—

They didn't give it. I heard a bounding behind me, caught the acrid smell, and whimpered. A weretiger could go as fast as I.

For a moment I remembered an old guide I'd had in Alaska, and wished to blazes he were here. He was a were-Kodiak bear. Then I whirled and met the tiger before he could pounce.

He was a big one, five hundred pounds at least. His eyes smoldered above the great fangs, and he lifted a paw that could crack my spine

like a dry twig. I rushed in, snapping, and danced back before he could strike.

Part of me heard the enemy, blundering around in the underbrush trying to find us. The tiger leaped. I evaded him and bolted for the nearest thicket. Maybe I could go where he couldn't. He ramped through the woods behind me, roaring.

I saw a narrow space between a pair of giant oaks, too small for him, and hurried that way. But it was too small for me also. In the half second that I was stuck, he caught up. The lights exploded and went out.

# IV

I was nowhere and nowhen. My very body had departed from me, or I from it. How could I think of infinite eternal dark and cold and emptiness when I had no senses? How could I despair when I was nothing but a point in spacetime? . . . No, not even that, for there was nothing else, nothing to find or love or hate or fear or be related to in any way whatsoever. The dead were less alone than I, for I was all which existed.

*This* was my despair.

But on the instant, or after a quadrillion years, or both or neither, I came to know otherwise. I was under the regard of the Solipsist. Helpless in unconsciousness, I could but share that egotism so ultimate that it would yield no room even to hope. I swirled in the tides and storms of thoughts too remote, too alien, too vast for me to take in save as I might brokenly hear the polar ocean while it drowned me.

*—danger, this one—he and those two—somehow they can be a terrible danger—not now* (scornfully) *when they merely help complete the ruin of a plan already bungled into wreck—no, later, when the next plan is ripening, the great one of which this war was naught but an early leaf—something about them warns thinly of danger—could I only scan more clearly into time!—they must be diverted, destroyed, somehow dealt with before their potential has grown—but I cannot originate anything yet—maybe they will be slain by the normal chances of war—if not, I must remember them and try later—now I have too much else to do, saving those seeds I planted in the world—the birds of the enemy fly thick across my fields, hungry crows and eagles to guard them—*(with ever wilder hate) *my snares shall take you yet, birds—and the One Who loosed you!*

So huge was the force of that final malevolence that I was cast free.

# V

I opened my eyes. For a while I was aware entirely of the horror. Physical misery rescued me, driving those memories back to where half-forgotten nightmares dwell. The thought flitted by me that shock must have made me briefly delirious.

A natural therianthrope in his beast shape isn't quite as invulnerable as most people believe. Aside from things like silver—biochemical poisons to a metabolism in that semifluid state—damage which stops a vital organ will stop life; amputations are permanent unless a surgeon is near to sew the part back on before its cells die; and so on and so on, no pun intended. We are a hardy sort, however. I'd taken a blow that probably broke my neck. The spinal cord not being totally severed, the damage had healed at standard therio speed.

The trouble was, they'd arrived and used my flash to make me human before the incidental hurts had quite gone away. My head drummed and I retched.

"Get up." Someone stuck a boot in my ribs.

I lurched erect. They'd removed my gear, including the flash. A score of them trained their guns on me. Tiger Boy stood close. In man-shape he was almost seven feet tall and monstrously fat. Squinting through the headache, I saw he wore the insignia of an emir—which was a military rank these days rather than a title, but pretty important nevertheless.

"Come," he said. He led the way, and I was hustled along behind.

I saw their carpets in the sky and heard the howling of their own weres looking for spoor of other Americans. I was still too groggy to care very much.

We entered the town, its pavement sounding hollow under the

boots, and went toward the center. Trollburg wasn't big, maybe five thousand population once. Most of the streets were empty. I saw a few Saracen troops, anti-aircraft guns poking into the sky, a dragon lumbering past with flames flickering around its jaws and cannon projecting from the armored howdah. No trace of the civilians, but I knew what had happened to them. The attractive young women were in the officers' harems, the rest dead or locked away pending shipment to the slave markets.

By the time we got to the hotel where the enemy headquartered, my aches had subsided and my brain was clear. That was a mixed blessing under the circumstances. I was taken upstairs to a suite and told to stand before a table. The emir sat down behind it, half a dozen guards lined the walls, and a young pasha of Intelligence seated himself nearby.

The emir's big face turned to that one, and he spoke a few words—I suppose to the effect of "I'll handle this, you take notes." He looked back at me. His eyes were the pale tiger-green.

"Now then," he said in good English, "we shall have some questions. Identify yourself, please."

I told him mechanically that I was called Sherrinford Mycroft, Captain, AUS, and gave him my serial number.

"That is not your real name, is it?" he asked.

"Of course not!" I replied. "I know the Geneva Convention, and you're not going to cast name-spells on me. Sherrinford Mycroft is my official johnsmith."

"The Caliphate has not subscribed to the Geneva Convention," said the emir quietly, "and stringent measures are sometimes necessary in a jihad. What was the purpose of this raid?"

"I am not required to answer that," I said. Silence would have served the same end, delay to gain time for Virginia, but not as well.

"You may be persuaded to do so," he said.

If this had been a movie, I'd have told him I was picking daisies, and kept on wisecracking while they brought out the thumbscrews. In practice it would have fallen a little flat.

"All right," I said. "I was scouting."

"A single one of you?"

"A few others. I hope they got away." That might keep his boys busy hunting for a while.

"You lie," he said dispassionately.

"I can't help it if you don't believe me," I shrugged.

His eyes narrowed. "I shall soon know if you speak truth," he said. "If not, may Eblis have mercy on you."

I couldn't help it, I jerked where I stood and sweat pearled out on my skin. The emir laughed. He had an unpleasant laugh, a sort of whining growl deep in his fat throat, like a tiger playing with its kill.

"Think over your decision," he advised, and turned to some papers on the table.

It grew most quiet in that room. The guards stood as if cast in bronze. The young shavetail dozed beneath his turban. Behind the emir's back, a window looked out on a blankness of night. The sole sounds were the loud tickings of a clock and the rustle of papers. They seemed to deepen the silence.

I was tired, my head ached, my mouth tasted foul and thirsty. The sheer physical weariness of having to stand was meant to help wear me down. It occurred to me that the emir must be getting scared of us, to take this much trouble with a lone prisoner. That was kudos for the American cause, but small consolation to me.

My eyes flickered, studying the tableau. There wasn't much to see, standard hotel furnishings. The emir had cluttered his desk with a number of objects: a crystal ball useless because of our own jamming, a fine cut-glass bowl looted from somebody's house, a set of nice crystal wineglasses, a cigar humidor of quartz glass, a decanter full of what looked like good Scotch. I guess he just liked crystal.

He helped himself to a cigar, waving his hand to make the humidor open and a Havana fly into his mouth and light itself. As the minutes crawled by, an ashtray soared up from time to time to receive from him. I guessed that everything he had was 'chanted so it would rise and move easily. A man that fat, paying the price of being a really big werebeast, needed such conveniences.

It was very quiet. The light glared down on us. It was somehow hideously wrong to see a good ordinary GE saintelmo shining on those turbaned heads.

I began to get the forlorn glimmerings of an idea. How to put it into effect I didn't yet know, but just to pass the time I began composing some spells.

Maybe half an hour had passed, though it seemed more like half a century, when the door opened and a fennec, the small fox of the African desert, trotted in. The emir looked up as it went into a closet, to find darkness to use its flash. The fellow who came out was, naturally, a dwarf barely one foot high. He prostrated himself and spoke rapidly in a high thready voice.

"So." The emir's chins turned slowly around to me. "The report is that no trace was found of other tracks than yours. You have lied."

"Didn't I tell you?" I asked. My throat felt stiff and strange. "We used owls and bats. I was the lone wolf."

"Be still," he said tonelessly. "I know as well as you that the only werebats are vampires, and that vampires are—what you say—4-F in all armies."

That was true. Every so often, some armchair general asks why we don't raise a force of Draculas. The answer is routine: they're too light and flimsy; they can't endure sunshine; if they don't get a steady blood ration they're apt to turn on their comrades; and you can't possibly use them around Italian troops. I swore at myself, but my mind had been too numb to think straight.

"I believe you are concealing something," went on the emir. He gestured at his glasses and decanter, which supplied him with a shot of Scotch, and sipped judiciously. The Caliphate sect was also heretical with respect to strong drink; they maintained that while the Prophet forbade wine, he said nothing about beer, gin, whisky, brandy, rum, or akvavit.

"We shall have to use stronger measures," the emir said at last. "I was hoping to avoid them." He nodded at his guards.

Two held my arms. The pasha worked me over. He was good at that. The werefennec watched avidly, the emir puffed his cigar and went on with his paperwork. After a long few minutes, he gave an order. They let me go, and even set forth a chair for me, which I needed badly.

I sat breathing hard. The emir regarded me with a certain gentleness. "I regret this," he said. "It is not enjoyable." Oddly, I believed him. "Let us hope you will be reasonable before we have to inflict permanent injuries. Meanwhile, would you like a cigar?"

The old third degree procedure. Knock a man around for a while, then show him kindness. You'd be surprised how often that makes him blubber and break.

"We desire information about your troops and their plans," said the emir. "If you will cooperate and accept the true faith, you can have an honored position with us. We like good men in the Caliphate." He smiled. "After the war, you could select your harem out of Hollywood if you desired."

"And if I don't squeal—" I murmured.

He spread his hands. "You will have no further wish for a harem. The choice is yours."

"Let me think," I begged. "This isn't easy."

"Please do," he answered urbanely, and returned to his papers.

I sat as relaxed as possible, drawing the smoke into my throat and letting strength flow back. The Army geas could be broken by their technicians only if I gave my free consent, and I didn't want to. I considered the window behind the emir. It was a two-story drop to the street.

Most likely, I'd just get myself killed. But that was preferable to any other offer I'd had.

I went over the spells I'd haywired. A real technician has to know at least one arcane language—Latin, Greek, classical Arabic, Sanskrit, Old Norse, or the like—for the standard reasons of sympathetic science. Paranatural phenomena are not strongly influenced by ordinary speech. But except for the usual tag-ends of incantations, the minimum to operate the gadgets of daily life, I was no scholar.

However, I knew one slightly esoteric dialect quite well. I didn't know if it would work, but I could try.

My muscles tautened as I moved. It was a shudder-some effort to be casual. I knocked the end of ash off my cigar. As I lifted the thing again, it collected some ash from the emir's.

I got the rhyme straight in my mind, put the cigar to my lips, and subvocalized the spell.

*"Ashes-way of the urningbay,*
*upward-way ownay eturningray,*
*as-way the arksspay do yflay,*
*ikestray imhay in the eye-way!"*

I closed my right eye and brought the glowing cigar end almost against the lid.

The emir's El Fumo leaped up and ground itself into *his* right eye.

He screamed and fell backward. I soared to my feet. I'd marked the werefennec, and one stride brought me over to him. I broke his vile little neck with a backhanded cuff and yanked off the flash that hung from it.

The guards howled and plunged for me. I went over the table and down on top of the emir, snatching his decanter en route. He clawed at me, wild with pain, I saw the ghastliness in his eye socket, and meanwhile I was hanging on to the vessel and shouting:

*"Ingthay of ystalcray,*
*ebay a istralmay!*
*As-way I-way owthray,*
*yflay ouyay osay!"*

As I finished, I broke free and hurled the decanter at the guards. It was lousy poetics, and might not have worked if the fat man hadn't already sensitized his stuff. As it was, the ball, the ashtray, the bowl, the glasses, the humidor, and the windowpanes all took off after the decanter. The air was full of flying glass.

I didn't stay to watch the results, but went out that window like an exorcised devil. I landed in a ball on the sidewalk, bounced up, and began running.

# VI

Soldiers were around. Bullets sleeted after me. I set a record reaching the nearest alley. My witch-sight showed me a broken window, and I wriggled through that. Crouching beneath the sill, I heard the pursuit go by.

This was the back room of a looted grocery store, plenty dark for my purposes. I hung the flash around my neck, turned it on myself, and made the changeover. They'd return in a minute, and I didn't want to be vulnerable to lead.

Wolf, I snuffled around after another exit. A rear door stood half open. I slipped through into a courtyard full of ancient packing cases. They made a good hideout. I lay there, striving to control my lupine nature, which wanted to pant, while they swarmed through the area.

When they were gone again, I tried to consider my situation. The temptation was to hightail out of this poor, damned place. I could probably make it, and had technically fulfilled my share of the mission. But the job wasn't really complete, and Virginia was alone with the afreet—if she still lived—and—

When I tried to recall her, the image came as a she-wolf and a furry aroma. I shook my head angrily. Weariness and desperation were submerging my reason and letting the animal instincts take over. I'd better do whatever had to be done fast.

I cast about. The town smells were confusing, but I caught the faintest sulfurous whiff and trotted cautiously in that direction. I kept to the shadows, and was seen twice but not challenged. They must have supposed I was one of theirs. The brimstone reek grew stronger.

They kept the afreet in the courthouse, a good solid building. I went through the small park in front of it, snuffed the wind carefully,

and dashed over street and steps. Four enemy soldiers sprawled on top, throats cut open, and the broomstick was parked by the door. It had a twelve-inch switchblade in the handle, and Virginia had used it like a flying lance.

The man side of me, which had been entertaining stray romantic thoughts, backed up in a cold sweat; but the wolf grinned. I poked at the door. She'd 'chanted the lock open and left it that way. I stuck my nose in, and almost had it clawed off before Svartalf recognized me. He jerked his tail curtly, and I passed by and across the lobby. The stinging smell was coming from upstairs. I followed it through a thick darkness.

Light glowed in a second-floor office. I thrust the door ajar and peered in. Virginia was there. She had drawn the curtains and lit the elmos to see by. She was still busy with her precautions, started a little on spying me but went on with the chant. I parked my shaggy behind near the door and watched.

She'd chalked the usual figure, same as the Pentagon in Washington, and a Star of David inside that. The Solly bottle was at the center. It didn't look impressive, an old flask of hard-baked clay with its hollow handle bent over and returning inside—merely a Klein bottle, with Solomon's seal in red wax at the mouth. She'd loosened her hair, and it floated in a ruddy cloud about the pale beautiful face.

The wolf of me wondered why we didn't just make off with this crock of It. The man reminded him that undoubtedly the emir had taken precautions and would have sympathetic means to uncork it from afar. We had to put the demon out of action . . . somehow . . . but nobody on our side knew a great deal about his race.

Virginia finished her spell, drew the bung, and sprang outside the pentacle as smoke boiled from the flask. She almost didn't make it, the afreet came out in such a hurry. I stuck my tail between my legs and snarled. She was scared, too, trying hard not to show that but I caught the adrenalin odor.

The afreet must bend almost double under the ceiling. He was a monstrous gray thing, nude, more or less anthropoid but with wings and horns and long ears, a mouthful of fangs and eyes like hot embers. His assets were strength, speed, and physical near-invulnerability. Turned loose, he could break any attack of Vanbrugh's, and inflict frightful casualties on the most well-dug-in defense. Controlling him afterward, before he laid the countryside waste, would be a problem. But why should the Saracens care? They'd have exacted a geas from him, that he remain their ally, as the price of his freedom.

He roared something in Arabic. Smoke swirled from his mouth. Virginia looked tiny under those half-unfurled bat membranes. Her voice was less cool than she would have preferred: "Speak English, Marid. Or are you too ignorant?"

The demon huffed indignantly. "O spawn of a thousand baboons!" My eardrums flinched from the volume. "O thou white and gutless infidel thing, which I could break with my least finger, come in to me if thou darest!"

I was frightened, less by the chance of his breaking loose than by the racket he was making. It could be heard for a quarter mile.

"Be still, accursed of God!" Virginia answered. That shook him a smidgen. Like most of the hell-breed, he was allergic to holy names, though only seriously so under conditions that we couldn't reproduce here. She stood hands on hips, head tilted, to meet the gaze that smoldered down upon her. "Suleiman bin Daoud, on whom be peace, didn't jug you for nothing, I see. Back to your prison and never come forth again, lest the anger of Heaven smite you!"

The afreet fleered. "Know that Suleiman the Wise is dead these three thousand years," he retorted. "Long and long have I brooded in my narrow cell, I who once raged free through earth and sky and will now at last be released to work my vengeance on the puny sons of Adam." He shoved at the invisible barrier, but one of that type has a rated strength of several million p.s.i. It would hold firm—till some adept dissolved it. "O thou shameless unveiled harlot with hair of hell, know that I am Rashid the Mighty, the glorious in power, the smiter of rocs! Come in here and fight like a man!"

I moved close to the girl, my hackles raised. The hand that touched my head was cold. "Paranoid type," she whispered. "A lot of these harmful Low Worlders are psycho. Stupid, though. Trickery's our single chance. I don't have any spells to compel him directly. But—" Aloud, to him, she said: "Shut up, Rashid, and listen to me. I also am of your race, and to be respected as such."

"Thou?" He hooted with fake laughter. "Thou of the Marid race? Why, thou fish-faced antling, if thou'dst come in here I'd show thee thou'rt not even fit to—" The rest was graphic but not for any gentlewere to repeat.

"No, hear me," said the girl. "Look and hearken well." She made signs and uttered a formula. I recognized the self-geas against telling a falsehood in the particular conversation. Our courts still haven't adopted it—Fifth Amendment—but I'd seen it used in trials abroad.

The demon recognized it, too. I imagine the Saracen adept who

pumped a knowledge of English into him, to make him effective in this war, had added other bits of information about the modern world. He grew more quiet and attentive.

Virginia intoned impressively: "I can speak nothing to you except the truth. Do you agree that the name is the thing?"

"Y-y-yes," the afreet rumbled. "That is common knowledge."

I scented her relief. First hurdle passed! He had *not* been educated in scientific goetics. Though the name is, of course, in sympathy with the object, which is the principle of nymic spells and the like—nevertheless, only in this century has Korzybski demonstrated that the word and its referent are not identical.

"Very well," she said. "My name is Ginny."

He started in astonishment. "Art thou indeed?"

"Yes. Now will you listen to me? I came to offer you advice, as one jinni to another. I have powers of my own, you know, albeit I employ them in the service of Allah, the Omnipotent, the Omniscient, the Compassionate."

He glowered, but supposing her to be one of his species, he was ready to put on a crude show of courtesy. She couldn't be lying about her advice. It did not occur to him that she hadn't said the counsel would be good.

"Go on, then, if thou wilst," he growled. "Knowest thou that tomorrow I fare forth to destroy the infidel host?" He got caught up in his dreams of glory. "Aye, well will I rip them, and trample them, and break and gut and flay them. Well will they learn the power of Rashid the bright-winged, the fiery, the merciless, the wise, the . . ."

Virginia waited out his adjectives, then said gently: "But Rashid, why must you wreak harm? You earn nothing thereby except hate."

A whine crept into his bass. "Aye, thou speakest sooth. The whole world hates me. Everybody conspires against me. Had he not had the aid of traitors, Suleiman had never locked me away. All which I have sought to do has been thwarted by envious ill-wishers— Aye but tomorrow comes the day of reckoning!"

Virginia lit a cigaret with a steady hand and blew smoke at him. "How can you trust the emir and his cohorts?" she asked. "He too is your enemy. He only wants to make a cat's-paw of you. Afterward, back in the bottle!"

"Why . . . why . . ." The afreet swelled till the space-warp barrier creaked. Lightning crackled from his nostrils. It hadn't occurred to him before; his race isn't bright; but of course a trained psychologist would understand how to follow out paranoid logic.

"Have you not known enmity throughout your long days?" continued Virginia quickly. "Think back, Rashid. Was not the very first thing you remember the cruel act of a spitefully envious world?"

"Aye—it was." The maned head nodded, and the voice dropped very low. "On the day I was hatched . . . aye, my mother's wingtip smote me so I reeled."

"Perhaps that was accidental," said Virginia.

"Nay. Ever she favored my older brother—the lout!"

Virginia sat down cross-legged. "Tell me about it," she urged. Her tone dripped sympathy.

I felt a lessening of the great forces that surged within the barrier. The afreet squatted on his hams, eyes half-shut, going back down a memory trail of millennia. Virginia guided him, a hint here and there. I didn't know what she was driving at, surely you couldn't psychoanalyze the monster in half a night, but—

"—Aye, and I was scarce turned three centuries when I fell into a pit my foes must have dug for me."

"Surely you could fly out of it," she murmured.

The afreet's eyes rolled. His face twisted into still more gruesome furrows. "It was a pit, I say!"

"Not by any chance a lake?" she inquired.

"Nay!" His wings thundered. "No such damnable thing . . . 'twas dark, and wet, but—nay, not wet either, a cold which burned . . ."

I saw dimly that the girl had a lead. She dropped long lashes to hide the sudden gleam in her gaze. Even as a wolf, I could realize what a shock it must have been to an aerial demon, nearly drowning, his fires hissing into steam, and how he must ever after deny to himself that it had happened. But what use could she make of—

Svartalf the cat streaked in and skidded to a halt. Every hair on him stood straight, and his eyes blistered me. He spat something and went out again with me in his van.

Down in the lobby I heard voices. Looking through the door, I saw a few soldiers milling about. They'd come by, perhaps to investigate the noise, seen the dead guards, and now they must have sent for reinforcements.

Whatever Ginny was trying to do, she needed time for it. I went out that door in one gray leap and tangled with the Saracens. We boiled into a clamorous pile. I was almost pinned flat by their numbers, but kept my jaws free and used them. Then Svartalf rode that broomstick above the fight, stabbing.

We carried a few of their weapons back into the lobby in our jaws,

and sat down to wait. I figured I'd do better to remain wolf and be immune to most things than have the convenience of hands. Svartalf regarded a tommy gun thoughtfully, propped it along a wall, and crouched over it.

I was in no hurry. Every minute we were left alone, or held off the coming attack, was a minute gained for Ginny. I laid my head on my forepaws and dozed off. Much too soon I heard hobnails rattle on pavement.

The detachment must have been a good hundred. I saw their dark mass, and the gleam of starlight off their weapons. They hovered for a while around the squad we'd liquidated. Abruptly they whooped and charged up the steps.

Svartalf braced himself and worked the tommy gun. The recoil sent him skating back across the lobby, swearing, but he got a couple. I met the rest in the doorway.

Slash, snap, leap in, leap out, rip them and gash them and howl in their faces! After a brief whirl of teeth they retreated. They left half a dozen dead and wounded.

I peered through the glass in the door and saw my friend the emir. He had a bandage over his eye, but lumbered around exhorting his men with more energy than I'd expected. Groups of them broke from the main bunch and ran to either side. They'd be coming in the windows and the other doors.

I whined as I realized we'd left the broomstick outside. There could be no escape now, not even for Ginny. The protest became a snarl when I heard glass breaking and rifles blowing off locks.

That Svartalf was a smart cat. He found the tommy gun again and somehow, clumsy though paws are, managed to shoot out the lights. He and I retreated to the stairway.

They came at us in the dark, blind as most men are. I let them fumble around, and the first one who groped to the stairs was killed quietly. The second had time to yell. The whole gang of them crowded after him.

They couldn't shoot in the gloom and press without potting their own people. Excited to mindlessness, they attacked me with scimitars, which I didn't object to. Svartalf raked their legs and I tore them apart—whick, snap, clash, Allah Akbar and teeth in the night!

The stair was narrow enough for me to hold, and their own casualties hampered them, but the sheer weight of a hundred brave men forced me back a tread at a time. Otherwise one could have tackled

me and a dozen more have piled on top. As things were, we gave the houris a few fresh customers for every foot we lost.

I have no clear memory of the fight. You seldom do. But it must have been about twenty minutes before they fell back at an angry growl. The emir himself stood at the foot of the stairs, lashing his tail and rippling his gorgeously striped hide.

I shook myself wearily and braced my feet for the last round. The one-eyed tiger climbed slowly toward us. Svartalf spat. Suddenly he zipped down the banister past the larger cat and disappeared in the gloom. Well, he had his own neck to think about—

We were almost nose to nose when the emir lifted a paw full of swords and brought it down. I dodged somehow and flew for his throat. All I got was a mouthful of baggy skin, but I hung on and tried to work my way inward.

He roared and shook his head till I swung like a bell clapper. I shut my eyes and clamped on tight. He raked my ribs with those long claws. I skipped away but kept my teeth where they were. Lunging, he fell on me. His jaws clashed shut. Pain jagged through my tail. I let go to howl.

He pinned me down with one paw, raising the other to break my spine. Somehow, crazed with the hurt, I writhed free and struck upward. His remaining eye was glaring at me, and I bit it out of his head.

He screamed! A sweep of one paw sent me kiting up to slam against the banister. I lay with the wind knocked from me while the blind tiger rolled over in his agony. The beast drowned the man, and he went down the stairs and wrought havoc among his own soldiers.

A broomstick whizzed above the melee. Good old Svartalf! He'd only gone to fetch our transportation. I saw him ride toward the door of the afreet, and rose groggily to meet the next wave of Saracens.

They were still trying to control their boss. I gulped for breath and stood watching and smelling and listening. My tail seemed ablaze. Half of it was gone.

A tommy gun began stuttering. I heard blood rattle in the emir's lungs. He was hard to kill. *That's the end of you, Steve Matuchek,* thought the man of me. *They'll do what they should have done in the first place, stand beneath you and sweep you with their fire, every tenth round argent.*

The emir fell and lay gasping out his life. I waited for his men to collect their wits and remember me.

Ginny appeared on the landing, astride the broomstick. Her voice seemed to come from very far away. "Steve! Quick! Here!"

I shook my head dazedly, trying to understand. I was too tired, too canine. She stuck her fingers in her mouth and whistled. That fetched me.

She slung me across her lap and hung on tight as Svartalf piloted the stick. A gun fired blindly from below. We went out a second-story window and into the sky.

A carpet swooped near. Svartalf arched his back and poured on the Power. That Cadillac had legs! We left the enemy sitting there, and I passed out.

# VII

When I came to, I was prone on a cot in a hospital tent. Daylight was bright outside; the earth lay wet and steaming. A medic looked around as I groaned. "Hello, hero," he said. "Better stay in that position for a while. How're you feeling?"

I waited till full consciousness returned before I accepted a cup of bouillon. "How am I?" I whispered; they'd humanized me, of course.

"Not too bad, considering. You had some infection of your wounds—a staphylococcus that can switch species for a human or canine host—but we cleaned the bugs out with a new antibiotic technique. Otherwise, loss of blood, shock, and plain old exhaustion. You should be fine in a week or two."

I lay thinking, my mind draggy, most of my attention on how delicious the bouillon tasted. A field hospital can't lug around the equipment to stick pins in model bacteria. Often it doesn't even have the enlarged anatomical dummies on which the surgeon can do a sympathetic operation. "What technique do you mean?" I asked.

"One of our boys has the Evil Eye. He looks at the germs through a microscope."

I didn't inquire further, knowing that *Reader's Digest* would be waxing lyrical about it in a few months. Something else nagged at me. "The attack . . . have they begun?"

"The— Oh. That! That was two days ago, Rin-Tin-Tin. You've been kept under asphodel. We mopped 'em up along the entire line. Last I heard, they were across the Washington border and still running."

I sighed and went back to sleep. Even the noise as the medic dictated a report to his typewriter couldn't hold me awake.

Ginny came in the next day, with Svartalf riding her shoulder. Sunlight striking through the tent flap turned her hair to hot copper. "Hello, Captain Matuchek," she said. "I came to see how you were, soon as I could get leave."

I raised myself on my elbows, and whistled at the cigaret she offered. When it was between my lips, I said slowly: "Come off it, Ginny. We didn't exactly go on a date that night, but I think we're properly introduced."

"Yes." She sat down on the cot and stroked my hair. That felt good. Svartalf purred at me, and I wished I could respond.

"How about the afreet?" I asked after a while.

"Still in his bottle." She grinned. "I doubt if anybody'll ever be able to get him out again, assuming anybody would want to."

"But what did you *do?*"

"A simple application of Papa Freud's principles. If it's ever written up, I'll have every Jungian in the country on my neck, but it worked. I got him to spinning out his memories and illusions, and soon found he had a hydrophobic complex—which is fear of water, Rover, not rabies—"

"You can call me Rover," I growled, "but if you call me Fido, gives a paddling."

She didn't ask why I assumed I'd be sufficiently close in future for such laying on of hands. That encouraged me. Indeed, she blushed, but went on: "Having gotten the key to his personality, I found it simple to play on his phobia. I pointed out how common a substance water is and how difficult total dehydration is. He got more and more scared. When I showed him that all animal tissue, including his own, is about eighty percent water, that was that. He crept back into his bottle and went catatonic."

After a moment, she added thoughtfully: "I'd like to have him for my mantelpiece, but I suppose he'll wind up in the Smithsonian. So I'll simply write a little treatise on the military uses of psychiatry."

"Aren't bombs and dragons and elfshot gruesome enough?" I demanded with a shudder.

Poor simple elementals! They think they're fiendish, but ought to take lessons from the human race.

As for me, I could imagine certain drawbacks to getting hitched with a witch, but— "C'mere, youse."

She did.

I don't have many souvenirs of the war. It was an ugly time and

best forgotten. But one keepsake will always be with me, in spite of the plastic surgeons' best efforts. As a wolf, I've got a stumpy tail, and as a man I don't like to sit down in wet weather.

That's a hell of a thing to receive a Purple Heart for.

# VIII

Here we reach one of the interludes. I'll skip over them fast. They were often more interesting and important to us—to Ginny and me—than the episodes which directly involved our Adversary. The real business of people is not strife or danger or melodrama; it's work, especially if they're so fortunate as to enjoy what they do; it's recreation and falling in love and raising families and telling jokes and stumbling into small pleasant adventures.

But you wouldn't care especially about what happened to us in those departments. You have your personal lives. Furthermore, a lot of it is nobody's business but ours. Furthermore yet, I have only this one night to 'cast. Any longer, and the stress might have effects on me. I don't take needless chances with the unknown; I've been there.

Finally, the big events do matter to you. He's also your Adversary.

Let me therefore just use the interludes to put the episodes in context. Okay?

This first period covers roughly two years. For several months of them Ginny and I remained in service, though we didn't see combat again. Nor did we see each other, which was worse on two counts. Reassignment kept shuffling us around.

Not that the war lasted that long. The kaftans had been beaten off the Caliphate. It disintegrated like a dropped windowpane, in revolutions, riots, secessions, vendettas, banditry, and piecemeal surrenders. America and her allies didn't need armed forces to invade enemy-held territory. They did need them, and urgently, for its occupation, to restore order before famine and plague broke loose. Our special talents had Ginny and me hopping over half the world—but not in company.

We spent a barrel of pay on postage. Nevertheless I took a while

to decide I really had better propose; and while her answer was tender, it wasn't yes. Orphaned at a rather early age, she'd grown to womanhood with a need for warmth—and a capacity for it—which required that tough career-girl shell to guard her from hurt. She would not contract a marriage that she wasn't certain could be for life.

I was discharged somewhat before her and went home to reweave threads torn loose by the war. Surprisingly few showed in the United States. Though the invaders had overrun nearly half, throughout most of that conquest they were present only a short while before we rolled them back, and in that while we kept them too busy to wreak the degree of harm that luckless longer-held corners like Trollburg suffered. Civil government followed on the heels of the Army, more rapid and efficient in its work than I'd have expected. Or maybe civilization itself was responsible. Technology can produce widespread devastation, but likewise quick recoveries.

Thus I returned to a country which, apart from various shortages that soon disappeared, looked familiar. On the surface, I mean. The psyche was something else again. Shocked to their souls by what had happened, I suppose, shocked more deeply than they knew, a significant part of the population had come unbalanced. What saved us from immediate social disaster was doubtless the variety of their eccentricities. So many demagogues, self-appointed prophets, would-be necromancers, nut cultists in religion and politics and science and dieting and life style and Lord knows what else, tended to cancel each other out. A few of them did grow ominously, like the Johannine Church, of which much more anon.

However, that didn't happen in a revolutionary leap. Those of us who weren't afflicted with some fanaticism—and we were the majority, remember—seldom worried more than peripherally. We figured the body politic would stop twitching in the natural course of events. Meanwhile we had our careers and dreams to rebuild; we had the everydays to get through.

Myself, I went back to Hollywood and resumed werewolfing for Metro-Goldwyn-Merlin. That proved a disappointment. It was a nuisance wearing a fake brush over my bobbed tail, for me and the studio alike. They weren't satisfied with my performances, either; nor was I. For instance, in spite of honestly trying, I couldn't get real conviction into my role in *Dracula, Frankenstein, the Wolf Man, the Mummy, and the Thing Meet Paracelsus.* Not that I look down on pure entertainment, but I was discovering a newborn wish to do something more significant.

So there began to be mutual hints about my resignation. Probably only my medals delayed a crisis. But war heroes were a dime a coven. Besides, everybody knows that military courage is a large part training and discipline, another large part the antipanic geas; and the latter is routinely lifted upon discharge, because civilians *need* a touch of timidity. I don't claim any more than the normal share of natural guts.

About that time Ginny was demobbed. She came straight to visit me. That was quite a reunion. She wouldn't accept my repeated proposals—"Not yet, Steve, dear; not till we see what we're both like under ordinary conditions; don't you understand?"—but I seemed to be running well out in front.

In the course of several days, besides the expected things, we did considerable serious talking. She drew to the forefront of my mind what my true ambition was: taming Fire and Air to create an antigravity spell powerful enough that men could reach the planets. In fact, I'd set out to be an engineer. But funds ran low in my freshman year, and a talent scout happened to see me in some amateur theatricals, and one thing led to another. Like most people, I'd drifted through life.

Ginny was not like most people. However, she'd been doing some rethinking too. She was welcome back at Arcane, but wondered if she really wanted to work for a large organization. Wouldn't her own independent consulting agency give her freedom to explore her own ideas? For that she needed further goetic knowledge, and the obvious way to acquire it was to go for a Ph.D.

And . . . between our savings and our GI, we could both now afford a return to college.

The clincher came when, after some correspondence, Trismegistus University offered her an instructorship—since she already had an M.A. from Congo—while she did her advanced studies. I fired off an application to its school of engineering and was accepted. A few weeks later, Steven Matuchek and MGM parted ways with many polite noises, and he and Virginia Graylock boarded a supercarpet for the Upper Midwest.

At first everything went like lampwork. We found us decent inexpensive rooms, not far apart. Classes were interesting. We spent most of our free waking hours together. Her resistance to an early marriage was eroding at such a rate that I extrapolated she'd accept me by Christmas and we'd hold the wedding right after the spring finals.

But then we felt the kicker. Right in the belly.

We'd known that the generally good faculty was saddled with a pompous mediocrity of a president, Bengt Malzius, whose chief ac-

complishment had been to make the trustees his yes-men. What he said, went. As a rule that didn't affect anybody on a lower level, at least not much. But in the past year he had decreed that academic personnel, without exception, must take a geas to obey every University regulation while their contracts were in force.

Few persons objected strongly. By and large, the rules were the standard ones; and salaries were good; and the new compulsion was intended as a partial check on the rebelliousness, nuttiness, and outright nihilism that had been growing to a disturbing extent of late, not only among students but among faculties. Ginny went along.

We'd been around for a couple of weeks when someone noticed we were going steady, and blabbed. Ginny was called into the president's presence. He showed her the fine print in his regulations, that she had not thought to read.

Students and faculty, right down to the instructor level, were not permitted to date each other.

We had a grim session that evening.

Naturally, next day I stormed past every clerk and secretary to confront Malzius in his office. No use. He wasn't going to revise the book for us. "Bad precedent, Mr. Matuchek, bad precedent." I agreed furiously that it was, indeed, a bad president. The rule would have had to be stricken altogether, as the geas didn't allow special dispensations. Nor did it allow for the case of a student from another school, so it was pointless for me to transfer.

The sole solution, till Ginny's contract expired in June, would have been for me to drop out entirely, and her cold-iron determination wouldn't hear of that. Lose a whole year? What was I, a wolf or a mouse? We had a big fat quarrel about it, right out in public. And when you can only meet by chance, or at official functions, it isn't just easy to kiss and make up.

Oh, sure, we were still "good friends" and still saw each other at smokers, teas, certain lectures . . . real *dolce vita.* Meanwhile, as she stated with the icy logic I knew was defensive but never could break past, we were human. From time to time she would be going out with some bachelor colleague, wishing he were me, and I'd squire an occasional girl around—

That's how matters stood in November.

The sky was full of broomsticks and the police were going nuts trying to handle the traffic. The Homecoming game always attracts an overflow crowd, also an overflow of high spirits. These I did not share. I edged my battered prewar Chevy past a huge two-hundred-dragon-power Lincoln with sky-blue handle, polyethylene straw, and blatting radio. It sneered at me, but I got to the vacant rack first. Dismounting, I pocketed the runekey and mooched glumly through the mob.

The Weather Bureau kachinas are obliging about game nights. There was a cool crisp tang to the air, and dry leaves scrittled across the sidewalks. A harvest moon was rising like a big yellow pumpkin over darkened campus buildings. I thought of Midwestern fields and woods, damp earthy smells and streaming mists, out beyond the city, and the wolf part of me wanted to be off and away after jackrabbits. But with proper training a were can control his reflexes and polarized light doesn't have to cause more than a primitive tingle along his nerves.

For me, the impulse was soon lost in bleaker thoughts. Ginny, my darling! She should have been walking beside me, face lifted to the wind and long hair crackling in the thin frost; but my only companion was an illegal hip flask. Why the hell was I attending the game anyhow?

Passing Teth Caph Sameth frat house, I found myself on the campus proper. Trismegistus was founded after the advent of modern science, and its layout reflects that fact. The largest edifice houses the Language Department, because exotic tongues are necessary for the more powerful spells—which is why so many African and Asian students come here to learn American slang; but there are two English halls, one for the arts college and one for Engineering Poetics. Nearby

is the Therioanthropology Building, which always has interesting displays of foreign technique: this month it was Eskimo, in honor of the visiting angekok Dr. Ayingalak. A ways off is Zoology, carefully isolated inside its pentagonal fence, for some of those long-legged beasties are not pleasant neighbors. The medical school has a shiny new research center, courtesy of the Rockefeller Foundation, from which has already come such stunning advances as the Polaroid filterlenses that make it possible for those afflicted with the Evil Eye to lead normal lives.

The law school is unaffected. Their work has always been of the other world.

Crossing the Mall, I went by the grimy little Physical Sciences Building just in time for Dr. Griswold to hail me. He came puttering down the steps, a small wizened fellow with goatee and merry blue eyes. Somewhere behind their twinkle lay a look of hurt bafflement; he was a child who could never quite understand why no one else was really interested in his toys.

"Ah, Mr. Matuchek," he said. "Are you attending the game?"

I nodded, not especially sociable, but he tagged along and I had to be polite. That wasn't to polish any apples. I was in his chemistry and physics classes, but they were snaps. I simply hadn't the heart to rebuff a nice, lonely old geezer.

"Me too," he went on. "I understand the cheerleaders have planned something spectacular between halves."

"Yeah?"

He cocked his head and gave me a birdlike glance. "If you're having any difficulty, Mr. Matuchek . . . if I can help you . . . that's what I'm here for, you know."

"Everything's fine," I lied. "Thanks anyway, sir."

"It can't be easy for a mature man to start in with a lot of giggling freshmen," he said. "I remember how you helped me in that . . . ah . . . unfortunate incident last month. Believe me, Mr. Matuchek, I am grateful."

"Oh, hell, that was nothing. I came here to get an education." *And to be with Virginia Graylock. But that's impossible now.* I saw no reason to load my troubles on him. He had an ample supply already.

Griswold sighed, perhaps feeling my withdrawal. "I often feel so useless," he said.

"Not in the least, sir," I answered with careful heartiness. "How on Midgard would—oh, say alchemy, be practical without a thorough

grounding in nuclear physics? You'd either get a radioactive isotope that could kill you, or blow up half a county."

"Of course, of course. You understand. You know something of the world—more than I, in all truth. But the students . . . well, I suppose it's only natural. They want to speak a few words, make a few passes, and get what they desire, just like that, without bothering to learn the Sanskrit grammar or the periodic table. They haven't realized that you never get something for nothing."

"They will. They'll grow up."

"Even the administration . . . this University simply doesn't appreciate the need for physical science. Now at California, they're getting a billion-volt Philosopher's Stone, but here—" Griswold shrugged. "Excuse me. I despise self-pity."

We came to the stadium, and I handed over my ticket but declined the night-seeing spectacles, having kept the witch-sight given me in basic training. My seat was on the thirty-yard line, between a fresh-faced coed and an Old Grad already hollering himself raw. An animated tray went by, and I bought a hot dog and rented a crystal ball. But that wasn't to follow the details of play. I muttered over the globe and peered into it and saw Ginny.

She was seated on the fifty, opposite side, the black cat Svartalf on her lap, her hair a shout of red against the human drabness around. That witchcraft peculiarly hers was something more old and strong than the Art in which she was so adept. Even across the field and through the cheap glass gazer, she made my heart stumble.

Tonight she was with Dr. Alan Abercrombie, assistant professor of comparative mantics, sleek, blond, handsome, the lion of the tiffins. He'd been paying her a lot of attention while I smoldered alone.

Quite alone. I think Svartalf considers my morals no better than his. I had every intention of fidelity, but when you've parked your broomstick in a moonlit lane and a cute bit of fluff is snuggled against you . . . those round yellow eyes glowing from a nearby tree are remarkably style-cramping. I soon gave up and spent my evenings studying or drinking beer.

Heigh-ho. I drew my coat tighter about me and shivered in the wind. That air smelled wrong somehow . . . probably only my bad mood, I thought, but I'd sniffed trouble in the future before now.

The Old Grad blasted my ears off as the teams trotted out into the moonlight, Trismegistus' Gryphons and the Albertus Magnus Wyverns. The very old grads say they can't get used to so many four-eyed runts wearing letters. Apparently a football team was composed of dinosaurs

back before the goetic age. But of course the Art is essentially intellectual and has given its own tone to sports—

This game had its interesting points. The Wyverns levitated off and their tiny quarterback turned out to be a werepelican. Dushanovitch, in condor shape, nailed him on our twenty. Andrevski is the best line werebuck in the Big Ten, and held them for two downs. In the third, Pilsudski got the ball and became a kangaroo. His footwork was beautiful as he dodged a tackle—the guy had a Tarnkappe, but you could see the footprints advance—and passed to Mstislav. The Wyverns swooped low, expecting Mstislav to turn it into a raven for a field goal, but with lightning a-crackle as he fended off their counterspells, he made it into a pig . . . greased. (These were minor transformations, naturally, a quick gesture at an object already sensitized, not the great and terrible Words I was to hear before dawn.)

A bit later, unnecessary roughness cost us fifteen yards: Domingo accidentally stepped on a scorecard which had blown to the field and drove his cleats through several of the Wyverns' names. But no real harm was done, and they got the same penalty when Thorsson was carried away by the excitement and tossed a thunderbolt. At the end of the first half, the score was Trismegistus 13, Albertus Magnus 6, and the crowd was nearly ripping the benches loose.

I pulled my hat back off my ears, gave the Old Grad a dirty look, and stared into the crystal. Ginny was more of a fan than I, she was jumping and hollering, hardly seeming to notice that Abercrombie had an arm around her. Or perhaps she didn't mind—? I took a long, resentful drag at my flask.

The cheering squad paraded out onto the field. Their instruments wove through an elaborate aerial maneuver, drumming and tootling, while they made the traditional march to the Campus Queen. I'm told it's also traditional that she ride forth on a unicorn to meet them, but for some reason that was omitted this year.

The hair rose stiff on my neck and I felt the blind instinctive tug of Skinturning. Barely in time I hauled myself back toward human and sat in a cold sweat. The air was suddenly rotten with danger. Couldn't *anyone* else smell it?

I focused my crystal on the cheering squad, looking for the source, only dimly aware of the yell—

"Aleph, beth, gimel, daleth, he, vau,
Nomine Domini, bow, wow, wow!
Melt 'em in the fire and stick 'em with pins,
Trismegistus always wins—"

MacIlwraith!

"Hey, what's wrong, mister?" The coed shrank from me, and I realized I was snarling.

"Oh . . . nothing . . . I hope." With an effort I composed my face and kept it from sprouting a snout.

The fattish blond kid down among the rooters didn't look harmful, but a sense of lightning-shot blackness swirled about his future. I'd dealt with him before, and—

Though I didn't snitch on him at the time, he was the one who had almost destroyed Griswold's chemistry class. Premed freshman, rich boy, not a bad guy at heart but with an unfortunate combination of natural aptitude for the Art and total irresponsibility. Medical students are notorious for merry pranks such as waltzing an animated skeleton through the girls' dorm, and he wanted to start early.

Griswold had been demonstrating the action of a catalyst, and MacIlwraith had muttered a pun-spell to make a cat boil out of the test tube. However, he slipped quantitatively and got a saber-toothed tiger. Because of the pun, it listed to starboard, but it was nonetheless a vicious, panic-raising thing. I ducked into a closet, used my pocket moonflash, and transformed. As a wolf I chased Pussy out the window and into a tree till somebody could call the Exorcism Department.

Having seen MacIlwraith do it, I took him aside and warned him that if he disrupted the class again I'd chew him out in the most literal sense. Fun is fun, but not at the expense of students who really want to learn and a pleasant elderly anachronism who's trying to teach them.

—"TEAM!"

The cheerleader waved his hands and a spurt of many-colored fire jumped out of nothingness. Taller than a man it lifted, a leaping glory of red, blue, yellow, haloed with a wheel of sparks. Slitting my eyes, I could just discern the lizard like form, white-hot and supple, within the aura.

The coed squealed. "Thrice-blessed Hermes," choked the Old Grad. "What is that? A demon?"

"No, a fire elemental," I muttered. "Salamander. Hell of a dangerous thing to fool around with."

My gaze ran about the field as the burning shape began to do its tricks, bouncing, tumbling, spelling out words in long flame-bands. Yes, they had a fireman close by in full canonicals, making the passes that kept the creature harmless. The situation ought to be okay. I lit a cigaret, shakily. It is not well to raise Loki's pets, and the stink of menace to come was acrid in my nostrils.

A good show, but— The crystal revealed Abercrombie clapping. Ginny, though, sat with a worried frown between the long green eyes. She didn't like this any better than I. Switch the ball back to MacIlwraith, fun-loving MacIlwraith.

I was perhaps the single member of the audience who saw what happened. The boy gestured at his baton. It sprouted wings. The fat fireman, swaying back and forth with his gestures, was a natural target for a good healthy goose. "Yeowp!"

He rocketed heavenward. The salamander wavered. All at once it sprang on high, thinning out till it towered over the walls. We glimpsed a spinning, dazzling blur, and the thing was gone.

My cigaret burst luridly into flame. I tossed it from me. Hardly thinking, I jettisoned my hip flask. It exploded from a touch of incandescence and the alcohol burned blue. The crowd howled, hurling away their smokes, slapping at pockets where matches had kindled, getting rid of bottles. The Campus Queen shrieked as her thin dress caught fire. She got it off in time to prevent serious injury and went wailing across the field. Under different circumstances, I would have been interested.

The salamander stopped its lunatic shuttling and materialized between goalposts that began to smoke: an intolerable blaze, which scorched the grass and roared. The fireman dashed toward it, shouting the spell of extinguishment. From the salamander's mouth licked a tongue of fire, I heard a distinct Bronx cheer, then it was gone again.

The announcer, who should have been calming the spectators, screeched as it flickered before his booth. That touched off the panic! In one heartbeat, five thousand people were clawing and trampling, choking each other in the gates, blind with the maniac need to escape.

I vaulted across benches and an occasional head, down to the field. There was death on those jammed tiers. "Ginny! Ginny, come here where it's safe!"

She couldn't have heard me above the din, but came of herself, dragging a terrified Abercrombie by one wrist. We faced each other in a ring of ruin. She drew the telescoping wand from her purse.

The Gryphons came boiling out of their locker room. Boiling is the right word: the salamander had materialized down there and playfully wrapped itself around the shower pipes.

Sirens hooted under the moon and police broomsticks shot above us, trying to curb the stampede. The elemental flashed for a moment across one besom. The rider dove it till he could jump off, and the burning stick crashed on the grass.

"God!" exclaimed Abercrombie. "The salamander's loose!"

"Tell me more," I snorted. "Ginny, you're a witch. Can you do anything about this?"

"I can extinguish the brute if it'll hold still long enough for me to recite the spell," she said. Disordered ruddy hair had tumbled past her pale, high-boned face to the fur-clad shoulders. "That's our one chance—the binding charm is broken, and it knows that!"

I whirled, remembering friend MacIlwraith, and collared him. "Were you possessed?" I shouted.

"I didn't do anything," he gasped. His teeth rattled as I shook him.

"Don't hand me that guff. I saw!"

He collapsed on the ground. "It was only for fun," he whimpered. "I didn't know—"

Well, I thought grimly, that was doubtless true. There's the trouble with the Art: with every blind powerful force man uses, fire or dynamite or atomic energy or goetics. Any meathead can learn how to begin something; these days, they start them in the third grade with spelling bees. But it's not always so easy to halt the something.

Student pranks were a standing problem at Trismegistus, as at all colleges. They were usually harmless, like sneaking into the dorms after curfew with Tarnkappen, or chanting female lingerie out through the windows. Sometimes they could be rather amusing, like the time the statue of a revered and dignified former president was animated and marched downtown singing bawdy songs. Often they fell quite flat, as when the boys turned Dean Hornsby into stone and it wasn't noticed for three days.

This one had gotten out of hand. The salamander could ignite this entire city.

I turned to the fireman, who was jittering about trying to flag down a police broom. In the dim shifty light, none of the riders saw him. "What'd you figure to do?" I asked.

"I gotta report back for duty," he said harshly. "And we'll need a water elemental, I guess."

"I have experience with the Hydros," offered Ginny. "I'll come along."

"Me too," I said at once.

Abercrombie glowered. "What can you do?"

"I'm were," I snapped. "In wolf shape I can't easily be harmed by fire. That might turn out useful."

"Wonderful, Steve!" Ginny smiled at me, the old smile which had

so often gone between us. Impulsively, I grabbed her to me and kissed her.

She didn't waste energy on a slap. I collected an uppercut that tumbled me on my stern. "Not allowed," she clipped. That double-damned geas! I could see misery caged within her eyes, but her mind was compelled to obey Malzius' rules.

"That's . . . ah . . . no place for a woman . . . a lady as charming as you," murmured Abercrombie. "Let me take you home, my dear."

"I've work to do," she said impatiently. "What the devil is wrong with those cops? We've got to get a lift out of here."

"Then I shall come too," said Abercrombie. "I am not unacquainted with blessings and curses, though—ha!—I fear that ever-filled purses are a trifle beyond my scope. In any event, the Treasury Department frowns on them."

Even in that moment, with riot thundering and hell let loose on earth, I was pleased to note that Ginny paid no attention to his famous wit. She scowled abstractedly and looked around. The Campus Queen was huddled near the benches, wearing somebody's overcoat. Ginny grinned and waved her wand. The Campus Queen shucked the coat and ran toward us. Thirty seconds later, three police broomsticks had landed. The fireman commandeered them and our party was whirled over the stadium and into the street.

During that short hop, I saw three houses ablaze. The salamander was getting around!

We gathered at the district police station, a haggard and sooty crew with desperate eyes. The fire chief and police chief were there, and a junior officer going crazy at the switchboard. Ginny, who had collected her own broom at her lodgings, arrived with Svartalf on one shoulder and the *Handbook of Alchemy and Metaphysics* under her arm. Abercrombie was brow-beating the terrified MacIlwraith till I told him to lay off.

"My duty—" he began. "I'm a proctor, you know."

I suppose it's necessary to have witch-smellers on campus, to make sure the fellows don't 'chant up liquor in the frat houses or smuggle in nymphs. And every year somebody tries to get by an exam with a familiar under his coat whispering the answers from a cribsheet. Nevertheless, I don't like professional nosy parkers.

"You can deal with him later," I said, and gave the boy a push out the door. "The salamander can fight back."

President Malzius huffed into the room. "What is the meaning of this?" he demanded. His pince-nez bobbed above full jowls. "I'll have you know, sir, I was preparing a most important address. The Lions Totem is holding a luncheon tomorrow, and—"

"Might not be any lunch," grunted the cop who had fetched him. "We got a salamander loose."

"Sala—No! It's against the rules! It is positively forbidden to—"

The man at the switchboard looked toward us. "It's just kindled the Methodist church at Fourteenth and Elm," he said. "And my God, all our equipment is already in service."

"Impossible!" cried Malzius. "A demon can't go near a church."

"How stupid does a man have to be to get your job?" Ginny fairly

spat. "This *isn't* a demon. It's an elemental." When her temper was again sheathed in ice, she continued slowly: "We haven't much hope of using a Hydro to put out the salamander, but we can raise one to help fight the fires. It'll always be three jumps behind, but at least the whole city won't be ruined."

"Unless the salamander gets too strong," cut in Abercrombie. His face was colorless and he spoke through stiff lips. "Then it can evaporate the Hydro."

"Summon two water beings," stammered Malzius. "Summon a hundred. I'll waive the requirement of formal application for permission to—"

"That possibility is limited, sir," Abercrombie told him. "The restraining force required is an exponential function of the total embodied mass. There probably aren't sufficient adepts in this town to control more than three at a time. If we raised four . . . we'd flood the city, and the salamander need merely skip elsewhere."

"Alan—" Ginny laid her handbook on the desk and riffled its pages. Abercrombie leaned over her shoulder, remembering to rest one hand carelessly on her hip. I choked back my prize cusswords. "Alan, for a starter, can you summon one Hydro and put it to work at plain fire fighting?"

"Of course, gorgeous one," he smiled. "That is a, ha, elemental problem."

She gave him a worried glance. "They can be as tricky as Fire or Air," she warned. "It's not enough just to know the theory."

"I have some small experience," he preened. "During the war— After this is over, come around to my place for a drink and I'll tell you about it." His lips brushed her cheek.

"Mr. Matuchek!" yelled Malzius. "Will you please stop growing fangs?"

I shook myself and suppressed the rage which had been almost as potent as moonlight.

"Look here," said the police chief. "I gotta know what's going on. You longhairs started this trouble and I don't want you making it worse."

Seeing that Ginny and Pretty Boy were, after all, legitimately busy, I sighed and whistled for a cigaret. "Let me explain," I offered. "I learned a few things about the subject, during the war. An elemental is not the same as a demon. Any kind of demon is a separate being, as individual as you and I. An elemental is part of the basic force involved: in this case, fire, or more accurately energy. It's raised out

of the basic energy matrix, given temporary individuality, and restored to the matrix when the adept is through with it."

"Huh?"

"Like a flame. A flame only exists potentially till someone lights a fire, and goes back to potential existence when you put the fire out. And the second fire you light, even on the same log, is not identical with the first. So you can understand why an elemental isn't exactly anxious to be dismissed. When one breaks loose, as this one did, it does its damnedest to stay in this world and to increase its power."

"But how come can it burn a church?"

"Because it's soulless, a mere physical force. Any true individual, human or otherwise, is under certain constraints of a . . . a moral nature. A demon is allergic to holy symbols. A man who does wrong has to live with his conscience in this world and face judgment in the next. But what does a fire care? And that's what the salamander is—a glorified fire. It's only bound by the physical laws of nature and paranature."

"So how do you, uh, put one out?"

"A Hydro of corresponding mass could do it, by mutual annihilation. Earth could bury it or Air withdraw from its neighborhood. Trouble is, Fire is the swiftest of the lot; it can flick out of an area before any other sort of elemental can injure it. So we're left with the dismissal spell. But that has to be said in the salamander's presence, and takes about two minutes."

"Yeah . . . and when the thing hears you start the words, it'll burn you down or scram. *Very* nice. What're we gonna do?"

"I don't know, chief," I said, "except it's like kissing a sheep dog." I blew hard and immediately smacked my lips. "You got to be quick. Every fire the critter starts feeds it more energy and makes it that much stronger. There's a limit somewhere—the square-cube law—but by then, it could be too powerful for humans to affect it."

"And what'd happen next?"

"Ragnarök. . . . No, I suppose not quite. Men would naturally raise correspondingly strong counter-elementals, like Hydros. But think of the control difficulties, and the incidental damage. Compared to that, the Caliphists were pikers."

Ginny turned from the desk. Abercrombie was chalking a pentagram on the floor while a sputtering Malzius had been deputized to sterilize a pocket knife with a match. (The idea was to draw a little blood from somebody. It can substitute for the usual powders, since it contains the same proteins.) The girl laid a hand on mine. "Steve, we'd

take too long getting hold of every local adept and organizing them," she said. "I'm afraid the same's true of the state police or the National Guard. God knows what the salamander will do while this office is calling for help. We, though, you and I, we could at least keep track of it, with less danger to ourselves than most. Are you game?"

"Sure," I agreed. "It can't hurt me in my wolf shape . . . not permanently . . . not if I'm careful. But you're staying put."

"Ever hear about the oath of my order? Come on."

As we went out the door, I gave Abercrombie a smug look. He had nicked his wrist and sprinkled the Signs; now he was well into the invocation. I felt cold dampness swirl through the room.

Outside, the night remained autumnally sharp, the moon high. Roofs made a saw-toothed silhouette against the leaping red glare at a dozen points around us, and sirens howled in the streets. Overhead, across the small indifferent stars, I saw what looked like a whirl of dry leaves, refugees fleeing on their sticks.

Svartalf jumped to the front end of Ginny's Cadillac, and I took the saddle behind hers. We whispered skyward.

Below us, blue fire spat and the station lights went out. Water poured into the street, a solid roar of it with President Malzius bobbing like a cork in the torrent.

"Unholy Sathanas!" I choked. "What's happened now?"

Svartalf ducked the stick low. "That idiot," groaned Ginny. "He let the Hydro slop clear over the floor . . . short circuits—" She made a few rapid passes with her wand. The stream quieted, drew into itself, became a ten-foot-high blob glimmering in the moonlight. Abercrombie scuttled out and started it squelching toward the nearest fire.

I laughed. "Go visit his place and listen to him tell about his vast experience," I said.

"Don't kick a man when he's down," Ginny snapped. "You've pulled your share of boners, Steve Matuchek."

Svartalf whisked the broom aloft again and we went above the chimney pots. *Oof!* I thought. Could she really be falling for that troll? A regular profile, a smooth tongue, and proximity. . . . I bit back an inward sickness and squinted ahead, trying to find the salamander.

"There!" Ginny yelled over the whistle of cloven air. Svartalf bottled his tail and hissed.

The University district is shabby-genteel: old pseudo-Gothic caves of wood which have slipped from mansions to rooming houses, flyspecked with minor business establishments. It had begun burning merrily, a score of red stars flickering in the darkness between street lamps.

Rushing near, we saw one of the stars explode in a white puff of steam. The Hydro must have clapped a sucker onto a fireplug and blanketed the place. I had a brief heretical thought that the salamander was doing a public service by eliminating those architectural teratologies. But lives and property were involved—

Tall and terrible, the elemental wavered beside the house on which it was feeding. It had doubled in size, and its core was too bright to look at. Flames whirled about the narrow head.

Svartalf braked and we hovered a few yards off, twenty feet in the air and level with the hungry mouth. Ginny was etched wild against night by that intolerable radiance. She braced herself in the stirrups and began the spell, her voice almost lost in the roar as the roof caved in. *"O Indra, Abaddon, Lucifer, Moloch, Hephaestos, Loki—"*

It heard. The seething eyes swung toward us and it leaped.

Svartalf squalled when his whiskers shriveled—perhaps only hurt vanity—and put the stick through an Immelmann turn and whipped away. The salamander bawled with the voice of a hundred blazing forests. Suddenly the heat scorching my back was gone, and the thing had materialized in front of us.

"That way!" I hollered, pointing. "In there!"

I covered Ginny's face and buried my own against her back as we went through the plate-glass front of Stub's Beer Garden. The flame-tongue licked after us, recoiled, and the salamander ramped beyond the door.

We tumbled off the broom and looked around. The tavern was empty, full of a fire-spattered darkness; everyone had fled. I saw a nearly full glass of beer on the counter and tossed it off.

"You might have offered me a drink," said Ginny. "Alan would have." Before I could recover enough to decide whether she was taunting or testing me, she went on in a rapid whisper: "It isn't trying to escape. It's gained power—confidence—it means to kill us!"

Even then, I wanted to tell her that red elflocks and a soot-smudge across an aristocratic nose were particularly enchanting. But the occasion didn't seem appropriate. "Can't get in here," I panted. "Can't do much more than ignite the building by thermal radiation, and that'll take a while. We're safe for the moment."

"Why . . . oh, yes, of course. Stub's is cold-ironed. All these college beer parlors are, I'm told."

"Yeah." I peered out the broken window. The salamander peered back, and spots danced before my eyes. "So the clientele won't go jazzing up the brew above 3.2— Quick, say your spell."

Ginny shook her head. "It'll just flicker away out of earshot. Maybe we can talk to it, find out—"

She trod forth to the window. The thing crouched in the street extended its neck and hissed at her. I stood behind my girl, feeling boxed and useless. Svartalf, lapping spilled beer off the counter, looked toward us and sneered.

"Ohé, Child of Light!" she cried.

A ripple went down the salamander's back. Its tail switched restlessly, and a tree across the way kindled. I can't describe the voice that answered: crackling, bellowing, sibilant, Fire given a brain and a throat. "Daughter of Eve, what have you to say to the likes of Me?"

"I command you by the Most High, return to your proper bonds and cease from troubling the world."

"Ho—oh, ho, ho, ho!" The thing sat back on its haunches—asphalt bubbled—and shuddered its laughter into the sky. *"You* command me, combustible one?"

"I have at my beck powers so mighty they could wither your puny spark into the nothingness whence it came. Cease and obey, lest worse befall you than dismissal."

I think the salamander was, for a moment, honestly surprised. "Greater than *Me?*" Then it howled so the tavern shook. "You dare say there are mightier forces than Fire? Than Me, who am going to consume the earth?"

"Mightier and more beautiful, O Ashmaker. Think. You cannot even enter this house. Water will extinguish you. Earth will smother you, Air alone can keep you alive. Best you surrender now—"

I remembered the night of the afreet. Ginny must be pulling the same trick—feeling out the psychology of the thing that raged and flared beyond the door—but what could she hope to gain?

"*More beautiful!*" The salamander's tail beat furrows in the street. It threw out bursting fireballs and a rain of sparks, red, blue, yellow, a one-being Fourth of July. I thought crazily of a child kicking the floor in a tantrum.

"More beautiful! Stronger! You dare say— Haaaaa—" Teeth of incandescence gleamed in a mouth that was jumping fire. "We shall see how beautiful you are when you lie a choked corpse!" Its head darted to the broken glass front. It could not pass the barrier of cold iron, but it began to suck air, in and out. A furnace wave of heat sent me gasping back.

"My God . . . it's going to use up our oxygen. . . . Stay here!" I

sprang for the door. Ginny shrieked, but I scarcely heard her "No!" as I went through.

Moonlight flooded me, cool and tingling between the unrestful guttering fires. I crouched to the hot sidewalk and felt a shudder when my body changed.

Wolf I was, but a wolf that my enemy could not kill . . . I hoped. My abbreviated tail thrust against the seat of my pants, and I remembered that some injuries are beyond the healing powers of even the therio shape.

Pants! Hell and damnation! In the excitement, I'd forgotten. Have you ever tried being a wolf while wrapped in shirt, trousers, underwear, and topcoat designed for a man?

I went flat on my moist black nose. My suspenders slid down and wrapped themselves about my hind legs. My tie tripped me in front and my coat gleefully wrapped everything into a bundle.

Frantic, I rolled over and tore at the cloth with my fangs. The salamander grew aware of me. Its tail slammed across my back. For a moment of searing pain, hair and skin scorched with the fabric. But that burning shredded it and I was free. The labile molecules of my body rebuilt themselves in seconds. The salamander had turned its attention away, deeming me out of action. Hardly realizing what I did, I snatched with my jaws a shoe which had dropped from my now smaller foot, laid it on the salamander's nearest white-hot toe, and bore down with both forepaws.

It bellowed and swung around to attack me afresh. That mouth gaped wide enough to bite me in half. I skittered aside. The monster paused, gauged the distance, flicked into nothingness, and materialized right on top of me.

This time I had no escape. Weighted down, I inhaled the fire that cooked my flesh. Agony sent my being whirling out of me like another flame.

Aloneness was not broken by the face which looked upon me, a face for which I have no words save that it was huge and its eyes were those of a corpse. But then, I did not see it, nor feel the cold which was deeper and stabbed me more cruelly than any I had known since last the thought-voice came through not-space and not-time to shake the senses I did not have. And the end of every hope and every faith was upon me.

"Be proud, Steven. I myself have worked to bring the death of you and your companions. To that end, I myself planted a prank in the head of a fool; for know, only thus may we safely work in the world, and I would not trust the subtleties of this one task to any minion. Pleasing though the general destruction is, material harm to men is not the true aim, and indeed my maneuverings to encompass the doom of you twain could prove costly if they provoke retaliation from the Other Side. But the danger to ours that you represent has become ever more clear as time runs toward a certain moment. I cannot know when that moment waits or what lineaments it will bear; but I know you must not be part of it."

That which was I would have cringed, were it not less than a point in nothingness.

"And yet," tolled through me, "and yet, Steven, you need not be dead. I forebode that the woman Virginia can be a worse enemy than you. Yes, I forebode that, lacking her, you are no threat to the Plan; but she, without you, might well prove so, if not as great a menace as you two conjoined. How this may be, there is no augury. But note her skills and her Gift; note that she has not twice been trapped like you; note what a spirit she bears within her. Vengefulness for you may drive

her to search below the appearance of things. Or she may take some other course. I cannot tell what. But I see that although you burn, she is not absolutely inescapably caught.

"Would you live, and live well, Steven?"

Fainter than light from the farthest star flickered out of me:—What must I do?

"Take my service. Accept my geas. The salamander will release you before irreparable injury has occurred. When your hurts have knit, the geas will make you do a single thing—nothing else for a long, rich lifetime. You will call her outside, stand well clear, and distract her wariness for the moment the salamander will need to materialize upon her as it did upon you.

"If you refuse this, return to the instant of your own cremation alive."

Virginia was more than infinitely remote, and I had no body to feel with nor tongue to speak yea or nay. But the focus that was I considered her within the anguish it had known; and it became absolute rage, to match the absolute hate that had stormed it free of another timelessness; and the not-scene exploded back into the void whence it had come.

# XII

I *think* that my fury overcame my torment to the degree that I started fighting. I am told I got a fang-grip on the obvious place to bite a beast that is sitting on you, and did not let go. But the pain was too great for me to recall anything other than itself.

Then the salamander had vanished. The street lay bare, dark except for the moon and a distant unbroken lamp and the uneasy red glow from kindled houses, quiet except for the crackle and crash of their burning. When I'd recovered to the point of having a functional nose, what I first noticed was the acrid smoke.

That took several minutes. Barely enough unseared tissue remained to provide a DNA pattern for reconstructing the rest. When sanity returned, my shaggy head was in Ginny's lap. She was stroking it and crying. I licked her hand, feebly, with a tongue like dried-out leather. If a man, I'd have stayed a while where she had me. But being a wolf with lupine instincts, I struggled to sit up and uttered a faint, hoarse yip.

"Steve . . . almighty Father, Steve, you saved our lives," Ginny whispered. "Another couple of minutes and we'd have been suffocating. My throat still feels like mummy dust."

Svartalf trotted from the bar, looking as smug as a cat with singed whiskers is able. He meowed. Ginny gave a shaken laugh and explained:

"But you owe this fellow a pint of cream or something. He may have tipped the scales for you, same as you did for us. At least, he showed me a way to help you."

I cocked my ears.

"He manned the beer taps," she said. "I filled pitcher after pitcher

and threw them out the door at the salamander. They discommoded it. It shifted around. That may've taken the heat off you, and the pressure, till you could manage to use your bite." She gripped my ruff. "And what an epic that was, those seconds while you clung!"

Beer! I wavered to my feet and back inside Stub's. They followed me, puzzled until I whined and pointed with my muzzle at the nearest glass. "Oh, I see." Ginny snapped her fingers. "You're thirsty. No, you're dehydrated!"

She drew me a quart. I lapped it down in a cataract and signaled for more. She shook her head. "You may have forced the salamander to skip, but we have to deal with it yet. The rest will be plain water."

My therio metabolism redistributed the fluid and brought me back to complete health. My first truly clear thought was that I hoped no more beer would have to be spent on fighting the elemental. My second was that whatever the means, we'd better apply them soon.

Penalties attach to everything. The trouble with being were is that in the other shape you have, essentially, an animal brain, with a superficial layer of human personality. Or in plain language, as a wolf I'm a rather stupid man. I was only able to realize I'd better reassume the human form . . . so I trotted to the open doorway where the moonlight could touch me, and did.

Ever see a cat grin? "Omigawd!" I yelped, and started to change back.

"Hold on," said Ginny crisply. "If you must fret about my maidenly modesty, here." She peeled off her scorched but serviceable fur coat. I doubt if one has ever been donned faster than by me. It was a pretty tight fit around the shoulders but went low enough—if I was careful. Though the night wind nipped my bare shanks, my face was of salamander temperature.

That was one reason I dismissed from among my worries the vision I had had. Another was the immediacy of the peril that confronted us, now and in the flesh. Besides, even more than on the previous occasion, the physical pain which followed the restoration of consciousness had blurred memory of so insubstantial an experience. Finally, I don't suppose I wanted to think further about it.

The idea flitted through my head: Twice I've had a similar illusion while passed out. Maybe I should see a psychiatrist? No, that'd be silly. This can't be more than an idiosyncratic reaction to a kind of trauma that isn't likely to hit me again in my life.

I forgot about the matter.

Instead, I asked quickly, "Now where? The damned critter could be anyplace."

"I think it'll hang around the campus," Ginny said. "Ample grazing, and it's not particularly smart. Let's get moving."

She fetched her stick from the smoldering barroom and we lifted. "So far," I said, "we've done nothing but waste time."

"N-no, not entirely. I did get a line on its mind." We cleared the rooftops and Ginny looked back around at me. "I wasn't sure of the precise form into which it had been conjured. You can mold the elemental forces into almost anything. But apparently the cheerleader was satisfied to give it a knowledge of English and a rudimentary intelligence. Add to that the volatile nature of Fire, and what have you got? A child."

"Some child," I muttered, hugging her coat to me.

"No, no, Steve, this is important. It has all the child's limiting traits. Improvidence, carelessness, thoughtlessness . . . A wise salamander would lie low, gathering strength slowly. It'd either realize it couldn't burn the entire planet, or if it didn't know, would never think of such a thing. Because what would it use for oxygen afterward?

"Remember, too, its fantastic vanity. It went into an insane rage when I said that powers existed more strong and beautiful than it, and the crack about beauty hurt as much as the one about strength.

"Short span of attention. It could have destroyed either you first, or Svartalf and me first, before taking care of the minor nuisance the other provided. Instead, it let its efforts be split. And it could have gritted its teeth when you took that mouthful, standing the pain for the short time needed to weight you down firmly again till you—you were dead." Her voice wavered at that, and she hastened on:

"At the same time, within that short span, if nothing distracts it, it focuses on one issue only, to the exclusion of any parts of a larger whole." She nodded thoughtfully. The long blowing hair tickled my face. "I don't know how, but some way its psychology must provide us with a lever."

My own vanity is not small. "I wasn't such a minor nuisance," I grumbled.

Ginny smiled and reached to pat my cheek. "All right, Steve, all right. I like you just the same, and now I *know* you'd make a good husband."

That left me in a comfortable glow until I wondered precisely what she was thinking of.

We spotted the salamander below us, igniting a theater, but it

flicked away as I watched, and a mile off it appeared next to the medical research center. Glass brick doesn't burn so well. As we neared, I saw it petulantly kick the wall and vanish again. Ignorant and impulsive . . . a child . . . a brat from hell!

Sweeping over the campus, we saw lights in the Administration Building. "Probably that's become headquarters for our side," said Ginny. "We'd better report." Svartalf landed us on the Mall in front of the place and strutted ahead up the stairs.

A squad of cops armed with fire extinguishers guarded the door. "Hey, there!" One of them barred our path. "Where you going?"

"To the meeting," said Ginny, smoothing her tresses.

"Yeah?" The policeman's eye fell on me. "Really dressed for it, too, aren't you? Haw, haw, haw!"

I'd had about my limit for this night. I wered and peeled off his own trousers. As he lifted his billy, Ginny turned it into a small boa constrictor. I switched back to human; we left the squad to its problems and went down the hall.

The faculty meeting room was packed. Malzius had summoned every one of his professors. As we entered, I heard his orotund tones: "—disgraceful. The authorities won't so much as listen to me. Gentlemen, it is for us to vindicate the honor of Gown against Town." He blinked when Ginny and Svartalf came in, and turned a beautiful Tyrian purple as I followed in the full glory of mink coat and stubbly chin. "*Mister* Matuchek!"

"He's with me," said Ginny curtly. "We were out fighting the salamander while you sat here."

"Possibly something other than brawn, even lupine brawn, is required," smiled Dr. Alan Abercrombie. "I see that Mr. Matuchek lost his pants in a more than vernacular sense."

Like Malzius, he had changed his wet clothes for the inevitable tweeds. Ginny gave him a cold look. "I thought you were directing the Hydro," she said.

"Oh, we got enough adepts together to use three water elementals," he said. "Mechanic's work. I felt my job was here. We can readily control the fires—"

"If the salamander weren't always lighting fresh ones," clipped Ginny. "And each blaze it starts, it gets bigger and stronger, while you sit here looking beautiful."

"Why, thank you, my dear," he laughed.

I jammed my teeth together so they hurt. She had actually smiled back at him.

"Order, order!" boomed President Malzius. "Please be seated, Miss Graylock. Have you anything to contribute to the discussion?"

"Yes. I understand the salamander now." She took a place at the end of the table. That was the last vacant chair, so I hovered miserably in the background wishing her coat had more buttons.

"Understand it sufficiently well to extinguish it?" asked Professor van Linden of Alchemy.

"No. But I know how it thinks."

"We're more interested in how it operates," said van Linden. "How can we make it hold still for a dismissal?" He cleared his throat. "Obviously, we must first know by what process it shuttles around so fast—"

"Oh, that's simple," piped Griswold. He was drowned by van Linden's fruity bass:

"—which is, of course, by the well-known affinity of Fire for Quicksilver. Since virtually every home these days has at least one thermometer—"

"With due respect, my good sir," interrupted Vittorio of Astrology, "you are talking utter hogwash. It is a simple matter of the conjunction of Mercury and Neptune in Scorpio—"

"You're wrong, sir!" declared van Linden. "Dead wrong! Let me show you the *Ars Thaumaturgica.*" He glared around after his copy, but it had been mislaid and he had to use an adaptation of the Dobu yam-calling chant to find it. Meanwhile Vittorio was screaming:

"No, no, no! The conjunction, with Uranus opposing in the ascendant . . . as I can easily prove—" He went to the blackboard and started to draw a diagram.

"Oh, come now!" snorted Jasper of Metaphysics. "I don't understand how you can both be so wrong. As I showed in the paper I read at the last Triple-A-S meeting, the intrinsic nature of the matrix—"

"That was disproved ten years ago!" roared van Linden. "The affinity—"

*"Ding an sich—"*

"—up Uranus—"

I sidled over and tugged at Griswold's sleeve. He pattered into a corner with me. "Okay, how does the bloody thing work?" I asked.

"Oh . . . merely a question of wave mechanics," he whispered. "According to the Heisenberg uncertainty principle, a photon has a finite probability of being at any point of space. The salamander uses a simple diffraction process to change the spatial coordinates of psi squared, in effect going from point to point without crossing the in-

tervening distance, much like an electron making a quantum jump, although, to be sure, the analogy is not precise due to the modifying influence of—"

"Never mind," I sighed. "This confab is becoming a riot. Wouldn't we do better to—"

"—stick by the original purpose," agreed Abercrombie, joining us. Ginny followed. Van Linden blacked Vittorio's eye while Jasper threw chalk at both of them. Our rump group went over near the door.

"I've already found the answer to our problem," said Abercrombie, "but I'll need help. A transformation spell. We'll turn the salamander into something we can handle more easily."

"That's dangerous," said Ginny. "You'll need a really strong T-spell, and that sort can backfire. What happens then is unpredictable."

Abercrombie straightened himself with a look of pained nobility. "For you, my dear, no hazard is too great."

She regarded him with admiration. It does take guts to use the ultimate runes. "Let's go," she said. "I'll help."

Griswold plucked at my arm. "I don't like this, Mr. Matuchek," he confided. "The Art is too unreliable. There ought to be some method grounded in nature and nature's quantitative laws."

"Yeah," I said disconsolately. "But what?" I paddled after Ginny and Abercrombie, who had their heads together over the handbook. Griswold marched beside me and Svartalf made a gesture with his tail at the Trismegistus faculty. They were too embroiled to notice.

We went out past an enraged but well-cowed squad of cops. The Physical Sciences hall stood nearby, and its chemistry division held stuff that would be needed. We entered an echoing gloom.

The freshman lab, a long room full of workbenches, shelves, and silence, was our goal. Griswold switched on the lights and Abercrombie looked around. "But we'll have to bring the salamander here," he said. "We can't do anything except in its actual presence."

"Go ahead and make ready," the girl told him. "I know how to fetch the beast. A minor transformation—" She laid out some test tubes, filled them with various powders, and sketched her symbols on the floor. Those ball-point wands are handy.

"What's the idea?" I asked.

"Oh, get out of the way," she snapped. I told myself she was only striking at her own weariness and despair, but it hurt. "We'll use its vanity, of course. I'll prepare some Roman candles and rockets and stuff . . . shoot them off, and naturally it'll come to show it can do more spectacular things."

Griswold and I withdrew into a corner. This was big-league play. I was frankly scared, and the little scientist's bony knees were beating a tattoo in march time. Even Ginny—yes, sweat beaded that smooth forehead. If this didn't work, we here were probably done for: either the salamander or the backlash of the spell could finish us. And we had no way of knowing whether the beast had grown too strong for a transformation.

The witch got her fireworks prepared, and went to an open window and leaned out. Hissing balls of blue and red, streamers of golden sparks, flew skyward and exploded.

Abercrombie had completed his diagrams. He turned to smile at us. "It's all right," he said. "Everything under control. I'm going to turn the salamander's energy into matter. E equals m c squared, you know. Just light me a Bunsen burner, Matuchek, and set a beaker of water over it. Griswold, you turn these lights off and the Polaroid bulbs on. We need polarized radiation."

We obeyed, though I hated to see an old and distinguished man acting as lab assistant to this patronizing slick-paper adman's dream. "You *sure* it'll work?" I asked.

"Of course," he smiled. "I've had experience. I was in the Quartermaster Corps during the war."

"Yeah," I said, "but turning dirt into K rations isn't the same thing as transforming that monster. You and your experience!"

Suddenly and sickly, remembering how he had bungled with the Hydro, I realized the truth. Abercrombie was confident, unafraid—because he didn't *know* enough!

For a minute I couldn't unfreeze my muscles. Griswold fiddled unhappily with some metallic samples. He'd been using them the other day for freshman experiments, trying to teach us the chemical properties; Lord, it seemed a million years ago. . . .

"Ginny!" I stumbled toward her where she stood at the window throwing rainbows into the air. "My God, darling, stop—"

*Crack!* The salamander was in the room with us.

I lurched back from it, half-blinded. Grown hideously bigger, it filled the other end of the lab, and the bench tops smoked.

"Oh, so!" The voice of Fire blasted our eardrums. Svartalf shot to a shelf top and upset bottles of acid onto the varmint. It didn't notice. "So, small moist pests, you would try to outdo Me!"

Abercrombie and Ginny lifted their wands and shouted the few brief words of transformation.

Crouched back into my corner, peering through a sulfurous reek

of fumes, I saw Ginny lurch and then jump for safety. She must have sensed the backlash. There came a shattering explosion and the air was full of flying glass.

My body shielded Griswold, and the spell didn't do more to me than turn me lupine. Ginny was on her hands and knees behind a bench, half-unconscious . . . but unhurt, unhurt, praise the good Powers forever. Svartalf—a Pekingese dog yapped on the shelf. Abercrombie was gone, but a chimpanzee in baggy tweeds scuttered wailing toward the door.

A fire-blast rushed before the ape. He whirled, screamed, and shinnied up a steam pipe. The salamander arched its back and howled with laughter.

"You would use your tricks on Me? Almighty Me, terrible Me, beautiful Me? Ha, they bounce off like water from a hot skillet! And I, I, I am the skillet which is going to fry you!"

Somehow, the low-grade melodrama of its speech was not in the least ridiculous. For this was the childish, vainglorious, senselessly consuming thing which was loose on earth to make ashes of men and the homes of men.

Under the Polaroids, I switched back to human and rose to my feet behind a bench. Griswold turned on a water faucet and squirted a jet with his finger. The salamander hissed in annoyance—yes, water still hurt, but we had too little liquid here to quench it, you'd need a whole lake by this time— It swung its head, gape-mouthed, aimed at Griswold, and drew a long breath.

*All is vanity. . . .*

I reeled over to the Bunsen burner that was heating a futile beaker of water. Ginny looked at me through scorched bangs. The room roiled with heat, sweat rivered off me. I didn't have any flash of genius, I acted on raw instinct and tumbled memories.

"Kill us," I croaked. "Kill us if you dare. Our servant is more powerful than you. He'll hound you to the ends of creation."

*"Your servant?"* Flame wreathed the words.

"Yeah . . . I mean yes . . . our servant, that Fire which fears not water!"

The salamander stepped back a pace, snarling. It was not yet so strong that the very name of water didn't make it flinch. "Show me!" it chattered. "Show me! I dare you!"

"Our servant . . . small, but powerful," I rasped. "Brighter and more beautiful than you, and above taking harm from the Wet Ele-

ment." I staggered to the jars of metal samples and grabbed a pair of tongs. "Have you the courage to look on him?"

The salamander bristled. "Have I the *courage?* Ask rather, does it dare confront Me?"

I flicked a glance from the corner of my eye. Ginny had risen and was gripping her wand. She scarcely breathed, but her eyes were narrowed.

There was a silence. It hung like a world's weight in that room, smothering what noises remained: the crackle of fire, Abercrombie's simian gibber, Svartalf's indignant yapping. I took a strip of magnesium in the tongs and held it to the burner flame.

It burst into a blue-white actinic radiance from which I turned dazzled eyes. The salamander was less viciously brilliant. I saw the brute accomplish the feat of simultaneously puffing itself up and shrinking back.

"Behold!" I lifted the burning strip. Behind me, Ginny's rapid mutter came: *"O Indra, Abaddon, Lucifer—"*

The child mind, incapable of considering more than one thing at a time . . . but for how long a time? I had to hold its full attention for the hundred and twenty seconds required.

"Fire," said the salamander feverishly. "Only another fire, one tiny piece of that Force from which I came."

"Can you do this, buster?"

I plunged the strip into the beaker. Steam puffed from the water, it boiled and bubbled—and the metal went on burning!

*"—abire ex Orbis terrestris—"*

"Mg plus $H_2O$ yields MgO plus $H_2$," whispered Griswold reverently.

"Keek-eek-eek!" said Abercrombie.

"Yip-yip-yip!" said Svartalf.

"It's a trick!" screamed the salamander. "It's impossible! If even I cannot— No!"

"Stay where you are!" I barked in my best Army manner. "Do you doubt that my servant can follow you wherever you may flee?"

"I'll kill that little monster!"

"Go right ahead, chum," I agreed. "Want to fight the duel under the ocean?"

Whistles skirled above our racket. The police had seen through these windows.

"I'll show you, I will!" The roar was almost a sob. I ducked behind

the bench, pulling Griswold with me. A geyser of flame rushed where I had been.

"Nyaah, nyaah, nyaah," I called. "You can't catch me! Scaredy-cat!"

Svartalf gave me a hard look.

The floor trembled as the elemental came toward me, not going around the benches but burning its way through them. Heat clawed at my throat. I spun down toward darkness.

And it was gone. Ginny cried her triumphant *"Amen!"* and displaced air cracked like thunder.

I lurched to my feet. Ginny fell into my arms. The police entered the lab and Griswold hollered something about calling the fire department before his whole building whiffed off in smoke. Abercrombie scampered out a window and Svartalf jumped down from the shelf. He forgot that a Pekingese isn't as agile as a cat, and his popeyes bubbled with righteous wrath.

# XIII

Outside, the Mall was cool and still. We sat on dewed grass and looked at the moon and thought what a great and simple wonder it is to be alive.

The geas held us apart, but tenderness lay on Ginny's lips. We scarcely noticed when somebody ran past us shouting that the salamander was gone, nor when church bells began pealing the news to men and Heaven.

Svartalf finally roused us with his barking. Ginny chuckled. "Poor fellow. I'll change you back as soon as I can, but now I've more urgent business. Come on, Steve."

Griswold, assured that his priceless hall was safe, followed us at a tactful distance. Svartalf merely sat where he was . . . too shocked to move, I guess, at the idea that there could be more important affairs than turning him back into a cat.

Dr. Malzius met us halfway, under one of the campus elms. Moonlight spattered his face and gleamed in the pince-nez. "My dear Miss Graylock," he began, "is it indeed true that you have overcome that menace to society? Most noteworthy. Accept my congratulations. The glorious annals of this great institution of which I have the honor to be president—"

Ginny faced him, arms akimbo, and nailed him with surely the chilliest gaze he had ever seen. "The credit belongs to Mr. Matuchek and Dr. Griswold," she said. "I shall so inform the press. Doubtless you'll see fit to recommend a larger appropriation for Dr. Griswold's outstanding work."

"Oh, now, really," stammered the scientist. "I didn't—"

"Be quiet, you ninnyhammer," whispered Ginny. Aloud: "Only

through his courageous and farsighted adherence to the basic teachings of natural law— Well, you can fill in the rest for yourself, Malzius. I don't think you'd be awfully popular if you went on starving his department."

"Oh . . . indeed . . . after all—" The president expanded himself. "I have already given careful consideration to the idea. Was going to recommend it at the next meeting of the board, in fact."

"I'll hold you to that," Ginny said. "Next: this stupid rule against student-faculty relationships. Mr. Matuchek will shortly be my husband—"

Whoosh! I tried to regain my breath.

"My dear Miss Graylock," sputtered Malzius, "decorum . . . propriety . . . why, he isn't even decent!"

I realized with horror that somehow, in the hullabaloo, I'd lost Ginny's coat.

A pair of cops approached, dragging a hairy form that struggled in their arms. A third man carried the garments the chimp had shed. "Begging your pardon, Miss Graylock." The tone was pure worship. "We found this monkey loose and—"

"Oh, yes." She laughed. "We'll have to restore him. But not right away. Steve needs those pants worse."

I got into them like a snake headed down a hole. Ginny turned back to smile with angelic sweetness at Malzius.

"Poor Dr. Abercrombie," she sighed. "These things will happen when you deal with paranatural forces. Now I believe, sir, that you have no rule against faculty members conducting research."

"Oh, no," said the president shakily. "Of course not. On the contrary! We expect our people to publish—"

"To be sure. Well, I have in mind a most interesting research project involving transformations. I'll admit it's a teeny bit dangerous. It could backfire as Dr. Abercrombie's spell did." Ginny leaned on her wand and regarded the turf thoughtfully. "It could even . . . yes, there's even a small possibility that it could turn *you* into an ape, dear Dr. Malzius. Or, perhaps, a worm. A long slimy one. But we mustn't let that stand in the way of science, must we?"

"What? But—"

"Naturally," purred the witch, "if I were allowed to conduct myself as I wish with my fiancé, I wouldn't have time for research."

Malzius took a bare fifty words to admit defeat. He stumped off in tottery grandeur while the last fireglow died above the campus roofs.

Ginny gave me a slow glance. "The rule can't officially be stricken till tomorrow," she murmured. "Think you can cut a few classes then?"

"Keek-eek-eek," said Dr. Alan Abercrombie. Then Svartalf arrived full of resentment and chased him up the tree.

# XIV

A short interlude this time. We finished our first academic year okay. Ginny was proud of my straight A's in shamanistics and calculus, and assisted me over some humps in arcane languages. (Griswold did me a similar service for electronics.) She had to modify her own plan of further study somewhat, if we were to get married in June.

You might think a former high-salaried New York witch would be anything but innocent. Certainly Ginny had a temper and her special kind of sophistication. However, quite apart from a stubbornly loyal and clean personality, she'd concentrated on those branches of the Art which require maidenhood. That kind of specialist commands fees in proportion to rarity.

Now my fire-and-ice girl was to become only another bride. And what's so only about that? Next year she could acquire the techniques necessary to compensate for being wedded.

We couldn't entirely hide our roles in snuffing the salamander from the news media; but with the eager cooperation of Malzius, who kept blaring about how the University Team had saved this fair city, we managed to obfuscate it so that we soon dropped out of the public eye. Griswold was conscience-stricken at receiving more credit than he thought he deserved, and indignant at our receiving less than we deserved, till we pointed out that the first was essential to getting his department modernized and the second to protecting our privacy. Besides, if we wanted to be sure the rule on dating was rescinded, and that conditions at Trismegistus would remain tolerable for us in other respects, we had to give Malzius tacit cooperation in rescuing his pride and not getting stuck with a craven image.

So, in brief, that winter and spring were wonderful and full of

wonder. I could skip well ahead, but can't help dwelling on—oh, at least the moment when:

"No," I said to my bride's business associate. "You are not coming along on the honeymoon."

He laid back his ears. "Mneowrr!" he said resentfully.

"You'll do fine by yourself in this apartment for a month," I told him. "The superintendent has promised to feed you every evening, the same time as he sets out the milk for the Brownie. And don't forget, when the Brownie comes in here, you are not to chase after him. After the last time you did that, three times in a row when Ginny and I went out to dinner, the Good People sweetened our martinis."

Svartalf glowered, yellow-eyed, and switched his tail. I imagine that was cat for, Well, dammit, anything the size of a mouse, which scuttles like a mouse, has got to expect to be treated like a mouse.

"He'll be here to dust and change *your* litterbox," I reminded Svartalf in my sternest voice. "You'll have the run of the place, and you can fly up the chimney on the whisk broom anytime you want fresh air. But the Brownie is off limits, bucko, and if I come back and hear you've been after him, I'll take wolf-shape and tree you. Understand?"

Svartalf jerked his tail at me, straight upward.

Virginia Graylock, who had for an incredible few hours been Mrs. Steven Matuchek, entered the living room. I was so stunned by the view of tall slenderness in a white dress, straight aristocratic features and red hair shouting down to her shoulders, that the voice didn't register except as a symphonic accompaniment. She had to repeat: "Darling, are you absolutely sure we can't take him? His feelings are hurt."

I recovered enough to say, "His feelings are made of tool steel. It's okay if he wants to share our bed when we get back, I guess—within reason—but fifteen pounds of black witchcat on my stomach when I'm honeymooning is out of reason. Besides, what's worse, he'd prefer your stomach."

Ginny blushed. "It will be odd without my familiar, after these many years. If he promised to behave—"

Svartalf, who had been standing on a table, rubbed against her hip and purred. Which was not a bad idea, I thought. However, I had my foot down and wasn't about to lift it. "He's incapable of behaving," I said. "And you won't need him. We're going to forget the world and its work, aren't we? I'm not going to study any texts, nor visit any of my fellow theriomorphs, even that were-coyote family down at Acapulco who invited us to drop in. It's going to be just us two, and I don't want any pussy—" I braked as fast as possible. She didn't

notice, only sighed a little, nodded, and stroked a soothing hand across the cat's back.

"Very well, dear," she said. With a flick of her earlier self: "Enjoy wearing the family pants while you can."

"I intend to do so all the time," I bragged.

She cocked her head. "*All* the time?" Hastily: "We'd best be on our way. Everything's packed."

"Check, mate," I agreed. She stuck out her tongue at me. I patted Svartalf. "So long, chum. No grudges, I trust?" He bit a piece out of my hand and said he supposed not. Ginny hugged him, seized my arm, and hurried me out.

The home to which we'd be coming back was a third-floor apartment near Trismegistus University. Our wedding this morning had been quiet, a few friends at the church, a luncheon afterward at somebody's house, and then we made our farewells. But Ginny's connections in New York and mine in Hollywood have money. Several people had clubbed together to give us a Persian carpet: a somewhat overwhelming present, but show me the bridal couple who don't like a touch of luxury.

It lay on the landing, its colors aglow in the sun. Our baggage was piled in the rear. We snuggled down side by side on cushions of polymerized sea foam. Ginny murmured the command words. We started moving so smoothly I didn't notice when we were airborne. The carpet wasn't as fast or flashy as a sports-model broomstick, but the three hundred dragonpower spell on it got us out of the city in minutes.

Midwestern plains rolled green and enormous beneath us, here and there a river like argent ribbon; but we were alone with birds and clouds. No wind of our passage got by the force screen. Ginny slipped off her dress. She had a sunsuit beneath it, and now I understand transistor theory; the absence of material has as real an existence as the presence. We sunbathed on our way south, stopped at twilight for supper at a charming little restaurant in the Ozarks, but decided not to stay in a broomotel. Instead, we flew on. The carpet was soft and thick and roomy. I started to raise the convertible top, but Ginny said we'd keep warm if we flew low, and she was right. Stars crowded the sky, until a big yellow Southern moon rose to drown half of them, and the air was murmurous, and we could hear crickets chorus from the dark earth below, and nothing else is any of your business.

I knew exactly where I was bound. A wartime friend of mine, Juan Fernández, had put his Army experience to good use. He'd been in the propaganda section, and done many excellent scripts. These days, instead of preparing nightmares to send the enemy, he was broadcasting a popular dream series, and his sponsors were paying him accordingly. In fact, everyone loved Fernández except the psychoanalysts, and they're obsolete now that scientific research has produced some really efficient antipossession techniques. Last year he had built a lodge in the country of his ancestors. It stood entirely by itself on the Sonora coast, at one of the loneliest spots on Midgard and one of the most beautiful. Fernández had offered me the use of it this month, and Ginny and I had set our wedding date accordingly.

We glided down about noon the next day. Westward the Gulf of California burned blue and molten white. Surf broke on a wide strip of sand beach, cliffs rose tier upon tier, finally the land itself rolled off to the east, dry, stark, and awesome. The lodge made a spot of green, perched on a bluff just above the strand.

Ginny clapped her hands. "Oh! I wouldn't have believed it!"

"You Easterners don't know what big country is," I said smugly.

She shaded her eyes against the sun-dazzle and pointed. "What's that, though?"

My own gaze traveled no further than her arm, but I remembered. Atop a cliff, about a mile north of the lodge and several hundred feet higher, crumbling walls surrounded a rubble heap; the snag of a tower stood at the northwest angle, to scowl among winds. "La Fortaleza," I said. "Spanish work, seventeenth century. Some don had an idea he could exploit this area for profit. He erected the castle as a strong

point and residence, brought a wife here from Castile. But everything went wrong and the place was soon abandoned."

"Can we explore it?"

"If you like."

Ginny laid a hand on my shoulder. "What's wrong, Steve?"

"Oh . . . nothing. I don't care for the Fortaleza myself. Even as a human by daylight, I sense wrongness. I went over there once after dark, wolf-shape, and it stank. Not so much in a physical way, but— Oh, forget it."

She said soberly: "The Spaniards enslaved the Indians in those times, didn't they? I imagine a lot of human agony went into that castle."

"And left a residuum. Yeah, probably. But hell, it was long ago. We'll have a look around. The ruins are picturesque, and the view from there is tremendous."

"If you really are worried about ghosts—"

"Forget it, darling! I'm not superstitious!"

And we landed at the lodge and did indeed forget it.

The place was built in cloister style, white walls and red tile roof enclosing a courtyard where a fountain played. But there was also a garden surrounding the outside, green with leaves and grass, red and white and purple and gold with flower beds. We were quite alone. The grounds were elementalized for Earth and Water, hence needed no attendants; the other two elemental forces kept the house air-conditioned, and an expensive cleanliness spell had also been put on it. Since Ginny was now temporarily out of the goetic game, she prepared a Mexican lunch from the supplies we'd brought along. She was so beautiful in shorts, halter, and frilly apron that I hadn't the heart to offer to teach her to cook. She exclaimed aloud when the dirty dishes floated back to the kitchen and followed to watch them dive into soapy water and frisk around. "It's the most up-to-date automatic dishwasher I've heard of!" she cried.

So we had plenty of time for an afternoon of surf bathing. At sunset we climbed back a stairway hewn from the yellow rock, ravenous, and I prepared steaks by introducing them to a charcoal fire but allowing no further conversation. Afterward we moved onto a patio overlooking the sea. We sat in deck chairs, holding hands, and the stars came out to greet us.

"Let's Skinturn at moonrise and frolic a bit," I suggested. "You'd make a delightful lady wolf. Or, hm, I wou— Never mind!"

She shook her head. "I can't, Steve, dear."

"Sure, you can. You'd need a T-spell, of course, but—"

"That's just it. You have lycanthropic genes; all you need to change species is polarized light. But for me it's a major transformation, and . . . I don't know . . . I don't feel able to do it. I can't even remember the formulas. I guess I'm not able, any more. My knowledge has gotten even fuzzier than I expected. I'll need refresher courses in the most elementary things. Right now, only a professional could change me."

I sighed. I'd been looking forward to wolfing it. You don't really know the world till you've explored it with animal as well as human senses, and Ginny was certainly a part of the world— Whoa, there! "Okay," I said. "Later, when you're an adept again."

"Of course. I'm sorry, darling. If you want to run off by yourself, werewise, go ahead."

"Not without you."

She chuckled. "You might get fleas, anyhow." She was leaning over to nibble my ear when we both heard the footsteps.

I rose to my feet, muttering inhospitable things. A form, shadowy under the velvet sky, approached us over a path which snaked inland. Who the devil, I thought. Someone from the village, ten miles hence? But— My nose in human shape is dull by my wolf standards, but suddenly caught a smell I didn't like. It wasn't an unpleasant odor; indeed, its pungency seemed at once to heighten Ginny's half-visible beauty to an unbearable degree. And yet something in me bristled.

I stepped forward as the stranger reached our patio. He was medium-tall for a Mexican, which made him shorter than me. He moved so gracefully, no more loud than smoke, that I wondered if he could be a werecougar. A dark cape over an immaculate white suit garbed the supple body. His wide-brimmed hat made the face obscure, till he took it off and bowed. Then light from a window touched him. I had never met a handsomer man, high cheekbones, Grecian nose, pointed chin, wide-set eyes of a gold-flecked greenish gray. His skin was whiter than my wife's, and the sleek hair was ash-blond. I wondered if he was a Mexican national, let alone of native stock.

"Buenas noches, señor," I said curtly. "Pardón, pero no hablamos español." Which was not quite true, but I didn't want to make polite chitchat.

The voice that answered was tenor or contralto, I couldn't decide which, but music in any case. "I' faith, good sir, I speak as many tongues as needful. I pray forgiveness, yet having observed from afar

that this house was lighted, methought its master had returned, and I did come with neighborly greeting."

His pronunciation was as archaic as the phrasing: the vowels, for instance, sounded Swedish, though the sentences didn't have a Swedish rhythm. At the moment, however, I was surprised by the words themselves. "Neighbor?"

"My sister and I have made abode within yon ancient castle."

"What? But— Oh." I stopped. Fernández hadn't mentioned anything like this, but then, he himself hadn't been here for months. The Fortaleza and grounds belonged to the Mexican government, from which he had purchased several acres for his hideaway. "Did you buy it?"

"A few rooms were made a right comfortable habitation for us, sir," he evaded. "I hight Amaris Maledicto." The mouth, so cleanly shaped that you scarcely noticed how full it was, curved into an altogether charming smile. Had it not been for the odor low in my nostrils, I might have been captivated. "You and your fair lady are guests of Señor Fernández? Be welcome."

"We've borrowed the lodge." Ginny's voice was a tad breathless. I stole a glance, and saw by the yellow windowlight that her eyes were full upon his, and brilliant. "Our . . . our name . . . Virginia. Steven and Virginia . . . Matuchek." I thought, with a cold sort of puzzlement, that brides were supposed to make a great show of being Mrs. So-and-So, not play it down in that fashion. "It's very kind of you to walk this far. Did your . . . your sister . . . come too?"

"Nay," said Maledicto. "And truth to tell, however glad of your society, 'tis belike well she was spared the sight of such loveliness as is yours. 'Twould but excite envy and wistfulness."

From him, somehow, unbelievably, in that flowering night above the great dim sea, under stars and sheer cliffs, that speech to another man's wife wasn't impudent, or affected, or anything except precisely right. By the half-illumination on the patio, I saw Ginny blush. Her eyes broke free of Maledicto's, the lashes fluttered birdlike, she answered confusedly: "It's kind of you . . . yes . . . won't you sit down?"

He bowed again and flowed into a chair. I plucked at Ginny's dress, drew her back toward the house and hissed furiously: "What the devil are you thinking of? Now we won't get rid of this character for an hour!"

She shook free with an angry gesture I remembered from past quarrels. "We have some cognac, Señor Maledicto," she said. It would have been her best smile she gave him, slow and sideways, except that

the faintest tremble remained upon her lips. "I'll get it. And would you like a cigar? Steve brought some Perfectos."

I sat down while she bustled inside. For a moment I was too outraged to speak. Maledicto took the word. "A charming lass, sir. A creature of purest delight."

"My *wife,*" I growled. "We came here for privacy."

"Oh, misdoubt me not!" His chuckle seemed to blend with the sea-murmur. Where he sat, in shadow, I could only make him out as a white and black blur, those oblique eyes glowing at me. "I understand, and shall not presume upon your patience. Mayhap later 'twould please you to meet my sister—"

"I don't play bridge."

"Bridge? Oh, aye, indeed, I remember. 'Tis a modern game with playing cards." His hand sketched an airy dismissal. "Nay, sir, our way is not to force ourselves unwanted. Indeed, we cannot visit save where some desire for us exists, albeit unspoken. 'Twas but . . . how should a man know aught from our dwelling, save that neighbors had arrived? And now I cannot churlishly refuse your lady's courtesy. But 'tis for a short time only, sir."

Well, that was as soft an answer as ever turned away wrath. I still couldn't like Maledicto, but my hostility eased till I could analyze my motives. Which turned out to be largely reaction to a third wheel. Something about him, maybe the perfume he used, made me desire Ginny more than ever before.

But my rage came back as she hovered over him with the cognac, chattered too loudly and laughed too much and insisted on having the Maledictos to dinner tomorrow! I hardly listened to their conversation. He talked smoothly, wittily, never quite answering my questions about himself. I sat and rehearsed what I'd say after he left.

Finally he rose. "I must not keep you," he said. "Moreover, 'tis a stony path to the Fortaleza, one with which I am not well familiar. Thus I must go slowly, lest I lose my way."

"Oh! But that could be dangerous." Ginny turned to me. "You've been over the trail, Steve. Show him home."

"I'd not afford you that trouble," demurred Maledicto.

"It's the least we can do. I insist, Amaris. It won't take you long, Steve. You said you felt like a run in the moonlight, and look, the moon is almost due up."

"Okay, okay, okay!" I snapped, as ungraciously as possible. I could, indeed, turn wolf on the way back, and work some of my temper off.

If I tried to argue with her now, the way I felt, our second night would see one Armageddon of a quarrel. "Let's go."

He kissed her hand. She said farewell, in a soft, blurry voice, like a schoolgirl in love for the first time. He had a flashlight; it made a small, bobbing puddle of radiance before us, picking out stones and clumps of sagebrush. The moonglow on the eastern ridges grew stronger. I felt it tingle along my nerves. For a while, as we wound across the mountainside, only the scrunch of our shoes made any noise.

"You brought no torch of your own, sir," he said at last. I grunted. Why should I tell him of my witchsight—to say nothing of the fact that I was a werewolf who in my alternate species had no need of flashlights? "Well, you shall take mine back," he continued. "The way were perilous otherwise."

That I knew. An ordinary human would blunder off the trail, even in bright moonlight. It was a dim, nearly obliterated path, and the land was gnarled and full of shadows. If he then got excited, the man would stumble around lost till dawn—or, quite probably, go off a precipice and smash his skull.

"I will call for it tomorrow evening." Maledicto sighed happily. "Ah, sir, 'tis rare good you've come. New-wedded folk are aye overflowingly full of love, and Cybelita has long been as parched as Amaris."

"Your sister?" I asked.

"Yes. Would you care to meet her this eventide?"

"No."

Silence fell again. We dipped into a gut-black ravine, rounded a crag, and could no more see the lodge. Nothing but the dim sheen of waters, the moonglow opposite, the suddenly very far and cold stars, lit that country. I saw the broken walls of the Fortaleza almost over my head, crowning their cliff like teeth in a jaw. Maledicto and I might have been the last living creatures on Midgard.

He stopped. His flashlight snapped out. "Good night, Señor Matuchek!" he cried. His laughter rang evil and beautiful.

"What?" I blinked bewildered into the murk that had clamped on me. "What the hell do you mean? We're not at the castle yet!"

"Nay. Proceed thither if thou wilst. And if thou canst."

I heard his feet start back down the path. They didn't crunch the gravel any more. They were soft and rapid, like the feet of a bounding animal.

Back toward the lodge.

A moment I stood as if cast in lead. I could hear the faintest

movement of air, rustling dry sagebrush, the ocean. Then my heartbeat shook all other noises out of me.

"*Ginny!*" I screamed.

I whirled and raced after him. My toes caught a rock, I pitched over, bloodied my hands with the fall. I staggered up, the bluffs and gullies flung my curses back at me, I went stumbling down a slope and through brush and cactus.

Again my foot snagged on something and I fell. This time I cracked my head against a boulder. The impact wasn't serious, but pain speared through me, lights burst, and for a minute or two I lay half-stunned.

And I felt a new presence in the night.

And through the hopeless aloneness that streamed from it and into my heart and marrow, I felt wire-taut expectation.

*—success in my grasp, this third time—both of them, he dead and she corrupted, afterward broken by remorse—safety from the threat that can be seen over them like a stormcloud as that certain moment draws nigh—safety at last—*

And the thought jagged more dreadfully sharp than any pain: Maledicto couldn't affect her by himself, not that strongly anyhow, not overcoming the love and pride and decency of her . . . no, the Tempter has worked in person on my girl—

I did not know what evil was intended. But in one flash, the vision of her alone with Maledicto burned me free of everything else, of hurt, weakness, the sense and even for a while the memory of a sneering Observer. I howled forth my rage and desperation, sprang erect, and ran.

That was sheer berserkergang. I didn't consciously notice what I was doing. Doubtless this had been planned, so I'd fall over a cliff to my death. But half-animal instincts and reflexes—I suppose—guarded me.

Presently I'd exhausted my wind and had to stop and gasp awhile. That forced pause gave my sanity a chance to take over.

Glaring around, I saw neither castle nor lodge. I'd lost my way.

# XVI

My gaze swept down the slope to the drop-off. The sea was a wan glimmer beyond. More of my wits came back. Maledicto had adroitly removed me from the scene, perhaps murdered me: if I were the untrained unspecial Homo sapiens he assumed. But I had a little more in reserve than he knew, such as witch-sight. I mumbled the formula and felt the retinal changes. At once I could see for miles. The view was blurred, of course; the human eyeball can't focus infrared wavelengths very well; but I could recognize landmarks. I set a general course and made for home.

With nightmare slowness. Maledicto had gone faster than human.

Nearly full, the moon broke over the hills.

The change was on me before I had overtly willed it. I didn't stop to undress, bundle my clothes and carry them in my mouth. My wolf-jaws ripped everything to rags except the elastic-banded shorts, and I went shadow-swift over the mountainside. If you think a giant bobtailed wolf in shorts is ridiculous, you're probably right; but it didn't occur to me just then.

I couldn't see as far with lupine eyes. However, I could smell my own trail, in bruised vegetation, vivid as a cry. I found the path and drank another scent. Now I knew what the undertone of Maledicto's odor had been.

Demon.

I'd never caught that exact whiff before, and my wolf brain wasn't up to wondering about his species. Nor did it wonder what he desired of Ginny. There was only room in my narrow skull for hate, and for hurrying.

The lodge came into view. I sprang onto the patio. No one was

about. But the master bedroom faced the sea, its window open to the moonbeams. I went through in a leap.

He had her in his arms. She was still pressing him away, resisting, but her eyes were closed and her strength faded. "No," she whispered. "No, help, don't, Amaris, Amaris, Amaris." Her hands moved to his throat, slid to his neck, drew his face to hers. They swayed downward together in the gloom.

I howled, once, and sank my teeth in him.

His blood did not taste human. It was like liquor, it burned and sang within me. I dared not bite him again. Another such draught and I might lie doglike at his feet, begging him to stroke me. I willed myself human.

The flow of transformation took no longer than he needed to release Ginny and turn around. Despite his surprise, he didn't snarl back at me. A shaft of moonlight caught his faerie visage, blazed gold in his eyes, and he was laughing.

My fist smashed forward with my weight behind it. Poor, slow man-flesh, how shall it fight the quicksilver life of Air and Darkness? Maledicto flickered aside. He simply wasn't there. I caromed into a wall and fell down, my knuckles one crumple of anguish.

His laughter belled above me. "And this puling thing should deserve as lively a wench as thee? Say but the word, Virginia, and I whip him to his kennel."

"Steve. . . ." She huddled back in a corner, not coming to me. I reeled onto my feet. Maledicto grinned, put an arm about Ginny's waist, drew her to him. She shuddered, again trying to pull away. He kissed her, and she made a broken sound and the motions of resistance started again to become motions of love. I charged. Maledicto shoved with his free hand. I went down, hard. He set a foot on my head and held me.

"I'd liefer not break thy bones," he said, "but if thou'rt not so gentle as to respect the lady's wishes—"

*"Wishes?"* Ginny broke from him. "God in Heaven!" she wailed. "Get out!"

Maledicto chuckled. "I must needs flee the holy names, if a victim of mine invoke them in full sincerity," he murmured. "And yet thou seest that I remain here. Thine inmost desire is to me, Virginia."

She snatched a vase and hurled it at him. He fielded it expertly, dropped it to shatter on me, and went to the window. "Oh, aye, this time the spell has been broken," he said. "Have no fear, though. At a more propitious hour, I shall return."

There was a moment's rippling, and he had gone over the sill. I crawled after him. The patio lay white and bare in the moonlight.

I sat down and held my head. Ginny flung herself sobbing beside me. A long time passed. Finally I got up, switched on the light, found a cigaret and slumped on the edge of the bed. She crouched at my knees, but I didn't touch her.

"What was it?" I asked.

"An incubus." Her head was bent, I saw just the red hair flowing down her back. She had put on her frilliest nightgown while we were gone—for whom? Her voice came small and thin. "He . . . it . . . it must haunt the ruins. Came over with the Spaniards. . . . Maybe it was responsible for their failure to—"

I dragged smoke into my lungs. "Why hasn't it been reported?" I wondered aloud, dully. And: "Oh, yeah, sure. It must have a very limited range of operation. A family curse on a family now extinct, so it's confined to the home and lands of that old don. Since his time, no one has been here after dark."

"Until we—" Her whisper trailed off.

"Well, Juan and his wife, with occasional guests." I smoked more fiercely. "You're the witch. You have the information. I barely know that an incubus is an erotic demon. Tell me, why did it never bother the Fernándezes?"

She began to weep afresh, deep hopeless gasps. I thought that despair had combined with the earlier loss of witchpower to drive her thaumaturgic training clean out of reach. My own mind was glass-clear as I continued. "Because it did speak the truth, I suppose, about holy symbols being a shield for people who really want to be shielded. Juan and his wife are good Catholics. They wouldn't come here without hanging crucifixes in every room. And neither of them wishes to be unfaithful to the other."

The face she raised was wild. "Do you think that I—"

"Oh, not consciously. If we'd thought to put up some crosses when we arrived, or offered an honest prayer, we'd have been safe too. We might never have known there was an incubus around. But we had too much else to think about, and it's too late now. Subconsciously, I suppose, you must have toyed with the idea that a little vacation from strict monogamy could do no one any harm—"

"Steve!" She scrambled stiffly to her feet. "On our honeymoon! You could say such a thing!"

"Could and did." I ground out the cigaret, wishing it were Maledicto's face. "How else could it lay a spell on you?"

"And you— Steve— Steve, I love you. Nobody else but you."

"Well, you better rev up the carpet," I sighed. "Fly to, oh, I imagine Guaymas is the nearest town big enough to have an exorcist on the police force. Report this and ask for protection. Because if I remember my demonology, it can follow you anywhere, once you've come under its influence."

"But nothing happened!" She cried that as if I were striking her: which, in a sense, I was.

"No, there wasn't time. Then. And, of course, you'd have been able to bounce any demon off with a purely secular spell, if you'd possessed your witch-powers. But those are gone. Until you relearn them, you'll need an exorcist guard, every hour of the day you aren't in a church. Unless—" I rose too.

"What?" She caught me with cold frantic hands. I shook her off, blinded by the double hurt to my manhood, that Maledicto had whipped me in fight and almost seduced my bride. "Steve, what are you thinking?"

"Why, that I might get rid of him myself."

"You *can't!* You're no warlock, and he's a demon!"

"I'm a werewolf. It may be a fair match." I shuffled into the bathroom, where I began to dress my wounds. They were superficial, except for swollen knuckles. She tried to help, but I gestured her away from me.

I knew I wasn't rational. Too much pain and fury filled me. I had some vague idea of going to the Fortaleza, whither Maledicto had presumably returned. In wolf-shape, I'd be as fast and strong as he. Of course, I dare not bite . . . but if I could switch to human as occasion warranted, use the unarmed combat techniques I'd learned in the Army. . . . The plan was as hopeless as any men ever coughed forth, but my own demon was driving me.

Ginny sensed it: that much witchcraft remained to her, if it was not simply inborn. She was quite pale in the unmerciful glare of the saintelmo, she shivered and gulped, but after a while she nodded. "If you must. We'll go together."

"No!" the roar burst from my gullet. "Be off to Guaymas, I said! Haven't I troubles enough? Let me alone till I can decide if I want you back!"

Another instant she stared at me. May I never again see such eyes. Then she fled.

I went out on the patio and became a wolf. The demon stench was thick on the air. I followed it over the mountainside.

# XVII

The earth was a dazzle of moonlight. My nose caught smells of dust, sage, cactus, kelp, and salt more remotely; my ears heard a bat's sonar squeak, the terrified scuttering of a jackrabbit; my pelt tingled with sensations for which men have no words. I felt my human torture no longer. The lupine brain could only hold clean, murderous carnivore thoughts. It was like being reborn. I understand that some psychiatrists have gotten good results by turning their patients temporarily into animals.

Presently the old watchtower lifted its corroded outline across the moon. Every nerve abristle for attack, I entered what had been a gateway. The courtyard lay empty around me. Sand had blown in during the centuries, weeds thrust between the flagstones, a shard of paving jutted here and there. Near the center was a heap which had been a building. Cellars lay underneath. I'd explored them a trifle, once, not deeply enough to come on the lair of the incubus.

I bayed my challenge.

It rustled in the tower door. A white form stepped out. My heart made one leap, and I crouched back. I thought wildly, Could I slash his jugular on the first bite, it wouldn't matter if I swallowed that drug-blood, he would be dead. . . .

Laughter ran around me on soft little feet. She made another stride outward, so that she could stand under a cataract of moonlight, impossibly white against the black moldering walls. "Good even, fair youth," she said. "I had not hoped for this fortune."

Her scent entered my lungs and my veins. I growled, and it turned into a whine. I wagged the stump of my tail. She came to me and scratched me behind the ears. I licked her arm; the taste was dizzying.

Somewhere in a thunderful wilderness, I thought it was no use remaining lupine. The currents of change ran through me. I stood up a man.

She was as tall and ripplesome as Amaris, and she had the same strange pointed face and eyes that fluoresced under the moon. But the pale hair fell past her waist in a cloud, and she wore a gown obviously woven by stingy spiders, on a figure that— Oh, well, I won't try to describe it. I suppose half the fun was simply in the way it moved.

"Cybelita . . . I presume?" I managed to husk.

"And thou art Steven." A slender hand fell upon mine and lingered. "Ah, welcome!"

I wet my lips. "Er . . . is your brother at home?"

She swayed closer. "What matters that?"

"I . . . uh . . ." I thought crazily that one can't politely explain one's business with a lady's brother as being to kill him. And after all, well, anyhow— "Look here," I blurted. "You, he, you've got to leave us alone!"

Cybelita smiled yieldingly. "Ah, thy grief is mine, Steven. And yet, canst thou not find it in thy heart to pity us? Knowest thou what damnation in truth consists of? To be a creature in whom the elements exist unblent—Fire of lust, Air of impulse, Water of wantonness, and the dark might of Earth—to be of such a nature, yet doomed to slink like a rat in these ruins, and howl to empty skies, and hunger and hunger for three hundred years! If thou wert starving, and two folk passing by spread a feast, wouldst thou not take such few crumbs as they could well spare?"

I croaked something about the analogic fallacy.

" 'Tis not malignancy," she pleaded. She drew close, her arms reached to my shoulders and her bosom nudged mine. " 'Tis need which forces us. And after all, Steven, ye mortals are not perfect either. Were ye saints with never an impure thought, no demon could venture near. We are drawn by that in ye which is akin to ourselves."

"Uh, well, yes," I choked. "You have two points there . . . a point, I mean. Yes."

Cybelita laughed anew. "But la, sweet youth! Here I stand in moonlight, embracing the most beautiful unclothed lad in this world—"

"Oh, my God!" I remembered that my outfit was a pair of skivvies. Since she didn't shrink away, my exclamation must not have counted as a prayer.

"—and discourse on metaphysic! Nay, now thou'rt a-flush." Cybelita pirouetted from me. "I'd not have the advantage of thee. That's not true friendship. Let us be alike in garb." She snapped her fingers

and the gown vanished. Not that it made any big difference, except morally, and by then morals seemed irrelevant.

"And now, come, come, my darling. My wolf, thou'rt my first *loup-garou*—had I suspected so new a wonder, no time would have been wasted on the woman— Come!" She threw herself against me. I don't know exactly what made me respond to her kiss. It was like being caught in a rose-colored cyclone.

Somehow I found a last resting place in the fragments of my will power. "No! I have a wife!"

Cybelita laughed less pleasantly. "Ha! Where thinkest thou Amaris has been since the moment thou left the wench alone?"

I made one garroted sound.

" 'Tis happened now," she purred. "What's done can ne'er be undone. Blame not thy wife. She is but mortal. Shouldst thou be more?"

I previewed Purgatory for about a minute. Then, hardly aware what was happening, I snatched Cybelita to me. My kisses broke her lips a little and I tasted the demon blood. "Come," she crooned, "my lover, my lover, bear me to the tower. . . ."

I picked her up and started across the courtyard.

"Steve!"

Ginny's scream was a knife driven through me.

I dropped my burden. Cybelita landed on her lovely tokus and said a most unlovely word. I gaped at Ginny. She crouched on our Persian carpet, it hovered over the broken gateway, her red hair tumbled past her bare shoulders and I knew, in that moment when I had already lost her to Amaris (for it could nevermore be the same between us two), that she was all I would ever want.

Cybelita rose. She looked bleached in the moonlight. I had no further desire for her. To hell with her.

To hell itself with her.

She sneered toward Ginny, turned back and opened her arms to me. I said: "Defend yourself!" and became a wolf.

Cybelita skipped back from my lunge. I heard Ginny cry out again, as if from another existence. My whole attention was on the succubus. Cybelita's body pulsed, grayed, suddenly she was a wolf too. She grinned shamelessly at me and her femaleness hit me like a club.

I didn't take the offer. I went for her throat. We rolled over and fought. She was tough, but hadn't been trained in combat lycanthropy. I know the judo breaks for my animal-shape, too. I got under her jaws and clamped my teeth where I wanted them.

The demon blood was sweet and horrible to taste. But this time it

couldn't rouse my wishes. The powers in me of Love, for my wife, and Hate, for the thing I fought, were too strong. Or, if you insist on outmoded terms, my glands were supplying enough testosterone and adrenalin to swamp whatever hormone was in that ichor.

I killed her.

In the last fragmented second, I heard—not with my ears—the shriek of the foul spirit within. I felt—not with my nerves—the space-time turbulence as it struggled to change the mathematical form of its Schrödinger function, thus fleeing to the Low Continuum where it belonged and leaving me with the exchange mass. But my fangs had been too quick and savage. The body perished and the soulless demon was no more.

I lay by the wolf corpse, gasping. It writhed horribly through shapes of woman, man, horned and tailed satanoid. When its last cohesive forces were spent, it puffed away in gas.

Piece by tattered piece, my wits returned. I lay across Ginny's dear lap. Moonlight poured cool over us, under friendly stars, down to a castle which was nothing but piled stones. Ginny laughed and wept and held me close.

I became a man again and drew her to me. "It's okay, darling," I breathed. "Everything's okay. I finished her. I'll get Amaris next."

"What?" Her wet face lifted from my breast toward my lips. "Don't you n-n-n-know? You have!"

"Huh?"

"Yes. Some of my education c-c-came back to me . . . after you'd gone." She drew a shaking breath. "Incubi and succubi are identical. They change their sex as . . . as . . . indicated. . . . Amaris and that hussy were the same!"

"You mean she didn't—he didn't—you didn't—" I let out a yell which registered on seismographs in Baja California. And yet that noise was the most fervent prayer of thanks which Our Father had ever gotten from me.

Not that I hadn't been prepared to forgive my dearest, having had experience of the demon's power. But learning that there wasn't anything which needed to be forgiven was like a mountain off my back.

"Steve!" cried Ginny. "I love you too, but my ribs aren't made of iron!"

I climbed to my feet. "It's done with," I whispered, incredulous. In a moment: "More than done with. We actually came out ahead of the game."

"How's that?" she asked, still timid but with a sunrise in her eyes.

"Well," I said, "I guess we've had a useful lesson in humility. Neither of us turns out to own a more decorous subconscious mind than the average person."

An instant's chill possessed me. I thought: No average persons would have come as near falling as we did . . . on the second night after their wedding! Nor would we ourselves. More than the resources of a petty demon was marshaled against us. More than chance brought us to its haunts. Something else wanted us destroyed.

I believe, now, that that Force was still at hand, watching. It could not strike at us directly. No new agents of temptation were near, and we were fire-tempered against them anyway. It could not again use our latent suspicions and jealousies to turn us on each other; we were as purged of those as common mortals can be.

But did it, in its time-abiding craftiness, *withdraw* the last evil influences from around and within us—did it free us of aches and weariness—and itself depart?

I don't know. I do know that suddenly the night was splendor, and my love for Ginny rose in a wave that left no room in me for anything else, and when many days later I remembered that encounter on the sea cliff, it was as vague to me as the former ones and I dismissed it with the same casual half-joke: "Funny how a bonk on the conk always gives me that particular hallucination."

There in the courtyard, I looked upon her, drew her to me, and said—my throat so full of unshed tears that the words came hoarse—"In what counts, darling, I learned how you do care for me. You followed me here, not knowing what might be waiting, when I'd told you to run for safety. . . ."

Her tousled head rubbed my shoulder. "I learned likewise about you, Steve. It's a good feeling."

We walked onto the carpet. "Home, James," I said. After a pause, when James was airborne: "Uh, I suppose you're dead tired."

"Well, actually not. I'm too keyed up yet . . . no, by gosh, I'm too happy." She squeezed my hand. "But you, poor dear—"

"I feel fine," I grinned. "We can sleep late tomorrow."

"Mister Matuchek! What are you thinking?"

"The same as you, Mrs. Matuchek."

I imagine she blushed in the moonlight. "So I see. Very good, sir."

Which turned out to be a prophecy.

# XVIII

After we returned to our apartment we took summer jobs, quitting when classes reopened in fall. Like most newlyweds, we ran into budgetary difficulties: nothing too serious, but we had to sell the carpet, for instance, when Ginny got pregnant. Otherwise, that first couple of married years, we lived unspectacular lives, except when we were alone together.

And then a nurse led me to the bed where my darling lay. Always fair-hued, she was white after her battle, and the beautiful bones stood sharply in her face. But her hair was fire across the pillow, and though the lids drooped on her eyes, that green had never shone brighter.

I bent and kissed her, as gently as I could. "Hi, there," she whispered.

"How are you?" was the foolish single thing that came to me to say.

"Fine." She regarded me for a moment before, abruptly, she grinned. "But you look as if couvade might be a good idea."

As a matter of fact, some obstetricians do put the father to bed when a child is being born. Our doctor followed majority opinion in claiming that I'd give my wife the maximum possible sympathetic help by just sweating it out in the waiting room. I'd studied the subject frantically enough, these past months, to become somewhat of an authority. A first birth for a tall slim girl like Ginny was bound to be difficult. She took the prospect with her usual coolness, unbending only to the extent of casting runes to foretell the sex of the child, and that only so we wouldn't be caught flat-footed for a name.

"How do you like your daughter?" she asked me.

"Gorgeous," I said.

"Liar," she chuckled. "The man never lived who wasn't horrified when they told him he'd sired that wrinkled blob of red protoplasm." Her hand reached for mine. "But she will be lovely, Steve. She can't help being. It's so lovely between us."

I told myself that I would *not* bawl right in front of the mothers in this room. The nurse saved me with a crisp: "I think we had better let your wife rest, Mr. Matuchek. And Dr. Ashman would like to finish things so he can go home."

He was waiting for me in the naming office. When I had passed through the soundproof door, the nurse sealed it behind me with wax and a davidstar. This was an up-to-date hospital where they took every care. Thomas Ashman was a grizzled, craggy six-footer with a relaxed manner, at present a bit droopy from weariness. I saw that beneath the impressive zodiacal traceries on his surgical gown, he'd been wearing white duck pants and a tee shirt—besides his amulet, of course.

We shook hands. "Everything's good," he assured me. "I've gotten the lab report. You understand that, with no therianthropes on the maternal side, none of your children will ever be a natural werewolf. But since this one has inherited the complete recessive gene complex from you, she'll take transformation spells quite easily. A definite advantage, especially if she goes in for a thaumaturgic career like her mother. It does mean, however, that certain things should be guarded against. She'll be more subject to paranatural influences than most people are."

I nodded. Ginny and I had certainly had an undue share of adventures we didn't want.

"Marry her off right," Ashman joked, "and you'll have werewolf grandchildren."

"If she takes after her old lady," I said, "Lord help any poor boy we tried to force on her!" I felt as idiotic as I sounded. "Look, Doctor, we're both tired. Let's make out the birth certificates and turn in."

"Sure." He sat down at the desk. The parchments were already inscribed with parental names, place and date, and the file number they bore in common. "What're you calling her?"

"Valeria."

"Yes, I suppose your wife would pick something like that. Her idea, wasn't it? Any middle name?"

"Uh . . . Mary. My decision—for my own mother—" I realized I was babbling again.

"Good thought. She can take refuge in it if she doesn't like the fancy monicker. Though I suspect she will." He typed out the information, signed, gave me the document, and dropped the carbon in an out box. Rather more ceremoniously, he laid down the primary certificate that bore her fingerprints. "And the true name?"

"Victrix."

"Hm?"

"Ginny always liked it. Valeria Victrix. The last Roman legion in Britain." The last that stood against Chaos, she had said in one of her rare wholly serious moments.

Ashman shrugged. "Well, it isn't as if the kid's going to use it."

"I hope she never has to!"

"That'd imply a bad emergency," he agreed. "But don't fret. I see too many young husbands, shaken up by what they've undergone, be knocked for a loop at the grim possibilities they have to face now. Really, though, this is nothing more than another sensible precaution, like a vaccination."

"I know," I said. "Wish they'd had the idea when I was born." It isn't likely that anyone will try nymic tricks against an ordinary peaceful citizen, but you've seen how my career has gotten turbulent every once in a while, and maintaining the counterspells is a bloody nuisance—not always reliable, either. Medical science is one of the few areas where I'll admit that genuine progress gets made.

Ashman dipped an eagle quill in a well of oak-gall ink. "By the bird of thy homeland and the tree of the lightning," he intoned, "under their protection and God's, child of this day, be thy true name, known on this earth but to thy parents, thy physician, and thee when thou shalt come of age: Victrix; and may thou bear it in honor and happiness while thy years endure. Amen." He wrote, dusted sand from Galilee across the words, and stood up again. "This one I'll file personally," he said. Yawning: "Okay, that's all."

We repeated our handshake. "I'm sorry you had to deliver her at such an unsanctified hour," I said.

"Nothing we GP's aren't used to," he answered. The sleepiness left him. He regarded me very steadily. "Besides, in this case I expected it."

"Huh?"

"I'd heard something about you and your wife already," Ashman said. "I looked up more. Cast a few runes of my own. Maybe you don't know it yourself, but that kid was begotten on the winter solstice. And, quite apart from her unusual heredity, there's something else about

her. I can't identify it. But I felt pretty sure she'd be born this night—because a full moon was due on Matthewsmas. I'm going to watch her with a great deal of interest, Mr. Matuchek, and I suggest you take extra special care of her. . . . Good night, now."

Nothing spectacular happened to us in the following three years. Or so you would have thought; but you are somebody else. For our little circle, it was when the world opened up for our taking and, at the same time, buckled beneath our feet.

To start with, Valeria was unexpected. We found out later that Svartalf had been chasing the Brownie again and, in revenge, the Good Folk had turned Ginny's pills to aspirin. Afterward I've wondered if more didn't lie behind the incident than that. The Powers have Their ways of steering us toward situations that will serve Their ends.

At first Ginny intended to go ahead according to our original plan, as soon as the youngster was far enough along that a babysitter could handle things by day. And she did take her Ph.D. in Arcana, and had some excellent job offers. But once our daughter was part of our home, well, mama's emancipation kept getting postponed. We weren't about to let any hireling do slobwork on Valeria! Not yet, when she was learning to smile, when she was crawling everywhere around, when her noises of brook and bird were changing into language—later, later.

I quite agreed. But this meant giving up, for a while if not forever, the condition we'd looked forward to: of a smart young couple with a plump double income, doing glamorous things in glamorous places among glamorous people. I did propose trying to take up my Hollywood career again, but would have been astounded if Ginny had been willing to hear word one of that idea. "Do you imagine for half a second," she said, "that I'd want a mediocre player of Silver Chief and Lassie, when I could have a damn good engineer?" Personally, I don't think the pictures I made were all that bad; but on the whole, her answer relieved me.

A newly created B.Sc. doesn't step right into the kind of challenging project he hopes for, especially when he's older than the average graduate. I had to start out with what I could get. By luck—we believed then—that was unexpectedly good.

The Nornwell Scryotronics Corporation was among the new outfits in the booming postwar communications and instrument business. Though small, it was upward bound on an exponential curve. Besides manufacture, it did R & D, and I was invited to work on the latter. This was not simply fascinating in itself, it was a long step toward my ultimate professional goal. Furthermore, an enlightened management encouraged us to study part time for advanced degrees, on salary. That pay wasn't bad, either. And before long, Barney Sturlason was my friend as much as he was my boss.

The chief drawback was that we had to stay in this otherwise dull city and endure its ghastly Upper Midwestern winters. But we rented a comfortable suburban house, which helped. And we had each other, and little Valeria. Those were good years. It's just that nobody else would find an account of them especially thrilling.

That's twice true when you consider what went on meanwhile at large. I suppose mankind has always been going to perdition in a roller coaster and always will be. Still, certain eras remind you of the old Chinese curse: "May you live in interesting times!"

Neither Ginny nor I had swallowed the propaganda guff about how peace and happiness would prevail forevermore once the wicked Caliphate had been defeated. We knew what a legacy of wretchedness all wars must leave. Besides, we knew this conflict was more a symptom than a cause of the world's illness. The enemy wouldn't have been able to overrun most of the Eastern Hemisphere and a chunk of the United States if Christendom hadn't been divided against itself. For that matter, the Caliphate was nothing but the secular arm of a Moslem heresy; we had plenty of good Allah allies.

It did seem reasonable, though, to expect that afterward people would have learned their lesson, put their religious quarrels aside, and settled down to reconstruction. In particular, we looked for the Johannine Church to be generally discredited and fade away. True, its adherents had fought the Caliph too, had in fact taken a leading role in the resistance movements in the occupied countries. But wasn't its challenge to the older creeds—to the whole basis of Western society—what had split and weakened our civilization in the first place? Wasn't its example what had stimulated the rise of the lunatic Caliphist ideology in the Middle East?

I now know better than to expect reasonableness in human affairs.

Contrary to popular impression, the threat didn't appear suddenly. A few men warned against it from the beginning. They pointed out how the Johnnies had become dominant in the politics of more than one nation, which thereupon stopped being especially friendly to us, and how in spite of this they were making converts throughout America. But most of us hardly listened. We were too busy repairing war damage, public and personal. We considered those who sounded the alarm to be reactionaries and would-be tyrants (which some, perhaps, were). The Johannine theology might be nuts, we said, but didn't the First Amendment guarantee its right to be preached? The Petrine churches might be in trouble, but wasn't that their problem? And really, in our scientific day and age, to talk about subtle, pervasive dangers in a religious-philosophical system . . . a system which emphasized peacefulness almost as strongly as the Quakers, which exalted the commandment to love thy neighbor above every other—well, it just might be that our materialistic secular society and our ritualistic faiths would benefit from a touch of what the Johnnies advocated.

So the movement and its influence grew. And then the activist phase began: and somehow orderly demonstrations were oftener and oftener turning into riots, and wildcat strikes were becoming more and more common over issues that made less and less sense, and student agitation was paralyzing campus after campus, and person after otherwise intelligent person was talking about the need to tear down a hopelessly corrupt order of things so that the Paradise of Love could be built on the ruins . . . and the majority of us, that eternal majority which wants nothing except to be left alone to cultivate its individual gardens, wondered how the country could have started to disintegrate overnight.

Brother, it did not happen overnight. Not even over Walpurgis Night.

# XX

I came home early that June day. Our street was quiet, walled in between big old elms, lawns, and houses basking in sunlight. The few broomsticks in view were ridden by local women, carrying groceries in the saddlebags and an infant or two strapped in the kiddie seat. This was a district populated chiefly by young men on the way up. Such tend to have pretty wives, and in warm weather these tend to wear shorts and halters. The scenery lightened my mood no end.

I'd been full of anger when I left the turbulence around the plant. But here was peace. My roof was in sight. Ginny and Val were beneath it. Barney and I had a plan for dealing with our troubles, come this eventide. The prospect of action cheered me. Meanwhile, I was home!

I passed into the open garage, dismounted, and racked my Chevvy alongside Ginny's Volksbesen. As I came out again, aimed at the front door, a cannonball whizzed through the air and hit me. "Daddy! Daddy!"

I hugged my offspring close, curly yellow hair, enormous blue eyes, the whole works. She was wearing her cherub suit, and I had to be careful not to break the wings. Before, when she flew, it had been at the end of a tether secured to a post, and under Ginny's eye. What the deuce was she doing free—?

Oh. Svartalf zoomed around the corner of the house on a whisk broom. His back was arched, his tail was raised, and he used bad language. Evidently Ginny had gotten him to supervise. He could control the chit fairly well, no doubt, keep her in the yard and out of trouble . . . until she saw Daddy arrive.

"Okay!" I laughed. "Enough. Let's go in and say boo to Mother."

"Wide piggyback?"

For Val's birthday last fall I'd gotten the stuff for an expensive spell and had Ginny change me. The kid was used to playing with me in my wolf form, I'd thought; but how about a piggyback ride, the pig being fat and white and spotted with flowers? The local small fry were still talking about it. "Sorry, no," I had to tell her. "After that performance of yours, you get the Air Force treatment." And I carried her by her ankles, squealing and wiggling, while I sang,

*"Up in the air, junior birdman,*
*Up in the air, upside down—"*

Ginny came into the living room, from the workroom, as we did. Looking behind her, I saw why she'd deputized the supervision of Val's flytime. Washday. A three-year-old goes through a lot of clothes, and we couldn't afford self-cleaning fabrics. She had to animate each garment singly, and make sure they didn't tie themselves in knots or something while they soaped and rinsed and marched around to dry off and so forth. And, since a parade like that is irresistible to a child, she had to get Val elsewhere.

Nonetheless, I wondered if she wasn't being a tad reckless, putting her familiar in charge. Hitherto, she'd done the laundry when Val was asleep. Svartalf had often shown himself to be reliable in the clutch. But for all the paranatural force in him, he remained a big black tomcat, which meant he was not especially dependable in dull everyday matters. . . . Then I thought, What the blazes, since Ginny stopped being a practicing witch, the poor beast hasn't had much excitement; he hasn't even got left a dog or another cat in the whole neighborhood that dares fight him; this assignment was probably welcome; Ginny always knows what she's doing; and—

"—and I'm an idiot for just standing here gawping," I said, and gathered her in. She was dressed like the other wives I'd seen, but if she'd been out there too I wouldn't have seen them.

She responded. She knew how.

"What's a Nidiot?" Val asked from the floor. She pondered the matter. "Well, Daddy's a *good* Nidiot."

Svartalf switched his tail and looked skeptical.

I relaxed my hold on Ginny a trifle. She ran her fingers through my hair. "Wow," she murmured. "What brought that on, tiger?"

"Daddy's a woof," Val corrected her.

"You can call me tiger today," I said, feeling happier by the minute.

Ginny leered. "Okay, pussycat."

"Wait a bit—"

She shrugged. The red tresses moved along her shoulders. "Well, if you insist, okay, Lame Thief of the Waingunga."

Val regarded us sternly. "When you fwoo wif you' heads," she directed, "put 'em outside to melt."

The logic of this, and the business of getting the cherub rig off her, took time to unravel. Not until our offspring was bottoms up on the living-room floor, watching cartoons on the crystal ball, and I was in the kitchen watching Ginny start supper, did we get a chance to talk.

"How come you're home so early?" she asked.

"How'd you like to reactivate the old outfit tonight?" I replied.

"Which?"

"Matuchek and Graylock—no, Matuchek and Matuchek—Troubleshooters Extraordinary, Licensed Confounders of the Ungodly."

She put down her work and gave me a long look. "What are you getting at, Steve?"

"You'll see it on the ball, come news time," I answered. "We aren't simply being picketed any more. They've moved onto the grounds. They're blocking every doorway. Our personnel had to leave by skylight, and rocks got thrown at some of them."

She was surprised and indignant, but kept the coolness she showed to the world outside this house. "You didn't call the police?"

"Sure, we did. I listened in, along with Barney, since Roberts thought a combat veteran might have some useful ideas. We can get police help if we want it. The demonstrators have turned into trespassers; and windows are broken, walls defaced with obscene slogans, that sort of thing. Our legal case is plenty clear. Only the opposition is out for trouble. Trouble for us, as much as possible, but mainly they're after martyrs. They'll resist any attempt to disperse them. Just like the fracas in New York last month. A lot of these characters are students too. Imagine the headlines: Police Brutality Against Idealistic Youths. Peaceful Protesters Set On With Clubs and Geas Casters.

"Remember, this is a gut issue. Nornwell manufactures a lot of police and defense equipment, like witchmark fluorescers and basilisk goggles. We're under contract to develop more kinds. The police and the armed forces serve the Establishment. The Establishment is evil. Therefore Nornwell must be shut down."

"*Quod erat demonstrandum* about," she sighed.

"The chief told us that an official move to break up the invasion would mean bloodshed, which might touch off riots at the University, along Merlin Avenue—Lord knows where it could lead. He asked us

to stop work for the rest of the week, to see if this affair won't blow over. We'd probably have to, anyway. Quite a few of our men told their supervisors they're frankly scared to come back, the way things are."

The contained fury sparked in her eyes. "If you knuckle under," she said, "they'll proceed to the next on their list."

"You know it," I said. "We all do. But there is that martyrdom effect. There are those Johnny priests ready to deliver yet another sanctimonious sermon about innocent blood equals the blood of the Lamb. There's a country full of well-intentioned bewildered people who'll wonder if maybe the Petrine churches aren't really on the way out, when the society that grew from them has to use violence against members of the churches of Love. Besides, let's face the fact, darling, violence has never worked against civil disobedience."

"Come back and tell me that after the machine guns have talked," she said.

"Yeah, sure. But who'd want to preserve a government that resorts to massacre? I'd sooner turn Johnny myself. The upshot is, Nornwell can't ask the police to clear its property for it."

Ginny cocked her head at me. "You don't look too miserable about this."

I laughed. "No. Barney and I brooded over the problem for a while and hatched us quite an egg. I'm actually enjoying myself by now, sort of. Life's been too tame of late. Which is why I asked if you'd like to get in on the fun."

"Tonight?"

"Yes. The sooner the better. I'll give you the details after our young hopeful's gone to bed."

Ginny's own growing smile faded. "I'm not sure I can get a sitter on notice that short. This is final exam week at the high school."

"Well, if you can't, what about Svartalf?" I suggested. "You won't be needing a familiar, and he can do the elementary things, keep guard, dash next door and yowl a neighbor awake if she gets collywobbles—"

"She might wake up and want us," Ginny objected, not too strongly.

I disposed of that by reminding her we'd bought a sleep watcher for Val, after a brief period when she seemed to have occasional nightmares. The little tin soldier didn't merely stand by her bed, the dream of him stood with his musket at the edge of her dreams, ready to chase away anything scary. I don't believe gadgets can substitute for parental love and presence; but they help a lot.

Ginny agreed. I could see the eagerness build up in her. Though

she'd accepted a housewife's role for the time being, no race horse really belongs on a plowing team.

In this fashion did we prepare the way for hell to break loose, literally.

The night fell moonless, a slight haze dulling the stars. We left soon after, clad alike in black sweaters and slacks, headlights off. Witch-sight enabled us to make a flight that was safe if illegal, high over the city's constellated windows and lamps until our stick swung downward again toward the industrial section. It lay still darker and emptier than was normal at this hour. I saw practically no tiny bluish glimmers flit around the bulks of shops and warehouses. The Good Folk were passing up their nocturnal opportunity for revels and curious window-peeking when man wasn't around. That which was going on had frightened them.

It centered on Nornwell's grounds. They shone forth, an uneasy auroral glow in the air. As we neared, the wind that slid past, stroking and whispering to me, bore odors—flesh and sweat, incense, an electric acridity of paranatural energies. The hair stood erect along my spine. I was content not to be in wolf-shape and get the full impact of that last.

The paved area around the main building was packed close to solid with bodies. So was the garden that had made our workers' warm-weather lunches pleasant; nothing remained of it except mud and cigaret stubs. I estimated five hundred persons altogether, blocking any except aerial access. Their mass was not restless, but the movement of individuals created an endless rippling through it, and the talk and footshuffle gave those waves a voice.

Near the sheds, our lot was less crowded. Scattered people there were taking a break from the vigil to fix a snack or flake out in a sleeping bag. They kept a respectful distance from a portable altar at the far end: though from time to time, someone would kneel in its direction.

I whistled, long and low. "That's arrived since I left." Ginny's arms caught tighter around my waist.

A Johannine priest was holding service. Altitude or no, we couldn't mistake his white robe, high-pitched minor-key chanting, spread-eagle stance which he could maintain for hours, the tau crucifix that gleamed tall and gaunt behind the altar, the four talismans—Cup, Wand, Sword, and Disc—upon it. Two acolytes swung censers whence came the smoke that sweetened and, somehow, chilled the air.

"What's he up to?" I muttered. I'd never troubled to learn much about the new church. Or the old ones, for that matter. Not that Ginny and I were ignorant of modern scientific discoveries proving the reality of the Divine and things like absolute evil, atonement, and an afterlife. But it seemed to us that so little is known beyond these bare hints, and that God can have so infinitely many partial manifestations to limited human understanding, that we might as well call ourselves Unitarians.

"I don't know," she answered. Her tone was bleak. "I studied what's public about their rites and doctrines, but that's just the top part of the iceberg, and it was years ago for me. Anyhow, you'd have to be a communicant—no, a lot more, an initiate, ultimately an adept, before you were told what a given procedure really means."

I stiffened. "Could he be hexing our side?"

Whetted by alarm, my vision swept past the uneasy sourceless illumination and across the wider scene. About a score of burly blue policemen were posted around the block. No doubt they were mighty sick of being jeered at. Also, probably most of them belonged to traditional churches. They wouldn't exactly mind arresting the agent of a creed which said that their own creeds were finished.

"No," I replied to myself, "he can't be, or the cops'd have him in the cooler this minute. Maybe he's anathematizing us. He could do that under freedom of religion, I suppose, seeing as how man can't control God but can only ask favors of Him. But actually casting a spell, bringing goetic forces in to work harm—"

Ginny interrupted my thinking aloud. "The trouble is," she said, "when you deal with these Gnostics, you don't know where their prayers leave off and their spells begin. Let's get cracking before something happens. I don't like the smell of the time stream tonight."

I nodded and steered for the principal building. The Johnny didn't fret me too much. Chances were he was just holding one of his esoteric masses to encourage the demonstrators. Didn't the claim go that his church was the church of universal benevolence? That it actually had

no need of violence, being above the things of this earth? "The day of the Old Testament, of the Father, was the day of power and fear; the day of the New Testament, of the Son, has been the day of expiation; the day of the Johannine Gospel, of the Holy Spirit, will be the day of love and unveiled mysteries." No matter now.

The police were interdicting airborne traffic in the immediate vicinity except for whoever chose to leave it. That was a common-sense move. None but a minority of the mob were Johnnies. To a number of them, the idea of despising and renouncing a sinful material world suggested nothing more than that it was fashionable to wreck that world. The temptation to flit overhead and drop a few Molotov cocktails could get excessive.

Naturally, Ginny and I might have insisted on our right to come here, with an escort if need be. But that could provoke the explosion we wanted to avoid. Altogether, the best idea was to slip in, unnoticed by friend and foe alike. Our commando-type skills were somewhat rusty, though; the maneuver demanded our full attention.

We succeeded. Our stick ghosted through a skylight left open, into the garage. To help ventilate the rest of the place, this was actually a well from roof to ground floor. Normally our employees came and went by the doors. Tonight, however, those were barred on two sides—by the bodies of the opposition, and by protective force-fields of our own which it would take an expert wizard to break.

The Pinkerton technician hadn't conjured quite fast enough for us. Every first-story window was shattered. Through the holes drifted mumbled talk, background chant. Racking the broom, I murmured in Ginny's ear—her hair tickled my lips and was fragrant—"You know, I'm glad they did get a priest. During the day, they had folk singers."

"Poor darling." She squeezed my hand. "Watch out for busted glass." We picked our way in the murk to a hall and upstairs to the R & D section. It was defiantly lighted. But our footfalls rang too loud in its emptiness. It was a relief to enter Barney Sturlason's office.

His huge form rose behind the desk. "Virginia!" he rumbled. "What an unexpected pleasure." Hesitating: "But, uh, the hazard—"

"Shouldn't be noticeable, Steve tells me," she said. "And I gather you could use an extra thaumaturgist."

"Sure could." I saw how his homely features sagged with exhaustion. He'd insisted that I go home and rest. This was for the practical reason that, if things went sour and we found ourselves attacked, I'd have to turn wolf and be the main line of defense until the police could act. But he'd stayed on, helping his few volunteers make ready. That,

far more than his great competence as a research man, was his mark of bosshood.

"Steve's explained our scheme?" he went on. His decision to accept her offer had been instantaneous. "Well, we need to make sure the most delicate and expensive equipment doesn't suffer. Quite apart from stuff being ruined, imagine the time and cost of recalibrating every instrument we've got, from dowsers to tarots! I think everything's adequately shielded, but I'd certainly appreciate an independent check by a fresh mind. Afterward you might cruise around the different shops and labs, see what I've overlooked and arrange its protection."

"Okay." She'd visited sufficiently often to be familiar with the layout. "I'll help myself to what I need from the stockroom, and ask the boys in—in the alchemistry section, did you say, dear?—for help if necessary." She paused. "I expect you two'll be busy for a while."

"Yes, I'm going to give them one last chance out there," Barney said, "and in case somebody gets overexcited, I'd better have Steve along for a bodyguard."

"And *I* still believe you might as well save your breath," I snorted.

"No doubt you're right, as far as you go," Barney said, "but don't forget the legal aspect. I don't own this place, I only head up a department. We're acting on our personal initiative after the directors agreed to suspend operations. Jack Roberts' approval of our plan was strictly *sub rosa.* Besides, ownership or not, we can no more use spells offensively against trespassers than we could use shotguns. The most we're allowed is harmless defensive forces to preserve life, limb, and property."

"Unless we're directly endangered," I said.

"Which is what we're trying to prevent," he reminded me. "Anyhow, because of the law, I have to make perfectly clear before plenty of witnesses that we intend to stay within it."

I shrugged and shed my outer garments. Underneath was the elastic knit one-piecer that would keep me from arrest for indecent exposure as a human, and not hamper me as a wolf. The moonflash already hung around my neck like a thick round amulet. Ginny kissed me hard. "Take care of yourself, tiger," she whispered.

She had no strong cause to worry. The besiegers were unarmed, except for fists and feet and possibly some smuggled billies or the like—nothing I need fear after Skinturning. Even knives and bullets and fangs could only inflict permanent harm under rare and special conditions, like those which had cost me my tail during the war. Besides, the likelihood of a fight was very small. Why should the oppo-

sition set on us? That would launch the police against them; and, while martyrdom has its uses, closing down our plant was worth more. Nonetheless, Ginny's tone was not completely level, and she watched us go down the hall till we had rounded a corner.

At that time, Barney said, "Wait a tick," opened a closet, and extracted a blanket that he hung on his arm. "If you should have to change shape," he said, "I'll throw this over you."

"Whatever for?" I exclaimed. "That's not sunlight outside, it's elflight. It won't inhibit transformation."

"It's changed character since that priest set up shop. I used a spectroscope to make certain. The glow's acquired enough ultraviolet—3500 angstroms to be exact—that you'd have trouble. By-product of a guardian spell against any that we might try to use offensively."

"But we *won't!*"

"Of course not. It's pure ostentation on his part. Clever, though. When they saw a shieldfield established around them, the fanatics and naive children in the mob leaped to the conclusion that it was necessary; and thus Nornwell gets reconfirmed as the Enemy." He shook his head. "Believe me, Steve, these demonstrators are being operated like gloves, by some mighty shrewd characters."

"You sure the priest himself raised the field?"

"Yeah. They're all Maguses in that clergy, remember—part of their training—and I wonder what else they learn in those lonesome seminaries. Let's try talking with him."

"Is he in charge?" I wondered. "The Johannine hierarchy does claim that when its members mix in politics, they do it strictly as private citizens."

"I know," Barney said. "And I am the Emperor Norton."

"No, really," I persisted. "These conspiracy theories are too bloody simple to be true. What you've got is a, uh, a general movement, something in the air, people disaffected—"

But then, walking, we'd reached one of the ornamental glass panels that flanked the main entrance. It was smashed like the windows, but no one had thought to barricade it, and our protective spell forestalled entry. Of course, it did not affect us. We stepped through, onto the landing, right alongside the line of bodies that was supposed to keep us in.

We couldn't go farther. The stairs down to the ground were packed solid. For a moment we weren't noticed. Barney tapped one scraggle-bearded adolescent on the shoulder. "Excuse me," he said from his towering height. "May I?" He plucked a sign out of the unwashed

hand, hung the blanket over the placard, and waved his improvised flag of truce aloft. The color was bilious green.

A kind of gasp, like the puff of wind before a storm, went through the crowd. I saw faces and faces and faces next to me, below me, dwindling off into the dusk beyond the flickering elflight. I don't think it was only my haste and my prejudice that made them look eerily alike.

You hear a lot about long-haired men and short-haired women, bathless bodies and raggedy clothes. Those were certainly present in force. Likewise I identified the usual graybeard radicals and campus hangers-on, hoodlums, unemployables, vandals, True Believers, and the rest. But there were plenty of clean, well-dressed, terribly earnest boys and girls. There were the merely curious, too, who had somehow suddenly found themselves involved. And everyone was tall, short, or medium, fat, thin, or average, rich, poor, or middleclass, bright, dull, or normal, heterosexual, homosexual, or I know not what, able in some fields, inept in others, interested in some things, bored by others, each with an infinite set of memories, dreams, hopes, terrors, loves—each with a soul.

No, the sameness appeared first in the signs they carried. I didn't count how many displayed ST. JOHN 13:34 or I JOHN 2:9–11 or another of those passages; how many more carried the texts, or some variation like LOVE THY NEIGHBOR or plain LOVE: quite a few, anyway, repeating and repeating. Others were less amiable:

DEMATERIALIZE THE MATERIALISTS!

WEAPONMAKERS, WEEP!

STOP GIVING POLICE DEVILS HORNS

KILL THE KILLERS, HATE THE HATERS, DESTROY THE DESTROYERS!

SHUT DOWN THIS SHOP

And so it was as if the faces—worse, the brains behind them—had become nothing but placards with slogans written across.

Don't misunderstand me. I wouldn't think much of a youngster who never felt an urge to kick the God of Things As They Are in his fat belly. It's too bad that most people lose it as they get old and fat themselves. The Establishment is often unendurably smug and stupid; the hands it folds so piously are often bloodstained.

And yet . . . and yet . . . it's the only thing between us and the Dark Ages that'd have to intervene before another and probably worse Establishment could arise to restore order. And don't kid yourself that none would. Freedom is a fine thing until it becomes somebody else's freedom to enter your house, kill, rob, rape, and enslave the people

you care about. Then you'll accept any man on horseback who promises to bring some predictability back into life, and you yourself will give him his saber and knout.

Therefore isn't our best bet to preserve this thing we've got? However imperfectly, it does function; and it's ours, it shaped us, we may not understand it any too well but surely we understand it better than something untried and alien. With a lot of hard work, hard thinking, hard-nosed good will, we can improve it.

You will not, repeat not, get improvement from wild-blue-yonder theorists who'd take us in one leap outside the whole realm of our painfully acquired experience; or from dogmatists mouthing the catchwords of reform movements that accomplished something two generations or two centuries ago; or from college sophomores convinced they have the answer to every social problem over which men like Hammurabi, Moses, Confucius, Aristotle, Plato, Marcus Aurelius, Thomas Aquinas, Hobbes, Locke, Voltaire, Jefferson, Burke, Lincoln, a thousand others broke their heads and their hearts.

But enough of that. I'm no intellectual; I try to think for myself. It depressed me to see these mostly well-meaning people made tools of the few whose aim was to bring the whole shebang down around their ears.

# XXII

The indrawn breath returned as a guttural sigh that edged toward a growl. The nearest males took a step or two in our direction. Barney waved his flag. "Wait!" he called, a thunderous basso overriding any other sound. "Truce! Let's talk this over! Take your leader to me!"

"Nothing *to* talk about, you murderers!" screamed a pimply girl. She swung her sign at me. I glimpsed upon it PEACE AND BROTHERHOOD before I had to get busy protecting my scalp. Someone began a chant that was quickly taken up by more and more: "Down with Diotrephes, down with Diotrephes, down with Diotrephes—"

Alarm stabbed through me. Though Diotrephes is barely mentioned in John's third epistle, the Johannines of today made him a symbol of the churches that opposed their movement. (No doubt he also meant other things to their initiates and adepts.) The unbelieving majority of the purely rebellious hadn't bothered to understand this. To them, Diotrephes became a name for the hated secular authority, or anyone else that got in their way. Those words had hypnotized more than one crowd into destructive frenzy.

I took her sign away from the girl, defended my eyes from her fingernails, and reached for my flash. But abruptly everything changed. A bell sounded. A voice cried. Both were low, both somehow penetrated the rising racket.

"Peace. Hold love in your hearts, children. Be still in the presence of the Holy Spirit."

My attacker retreated. The others who hemmed us in withdrew. Individuals started falling on their knees. A moan went through the mob, growing almost orgasmic before it died away into silence. Looking up, I saw the priest approach.

He traveled with bell in one hand, holding onto the upright of his tau crucifix while standing on its pedestal. Thus Christ nailed to the Cross of Mystery went before him. Nothing strange about that, I thought wildly, except that other churches would call it sacrilegious to give the central sign of their faith yonder shape, put an antigrav spell on it and use it like any broomstick. Yet the spectacle was weirdly impressive. It was like an embodiment of that Something Else on which Gnosticism is focused.

I'd regarded the Johnnies' "ineffable secrets" as unspeakable twaddle. Tonight I knew better. More was here than the ordinary paranatural emanations. Every nerve of my werewolf heritage sensed it. I didn't think the Power was of the Highest. But whence, then?

As the priest landed in front of us, though, he looked entirely human. He was short and skinny, his robe didn't fit too well, glasses perched precariously on his button nose, his graying hair was so thin I could hardly follow the course of his tonsure—the strip shaven from ear to ear, across the top of the head, that was said to have originated with Simon Magus.

He turned to the crowd first. "Let me speak with these gentlemen out of love, not hatred, and righteousness may prevail," he said in his oddly carrying tone. " 'He that loveth not knoweth not God; for God is love.' "

"Amen," mumbled across the grounds.

As the little man faced back toward us, I had a sudden belief that he really meant that dear quotation. It didn't drive away the miasma. The Adversary knows well how to use single-minded sincerity. But I felt less hostile to this priest as a person.

He smiled at us and bobbed his head. "Good evening," he said. "I am Initiate Fifth Class Marmiadon, at your service."

"Your, uh, ecclesiastical name?" Barney asked.

"Why, of course. The old name is the first of the things of this world that must be left behind at the Gate of Passage. I'm not afraid of a hex, if that is what you mean, sir."

"No, I suppose not." Barney introduced us, a cheap token of amity since we were both easily identifiable. "We came out hoping to negotiate a settlement."

Marmiadon beamed. "Wonderful! Blessings! I'm not an official spokesman, you realize. The Committee for National Righteousness called for this demonstration. However, I'll be glad to use my good offices."

"The trouble is," Barney said, "we can't do much about their basic

demands. We're not against world peace and universal disarmament ourselves, you understand; but those are matters for international diplomacy. In the same way, the President and Congress have to decide whether to end the occupation of formerly hostile countries and spend the money on social uplift at home. Amnesty for rioters is up to state or city governments. School courses in Gnostic philosophy and history have to be decided on by elected authorities. As for total income equalization and the phasing out of materialism, hypocrisy, injustice—" He shrugged. "That needs a Constitutional amendment at least."

"You can, however, lend your not inconsiderable influence to forwarding those ends," Marmiadon said. "For example, you can contribute to the Committee's public education fund. You can urge the election of the proper candidates and help finance their campaigns. You can allow proselytizers to circulate among your employees. You can stop doing business with merchants who remain obstinate." He spread his arms. "In the course of so doing, my children, you can rescue yourselves from eternal damnation!"

"Well, maybe; though Pastor Karlslund over at St. Olaf's Lutheran might give me a different opinion on that," Barney said. "In any case, it's too big a list to check off in one day."

"Granted, granted." Marmiadon quivered with eagerness. "We reach our ends a step at a time. 'While ye have light, believe in the light, that ye may be the children of light.' The present dispute is over a single issue."

"The trouble is," Barney said, "you want us to cancel contracts we've signed and taken money for. You want us to break our word and let down those who trust us."

His joy dropped from Marmiadon. He drew himself to his full meager height, looked hard and straight at us, and stated: "These soldiers of the Holy Spirit demand that you stop making equipment for the armed forces, oppressors abroad, and for the police, oppressors at home. Nothing more is asked of you at this time, and nothing less. The question is not negotiable."

"I see. I didn't expect anything else," Barney said. "But I wanted to put the situation in plain language before witnesses. Now I'm going to warn you."

Those who heard whispered to the rest, a hissing from mouth to mouth. I saw tension mount anew.

"If you employ violence upon those who came simply to remonstrate," Marmiadon declared, "they will either have the law upon you,

or see final proof that the law is a creature of the vested interests . . . which I tell you in turn are the creatures of Satan."

"Oh, no, no," Barney answered. "We're mild sorts, whether you believe it or not. But you are trespassing. You have interfered with our work to the point where we're delayed and shorthanded. We must carry on as best we can, trying to meet our contractual obligations. We're about to run an experiment. You could be endangered. Please clear the grounds for your own safety."

Marmiadon grew rigid. "If you think you can get away with a deadly spell—"

"Nothing like. I'll tell you precisely what we have in mind. We're thinking about a new method of transporting liquid freight. Before going further, we have to run a safety check on it. If the system fails, unprotected persons could be hurt." Barney raised his volume, though we knew some of the police officers would have owls' ears tuned in. "I order you, I warn you, I beg you to stop trespassing and get off company property. You have half an hour."

We wheeled and were back inside before the noise broke loose. Curses, taunts, obscenities, and animal howls followed us down the halls until we reached the blessed isolation of the main alchem lab.

The dozen scientists, technicians, and blue-collar men whom Barney had picked out of the volunteers to stay with him, were gathered there. They sat smoking, drinking coffee brewed on Bunsen burners, talking in low voices. When we entered, a small cheer came from them. They'd watched the confrontation on a closed-loop ball. I sought out Ike Abrams, the warehouse foreman. Ever since we soldiered together, I'd known him as a good man, and had gotten him his job here. "All in order?" I asked.

He made a swab-O sign. "By me, Cap'n, she's clear and on green. I can't wait."

I considered him for a second. "You really have it in for those characters, don't you?"

"In my position, wouldn't you?" He looked as if he were about to spit.

In your position, I thought, or in any of a lot of other positions, but especially in yours, Ike—yes.

As a rationalist, I detested the irrationality at the heart of Gnosticism. Were I a devout Christian, I'd have more counts against the Johannine Church: its claim to be the successor of all others, denying them any further right to exist; worse, probably, its esotericism, that would deny God's grace to nearly the whole of mankind. Rationalist

and religionist alike could revolt against its perversion of the Gospel According to St. John, perhaps the most beautiful and gentle if the most mystical book in Holy Writ.

But if you were Jewish, the Johnnies would pluck out of context and throw at you texts like "For many deceivers are entered into the world, who confess not that Jesus Christ is come in the flesh. This is a deceiver and an antichrist." You would see reviving around you the ancient nightmare of anti-Semitism.

A little embarrassed, I turned to Bill Hardy, our chief paracelsus, who sat swinging his legs from a lab bench. "How much stuff did you produce?" I asked.

"About fifty gallons," he said, pointing.

"Wow! With no alchemy?"

"Absolutely not. Pure, honest-to-Berzelius molecular interaction. I admit we were lucky to have a large supply of the basic ingredients on hand."

I winced, recalling the awful sample he'd whipped up when our scheme was first discussed. "How on Midgard did that happen?"

"Well, the production department is—was—filling some big orders," he said. "For instance, a dairy chain wanted a lot of rancidity preventers. You know the process, inhibit the reaction you don't want in a test tube, and cast a sympathetic spell to get the same effect in ton lots of your product. Then the government is trying to control the skunk population in the Western states, and—" He broke off as Ginny came in.

Her eyes glistened. She held her wand like a Valkyrie's sword. "We're set, boys." The words clanged.

"Let's go." Barney heaved his bulk erect. We followed him to the containers. They were ordinary flat one-gallon cans such as you buy paint thinner in, but Solomon's seal marked the wax that closed each screw top and I could subliminally feel the paranatural forces straining around them. It seemed out of keeping for the scientists to load them on a cart and trundle them off.

Ike and his gang went with me to my section. The apparatus I'd thrown together didn't look especially impressive either. In fact, it was a haywire monstrosity, coils and wires enclosing a big gasoline-driven electric generator. Sometimes you need more juice for an experiment than the carefully screened public power lines can deliver.

To cobble that stuff on, I'd have to remove the generator's own magnetic screens. What we had, therefore, was a mass of free cold iron; no spell would work in its immediate vicinity. Ike had been in

his element this afternoon, mounting the huge weight and awkward bulk on wheels for me. He was again, now, as he directed it along the halls and skidded it over the stairs.

No doubt he sometimes wished people had never found how to degauss the influences that had held paranatural forces in check since the Bronze Age ended. He wasn't Orthodox; his faith didn't prohibit him having anything whatsoever to do with goetics. But neither was he Reform or Neo-Chassidic. He was a Conservative Jew, who could make use of objects that others had put under obedience but who mustn't originate any cantrips himself. It's a tribute to him that he was nonetheless a successful and popular foreman.

He'd rigged a husky block-and-tackle arrangement in the garage. The others had already flitted to the flat roof. Ginny had launched the canisters from there. They bobbed about in the air, out of range of the magnetic distortions caused by the generator when we hoisted its iron to their level. Barney swung the machine around until we could ease it down beside the skylight. That made it impossible for us to rise on brooms or a word. We joined our friends via rope ladder.

"Ready?" Barney asked. In the restless pale glow, I saw sweat gleam on his face. If this failed, he'd be responsible for unforeseeable consequences.

I checked the connections. "Yeah, nothing's come loose. But let me first have a look around."

I joined Ginny at the parapet. Beneath us roiled the mob, faces and placards turned upward to hate us. They had spied the floating containers and knew a climax was at hand. Behind his altar, Initiate Marmiadon worked at what I took to be reinforcement of his defensive field. Unknown phrases drifted to me: *". . . Heliphomar Mabon Saruth Gefutha Enunnas Sacinos . . ."* above the sullen mumble of our besiegers. The elflight flickered brighter. The air seethed and crackled with energies. I caught a thunderstorm whiff of ozone.

My darling wore a slight, wistful smile. "How Svartalf would love this," she said.

Barney lumbered to our side. "Might as well start," he said. "I'll give them one last chance." He shouted the same warning as before. Yells drowned him out. Rocks and offal flew against our walls. "Okay," he growled. "Let 'er rip!"

I went back to the generator and started the motor, leaving the circuits open. It stuttered and shivered. The vile fumes made me glad we'd escaped depending on internal combustion engines. I've seen automobiles, as they were called, built around 1900, shortly before the first

broomstick flights. Believe me, museums are where they belong—a chamber of horrors, to be exact.

Ginny's clear call snapped my attention back. She'd directed the canisters into position. I could no longer see them, for they floated ten feet over the heads of the crowd, evenly spaced. She made a chopping gesture with her wand. I threw the main switch.

No, we didn't use spells to clear Nornwell's property. We used the absence of spells. The surge of current through the coils on the generator threw out enough magnetism to cancel every charm, ours and theirs alike, within a hundred-yard radius.

We'd stowed whatever gear might be damaged in safe conductive-shell rooms. We'd repeatedly cautioned the mob that we were about to experiment with the transportation of possibly dangerous liquids. No law required us to add that these liquids were in super-pressurized cans which were bound to explode and spray their contents the moment that the wall-strengthening force was annulled.

We'd actually exaggerated the hazard . . . in an attempt to avoid any slightest harm to trespassers. Nothing vicious was in those containers. Whatever might be slightly toxic was present in concentrations too small to matter, although a normal sense of smell would give ample warning regardless. Just a harmless mixture of materials like butyl mercaptan, butyric acid, methanethiol, skatole, cadaverine, putrescine . . . well, yes, the organic binder did have penetrative properties; if you got a few drops on your skin, the odor wouldn't disappear for a week or two. . . .

The screams reached me first. I had a moment to gloat. Then the stench arrived. I'd forgotten to don my gas mask, and even when I'm human my nose is quite sensitive. The slight whiff I got sent me gasping and retching backward across the roof. It was skunk, it was spoiled butter, it was used asparagus, it was corruption and doom and the wheels of Juggernaut lubricated with Limburger cheese, it was beyond imagining. I barely got my protection on in time.

"Poor dear. Poor Steve." Ginny held me close.

"Are they gone?" I sputtered.

"Yes. Along with the policemen and, if we don't get busy, half this postal district."

I relaxed. The uncertain point in our plan had been whether the opposition would break or would come through our now undefended doors in search of our lives. After my experience I didn't see how the latter would have been possible. Our chemists had builded better than they knew.

We need hardly expect a return visit, I thought in rising glee. If you suffer arrest or a broken head for the Cause, you're a hero who inspires others. But if you merely acquire for a while a condition your best friends won't tell you about because they can't come within earshot of you—hasn't the Cause taken a setback?

I grabbed Ginny to me and started to kiss her. Damn, I'd forgotten my gas mask again! She disentangled our snouts. "I'd better help Barney and the rest hex away those molecules before they spread," she told me. "Switch off your machine and screen it."

"Uh, yes," I must agree. "We want our staff returning to work in the morning."

What with one thing and another, we were busy for a couple of hours. After we finished, Barney produced some bottles, and the celebration lasted till well-nigh dawn. The eastern sky blushed pink when Ginny and I wobbled aboard our broom and hiccoughed, "Home, James."

The air blew cool, heaven reached high. "Know something?" I said over my shoulder. "I love you."

"Purr-rr-rr." She leaned forward to rub her cheek against mine. Her hands wandered.

"Shameless hussy," I said.

"You prefer some other kind?" she asked.

"Well, no," I said, "but you might wait a while. Here I am in front of you, feeling more lecherous every minute but without any way to lech."

"Oh, there are ways," she murmured dreamily. "On a broomstick yet. Have you forgotten?"

"No. But dammit, the local airlanes are going to be crowded with commuter traffic pretty soon, and I'd rather not fly several miles looking for solitude when we've got a perfectly good bedroom nearby."

"Right. I like that thought. Only fifteen minutes a day, in the privacy of your own home— Pour on the coal, James."

The stick accelerated.

I was full of glory and the glory that was her. She caught the paranatural traces first. My indication was that her head lifted from between my shoulder blades, her arms loosened around my waist while the fingernails bit through my shirt. "What the Moloch?" I exclaimed.

*"Hsh!"* she breathed. We flew in silence through the thin chill dawn wind. The city spread darkling beneath us. Her voice came at last, tense, but somehow dwindled and lost: "I said I didn't like the scent of the time-stream. In the excitement and everything, I forgot."

My guts crawled, as if I were about to turn wolf. Senses and extrasenses strained forth. I've scant thaumaturgic skill—the standard cantrips, plus a few from the Army and more from engineering training—but a lycanthrope has inborn instincts and awarenesses. Presently I also knew.

Dreadfulness was about.

As we flitted downward, we knew that it was in our house.

We left the broomstick on the front lawn. I turned my key in the door and hurled myself through. "Val!" I yelled into the dim rooms. "Svartalf!"

No lock had been forced or picked, no glass had been broken, the steel and stone guarding every paranatural entry were unmoved. But chairs lay tumbled, vases smashed where they had fallen off shaken tables, blood was spattered over walls, floors, carpets, from end to end of the building.

We stormed into Valeria's room. When we saw that little shape quietly asleep in her crib, we held each other and wept.

Finally Ginny could ask, "Where's Svartalf? What happened?"

"I'll look around," I said. "He gave an epic account of himself, at least."

"Yes—" She wiped her eyes. As she looked around the wreckage in the nursery, that green gaze hardened. She stared down into the crib. "Why didn't you wake up?" she said in a tone I'd never heard before.

I was already on my way to search. I found Svartalf in the kitchen. His blood had about covered the linoleum. In spite of broken bones, tattered hide, belly gashed open, the breath rattled faintly in and out of him. Before I could examine the damage further, a shriek brought me galloping back to Ginny.

She held the child. Blue eyes gazed dully at me from under tangled gold curls. Ginny's face, above, was drawn so tight it seemed the skin must rip on the cheekbones. "Something's wrong with her," she told me. "I can't tell what, but something's wrong."

I stood for an instant feeling my universe break apart. Then I went into the closet. Dusk was giving place to day, and I needed darkness. I shucked my outer clothes and used my flash. Emerging, I went to those two female figures. My wolf nose drank their odors.

I sat on my haunches and howled.

Ginny laid down what she was holding. She stayed completely motionless by the crib while I changed back.

"I'll call the police," I heard my voice say to her. "That thing isn't Val. It isn't even human."

# XXIII

I take care not to remember the next several hours in detail.

At noon we were in my study. Our local chief had seen almost at once that the matter was beyond him and urged us to call in the FBI. Their technicians were still busy checking the house and grounds, inch by inch. Our best service was to stay out of their way. I sat on the day bed, Ginny on the edge of my swivel chair. From time to time one of us jumped up, paced around, made an inane remark, and slumped back down. The air was fogged with smoke from ashtray-overflowing cigarets. My skull felt scooped out. Her eyes had retreated far back into her head. Sunlight, grass, trees were unreal in the windows.

"You really ought to eat," I said for the ?-th time. "Keep your strength."

"Same to you," she answered, not looking at me or at anything I could tell.

"I'm not hungry."

"Nor I."

We returned to the horror.

The extension phone yanked us erect. "A call from Dr. Ashman," it said. "Do you wish to answer?"

"For God's sake yes!" ripped from me. "Visual." Momentarily, crazily, I couldn't concentrate on our first message from the man who brought Valeria into the world. My mind spun off into the principles of telephony. Sympathetic vibrations, when sender and receiver are spelled to the same number; a scrying unit for video when desired; a partial animation to operate the assembly— Ginny's hand seized mine. Its cold shocked me into sanity.

Ashman's face looked well-nigh as exhausted as hers. "Virginia," he said. "Steve. We have the report."

I tried to respond and couldn't.

"You were right," he went on. "It's a homunculus."

"What took you so long?" Ginny asked. Her voice wasn't husky any more, just hoarse and harsh.

"Unprecedented case," Ashman said. "Fairy changelings have always been considered a legend. Nothing in our data suggests any motive for nonhuman intelligences to steal a child . . . nor any method by which they could if they wanted to, assuming the parents take normal care . . . and certainly no reason for such hypothetical kidnapers to leave a sort of golem in its place." He sighed. "Apparently we know less than we believed."

"What are your findings?" The restored determination in Ginny's words brought my gaze to her.

"The police chirurgeon, the crime lab staff, and later a pathologist from the University hospital worked with me," Ashman told us. "Or I with them. I was merely the family doctor. We lost hours on the assumption Valeria was bewitched. The simulacrum is excellent, understand. It's mindless—the EEG is practically flat—but it resembles your daughter down to fingerprints. Not till she . . . it . . . had failed to respond to every therapeutic spell we commanded between us, did we think the body might be an imitation. You told us so at the outset, Steve, but we discounted that as hysteria. I'm sorry. Proof required a whole battery of tests. For instance, the saline content and PBI suggest the makers of the homunculus had no access to oceans. We clinched the matter when we injected some radioactivated holy water; that metabolism is not remotely human."

His dry tone was valuable. The horror began to have some shadowy outline; my brain creaked into motion, searching for ways to grapple it. "What'll they do with the changeling?" I asked.

"I suppose the authorities will keep it in the hope of—of learning something, doing something through it," Ashman said. "In the end, if nothing else happens, it'll doubtless be institutionalized. Don't hate the poor thing. That's all it is, a poor thing, manufactured for some evil reason but not to blame."

"Not to waste time on, you mean," Ginny rasped. "Doctor, have you any ideas about rescuing Val?"

"No. It hurts me." He looked it. "I'm only a medicine man, though. What further can I do? Tell me and I'll come flying."

"You can start right away," Ginny said. "You've heard, haven't you,

my familiar was critically wounded defending her? He's at the vet's, but I want you to take over."

Ashman was startled. "What? Really— Look, I can't save an animal's life when a specialist isn't able."

"That's not the problem. Svartalf will get well. But vets don't have the expensive training and equipment used on people. I want him rammed back to health overnight. What runes and potions you don't have, you'll know how to obtain. Money's no object."

"Wait," I started to say, recalling what leechcraft costs are like.

She cut me off short. "Nornwell will foot the bill, unless a government agency does. They'd better. This isn't like anything else they've encountered. Could be a major emergency shaping up." She stood straight. Despite the sooted eyes, hair hanging lank, unchanged black garb of last night, she was once more Captain Graylock of the 14th United States Cavalry. "I am not being silly, Doctor. Consider the implications of your discoveries. Svartalf may or may not be able to convey a little information to me about what he encountered. He certainly can't when he's unconscious. At the least, he's always been a good helper, and we need whatever help we can get."

Ashman reflected a minute. "All right," he said.

He was about to sign off when the study door opened. "Hold it," a voice ordered. I turned on my heel, jerkily, uselessly fast.

The hard brown face and hard rangy frame of Robert Shining Knife confronted me. The head of the local FBI office had discarded the conservative business suit of his organization for working clothes. His feather bonnet seemed to brush the ceiling; a gourd stuck into his breechclout rattled dryly to his steps; the blanket around his shoulders and the paint on his skin were patterned in thunderbirds, sun discs, and I know not what else.

"You listened in," I accused.

He nodded. "Couldn't take chances, Mr. Matuchek. Dr. Ashman, you'll observe absolute secrecy. No running off to any blabbermouth shaman or goodwife you think should be brought in consultation."

Ginny blazed up. "See here—"

"Your cat'll be repaired for you," Shining Knife promised in the same blunt tone. "I doubt he'll prove of assistance, but we can't pass by the smallest possibility. Uncle Sam will pick up the tab—on the QT—and Dr. Ashman may as well head the team. But I want to clear the other members of it, and make damn sure they aren't told more than necessary. Wait in your office, Doctor. An operative will join you inside an hour."

The physician bristled. "And how long will he then take to certify each specialist I may propose is an All-American Boy?"

"Very little time. You'll be surprised how much he'll know about them already. You'd also be surprised how much trouble someone would have who stood on his rights to tell the press or even his friends what's been going on." Shining Knife smiled sardonically. "I'm certain that's a superfluous warning, sir. You're a man of patriotism and discretion. Good-bye."

The phone understood him and broke the spell.

"Mind if I close the windows?" Shining Knife asked as he did. "Eavesdroppers have sophisticated gadgets these days." He had left the door ajar; we heard his men move around in the house, caught faint pungencies and mutterings. "Please sit down." He leaned back against a bookshelf and watched us.

Ginny controlled herself with an effort I could feel. "Aren't you acting rather high-handed?"

"The circumstances require it, Mrs. Matuchek," he said.

She bit her lip and nodded.

"What's this about?" I begged.

The hardness departed from Shining Knife. "We're confirming what your wife evidently suspects," he said with a compassion that made me wonder if he had a daughter of his own. "She's a witch and would know, but wouldn't care to admit it till every hope of a less terrible answer was gone. This is no ordinary kidnaping."

"Well, of course—!"

"Wait. I doubt if it's technically any kind of kidnaping. My bureau may have no jurisdiction. However, as your wife said, the case may well involve the national security. I'll have to communicate with Washington and let them decide. In the last analysis, the President will. Meanwhile, we don't dare rock the boat."

I looked from him to Ginny to the horror that was again without form, not a thing to be fought but a condition of nightmare. "Please," I whispered.

Shining Knife's mouth contorted too for an instant. He spoke flatly and fast:

"We've ascertained the blood is entirely the cat's. There are some faint indications of ichor, chemical stains which may have been caused by it, but none of the stuff itself. We got better clues from scratches and gouges in floor and furnishings. Those marks weren't left by anything we can identify, natural or paranatural; and believe me, our gang is good at identifications.

"The biggest fact is that the house was never entered. Not in any way we can check for—and, again, we know a lot of different ones. Nothing was broken, forced, or picked. Nothing had affected the guardian signs and objects; their fields were at full strength, properly meshed and aligned, completely undisturbed. Therefore nothing flew down the chimney, or oozed through a crack, or dematerialized past the walls, or compelled the babysitter to let it in.

"The fact that no one in the neighborhood was alerted is equally significant. Remember how common hex alarms and second-sighted watchdogs are. Something paranatural and hostile in the street would've touched off a racket to wake everybody for three blocks around. Instead, we've only got the Delacortes next door, who heard what they thought was a catfight."

He paused. "Sure," he finished, "we don't know everything about goetics. But we do know enough about its felonious uses to be sure this was no forced entry."

"What, then?" I cried.

Ginny said it for him: "It came in from the hell universe."

"Theoretically, could have been an entity from Heaven." Shining Knife's grin was brief and stiff. "But that's psychologically—spiritually—impossible. The M.O. is diabolic."

Ginny sat forward. Her features were emptied of expression, her chin rested on a fist, her eyes were half-shut, the other hand drooped loosely over a knee. She murmured as if in a dream:

"The changeling fits your theory quite well, doesn't it? To the best of our knowledge, matter can't be transferred from one space-time plenum to another in violation of the conservation laws of physics. Psychic influences can go, yes. Visions, temptations, inspirations, that sort of thing. The uncertainty principle allows them. But not an actual object. If you want to take it from its proper universe to your own, you have to replace it with an identical amount of matter, whose configuration has to be fairly similar to preserve momentum. You may remember Villegas suggested this was the reason angels take more or less anthropomorphic shapes on earth."

Shining Knife looked uneasy. "This is no time to be unfriends with the Most High," he muttered.

"I've no such intention," Ginny said in her sleepwalker's tone. "He can do all things. But His servants are finite. They must often find it easier to let transferred matter fall into the shape it naturally wants to, rather than solve a problem involving the velocities of ten to the umpteenth atoms in order to give it another form. And the inhabitants of

the Low Continuum probably can't. They aren't creative. Or so the Petrine churches claim. I understand the Johannine doctrine includes Manichaean elements.

"A demon could go from his universe to a point in ours that was inside this house. Because his own natural form is chaotic, he wouldn't have to counter-transfer anything but dirt, dust, trash, rubbish, stuff in a high-entropy condition. After he finished his task, he'd presumably return that material in the course of returning himself. It'd presumably show effects. I know things got generally upset in the fight, Mr. Shining Knife, but you might run a lab check on what was in the garbage can, the catbox, and so forth."

The FBI man bowed. "We thought of that, and noticed its homogenized condition," he said. "If *you* could think of it, under these circumstances—"

Her eyes opened fully. Her speech became like slowly drawn steel: "Our daughter is in hell, sir. We mean to get her back."

I thought of Valeria, alone amidst cruelty and clamor and unnamable distortions, screaming for a Daddy and a Mother who did not come. I sat there on the bed, in the night which has no ending, and heard my lady speak as if she were across a light-years-wide abyss:

"Let's not waste time on emotions. I'll continue outlining the event as I reconstruct it; check me out. The demon—could have been more than one, but I'll assume a singleton—entered our cosmos as a scattered mass of material but pulled it together at once. By simple transformation, he assumed the shape he wanted. The fact that neither the Adversary nor any of his minions can create—if the Petrine tradition is correct—wouldn't handicap him. He could borrow an existing shape. The fact that you can't identify it means nothing. It could be a creature of some obscure human mythology, or some imaginative drawing somewhere, or even another planet.

"This is not a devout household. It'd be hypocrisy, and therefore useless, for us to keep religious symbols around that we don't love. Besides, in spite of previous experience with a demon or two, we didn't expect one to invade a middle-class suburban home. No authenticated case of that was on record. So the final possible barrier to his appearance was absent.

"He had only a few pounds of mass available to him. Any human who kept his or her head could have coped with him—if nothing else, kept him on the run, too busy to do his dirty work, while phoning for an exorcist. But on this one night, no human was here. Svartalf can't talk, and he obviously never got the chance to call in help by different

means. He may have outweighed the demon, but not by enough to prevail against a thing all teeth, claws, spines, and armor plate. In the end, when Svartalf lay beaten, the demon took our Val to the Low Continuum. The counter-transferred mass was necessarily in her form.

"Am I right?"

Shining Knife nodded. "I expect you are."

"What do you plan to do about it?"

"Frankly, at the moment there's little or nothing we can do. We haven't so much as a clue to motive."

"You've been told about last night. We made bad enemies. I'm inclined to take at face value the Johnnies' claim that their adepts have secret knowledge. Esotericism has always been associated more with the Low than the High. I'd say their cathedral is the place to start investigating."

Behind his mask of paint, Shining Knife registered unhappiness. "I explained to you before, Mrs. Matuchek, when we first inquired who might be responsible, that's an extremely serious charge to make on no genuine evidence. The public situation is delicately balanced. Who realizes that better than you? We can't afford fresh riots. Besides, more to the point, this invasion could be the start of something far bigger, far worse than a kidnaping."

I stirred. "Nothing's worse," I mumbled.

He ignored me, sensing that at present Ginny was more formidable. "We know practically zero about the hell universe. I'll stretch a point of security, because I suspect you've figured the truth out already on the basis of unclassified information; quite a few civilian wizards have. The Army's made several attempts to probe it, with no better success than the Faustus Institute had thirty years ago. Men returned in states of acute psychic shock, after mere minutes there, unable to describe what'd happened. Instruments recorded data that didn't make sense."

"Unless you adopt Nickelsohn's hypothesis," she said.

"What's it?"

"That space-time in that cosmos is non-Euclidean, violently so compared to ours, and the geometry changes from place to place." Her tone was matter-of-fact.

"Well, yes, I'm told the Army researchers did decide—" He saw the triumph in her eyes. "Damn! What a neat trap you set for me!" With renewed starkness: "Okay. You'll understand we dare not go blundering around when forces we can't calculate are involved for reasons we can scarcely guess. The consequences could be disastrous. I'm going to report straight to the Director, who I'm sure will report straight

to the President, who I'm equally sure will have us keep alert but sit tight till we've learned more."

"What about Steve and me?"

"You too. You might get contacted, remember."

"I doubt it. What ransom could a demon want?"

"The demon's master—"

"I told you to check on the Johnnies."

"We will. We'll check on everything in sight, reasonable or not. But it'll take time."

"Meanwhile Valeria is in hell."

"If you want a priest—we've clergy of most faiths cleared to serve our personnel. I can bring one here if you like."

The red head shook. "No, thanks. Ask them to pray for her. It can't hurt. I doubt it'll help much, either. Certainly none of them can help us two. What we want is a chance to go after our daughter."

My heart sprang. The numbness tingled out of me. I rose.

Shining Knife braced himself. "I can't permit that. Sure, you've both accomplished remarkable things in the past, but the stakes are too high now for amateurs to play. Hate me all you want. If it's any consolation, that'll pain me. But I can't let you jeopardize yourselves and the public interest. You'll stay put. Under guard."

"You—" I nearly jumped him. Ginny drew me back.

"Hold on, Steve," she said crisply. "Don't make trouble. What we'll do, you and I, if it won't interfere with the investigation, is choke down some food and a sleeping potion and cork off till we're fit to think again."

Shining Knife smiled. "Thanks," he said. "I was certain you'd be sensible. I'll go hurry 'em along in the kitchen so you can get that meal soon."

I closed the door behind him. Rage shivered me. "What the blue deuce is this farce?" I stormed. "If he thinks we'll sit and wait on a gaggle of bureaucrats—"

"Whoa." She pulled my ear down to her lips. "What he thinks," she whispered, "is that his wretched guard will make any particular difference to us."

"Oh-ho!" For the first time I laughed. It wasn't a merry or musical noise, but it was a laugh of sorts.

# XXIV

We weren't exactly under house arrest. The well-behaved young man who stayed with us was to give us what protection and assistance we might need. He made it clear, though, that if we tried to leave home or pass word outside, he'd suddenly and regretfully discover reason to hold us for investigation of conspiracy to overthrow the Interstate Commerce Commission.

He was a good warlock, too. An FBI agent must have a degree in either sorcery or accounting; and his boss wanted to be sure we didn't try anything desperate. But at supper Ginny magicked out of him the information she required. How she did that, I'll never understand. I don't mean she cast a spell in the technical sense. Rather, the charm she employed is the kind against which the only male protection is defective glands. What still seems impossible to me is that she could sit talking, smiling, flashing sparks of wit across a surface of controlled feminine sorrow, waggling her eyelashes and leading him on to relate his past exploits . . . when each corner of the place screamed that Valeria was gone.

We retired early, pleading exhaustion. Actually we were well rested and wire-taut. "He's sharp on thaumaturgy," my sweetheart murmured in the darkness of our bedroom, "but out of practice on mantics. A smoothly wrought Seeming ought to sucker him. Use the cape."

I saw her intent. A cold joy, after these past hours in chains, beat through me. I scrambled out of my regular clothes, into my wolf suit, and put the civvies back on top. As I reached for the Tarnkappe—unused for years, little more than a war souvenir—she came to me and pressed herself close. "Darling, be careful!" Her voice was not steady and I tasted salt on her lips.

She had to stay, allaying possible suspicion, ready to take the ransom demand that *might* come. Hers was the hard part.

I donned the cloak. The hood smelled musty across my face, and small patches of visibility showed where moths had gotten at the fabric. But what the nuts, it was merely to escape and later (we hoped) return here in. There are too many counter-agents these days for Tarnkappen to be effective for serious work, ranging from infrared detectors to spray cans of paint triggered by an unwary foot. Our friendly Fed no doubt had instruments ready to buzz him if an invisibilizing field moved in his vicinity.

Ginny went into her passes, *sotto voce* incantations, and the rest. She'd brought what was necessary into this room during the day. Her excuse was that she wanted to give us both as strong a protection against hostile influences as she was able. She'd done it, too, with the FBI man's admiring approval. In particular, while the spell lasted, I'd be nearly impossible to locate by paranatural means alone.

The next stage of her scheme was equally straightforward. While terrestrial magnetism is too weak to cancel paranatural forces, it does of course affect them, and so do its fluctuations. Therefore ordinary goetic sensor devices aren't designed to register minor quantitative changes. Ginny would establish a Seeming. The feeble Tarnkappe field would appear gradually to double in intensity, then, as I departed, oscillate back to its former value. On my return, she'd phase out the deception.

Simple in theory. In practice it took greater skill to pull off without triggering an alarm than her record showed she could possess. What the poor old FBI didn't know was that she had what went beyond training and equipment, she had a Gift.

At her signal, I slipped through the window. The night air was chill and moist; dew glistened on the lawn in the goblin glow of street lamps; I heard a dog howl. It had probably caught a whiff of my cloak. And no doubt the grounds were under surveillance . . . yes, my witchsight picked out a man in the shadows beneath the elms across the way. . . . I padded fast and softly down the middle of the pavement, where I'd be least likely to affect some watchbeast or sentry field. When it comes to that sort of business, I'm pretty good myself.

After several blocks, safely distant, I reached the local grade school and stowed my Tarnkappe in a playground trash can. Thereafter I walked openly, an unremarkable citizen on his lawful occasions. The night being new, I did have to be careful that no passer-by recognized me. At the first phone booth I called Barney Sturlason's home. He said

to come right on over. Rather than a taxi, I took a crosstown carpet, reasoning I'd be more anonymous as one of a crowd of passengers. I was.

Barney opened the door. Hallway light that got past his shoulders spilled yellow across me. He let out a soft whistle. "I figured you'd be too bushed to work today, Steve, but not that you'd look like Monday after Ragnarök. What's wrong?"

"Your family mustn't hear," I said.

He turned immediately and led me to his study. Waving me to one of the leather armchairs, he relocked the door, poured two hefty Scotches, and settled down opposite me. "Okay," he invited.

I told him. Never before had I seen anguish on those features. "Oh, no," he whispered.

Shaking himself, like a bear making ready to charge, he asked: "What can I do?"

"First off, lend me a broom," I answered.

"Hold on," he said. "I do feel you've been rash already. Tell me your next move."

"I'm going to Siloam and learn what I can."

"I thought so." The chair screaked under Barney's shifting weight. "Steve, it won't wash. Burgling the Johnny cathedral, maybe trying to beat an admission out of some priest— No. You'd only make trouble for yourself and Ginny at a time when she needs every bit of your resources. The FBI will investigate, with professionals. You could wreck the very clues you're after, assuming they exist. Face it, you are jumping to conclusions." He considered me. "A moral point in addition. You didn't agree that mob yesterday had the right to make its own laws. Are you claiming the right for yourself?"

I took a sip and let the whisky burn its loving way down my gullet. "Ginny and I've had a while to think," I said. "We expected you'd raise the objections you do. Let me take them in order. I don't want to sound dramatic, but how can we be in worse trouble? Add anything to infinity and, and, and"—I must stop for another belt of booze—"you've got the same infinity.

"About the FBI being more capable. We don't aim to bull around just to be doing something; give us credit for some brains. Sure, the Bureau must've had agents in the Johannine Church for a long while, dossiers on its leaders, the standard stuff. But you'll remember how at the HCUA hearings a few years back, no evidence could be produced to warrant putting the Church on the Attorney General's list, in spite of its disavowal of American traditions."

"The Johnnies are entitled to their opinions," Barney said. "Shucks, I'll agree with certain claims of theirs. This society has gotten too worldly, too busy chasing dollars and fun, too preoccupied with sex and not enough with love, too callous about the unfortunate—"

"Barney," I snapped, "you're trying to sidetrack me and cool me off, but it's no go. Either I get your help soon or I take my marbles elsewhere."

He sighed, fumbled a pipe from his tweed jacket and began stuffing it. "Okay, continue. If the Feds can't find proof that the Johannine hierarchy is engaged in activities illegal or subversive, does that prove the hierarchy is diabolically clever . . . or simply innocent?"

"Well, the Gnostics brag of having information and powers that nobody else does," I said, "and they do get involved one way or another in more and more of the social unrest going on—and mainly, who else, what else might be connected with this thing that's happened? Maybe even unwittingly; that's imaginable; but connected."

I leaned forward. "Look, Barney," I went on, "Shining Knife admits he'll have to move slow. And Washington's bound to keep him on tighter leash than he wants personally. Tomorrow, no doubt, he'll have agents interviewing various Johnnies. In the nature of the case, they'll learn nothing. You'd need mighty strong presumptive evidence to get a search warrant against a church, especially one that so many people are convinced bears the final Word of God, and most especially when the temple's a labyrinth of places that none but initiates in the various degrees are supposed to enter.

"Well, if and when you got your warrant, what could you uncover? This was no ordinary job. The usual tests for nigromancy and so forth aren't applicable. Why, if I were High Adept Zarathra, I'd invite the G-men to come inspect everything that's religiously permissible. What could he lose?"

"What could you gain?" Barney replied.

"Perhaps nothing," I said. "But I mean to act now, not a week from now; and I won't be handicapped by legal rules and public opinion; and I do have special abilities and experience in dark matters; and they won't expect me; and in short, if anything's there to find, I've the best chance in sight of finding it."

He scowled past me.

"As for the moral issue," I said, "you may be right. On the other hand, I'm not about to commit brutalities like some imaginary Special Agent Vee Eye Eye. And in spite of Shining Knife's fear, I honestly don't see what could provoke a major invasion from the Low World.

That'd bring in the Highest, and the Adversary can't afford such a confrontation.

"Which is worse, Barney, an invasion of property and privacy, maybe a profanation of a few shrines . . . or a child in hell?"

He set his glass down on an end table. "You win!" exploded from him. Blinking in surprise: "I seem to've smashed the bottom out of this tumbler."

"Finish mine," I said. "I'm on my way."

We rose together. "How about a weapon?" he offered.

I shook my head. "Let's not compound the felony. Whatever I meet, probably a gun won't handle." It seemed needless to add that I carried a hunting knife under my civvies and, in wolf-shape, a whole mouthful of armament. "Uh, we'll fix it so you're in the clear. I visited you; that can no doubt be proven if they try hard. But I sneaked back after I left and boosted your broom."

He nodded. "I suggest you take the Plymouth," he said. "It's not as fast as either sports job, but the spell runs quieter and the besom was tuned only the other day." He stood for a bit, thinking. Stillness and blackness pressed on the windowpanes. "Meanwhile I'll start research on the matter. Bill Hardy . . . Janice Wenzel from our library staff . . . hm, we could co-opt your Dr. Ashman, and how about Prof Griswold from the University? . . . and more, able close-mouthed people, who'll be glad to help and hang any consequences. If nothing else, we can assemble all unclassified data regarding the Low Continuum, and maybe some that aren't. We can set up equations delimiting various conceivable approaches to the rescue problem, and crank 'em through the computator, and eliminate unworkable ideas. Yeah, I'll get busy right off."

What can you say to a guy like that except thanks?

# XXV

It seemed in character for the Johannine Church to put its cathedral for the whole Upper Midwest not in Chicago, Milwaukee, or any other city, but off alone, a hundred miles even from our modest town. The placing symbolized and emphasized the Gnostic rejection of this world as evil, the idea of salvation through secret rites and occult knowledge. Unlike Petrine Christianity, this kind didn't come to you; aside from dismal little chapels here and there, scarcely more than recruiting stations, you came to it.

Obvious, yes. And therefore, I thought, probably false. Nothing about Gnosticism was ever quite what it seemed. That lay in its very nature.

Perhaps its enigmas, veils behind veils and mazes within mazes, were one thing that drew so many people these days. The regular churches made their theologies plain. They clearly described and delimited the mysteries as such, with the common-sense remark that we mortals aren't able to understand every aspect of the Highest. They declared that this world was given us to live in by the Creator, and hence must be fundamentally good; a lot of the imperfections are due to human bollixing, and it's our job to improve matters.

Was that overly unromantic? Did the Johannines appeal to the daydream, childish but always alive in us, of becoming omnipotent by learning a secret denied the common herd? I'd made that scornful assumption, and still believed it held a lot of truth. But the more I thought, the less it felt like the whole explanation.

I had plenty of time and chance and need for thought, flitting above the night land, where scattered lights of farms and villages looked nearly as remote as the stars overhead. The air that slid around

the windfield was turning cold. Its breath went through and through me, disrupting cobwebs in my head until I saw how little I'd really studied, how much I'd lazily taken for granted. But I saw, too, facts I'd forgotten, and how they might be fitted together in a larger understanding. Grimly, as I traveled, I set myself to review what I could about the Johannine Church, from the ground up.

Was it merely a thing of the past two or three generations, a nut cult that happened to appeal to something buried deep in Western man? Or was it in truth as old as it maintained—founded by Christ himself?

The other churches said No. Doubtless Catholic, Orthodox, and Protestant should not be lumped together as Petrine. But the popular word made a rough kind of sense. They did have a mutual interpretation of Jesus' charge to his disciples. They agreed on the special importance of Peter. No matter what differences had arisen since, including the question of apostolic succession, they all derived from the Twelve in a perfectly straightforward way.

And yet . . . and yet . . . there is that strange passage at the close of the Gospel According to St. John. "Then Peter, turning about, seeth the disciple whom Jesus loved following; which also leaned on his breast at supper, and said, Lord, which is he that betrayeth thee? Peter seeing him saith to Jesus, Lord, and what shall this man do? Jesus saith unto him, If I will that he tarry till I come, what is that to thee? follow thou me. Then went this saying abroad among the brethren, that that disciple should not die: yet Jesus said not unto him, He shall not die; but, If I will that he tarry till I come, what is that to thee? This is the disciple which testifieth of these things, and wrote these things: and we know that his testimony is true."

I don't understand it, and I'm not sure Biblical scholars do either, regardless of what they say. Certainly it gave rise to a fugitive tradition that here Our Lord was creating something more than any of them but John ever knew—some unproclaimed other Church, within or parallel to the Church of Peter, which would at the end manifest itself and guide man to a new dispensation. Today's cult might have originated entirely in this century. But the claim it trumpeted had been whispered for two thousand years.

The association of such a claim with otherworldliness was almost inevitable. Under many labels, Gnosticism has been a recurring heresy. The original form, or rather forms, were an attempt to fuse Christianity with a mishmash of Oriental mystery cults, Neoplatonism, and sorcery. Legend traced it back to the Simon Magus who appears in the eighth chapter of Acts, whose memory was accordingly held in horror by the

orthodox. Modern Johanninism was doubly bold in reviving that dawn-age movement by name, in proclaiming it not error but a higher truth and Simon Magus not a corrupter but a prophet.

Could that possibly be right? Might the world actually be at the morning of the Reign of Love? I didn't know; how could I? But by using my brains, as the Petrine tradition held we should, rather than my emotions, I'd decided the Johannine dogma was false. Its spreading acceptance I found due to plain human irrationality.

So you got communities of Truth Seekers, settling down to practice their rites and meditations where nobody would interfere. They drew pilgrims, who needed housing, food, services. The priests, priestesses, acolytes, and lay associates did too. A temple (more accurate than "cathedral," but the Johnnies insisted on the latter word to emphasize that they were Christians) needed income; and as a rule it had a substantial endowment, shrewdly managed. Thus a town often grew up around the original foundation—like Siloam, where I was headed.

Simple. Banal. Why did I bother marshaling information that any reader of the daily papers had? Merely to escape thinking about Valeria? No. To get as much as possible straight in my head, when most was tangled and ghostly.

The Something Else, the Thing Beyond . . . was it no illusion, but a deeper insight? And if so, an insight into what? I thought of the Johannines' intolerance and troublemaking. I thought of the frank assertion that their adepts held powers no one else imagined, and that more was revealed to them every year. I thought of stories told by certain apostates, who hadn't advanced far in their degrees when they experienced that which scared them off: nothing illegal, immoral, or otherwise titillating; merely ugly, hateful, sorrowful, and hence not very newsworthy; deniable or ignorable by those who didn't want to believe them. I thought of the Gnostic theology, what part of it was made public: terrible amidst every twist of revelation and logic, the identification of their Demiurge with the God of the Old Testament with Satan.

I thought of Antichrist.

But there I shied off, being agnostic about such matters, as I've said. I took my stand on the simple feeling that it didn't make sense the Almighty would operate in any such fashion.

Light glimmered into view, far off across the prairie. I was glad of journey's end, no matter what happened next. I didn't care to ride further with those reflections of mine.

Siloam was ordinary frame houses in ordinary yards along ordinary

streets. A sign beneath the main airlane, as you neared, said POP. 5240; another announced that the Lions Club met every Thursday at the Kobold Kettle Restaurant. There were a couple of small manufacturing enterprises, a city hall, an elementary school, a high school, a firehouse, a bedraggled park, a hotel, more service stations than needed. The business district held stores, a cafe or two, a bank, chirurgeon's and dentist's offices above a Rexall apothecary . . . the American works.

That homeliness made the rest freezingly alien. Though the hour lacked of midnight, downtown was a tomb. The residential streets were nearly as deserted—nobody out for a stroll, no teenagers holding hands, scarcely a stick or a wagon moving, beneath the rare lamps—once in a while a robed and hooded figure slowly pacing. Each home lay drawn into itself, behind drawn shades. Where the inhabitants weren't asleep, they were probably not watching crystal or playing cards or having a drink or making love, they were most likely at the devotions and studies they hoped would qualify them for a higher religious degree, more knowledge and power and surety of salvation.

And everything centered on the cathedral. It soared above the complex of boxlike ancillary buildings that surrounded it, above town and plain. The pictures I'd seen of it had not conveyed the enormity. Those flat, bone-white walls went up and up and *up,* till the roof climbed farther yet to make the vast central cupola. From afar, the windows looked like nailheads, one row to a story; but then I saw the stained-glass pair, each filling half the façade it occupied with murky colors and bewildering patterns, Mandala at the west end and Eye of God at the east. From the west, also, rose the single tower, which in a photograph only looked austere, but now became one leap into the stars.

Light played across the outside of the cathedral and shone dimly from its glass. I heard a chant, men's voices marching deep beneath the wild icy sweepings and soarings of women who sang on no scale I could identify, in no language of earth.

*". . . Helfioth Alaritha arbar Neniotho Melitho Tarasunt*
*Chanados Umia Theirura Marada Seliso . . ."*

The music was so amplified as to be audible to the very outskirts of town. And it never ended. This was a perpetual choir. Priests, acolytes, pilgrims were always on hand to step in when any of the six hundred and one wearied. I failed to imagine how it must be to live in that day-and-night haze of canticle. If you were a dweller in Siloam, perhaps not even a Johnny, you'd soon stop noticing on a conscious

level. But wouldn't the sound weave into your thoughts, dreams, bones, finally into your soul?

I couldn't interpret the extrasensation I felt, either, more powerful for every yard I approached. Wrongness—or rightness of a kind that I was simply unable to fathom?

After all, the attendant at the gate was a pleasant young man, his tow hair and blue eyes right out of the folk who'd been hereabouts for more than a hundred years, his friendliness out of Walt Whitman's own America. When I had parked my broom in the lot that stretched wide and bare into the dark, approached him, and asked, "Okay to go in?" he regarded me for a moment before answering lightly, "You're not a communicant, are you?"

"N-no," I said, a bit taken aback.

He chuckled. "Wanna know how I can tell? They've got to the Elphuë. We'd wait till Mary's invocation was finished before we entered."

"I'm sorry, I—"

" 'S okay. Nobody minds, long's you're quiet. In theory, you're damned anyway. I don't buy that myself, know what I mean? My girl's a Methodist. I'll go along with the red tape the priests want before they'll let me marry her, but I can't believe she'll burn." He realized he might have spoken too freely and added in haste: "How come you're this late? The tourists arrive in the daytime."

I decided he wasn't a lay brother, just an employee, and no more fanatical than the average Christian of any type—in short, one of the decent majority you find in all organizations, all countries. I was prepared for his question. "I travel in ankhs," I said. "Got an appointment in town early tomorrow morning before moving on. Got hung up today and didn't reach here till now. Your choir is so famous I didn't want to miss it."

"Thanks." He handed me a leaflet. "You know the rules? Use the main door. Take a seat in the Heath—uh, the Spectators' Corner. No noise, no picture-taking. When you want to leave, do it quietly, same way as you came."

I nodded and walked through the gate. The auxiliary buildings formed a square around a paved yard centered on the cathedral. Where they did not butt directly on each other, walls had been raised between, making the only entrances three portals closable by wire gates. The offices, storerooms, living quarters were plain, in fact drab. A few cenobites moved about, male scarcely distinguishable from female in their robes and overshadowing cowls. I remembered the complete ab-

sence of any scandals, anywhere in the world, though the Johannines mingled the sexes in celibacy. Well, of course their monks and nuns weren't simply consecrated; they were initiates. They had gone beyond baptism, beyond the elementary mystery rites and name-changing (with the old public name retained for secular use) that corresponded to a Petrine confirmation. For years they had mortified the flesh, disciplined the soul, bent the mind to mastering what their holy books called divine revelation, and unbelievers called pretentious nonsense, and some believers in a different faith called unrecognized diabolism. . . .

Blast it, I thought, I've got to concentrate on my job. Never mind those silent sad figures rustling past. Ignore, if you can, the overwhelmingness of the cathedral you are nearing and the chant that now swells from it to fill the whole night. Deny that your were-wolf heritage senses things it fears to a degree that is making you ill. Sweat prickles forth on your skin, runs cold down your ribs and reeks in your nostrils. You see the world through a haze of dream and relentless music. But Valeria is in hell.

I stopped where the vague shifty light was strongest and read the leaflet. It bade me a courteous welcome and listed the same regulations as the gatekeeper had. On the flip side was a floor plan of the basilica section of the main building. The rest was left blank. Everybody realized that an abundance of rooms existed in the levels of the north and south sides, the tower, and even the cupola. It was no secret that great crypts ran beneath. They were used for certain ceremonies—parts of them, anyhow. Beyond this information: nothing. The higher in degree you advanced, the more you were shown. Only adepts might enter the final sanctums, and only they knew what went on there.

I mounted the cathedral steps. A couple of husky monks stood on either side of the immense, open door. They didn't move, but their eyes frisked me. The vestibule was long, low-ceilinged, whitewashed, bare except for a holy water font. Here was no cheerful clutter of bulletin board, parish newsletter, crayon drawings from the Sunday school. A nun standing at the middle pointed me to a left entrance. Another one at that position looked from me to a box marked Offerings and back until I had to stuff in a couple of dollars. It might have been funny except for the singing, the incense, the gazes, the awareness of impalpable forces which drew my belly muscles taut.

I entered an aisle and found myself alone in a roped-off section of pews, obviously for outsiders. It took me a minute to get over the impact of the stupendous interior and sit down. Then I spent several more minutes trying to comprehend it, and failing.

The effect went beyond size. When everything was undecorated, naked white geometry of walls and pillars and vaulting, you had nothing to scale by; you were in a cavern that reached endlessly on. God's Eye above the altar, Mandala above the choir loft, dominated a thick dusk. But they were unreal too, more remote than the moon, just as the candles glimmering from place to place could have been stars. Proportions, curves, intersections, all helped create the illusion of illimitable labyrinthine spaces. Half a dozen worshipers, scattered along the edge of the nave, were lost. But so would any possible congregation be. This church was *meant* to diminish its people.

A priest stood at the altar with two attendants. I recognized them by their white robes as initiates. At their distance they were dwarfed nearly to nothing. Somehow the priest was not. In the midnight-blue drapery and white beard of an adept, he stood tall, arms outspread, and I feared him. Yet he wasn't moving, praying, anything. . . . Smoke from the hanging censers drugged my lungs. The choir droned and shrilled above me. I had never felt more daunted.

Hauling my glance away, I forced myself to study the layout as if this were an enemy fortress to be penetrated: which it was, for me tonight, whether or not it bore any guilt for what had happened to my little girl. The thought of her started a rage brewing that soon got strong enough to serve for courage. My witch-sight didn't operate here; counterspells against such things must have been laid. Normal night vision was adapting, though, stretched to the same ultimate as every other faculty I had.

The noncommunicants' section was as far as could be from the altar, at the end of the extreme left side aisle. So on my right hand were pews reaching to the nave, on my left a passage along the north wall. The choir loft hung over me like a thundercloud. Directly ahead, at the end of a field of empty benches, rose one of the screens that cut off most of the transept from view, ornamented with a black crux ansata.

This isn't helping me figure out how to burgle the joint, I thought.

A monk went past me on soft-sandaled feet. Over his robe he wore a long surplice embroidered with cabalistic symbols. Halfway to the transept he halted before a many-branched sconce, lit a candle, and prostrated himself for minutes. Rising, bowing, and backing off seven steps, he returned in my direction.

From pictures, I recognized his outer garment as the one donned by choristers. Evidently he'd been relieved and, instead of taking

straight off to shuck the uniform, had acquired a bit of merit first. When he'd gone by, I twisted around to follow his course. The pews did not extend the whole way back to the vestibule wall. They left some clear space at the rear end. The choral balcony threw it into such gloom that I could barely see the monk pass through a door in the corner nearest me.

The idea burst forth like a pistol from the holster. I sat outwardly still, inwardly crouched, and probed from side to side of the basilica. Nobody was paying attention to me. Probably I wasn't even visible to celebrants or worshipers; this placement was designed to minimize the obtrusiveness of infidels. My ears, which beneath the clamant song picked out the monk's footfalls, had detected no snick of key in lock. I could follow him.

Then what? I didn't know and didn't greatly care. If they nailed me at once, I'd be a Nosy Parker. They'd scold me and kick me out, and I'd try some different approach. If I got caught deeper in the building—well, that was the risk I'd come courting.

I waited another three hundred million microseconds, feeling each one. The monk needed ample time to get out of this area. During the interval I knelt, gradually hunching lower and lower until I'd sunk out of sight. It drew no stares or inquiries. Finally I was on all fours.

Now! I scuttled, not too fast, across to that shadowy corner. Risen, I looked behind me. The adept stood like a gaunt eidolon, the initiates handled the four sacred objects in complicated ways, the choir sang, a man signed himself and left via the south aisle. I waited till he had exited before gripping the doorknob. It felt odd. I turned it most slowly and drew the door open a crack. Nothing happened. Peering in, I saw dim blue lights.

I went through.

Beyond was an anteroom. A drapery separated it from a larger chamber, which was also deserted. That condition wouldn't last long. The second of the three curtained openings gave on a spiral staircase down which the hymn came pouring. The third led to a corridor. Most of the space was occupied by racks on which hung surplices. Obviously you borrowed one after receiving your instructions elsewhere, and proceeded to the choir loft. At the end of your period, you came back this way. Given six hundred and one singers, reliefs must show quite often. Maybe they weren't so frequent at night, when the personnel were mostly clergy with more training and endurance than eager-beaver laymen. But I'd best not stick around.

I could ditch my outer garments, that'd hamper a wolf, under one of those pullovers. However, somebody who happened to spy me barefoot, in skin-tight briefs, would be hard to convince of my bona fides. I settled for unsnapping the sheath from my inner belt and stuffing my knife in a jacket pocket before I stepped into the hall.

# XXVI

Lined with doors for the length of the building, the corridor might have been occupied by any set of prosaic offices. Mostly they were closed, and the light overhead was turned low. Names on the frosted glass ran to such as "I-2 Saktinos, Postal Propaganda." Well, a lot of territory was controlled from here. A few panels glowed yellow. Passing by one, I heard a typewriter. Within the endless chant, that startled me as if it'd been the click of a skeleton's jaws.

My plans were vague. Presumably Marmiadon, the priest at the Nornwell demonstration, operated out of this centrum. He'd have returned and asked his brethren to get the stench off him. An elaborate spell, too expensive for the average person, would clean him up sooner than nature was able. At least, he was my only lead. Otherwise I could ransack this warren for a fruitless decade.

Where staircases ran up and down, a directory was posted on the wall. I'd expected that. A lot of civilians and outside clergy had business in the nonreserved sections. Marmiadon's office was listed as 413. Because an initiate in the fifth degree ranked fairly high—two more and he'd be a candidate for first-degree adept status—I'd assumed he was based in the cathedral rather than serving as a mere chaplain or missionary. But it occurred to me that I didn't know what his regular job was.

I took the steps quietly, by twos. At the third-floor landing, a locked wrought-iron gate barred further passage. Not surprising, I thought; I'm getting into officer country. It wasn't too big for an agile man to climb over. What I glimpsed of that hall looked no different from below, but my skin prickled at a strengthened sense of abnormal energies.

The fourth floor didn't try for any resemblances to Madison Ave-

nue. Its corridor was brick, barrel-vaulted, lit by Grail-shaped oil lamps hung in chains from above, so that shadows flickered huge. The chant echoed from wall to wall. The atmosphere smelled of curious, acrid musks and smokes. Rooms must be large, for the pointed-arch doors stood well apart. They weren't numbered, but they bore nameplates and I guessed the sequence was the same as elsewhere.

One door stood open between me and my goal. Incongruously bright light spilled forth. I halted and stared in slantwise at shelves upon shelves of books. Some few appeared ancient, but mostly they were modern—yes, that squat one must be the *Handbook of Alchemy and Metaphysics,* and yonder set the *Encyclopaedia Arcanorum,* and there was a bound file of *Mind*—well, scientists need reference libraries, and surely very strange research was conducted here. It was my hard luck that someone kept busy this late at night.

I glided to the jamb and risked a closer peek. One man sat alone. He was huge, bigger than Barney Sturlason, but old, old; hair and beard were gone, the face might have belonged to Rameses' mummy. An adept's robe swathed him. He had a book open on his table, but wasn't looking at it. Deep-sunken, his eyes stared before him while a hand walked across the pages. I realized he was blind. That book, though, was not in Braille.

The lights could be automatic, or for another worker in the stacks. I slipped on by.

Marmiadon's place lay several yards further. Beneath his name and rank, the brass plate read "Fourth Assistant Toller." Not a bell ringer, for God's sake, that runt . . . was he? The door was locked. I should be able to unscrew the latch or push out the hinge pins with my knife. Better wait till I was quite alone, however. Meanwhile I could snoop—

"What walks?"

I whipped about. The adept stood in the hall at the library entrance. He leaned on a pastoral staff; but his voice reverberated so terribly that I didn't believe he needed support. Dismay poured through me. I'd forgotten how strong a Magus he must be.

"Stranger, what are you?" the bass cry bayed.

I tried to wet my sandpapery lips. "Sir—your Enlightenment—"

The staff lifted to point at me. It bore a Johannine capital, the crook crossed by a tau. I knew it was more than a badge, it was a wand. "Menace encircles you," the adept called. "I felt you in my darkness. Declare yourself."

I reached for the knife in my pocket, the wereflash under my shirt. Forlorn things; but when my fingers closed on them, they became tal-

ismans. Will and reason woke again in me. I thought beneath the hammering:

It'd have been more luck than I could count on, not to get accosted. I meant to try and use the circumstance if it happened. Okay, it has. That's a scary old son of a bitch, but he's mortal. Whatever his powers are, they don't reach to seeing me as I see him, or he'd do so.

Nonetheless I must clear my throat a time or two before speaking, and the words rang odd in my ears. "I—I beg your Enlightenment's pardon. He took me by surprise. Would he please tell me . . . where Initiate Marmiadon is?"

The adept lowered his staff. Otherwise he didn't move. The dead eyes almost rested on me, unwavering: which was worse than if they actually had. "What have you with him to do?"

"I'm sorry, your Enlightenment. Secret and urgent. As your Enlightenment recognizes, I'm a, uh, rather unusual messenger. I can tell him I'm supposed to get together with Initiate Marmiadon in connection with the, uh, trouble at the Nornwell company. It turns out to be a lot more important than it looks."

"That I know, and knew from the hour when he came back. I summoned—I learned—Enough. It is the falling stone that may loose an avalanche."

I had the eldritch feeling his words weren't for me but for someone else. And what was this about the affair worrying him also? I dared not stop to ponder. "Your Enlightenment will understand, then, why I'm in a hurry and why I can't break my oath of secrecy, even to him. If he'd let me know where Marmiadon's cell is—"

"The failed one sleeps not with his brothers. The anger of the Light-Bearer is upon him for his mismanagement, and he does penance alone. You may not seek him before he has been purified." An abrupt snap: "Answer me! Whence came you, what will you, how can it be that your presence shrills to me of danger?"

"I . . . I don't know either," I stammered.

"You are no consecrate—"

"Look, your Enlightenment, if you, if he would— Well, maybe there's been a misunderstanding. My, uh, superior ordered me to get in touch with Marmiadon. They said at the entrance I might find him here, and lent me a gate key." That unobtrusive sentence was the most glorious whopper I ever hope to tell. Consider its implications. Let them ramify. Extrapolate, extrapolate. Sit back in wonder. "I guess they were mistaken."

"Yes. The lower clerics have naturally not been told. However—"

The Magus brooded.

"If your Enlightenment 'ud tell me where to go, who to see, I could stop bothering him."

Decision. "The night abbot's secretariat, Room 107. Ask for Initiate-Six Hesathouba. Of those on duty at the present hour, he alone has been given sufficient facts about the Matuchek case to advise you."

*Matuchek* case?

I mumbled my thanks and got away at just short of a run, feeling the sightless gaze between my shoulder blades the whole distance to the stairs. Before climbing back over the gate, I stopped to indulge in the shakes.

I knew I'd scant time for that. The adept might suffer from a touch of senility, but only a touch. He could well fret about me until he decided to set inquiries afoot, which might not end with a phone call to Brother Hesathouba. If I was to have any chance of learning something real, I must keep moving.

Where to, though, in this Gormenghast house? How? What hope? I ought to admit my venture was sheer quixotry and slink home.

No! While the possibility remained, I'd go after the biggest windmills in sight. My mind got into gear. No doubt the heights as well as the depths of the cathedral were reserved for the ranking priests. But the ancient mystery religions had held their major rites underground. Weren't the crypts my best bet for locating Marmiadon?

I felt a grin jerk of itself across my face. They wouldn't lighten his ordeal by spelling the smell off him. Which was another reason to suppose he was tucked away below, out of nose range.

Human noses, that is.

I retraced my steps to the first level. From there I hastened downward. No one happened by. The night was far along; sorcerers might be at work, but few people else.

I descended past a couple of sublevels apparently devoted to storage, janitorial equipment, and the like. In one I glimpsed a sister hand-scrubbing the hall floor. Duty? Expiation? Self-abasement? It was a lonely sight. She didn't see me.

A ways beyond, I encountered another locked gate. On its far side the stairway steepened, concrete no longer but rough-hewn stone. I was down into bedrock. The well was chilly and wet to touch, the air to breathe. Modern illumination fell behind. My sole lights were candles, set in iron sconces far apart. They guttered in the draft from below. My shadow flapped misshapen around them. Finally I could not hear the mass. And still the path led downward.

And downward, until after some part of eternity it ended.

I stepped onto the floor of a natural cave. Widely spaced blue flames picked stalactites and stalagmites out of dense, unrestful murk. These burned from otherwise inactivated Hands of Glory fastened over the entrances to several tunnels. I knew that the Johannine hierarchy had used its influence to get special police licenses for such devices. Was that really for research? From one tunnel I heard the rushing of an underground river; from another glowed wan lights, drifted incense and a single quavering voice. Prayer, vigil, theurgy, or what? I didn't stop to investigate. Quickly I peeled off suit, socks, shoes, and hid them behind a rock. The knife I clipped back onto my elastic shorts.

Turning the lens on myself, I transformed, trying not to let the quasi-sexual sensation get to me, much. Instead I held tight in my diminished cerebral cortex the purpose I had, to use animal senses and sinews for my human end.

Therefore I noted a resistance to the change. I needed twice as long as normal to complete it. More counterspells, no doubt. I probably couldn't have lycoed if I'd not had the right chromosomes, unless I were a most powerful thaumaturge.

Never mind. I was wolf again!

The feeble illumination ceased being a handicap. Wolves don't depend on their eyes the way men do. Ears, feet, tongue, every hair on my body, before all else my nose, drank a flood of data. The cave was not now a hole to stumble in, it was a place that I understood.

And . . . yes, faint but unmistakable from one tunnel came a gust of unforgettable nastiness. I checked a hunter's yelp barely in time and trotted off in that direction.

# XXVII

The passage was lengthy, twisting, intersected by many others. Without my sense of smell for a guide, I'd soon have been lost. The lighting was from Hands, above the cells dug out of the rock at rare intervals. It was public knowledge that every candidate for primary initiation spent a day and night alone here, and the devout went back on occasion. Allegedly the soul benefited from undisturbed prayers and meditations. But I wasn't sure what extra influences crept in subliminally as well. Certain odors, at the edge of my lupine perception, raised the fur on my neck.

After a while they were drowned out by the one I was tracing. Wolves have stronger stomachs than people, but I began to gag. When finally I reached the source, I held my breath while looking in.

The dull blue glow from the fingers over the entrance picked out little more than highlights in the cubicle. Marmiadon was asleep on a straw pallet. He wore his robe for warmth; it was grubby as his skin. Otherwise he had some hardtack, a jerry can of water, a cup, a Johannine Bible, and a candle to read it by. He must only have been leaving his cell to visit an oubliette down the tunnel. Not that it would have made any large difference if he didn't. Phew!

I backed off and humanized. The effluvium didn't strike me too hard in that shape, especially after my restored reasoning powers took charge. No doubt Marmiadon wasn't even noticing it any more.

I entered his quarters, hunkered, and shook him. My free hand drew the knife. "Wake up, you."

He floundered to awareness, saw me, and gasped. I must have been a pretty grim sight, black-clad where I wasn't nude and with no mercy in my face. He looked as bad, hollow-eyed in that corpse-light. Before

he could yell, I clapped my palm over his mouth. The bristles of unshavenness felt scratchy, the flesh dough-like. "Be quiet," I said without emphasis, "or I'll cut your guts out."

He gestured agreement and I let go. "M-m-mister Matuchek," he whispered, huddling away from me till the wall stopped him.

I nodded. "Want to talk with you."

"I— How— In God's name, what about?"

"Getting my daughter home unharmed."

Marmiadon traced crosses and other symbols in the air. "Are you possessed?" He became able to look at me and answer his own question. "No. I could tell—"

"I'm not being puppeted by a demon," I grunted, "and I haven't got a psychosis. Talk."

"Bu-bu-but I haven't anything to say. Your daughter? What's wrong? I didn't know you had one."

That rocked me back. He wasn't lying, not in his state. "Huh?" I could only say. He grew a trifle calmer, fumbled around after his glasses and put them on, settled down on the pallet and watched me.

"It's holy truth," he insisted. "Why should I have information about your family? Why should anyone here?"

"Because you've appointed yourselves my enemies," I said in renewed rage.

He shook his head. "We're no man's foe. How can we be? We hold to the Gospel of Love." I sneered. His glance dropped from mine. "Well," he faltered, "we're sons of Adam. We can sin like everybody else. I admit I was furious when you pulled that . . . that trick on us . . . on those innocents—"

My blade gleamed through an arc. "Stow the crap, Marmiadon. The solitary innocent in this whole miserable business is a three-year-old girl, and she's been snatched into hell."

His mouth fell wide. His eyes frogged.

"Start blabbing," I said.

For a while he couldn't get words out. Then, in complete horror: "No. Impossible. I would never, never—"

"How about your fellow priests? Which of them?"

"None. I swear it. Can't be." I pricked his throat with the knife point. He shuddered. "Please. Let me know what happened. Let me help."

I lowered the blade, shifted to a sitting position, rubbed my brow, and scowled. This wasn't according to formula. "See here," I accused him, "you did your best to disrupt my livelihood. When my life itself

is busted apart, what am I supposed to think? If you're not responsible, you'd better give me a lot of convincing."

The initiate gulped. "I . . . yes, surely. I meant no harm. What you were doing, are doing—it's sinful. You're damning yourselves and aiding others to do likewise. The Church can't stand idle. More of its ministers volunteer to help than don't."

"Skip the sermon," I ordered. Apart from everything else, I didn't want him working up enough zeal to stop being dominated by me. "Stick to events. You were sent to abet that mob."

"No. Not— Well, I was on the list of volunteers. When this occasion arose, I was the one allowed to go. But not to . . . do what you say . . . instead to give aid, counsel, spiritual guidance—and, well, yes, defend against possible spells— Nothing else! You were the ones who attacked."

"Sure, sure. We began by picketing, and when that didn't work we started on trespass, vandalism, blockade, terrorizing— Uh-huh. And you were so strictly acting as a private citizen that when you failed, your superiors comforted you and you're back at your regular work already."

"My penance is for the sin of anger," he said.

A tiny thrill ran along my spine. We'd reached a significant item. "You aren't down here simply because you got irritated with us," I said. "What'd you actually do?"

Fear seized him afresh. He raised strengthless hands. "Please. I can't have— No." I brought my knife close again. He shut his eyes and said fast: "In my wrath when you were so obdurate, I laid a curse on your group. The Curse of Mabon. My reverend superiors—I don't know how they knew what I'd done, but adepts have abilities— When I returned here, I was taxed with my sin. They told me the consequences could be grave. No more. I wasn't told there . . . there'd been any. Were there really?"

"Depends," I said. "What is this curse?"

"No spell. You do understand the distinction, don't you? A spell brings paranatural forces to, to bear, by using the laws of goetics. Or it summons nonhuman beings or— It's the same principle as using a gun, any tool, or whistling up a dog, Mr. Matuchek. A prayer is different. It's an appeal to the Highest or His cohorts. A curse is nothing except a formula for asking Them to, well, punish somebody. They do it if They see fit—it's Them alone—"

"Recite it."

"*Absit omen!* The danger!"

"You just got through saying it's harmless in itself."

"Don't you know? Johannine prayers are different from Petrine. We're the new dispensation, we've been given special knowledge and divine favor, the words we use have a potency of their own. I can't tell what would happen if I said them, even without intent, under uncontrolled conditions like these."

That was very possibly right, I thought. The essence of Gnosticism in the ancient world had been a search for power through hidden knowledge, ultimately power over God Himself. Doubtless Marmiadon was sincere in denying his church had revived that particular concept. But he hadn't progressed to adept status; the final secrets had not been revealed to him. I thought, reluctantly, that he wasn't likely to make it, either, being at heart not a bad little guy.

My mind leaped forward. Let's carry on that idea, I thought in the space of half a second. Let's assume the founders of modern Gnosticism did make some discoveries that gave them capabilities not known before, results that convinced them they were exerting direct influence on the Divine. Let's further suppose they were mistaken—deceived—because, hang it, the notion that mortals can budge Omnipotence *is* unreasonable. What conclusion do these premises lead us to? This: that whether they know it or not, the blessings and curses of the Johannines are in fact not prayers, but peculiarly subtle and powerful spells.

"I can show you the text," Marmiadon chattered. "You can read for yourself. It's not among the forbidden chapters."

"Okay," I agreed.

He lit his candle and opened the book. I'd glanced at Johannine Bibles but never gotten up the steam to get through one. They replaced the Old Testament with something that even a gentile like me considered blasphemous, and followed the standard parts of the New with a lot of the Apocrypha, plus other stuff whose source never has been identified by reputable scholars. Marmiadon's shaky finger touched a passage in that last section. I squinted, trying to make out the fine print. The Greek was paralleled with an English translation, and itself purported to render the meaning of a string of words like those in the canticles upstairs.

*Holy, holy, holy. In the name of the seven thunders. O Mabon of righteousness, exceeding great, angel of the Spirit, who watcheth over the vials of wrath and the mystery of the bottomless pit, come thou to mine aid, wreak sorrow upon them that have done evil to me, that they may know contrition and afflict no longer the servants of the hidden truth and the Reign that is to come. By these words be thou summoned,*

*Heliphomar Mabon Saruth Gefutha Enunnas Sacinos. Amen. Amen. Amen.*

I closed the book. "I don't go for that kind of invocation," I said slowly.

"Oh, you could recite it aloud," Marmiadon blurted. "In fact, an ordinary communicant of the Church could, and get no response. But I'm a toller. A summoner, you'd call it. Not too high-ranking or skillful; nevertheless, certain masteries have been conferred."

"An, s-s-so!" The sickening explanation grew upon me. "You raise and control demons in your regular line of work—"

"Not demons. No, no, no. Ordinary paranatural beings for the most part. Occasionally a minor angel."

"You mean a thing that tells you it's an angel."

"But it is!"

"Never mind. Here's what happened. You say you got mad and spoke this curse, a black prayer, against us. I say that knowingly or not, you were casting a spell. Since nothing registered on detectors, it must've been a kind of spell unknown to science. A summons to something from out of this universe. Well, you Johnnies do seem to've acquired a pipeline to another world. You believe, most of you, that world is Heaven. I'm convinced you're fooled; it's actually hell."

"No," he groaned.

"I've got reason, remember. That's where my kid was taken."

"She couldn't have been."

"The demon answered your call. It happened that of the Nornwell people around, my wife and I had the one household exposed that night to his action. So the revenge was worked on us."

Marmiadon squared his puny shoulders. "Sir, I don't deny your child is missing. But if she was taken . . . as an unintended result of my action . . . well, you needn't fear."

"When she's in hell? Supposing I got her back this minute, what'll that place have done to her?"

"No, honestly, don't be afraid." Marmiadon ventured to pat my hand where it clenched white-knuckled around the knife. "If she were in the Low Continuum, retrieval operations would involve temporal phasing. Do you know what I mean? I'm not learned in such matters myself, but our adepts are, and a portion of their findings is taught to initiates, beginning at the fourth degree. The mathematics is beyond me. But as I recall, the hell universe has a peculiar, complex space-time geometry. It would be as easy to recover your daughter from the exact instant when she arrived there as from any other moment."

The weapon clattered out of my grasp. A roar went through my head. "Is that the truth?"

"Yes. More than I'm canonically allowed to tell you—"

I covered my face. The tears ran out between my fingers.

"—but I want to help you, Mr. Matuchek. I repent my anger." Looking up, I saw him cry too.

After a while we were able to get to business. "Of course, I must not mislead you," he declared. "When I said it would be as easy to enter hell at one point of time as another, I did not mean it would not be difficult. Insuperably so, indeed, except for our highest adepts. No geometers are alive with the genius to find their way independently through those dimensions.

"Fortunately, however, the question doesn't arise. I just wanted to reassure you enough so you'd listen to the real case. It may be that your daughter was removed in answer to my curse. That would account for the displeasure of my superiors with me. But if so, she's under angelic care."

"Prove it," I challenged.

"I can try. Again, I'm breaking the rules, especially since I'm under penance and you're an unbeliever. Still, I can try to summon an angel." He smiled timidly at me. "Who knows? If you recant, your girl could be restored to you on the spot. A man of your gifts and energy would make a wonderful convert. Conceivably that's been God's purpose right along."

I didn't like the idea of a Calling. In fact, I was bloody well chilled by it. Marmiadon might think the creature that arrived was from Heaven. I didn't. But I was prepared to face worse than devils on this trip. "Go ahead."

He turned his Bible to another passage I didn't recognize. Kneeling, he started to chant, a high-pitched rise and fall which sawed at my nerves.

A wind blew down the tunnel. The lights didn't go out, but a dimness came over my eyes, deepening each second, as if I were dying, until I stood alone in a whistling dark. And the night was infinite and eternal; and the fear left me, but in its place there fell the suddenly remembered absolute despair. Yet never had I known a grief like this—not the three times before, not when Valeria was taken, not when my mother died—for now I had reached in the body the final end of every hope and looked upon the ultimate emptiness of all things; love, joy, honor were less than ash, they had never been, and I stood hollow as the only existence in hollow creation.

Far, far away a light was kindled. It moved toward me, a spark, a star, a sun. I looked upon the vast mask of a face, into the lifeless eyes; and the measured voice beat through me:

"The hour is here. Despite the afreet, the salamander, the incubus, and mortal man, your destiny has endured, Steven. It was not my will or my planning. I foresaw you would be among my keenest enemies in this cycle of the world, the danger that you would wreck my newest great enterprise. But I could not know what would bring you to confront my works: the thoughtless call of one fool, the rash obedience of another. Now you would seek to storm my inner keep.

"Be afraid, Steven. I may not touch you myself, but I have mightier agents to send than those you met before. If you go further against me, you go to your destruction. Return home; accept your loss as humbly as befits a son of Adam; beget other children, cease meddling in public matters, attend solely to what is your own. Then you shall have pleasure and wealth and success in abundance, and your days shall be long in the land. But this is if you make your peace with me. If not, you will be brought down, and likewise those you care for. Fear me."

The sight, the sound, the blindness ended. I sagged, wet and a-reek with sweat, looking stupidly at Marmiadon in the candlelight. He beamed and rubbed his hands. I could scarcely comprehend him:

"There! Wasn't I right? Aren't you glad? Wasn't he glorious? I'd be down on my knees if I were you, praising God for His mercy."

"Hu-u-uh?" dragged out of me.

"The angel, the angel!"

I shook myself, as if I'd come from wild waters that nearly drowned me. My heart was still drained. The world felt remote, fragile. But my brain functioned, in a mechanical fashion. It made my lips move. "I could have seen a different aspect of the being. What happened to you?"

"The crowned head, the shining wings," he crooned. "Your child is safe. She will be given back to you when your penitence is complete. And because of having been among the blessed in her mortal life, she will become a saint of the true Church."

Well, trickled through my head, this doubtless isn't the first time the Adversary's made an instrument of people who honestly believe they're serving God. What about Jonathan Edwards, back in old New England? "The floors of hell are paved with the skulls of unbaptized children." Who really was the Jehovah he called upon?

"What did you experience?" Marmiadon asked.

I might or might not have told him my revelation. Probably not;

what good would that have done? A sound distracted us both—nearing footsteps, words.

"What if he hasn't been here?"

"We'll wait for some hours."

"In this thin garb?"

"The cause of the Lord, brother."

I stiffened. Two men coming: monks, from the noise of their sandals; big, from its volume on the stone. The adept I met upstairs must have grown suspicious; or Marmiadon's invocation and its effect had registered elsewhere; or both. If I got caught—I'd been warned. And my existence was beyond price, until I could get home the information that might help rescue Val.

I turned the flash on myself. Marmiadon whimpered as I changed shape. It's well I was in a hurry. Wolf, with wolf passions, I'd have torn his throat apart for what he'd done if there'd been time. Instead, I went out in a single gray streak.

The pair of monks didn't see me through the gloom until I was almost on them. They were beefy for sure. One carried a stick, the other a forty-five automatic. I darted between the legs of the latter, bowling him over. His buddy got a crack across my ribs with his cudgel. Pain slowed me for a moment. A bone may have been broken. It knitted with the speed of the were condition and I dashed on. The pistol barked. Slugs whanged nastily past. If they included argent rounds, a hit would stop me. I had to move!

Up the stairs I fled. The friars dropped from sight. But an alarm started ahead of me, bells crashing through the hymns. Did my pursuers have a walkie-talkie ball with them? Produced at Nornwell? I burst into the first-floor hallway. There must be other exits than the main door, but I didn't know them. A wolf can travel like bad news. I was through the curtain which screened off the choir vestry before any nightshifter had glanced out of an office or any sleepy monk arrived from another section.

The church was in a boil. I cracked the door to the aisle sufficiently for a look. The chant went on. But folk ran about in the nave, shouting. More to the point, a couple of them were closing doors to the vestibule. I couldn't get out.

Feet slapped floor in the corridor. The Johnnies weren't certain which way I'd skited, and were confused anyhow by this sudden unexplained emergency. Nevertheless, I'd scant time until someone thought to check here.

A possible tactic occurred to me. I didn't consider the wherefores

of it, which a wolf isn't equipped to do. Trusting instinct, I slapped the switch on my flash with a forepaw. The blue entry-room lights didn't interfere with my reverting to human. Darting back to the vestry, I grabbed a surplice and threw it over my head. It fell nearly to my feet. They stayed bare, but maybe no one would notice.

Ascending to the choir loft in record time, I stopped in the archway entrance and studied the situation. Men and women stood grouped according to vocal range. They held hymnals. Spare books lay on a table. The view from here, down to the altar and up to the cupola, was breathtaking. But I'd no breath to spend. I picked my spot, helped myself to a book, and moved solemnly forward.

I wouldn't have gotten away with it under normal conditions. Conditions not being normal, the choir was agitated too, its attention continually pulled down to the excitement on the floor. The song kept wandering off key. I found a place on the edge of the baritones and opened my hymnal to the same page as my neighbor.

*"Mephnounos Chemiath Aroura Maridon Elison,"* he chanted. I'd better make noises likewise. The trouble was, I'd not had the rehearsals they gave to laymen who wanted to participate. I couldn't even pronounce most of those words, let alone carry the tune.

My neighbor glanced at me. He was a portly, officious-looking priest. I oughtn't to stand around with my teeth in my mouth, he must be thinking. I gave him a weak smile. "*Thatis Etelelam Teheo abocia Rusar,*" he intoned in a marked manner.

I grabbed at the first melody I recalled which had some general resemblance to the one he was using. Mushing it up as much as I dared, I studied my book and commenced:

"*A sailor told me before he died—*

*I don't know whether the bastard lied—*"

In the general counterpoint, not to mention the uproar below, it passed. The cleric took his eyes off me. He continued with the canticle and I with *The Big Red Wheel.*

I trust I may be forgiven for some of the other expedients I found necessary in the hour that followed. An hour, I guessed, was an unsuspicious time for a lay singer to stay. Meanwhile, by eye and ear, I followed roughly the progress of the hunt for me. The size and complexity of the cathedral worked in my favor for once; I could be anywhere. Unquestionably, spells were being used in the search. But the wizards had little to go on except what Marmiadon could tell. And I had everything protective that Ginny, who's one of the best witches in the Guild, was able to give me before I left. Tracing me, identifying

me, would be no simple matter, even for those beings that the most potent of the adepts might raise.

Not that I could hold out long. If I didn't scramble soon I was dead, or worse. A part of me actually rejoiced at that. You see, the danger, the calling up of every resource I had to meet it, wiped away the despair at the core of hell which I had met in the crypts. I was alive, and it mattered, and I'd do my best to kill whatever stood between me and my loves!

After a while the main entrance was reopened, though watched by monks. I'd figured out a plan to get around them. After leaving the choir and disrobing, I turned wolf. The north corridor was again deserted, which was lucky for any Johnnies I might have encountered. Having doubtless posted a guard at every door, they were cooling their chase. It went on, but quietly, systematically, no longer disruptive of religious atmosphere. Lupine senses helped me avoid patrols while I looked for a window.

On the lower levels, these were in rooms that were occupied or whose doors were locked. I had to go to the sixth floor—where the scent of wrongness was almost more than I could bear—before finding a window in the corridor wall. It took resolution, or desperation, to jump through. The pain as the glass broke and slashed me was as nothing to the pain when I hit the concrete beneath.

But I was lyco. My injuries were not fatal or permanently crippling. The red rag of me stirred, grew together, and became whole. Sufficient of my blood was smeared around, unrecoverable, that I felt a bit weak and dizzy; but a meal would fix that.

The stars still glittered overhead. Vision was uncertain. And I doubted the outer gatekeepers had been told much, if anything. The hierarchy would be anxious to hush up this trouble as far as might be. I stripped off what remained of my clothes with my teeth, leaving the wereflash fairly well covered by my ruff, and trotted off to the same place where I'd entered. "Why, hullo, pooch," said my young friend. "Where'd you come from?" I submitted to having my ears rumpled before I left.

In Siloam's darkened downtown I committed a fresh crime, shoving through another window, this time in the rear of a grocery store. I could compensate the proprietor anonymously, later. Besides the several pounds of hamburger I found and ate, I needed transportation; and after humanizing I was more than penniless, I was naked. I phoned Barney. "Come and get me," I said. "I'll be wolf at one of these spots."

I gave him half a dozen possibilities, in case the pursuit of me spilled beyond cathedral boundaries.

"What happened to my broom?" he demanded.

"I had to leave it parked," I said. "You can claim it tomorrow."

"I'm eager to hear the story."

"Well, it was quite a night, I can tell you."

# XXVIII

My detailed relation I gave to Ginny after sneaking back into our house. I was numb with exhaustion, but she insisted on hearing everything at once, whispered as we lay side by side. Her questions drew each last detail from me, including a lot that had slipped my mind or that I hadn't especially noticed at the time. The sun was up before she fixed my breakfast and allowed me to rest. With a few pauses for nourishment and drowsy staring, I slept a full twenty-four hours.

Ginny explained this to our FBI man as the result of nervous prostration, which wasn't too mendacious. She also persuaded him and his immediate boss (Shining Knife had gone to Washington) that if they wanted to keep matters under wraps, they'd better not hold us incommunicado. Our neighbors already knew something was afoot. They could be stalled for but a short while, our close friends and business associates for a shorter while yet. If the latter got worried, they could bring more to bear in the way of sortileges than the average person.

The upshot was that we kept our guest. When Mrs. Delacorte dropped around to borrow a gill of brimstone, we introduced him as my cousin Louis and mentioned that we'd sent Val on an out-of-town visit while our burglary was being investigated. It didn't rate more than a paragraph on an inside page of the daily paper. However, I was allowed to work again, Ginny to go shopping. We were told what number to call if we received any demands. Nothing was said about the men who shadowed us. They were good; without our special skills, we'd never have known about them.

On the third morning, therefore, I showed at Nornwell. Barney Sturlason was primed. He found a do-not-disturb job for me to do in my office—rather, to fake doing while I paced, chain-smoked

my tongue to leather, drank coffee till it gurgled in my ears—until time for an after-lunch conference with some outside businessmen. I knew what that conference was really to be about. When the intercom asked me to go there, I damn near snapped my head off accelerating before I remembered to walk the distance and say hello to those I passed.

The meeting room was upstairs. Its hex against industrial espionage operated equally well against official surveillance. Barney bulked at the end of the table, collar open, cigar fuming. The assembled team comprised eleven, to help assure we'd harbor no Judas. I knew three well besides Barney and myself—Griswold, Hardy, Janice Wenzel—and another slightly, Dr. Nobu, a metaphysicist whom we had sometimes consulted. The rest were strangers to me. One turned out to be a retired admiral, Hugh Charles, who'd specialized in Intelligence operations; another was a mathematician named Falkenberg; a third was Pastor Karlslund from Barney's church. All of these looked weary. They'd worked like galley slaves, practically up to this minute. The last pair seemed fresh, and totally undistinguished except that one had a large sample case which he'd put on the table.

Before he got to their names, Barney made a pass and spoke a phrase. "Okay," he said, "the security field is back at full strength. Come on out and join the coven." He grinned at me. "Steve, I'd like you to meet Mr. Smith and Mr. Brown, representing the company whose proposal we're to discuss today."

Their outlines blurred, went smoky, and firmed again as the Seeming passed. Ginny's hair gleamed copper in the sunlight from the windows. Dr. Ashman opened his case. Svartalf poured out, restored to health, big, black, and arrogant as ever. He stretched cramped muscles. "Mee-owr-r-r," he scolded us. The pastor offered the cat a soothing hand. I didn't have time to warn him. Luckily, Ashman was in the habit of carrying Band-Aids. Svartalf sat down by Ginny and washed himself.

"How'd you manage it?" the admiral asked with professional interest.

Ginny shrugged. "Simple. Barney'd been in contact with Dr. Ashman, you know, and arranged a time when he'd've canceled his appointments. He went to the animal hospital and fetched Svartalf, who can lie quiet in a box if he must. We'd already verified there was no tail on the doctor." Svartalf switched his in a smug fashion. "Meanwhile I'd gone downtown. They're having a sale at Perlman's. Easiest

crowd in the world to disappear into, and who'll notice a bit of sorcery there? Having changed my looks, I rendezvoused with Dr. Ashman and altered him." Svartalf threw the man a speculative look. "We proceeded here. Barney knew exactly when we'd arrive, and had the field low enough that it didn't whiff our disguises."

She opened her purse, which hadn't needed much work to resemble a briefcase, got out her vanity, and inspected her appearance. In demure make-up and demure little dress, she hardly suggested a top-flight witch, till you noticed what else she was packing along.

"To business," Barney said. "We informed this team at once of what you'd discovered, Steve. From the strictly scientific angle, your hints, added to what'd already been assembled, were a jolt. Working together, certain of our people have developed some insights that should prove revolutionary." He paused. "But let's begin with the political mess we're in."

"Or the religious," Janice Wenzel said.

"In this case," Pastor Karlslund said, "I doubt if there's any clear distinction." He was a large, blond, scholarly-looking man.

"If the Johannine Church is indeed of diabolic origin—" Griswold grimaced. "I hate to believe that. I don't agree with its tenets, but to say they come not from error but from evil does go rather far. Are you sure, Mr. Matuchek, that you really encountered the Adversary?"

"One of his higher-ups, anyway," I said. "Or lower-downs, if you prefer. Not for the first time, either. Those earlier visions and experiences of mine fall into a pattern now."

"I mean, well, you were under considerable stress. A hallucination would be very reasonable . . . expectable, I mean."

"If the Johnnies are legit," my wife clipped, "why are they keeping quiet? They have Steve's identity. They've had ample time to get in touch with him, or to file an official complaint. But never a peep. Barney's man, sent to fetch his broomstick, took it from where it was parked with no questions asked. I say they can't risk an investigation."

"They might be trying to get your daughter returned to you through their paranatural contacts," Hardy suggested without conviction.

Admiral Charles snorted. "Big chance! I don't doubt the Adversary would like to cancel the whole episode. But how? He can return her with zero time-lapse in hell, you say, Mr. Matuchek—quite astounding, that. Nevertheless, I don't imagine he can change the past: the days we've lived without her, the things we've learned as a consequence."

"Our silence could be her ransom," Hardy said.

"What man would feel bound by that kind of bargain?" the admiral replied.

Karlslund added: "No contracts can be made with the Low Ones anyhow. Contract implies a meeting of minds, an intent to abide by the terms reached. Being incapable of probity, a devil is unable to believe humans won't try to cheat him in turn."

"So," Charles said, "he'd gain nothing by releasing her, and lose whatever hostage value she has."

Ashman said painfully: "He's already succeeded in dividing the forces of good. I get the impression this meeting is in defiance of the government, an actual conspiracy. Is that wise?"

"I suppose you mean we should make a clean breast to Uncle Sam and trust him to set everything right." The hurt in me powered my sneer.

"What resources have we in comparison?" Ashman asked. "What right have we to withhold the information you've gathered? It's vital to the common weal."

"Let me handle that question," Barney said. "I've got connections in Washington, and Admiral Charles, who has more, confirms my guess as to what's going on there. The key datum is this: that the facts of the kidnaping are being officially suppressed. Our local FBI head is a sharp boy. He saw at once that that's what policy would be, and acted in anticipation of a directive he knew he'd get.

"The reasons for such a policy are complicated, but boil down to two items. First, hardly anything is known about the hell universe. This is one of the few cases, maybe unique, that looks like a direct, physical assault from demon territory. Nobody can be sure what it portends. In those circumstances, caution is inevitable. They'll argue in the State Department that the truth could be altogether different from the semblance. They'll argue in Defense that we'd better not commit ourselves to anything before we have more data and especially a bigger military appropriation. The President, the Cabinet, the top men in Congress, will agree on sitting tight. That involves sitting on the news, to forestall an inconvenient public furore.

"Second, maybe less critical at the moment but definitely to be considered, the Johannine Church. This is a democratic country. A lot of perfectly sincere voters are either Johnnies or believe Johanninism is just another creed. A fair number of important people fall into the same classes. Remember what a stink went up when the House committee tried to probe a little. The present affair does suggest the faction is right which says the Johannine Church was instigated by the Lowest

as a means of discrediting religion, undermining society, and turning man against man. The last thing the Administration will want—at this ticklish juncture—is to go through that 'subversion' versus 'suppression' shouting match again. Secrecy buys peace, quiet, and time."

Barney halted to rekindle his cigar. The room had become very still as we listened. Smoke filled the sunbeams with blue strata and our nostrils with staleness. Ginny and I exchanged a forlorn look across the table. Yesterday I'd gone into the basement to replace a blown fuse. She'd come along, because these days we stayed together when we could. Some things of Valeria's stood on a shelf, lately outgrown and not yet discarded. The everfilled bottle, the Ouroboros teething ring, the winged training spoon, the little pot with a rainbow at the end— We went upstairs and asked our guard to change the fuse.

Her fists clenched before her. Svartalf rubbed his head on her arm, slowly, demanding no attention in return.

"The conclusion," Barney said, "is that, resources or no, the government isn't likely to use them for quite a while, if ever. As of today, we, this bunch of us, have the right and duty to take what action we can.

"You see, Doctor, we've done nothing technically illegal. Steve was not under arrest. He was free to go in and out of his home, in a Tarnkappe via the window if he chose, accountable to nobody. I was free to lend him my broom. The cathedral is open to the public. If Steve went into other parts of the building, looking for someone who might have information helpful in his hour of need, at most he committed a civil tort. Let the hierarchy sue him for damages if it wants. He can charge felonious assault, remember. One does not have the privilege of using lethal weapons in defense of mere privacy, and he was clubbed and shot at.

"Accordingly, no crime having been committed, none of us are accessories after the fact. No crime being contemplated, none of us are engaging in conspiracy. I grant you, soon the National Defense Act, and anything else the President finds handy, will be invoked. Then we would be in trouble if we behaved as we're doing. But no legally binding prohibition has been laid on us to date; and the Constitution forbids ex post facto proceedings."

"Hm." Ashman reflected.

"As for the withholding of essential information," Barney continued, "don't worry, we aren't about to do that either. We are sifting what we've been told, as responsible citizens who don't want to make

accusations that may be unfounded. But we will see that whatever is sound gets into the right hands."

"Must we act so fast?" Ashman demurred. "If the child can be recovered from the same instant as she arrived . . . yonder . . . isn't it best for her too that we let the government operate on her behalf at a slow, careful pace, rather than going off ourselves ill-prepared and underequipped?"

Admiral Charles' lean features darkened. "Frankly," he said, "if no further incidents occur, I don't expect this Administration will act. It's let unfriendly countries rob, imprison, or kill American nationals—some in uniform—without doing more than protest. What do you imagine they'll say in Foggy Bottom at the thought of taking on hell itself for one small girl? I'm sorry, Mrs. Matuchek, but that's the way matters are."

"Be that as it may," said Falkenberg in haste, for the look on Ginny's face had become terrifying, "as I understand the situation, the, ah, enemy are off balance at present. Mr. Matuchek took them by surprise. Evidently the, ah, Adversary is debarred from giving them direct help, counsel, or information. Or else he considers it inadvisable, as it might provoke intervention by the Highest. The, ah, Johannine Mages can do extraordinary things, no doubt. But they are not omniscient or omnipotent. They can't be sure what we have learned and what we will attempt. Give them time, however, in this universe, and they will, ah, recover their equilibrium, mend their fences, possibly make some countermove."

Ginny said out of her Medusa mask: "Whatever the rest of you decide, Steve and I won't sit waiting."

"Blazes, no!" exploded from me. Svartalf laid back his ears, fangs gleamed amidst his whiskers and the fur stood up on him.

"You see?" Barney said to the group. "I know these people. You can't stop them short of throwing them in jail for life; and I'm not convinced any jail would hold them. They might have to be killed. Do we let that happen, or do we help them while we still can?"

Voices rumbled around the table, hands went aloft, Janice Wenzel cried loudest: "I've got kids of my own, Virginia!" Eyes turned from us to Ashman. He flushed and said:

"I'm not going henhouse on you. Remember, all this has just been sprung on me without warning. I'm bound to raise the arguments that occur to me. I don't believe that encouraging Valeria's parents to commit suicide will do her any good."

"What do you mean?" Barney asked.

"Do I misunderstand? Isn't your intention to send Steven and Virginia—my patients—into the hell universe?"

That brought me up cold. I'd been ready and raging for action; but this was as if a leap had fetched me to the rim of Ginnungagap. The heart slammed in me. I stared at Ginny. She nodded.

The whole group registered various degrees of consternation. I scarely noticed the babble that lifted or Barney's quelling of it. Finally we all sat in a tautstrung silence.

"I must apologize to this committee," Barney said. His tone was deep and measured as a vesper bell's. "The problem that I set most of you was to collect and collate available information on the Low Continuum with a view to rescue operations. You did magnificently. When you were informed of Steve's findings, you used them to make a conceptual breakthrough that may give us the method we want. But you were too busy to think beyond the assignment, or to imagine that it was more than a long-range, rather hypothetical study: something that might eventually give us capabilities against further troubles of this nature. Likewise, those of you I discussed the political or religious aspects with didn't know how close we might be to facing them in reality.

"I saw no alternative to handling it that way. But Mrs. Matuchek reached me meanwhile, surreptitiously. I gave her the whole picture, we discussed it at length and evolved a plan of campaign." He bowed slightly toward Ashman. "Congratulations on your astuteness, Doctor."

She knew, I thought in the shards of thinking, and yet no one could have told it on her, not even me—not till this instant, and then solely because she chose. A part of me wondered if other husbands experienced corresponding surprises.

She raised her hand. "The case is this," she said with the same military crispness as when first I'd met her. "A small, skilled group has a chance of success. A large, unskilled group has none. It'd doubtless suffer more than the Army or the Faustus teams did, since they retreated quickly."

"Death, insanity, or imprisonment in hell with everything that that implies—" Ashman whispered. "You assume Steven will go."

"I know better than to try stopping him," she said.

That gave me a measure of self-control again. I was not unconscious of admiring glances. But mainly I listened to her:

"He and I and Svartalf are as good a squad as you'll find. If anybody has a hope of pulling the stunt off, we do. The rest of you can help with preparations and with recovering us. If we don't make

it back, you'll be the repositories of what has already been learned. Because this is a public matter. It goes far beyond our girl . . . agreed. That's your main reason for assisting us. To try and make sure your children and grandchildren will inherit a world worth having."

She reached in her purse. "Damn," she said, "I'm out of cigarettes."

She got a lot of offers, but accepted mine. Our hands clung for a second. Ashman sat staring at his intertwined fingers. Abruptly he straightened and said, with a kind of smile:

"All right, I apologize. You must admit my reaction was natural. But you're an able group. If you think you've found a way to enter hell and return unharmed, you could be right and you have my support. May I ask what your scheme is?"

Barney relaxed a trifle. "You may," he said. "Especially since we've got to explain it to some of the others."

He stubbed out his cigar and began on a fresh one. "Let me put the proposition in nickel words first," he said, "then the experts can correct and amplify according to their specialties. Our universe has a straightforward space-time geometry, except in odd places like the cores of white dwarf stars. Demons can move around in it without trouble—in fact, they can play tricks with distance and chronology that gave them the reputation of being supernatural in olden days—because their home universe is wildly complicated and variable. Modern researchers have discovered how to get there, but not how to travel around or remain whole of body and mind.

"Well, Steve's information that we could reach any point in hell time, if we knew the method, opened a door or broke a logjam or something. Suddenly there was a definite basic fact to go on, a relationship between the Low Continuum and ours that could be mathematically described. Dr. Falkenberg set up the equations and started solving them for different conditions. Dr. Griswold helped by suggesting ways in which the results would affect the laws of physics; Bill Hardy did likewise for chemistry and atomistics; et cetera. Oh, they've barely begun, and their conclusions haven't been subjected to experimental test. But at least they've enabled Dr. Nobu, as a metaphysicist, and me, as a practical engineer, to design some spells. We completed them this morning. They should project the expedition, give it some guardianship when it arrives, and haul it back fast. That's more than anybody previous had going for them."

"Insufficient." Charles was the new objector. "You can't have a full description of the hell universe—why, we don't have that even for

this cosmos—and you absolutely can't predict what crazy ways the metric there varies from point to point."

"True," Barney said.

"So protection which is adequate at one place will be useless elsewhere."

"Not if the space-time configuration can be described mathematically as one travels. Then the spells can be adjusted accordingly."

"What? But that's an impossible job. No mortal man—"

"Right," Ginny said.

We gaped at her.

"A passing thing Steve heard, down in the crypts, was the clue," Ginny said. "Same as your remark, actually, Admiral. No mortal man could do it. But the greatest geometers are dead."

A gasp went around the table.

With appropriate seemings laid on, and Svartalf indignantly back in the sample case, our community left the plant on a company carpet. It was now close to four. If my FBI shadow didn't see me start home around five or six o'clock, he'd get suspicious. But there wasn't a lot I could do about that.

We landed first at St. Olaf's while Pastor Karlslund went in to fetch some articles. Janice Wenzel, seated behind us, leaned forward and murmured: "I guess I'm ignorant, but isn't this appealing to the saints a Catholic rather than a Lutheran thing?"

The question hadn't been raised at the conference. Karlslund was satisfied with making clear the distinction between a prayer—a petition to the Highest, with any spells we cast intended merely to ease the way for whoever might freely respond—and necromancy, an attempt to force our will on departed spirits. (While the latter is illegal, that's mainly a concession to public taste. There's no reliable record of its ever having succeeded; it's just another superstition.)

"I doubt if the sect makes any odds," Ginny said. "What is the soul? Nobody knows. The observations that prove it exists are valid, but scattered and not repeatable under controlled conditions. As tends to be the case for many paranatural phenomena."

"Which, however," Dr. Nobu put in, "is the reason in turn why practical progress in goetics is so rapid once a correct insight is available. Unlike the force-fields of physics—gravitation, electromagnetism, and so on—the force-fields of paraphysics—such as similarity and ergody—are not limited by the speed of light. Hence they can, in principle, shift energy from any part of the plenum to any other. That is why a vanishingly small input can give an indefinitely large output.

Because of this, qualitative understanding is more important to control than quantitative. And so, a mere three days after learning about the time variability of hell, we feel some confidence that our new spells will work. . . . But as for the soul, I incline to the belief that its character is supernatural rather than paranatural."

"Not me," Ginny said. "I'd call it an energy structure within those parafields. It's formed by the body but outlives that matrix. Once free, it can easily move between universes. If it hangs around here for some reason, disembodied, isn't that a ghost? If it enters a newly fertilized ovum, isn't that reincarnation? If the Highest allows it to come nearer His presence, isn't that salvation? If the Lowest has more attraction for it, isn't that damnation?"

"Dear me," Janice said. Ginny uttered a brittle laugh.

Barney turned around in the pilot's seat. "About your question that started this seminar, Janice," he said, "it's true we Lutherans don't make a habit of calling on the saints. But neither do we deny they sometimes intervene. Maybe a Catholic priest or a Neo-Chassidic rabbi would know better how to pray for help. But I couldn't get any on short notice that I dared co-opt, while I've known Jim Karlslund for years. . . . Speak of the, er, pastor—" Everybody chuckled in a strained way as our man boarded with an armful of ecclesiastical gear.

We took off again and proceeded to Trismegistus University. Sunlight slanted gold across remembered lawns, groves, buildings. Few persons were about in this pause between spring and summer sessions; a hush lay over the campus, distantly backgrounded by the city's whirr. It seemed epochs ago that Ginny and I had been students here, a different cycle of creation. I glanced at her, but her countenance was unreadable.

Wings rustled near, a raven that paced us. An omen? Of what? It banked as we landed and flapped out of sight.

We entered the Physical Sciences building. Corridors and stairwells reached gloomy, full of echoes. Desertion was one reason we'd chosen it, another being Griswold's keys to each lab and stockroom. Karlslund would have preferred the chapel, but we were too likely to be noticed there. Besides, Ginny and Barney had decided in their plan-laying that the religious part of our undertaking was secondary.

We needed someone whose appeal would be unselfish and devout, or no saint was apt to respond. However, they seldom do anyway, compared to the number of prayers that must arise daily. The Highest expects us to solve our own problems. What we relied on—what gave us a degree of confidence we would get some kind of reaction—was

the progress we'd made, the direct access we believed we had to the Adversary's realm and our stiff resolve to use it. The implications were too enormous for Heaven to ignore . . . we hoped.

I thought, in the floating lightheadedness to which stress had brought me: Perhaps we'll be forbidden to try.

We picked the Berkeley Philosophical Laboratory for our calling. It was a new, large, splendidly outfitted wing tacked onto the shabby old structure that housed Griswold's department before the salamander episode. Here senior and graduate physical-science students learned how to apply paranatural forces to natural research. So it had every kind of apparatus we could imagine needing. The main chamber was wide and high, uncluttered by more than a few shelves and workbenches along the walls. Light fell cool through gray-green glass in the Gothic windows. Zodiacal symbols on the deep-blue ceiling encircled a golden Bohr atom. You'd never find a place further in spirit from that cathedral at Siloam. My kind of people had raised this. I felt some measure of its sanity enter me to strengthen.

Griswold locked the door. Ginny took off the Seemings and let Svartalf out. He padded into a corner, tail going like a metronome. Karlslund laid an altar cloth on a bench, arranged on it cross, bell, chalice, sacred bread, and wine. The rest of us worked under Barney. We established a shieldfield and an antispy hex around the area in the usual way. Next we prepared to open the gates between universes.

So the popular phrase has it, altogether inaccurately. In truth there are no gates, there are means of transmitting influences from one continuum to another, and fundamentally it does not depend on apparatus but on knowing how. The physical things we set out—Bible and Poimanderes opened to the appropriate passages, menorah with seven tall candles lit by flint and steel, vial of pure air, chest of consecrated earth, horn of Jordan water, Pythagorean harp—were symbolic more than they were sympathetic.

I want to emphasize that, because it isn't as well known as it should be: one reason why Gnosticism caught on. The Petrine tenet goes along with the higher non-Christian faiths and the findings of modern science. You *can't* compel Heaven. It's too great. You can exert an influence, yes, but it won't have effect unless the Highest allows, any more than a baby's tug on your trouser cuff can turn you from your path by itself.

Our prayer was an earnest of our appeal, which God had already read in our hearts. In a way, its purpose was to convince us that we really meant what we said we wanted. Likewise, our spells would help

any spirit that chose to come here. But he or she didn't really need assistance. What would matter was that we were doing our best.

Hell is another case entirely. In physical terms, it's on a lower energy level than our universe. In spiritual terms, the Adversary and his minions aren't interested in assisting us to anything except our destruction. We could definitely force our way in and lay compulsions on the demons by sheer power of wizardry—if we swung enough power!—and we would definitely have to if Val was to be rescued.

The formulas for trying to summon Heavenly aid aren't common knowledge, but they aren't hidden either. You can find them in the right reference works. Our hell spells were something else. I will never describe them. Since you may well guess they involve an inversion of the prayer ritual, I'll state that we employed these articles: a certain one of the Apocrypha, a Liber Veneficarum, a torch, a globe of wind from a hurricane, some mummy dust, thirteen drops of blood, and a sword. I don't swear to the truthfulness of my list.

We didn't expect we'd require that stuff right away, but it was another demonstration of intent. Besides, Ginny needed a chance to study it and use her trained intuition to optimize the layout.

Karlslund's bell called us. He was ready. We assembled before the improvised altar. "I must first consecrate this and hold as full a service as possible," he announced. I looked at my watch—damn near five—but dared not object. His feeling of respect for due process was vital.

He handed out prayer books and we commenced. The effect on me was curious. As said, I don't believe any set of dogmas is preferable to any other or to an upright agnosticism. On the rare occasions I've been in church, I've found that the high Episcopalians put on the best show, and that's it. Now, at first, I wanted to whisper to Ginny, "Hey, this is a secret service." But soon the wish for a joke slipped from me together with the racked emotions that generated it. Out of that simple rite grew peace and a wordless wonder. That's what religion is about, I suppose, a turning toward God. Not that I became a convert; but on this one occasion it felt as if some aspect of Him might be turning toward *us*.

"Let us pray."

"Our Father, Who art in Heaven—"

There was a knock on the door.

I didn't notice at first. But it came again, and again, and a voice trickled through the heavy panels: "Dr. Griswold! Are you in there? Phone call for you. A Mr. Knife from the FBI. Says it's urgent."

That rocked me. My mood went smash. Ginny's nostrils dilated

and she clutched her book as if it were a weapon. Karlslund's tones faltered.

Griswold pattered to the door and said to the janitor or whoever our Porlockian was: "Tell him I've a delicate experiment under way. It can't be interrupted. Get his number, and I'll call back in an hour or so."

Good for you! half of me wanted to shout. The rest was tangled in cold coils of wondering about God's mercy. Thy will be done . . . but what is Thy will? Can't be everything that happens, or men would be mere puppets in a cruel charade.

God won't frustrate us. He won't let a little girl stay in hell.

He's done it on occasion. Read police records.

But death finally released those victims, and they were given comfort. Or so the churches claim. How do the churches know? Maybe nothing exists but a blind interplay of forces; or maybe the Lowest and Highest are identical; or—No, that's the despair of hell, which you have met before. Carry on, Matuchek. Don't give up the crypt. "Onward, Christian so-oldiers" in your irregular baritone. If this doesn't work out, we'll try something else.

And at last we had struggled through the service to the benediction. Then Karlslund said, troubled: "I'm not sure we're going to get anywhere now. The proper reverence is lost."

Hardy replied unexpectedly, "Your church puts its prime emphasis on faith, Pastor. But to us Catholics, works count too."

Karlslund yielded. "Well—all right. We can make the attempt. What exact help do you wish?"

Barney, Ginny, and the rest exchanged blank looks. I realized that in the rush, they'd forgotten to get specific about that. It probably hadn't seemed urgent, since Heaven is not as narrowly literal-minded as hell. Our formula could be anything reasonable . . . presumably.

Barney cleared his throat. "Uh, the idea is," he said, "that a first-rank mathematician would go on learning, improving, gaining knowledge and power we can't guess at, after passing on. We want a man who pioneered in non-Euclidean geometry."

"Riemann is considered definitive," Falkenberg told us, "but he did build on the work of others, like Hamilton, and had successors of his own. We don't know how far the incomparable Gauss went, since he published only a fraction of his thought. On the whole, I'd favor Lobachevsky. He was the first to prove a geometry can be self-consistent that denies the axiom of parallels. Around 1830 or 1840 as I

recall, though the history of mathematics isn't my long suit. Everything in that branch of it stems from him."

"That'll do," Barney decided, "considering we don't know if we can get any particular soul for an ally. Any whatsoever, for that matter," he added raggedly. To Falkenberg: "You and the pastor work out the words while we establish the spell."

That took time also, but kept us busy enough that it wasn't as maddening as the service had been after the distraction. We made the motions, spoke the phrases, directed the will, felt the indescribable stress of energies build toward breaking point. This was no everyday hex, it was heap big medicine.

Shadows thickened out of nowhere until the windows shone like pale lamps at night. The seven candle flames burned unnaturally tall without casting a glow. The symbols overhead glowed with their own radiance, a mythic heaven, and began slowly turning. St. Elmo's fire crawled blue over our upraised hands and Ginny's wand, crackled from Svartalf's fur where he stood on her shoulders and from her unbound hair. The harp played itself, strings plangent with the music of the spheres. Weaving my way back and forth across the floor I couldn't see for darkness, hand in hand as one of the seven who trod the slow measures of the *bransle grave,* I heard a voice cry: "Aleph!" and long afterward: "Zain."

At that we halted, the harp ceased, the eternal silence of the infinite spaces fell upon us, and the zodiac spun faster and faster until its figures blurred together and were time's wheel. What light remained lay wholly on the pastor. He stood, arms lifted, before the altar. "Hear us, O God, from Heaven Thy dwelling place," he called. "Thou knowest our desire; make it pure, we pray Thee. In Thy sight stand this man Steven and this woman Virginia, who are prepared to harrow hell as best as is granted them to do, that they may confound Thine enemies and rescue an unstained child from the dungeons of the worm. Without Thine aid they have no hope. We beg Thee to allow them a guide and counselor through the wilderness of hell. If we are not worthy of an angel, we ask that Thou commend them unto Thy departed servant Nikolai Ivanovitch Lobachevsky, or whomever else may be knowledgeable in these matters as having been on earth a discoverer of them. This do we pray in the name of the Father, and of the Son, and of the Holy Ghost. Amen."

There was another stillness.

Then the cross on the altar shone forth, momentarily sun-bright, and we heard one piercing, exquisite note, and I felt within me a rush

of joy I can only vaguely compare to the first winning of first love. But another noise followed, as of a huge wind. The candles went out, the panes went black, we staggered when the floor shook beneath us. Svartalf screamed.

"Ginny!" I heard myself yell. Simultaneously I was whirled down a vortex of images, memories, a bulbous-towered church on an illimitable plain, a dirt track between rows of low thatch-roofed cottages and a horseman squeaking and jingling along it with saber at belt, an iron winter that ended in thaw and watery gleams and returning birdflocks and shy breath of green across the beechwoods, a disordered stack of books, faces, faces, hands, a woman who was my wife, a son who died too young, half of Kazan in one red blaze, the year of the cholera, the letter from Göttingen, loves, failures, blindness closing in day by slow day *and none of it was me.*

A thunderclap rattled our teeth. The wind stopped, the light came back, the sense of poised forces was no more. We stood bewildered in our ordinary lives. Ginny cast herself into my arms.

"*Lyubimyets,*" I croaked to her, "no, darling—*Gospodny pomiluie*—" while the kaleidoscope gyred within me. Svartalf stood on a workbench, back arched, tail bottled, not in rage but in panic. His lips, throat, tongue writhed through a ghastly fight with sounds no cat can make. He was trying to talk.

"What's gone wrong?" Barney roared.

# XXX

Ginny took over. She beckoned to the closest men. "Karlslund, Hardy, help Steve," she rapped. "Check him, Doc." I heard her fragmentarily through the chaos. My friends supported me. I reached a chair, collapsed, and fought for breath.

My derangement was short. The recollections of another land, another time, stopped rocketing forth at random. They had been terrifying because they were strange and out of my control. *Poko'y* sounded in my awareness, together with *Peace,* and I knew they meant the same. Courage lifted. I sensed myself thinking, with overtones of both formalism and compassion:

—I beg your pardon, sir. This re-embodiment confused me likewise. I had not paused to reflect what a difference would be made by more than a hundred years in the far realms where I have been. A few minutes will suffice, I believe, for preliminary studies providing the informational basis for a modus vivendi that shall be tolerable to you. Rest assured that I regret any intrusion and will minimize the same. I may add, with due respect, that what I chance to learn about your private affairs will doubtless be of no special significance to one who has left the flesh behind him.

Lobachevsky! I realized.

—Your servant, sir. Ah, yes, Steven Anton Matuchek. Will you graciously excuse me for the necessary brief interval?

This, and the indescribable stirring of two memory sets that followed, went on at the back of my consciousness. The rest of me was again alert: uncannily so. I waved Ashman aside with an "I'm okay" and scanned the scene before me.

In Svartalf's hysterical condition, he was dangerous to approach.

Ginny tapped a basin of water at a workbench sink and threw it over him. He squalled, sprang to the floor, dashed to a corner, crouched and glowered. "Poor puss," she consoled. "I had to do that." She found a towel. "Come here to mama and we'll dry you off." He made her come to him. She squatted and rubbed his fur.

"What got into him?" Charles asked.

Ginny looked up. Against the red hair her face was doubly pale. "Good phrase, Admiral," she said. "Something did. I shocked his body with a drenching. The natural cat reflexes took over, and the invading spirit lost its dominance. But it's still there. As soon as it learns its psychosomatic way around, it'll try to assume control and do what it's come for."

"Which is?"

"I don't know. We'd better secure him."

I rose. "No, wait," I said. "I can find out." Their eyes swiveled toward me. "You see, uh, I've got Lobachevsky."

"What?" Karlslund protested. "His soul in your— Can't be! The saints never—"

I brushed past, knelt by Ginny, took Svartalf's head between my hands, and said, "Relax. Nobody wants to hurt you. My guest thinks he understands what's happened. Savvy? Nikolai Ivanovitch Lobachevsky is his name. Who are you?"

The muscles bunched, the fangs appeared, a growing ululation swept the room. Svartalf was about to have another fit.

—Sir, by your leave, the thought went in me. He is not hostile. I would know if he were. He is disconcerted at what has occurred, and has merely a feline brain to think with. Evidently he is unacquainted with your language. May I endeavor to calm him?

Russian purled and fizzled from my lips. Svartalf started, then I felt him ease a bit in my grasp. He looked and listened as intently as if I were a mousehole. When I stopped, he shook his head and mewed.

—So he was not of my nationality either. But he appears to have grasped our intent.

Look, I thought, you can follow English, using my knowledge. Svartalf knows it too. Why can't his . . . inhabitant . . . do like you?

—I told you, sir, the feline brain is inadequate. It has nothing like a human speech-handling structure. The visiting soul must use every available cortical cell to maintain bare reason. But it can freely draw upon its terrestrial experience, thanks to the immense data storage capacity of even a diminutive mammalian body. Hence we can use what languages it knew before.

I thought: I see. Don't underrate Svartalf. He's pure-bred from a long line of witch familiars, more intelligent than an ordinary cat. And the spells that've surrounded him through his life must've had effects.

—Excellent. *"Sprechen Sie Deutsch?"*

Svartalf nodded eagerly. "Meeöh," he said with an umlaut.

*"Guten Tag, gnädiger Herr. Ich bin der Mathematiker Nikolai Iwanowitsch Lobatschewski, quondam Oberpfarrer zu der Kasans Universität in Russland. Je suis votre très humble serviteur, Monsieur."* That last was in French, as politeness called for in the earlier nineteenth century.

"W-r-r-rar-r." Claws gestured across the floor.

Ginny said, wide-eyed with awe: "He wants to write. . . . Svartalf, listen. Don't be angry. Don't be afraid. Let him do what he will. Don't fight, help him. When this is over, you'll have more cream and sardines than you can eat. I promise. There's a good cat." She rubbed him under the chin. It didn't seem quite the proper treatment for a visiting savant, but it worked, because at last he purred.

While she and Griswold made preparations, I concentrated on meshing with Lobachevsky. The rest stood around, shaken by what had happened and the sudden complete unknownness of the next hour. A fraction of me hearkened to their low voices.

Charles: "Damnedest apparition of saints I ever heard of."

Karlslund: "Admiral, please!"

Janice: "Well, it's true. They shouldn't have intruded in bodies like, like demons taking possession."

Griswold: "Maybe they had to. We did neglect to provide counter-transferral mass for inter-continuum crossing."

Karlslund: "They aren't devils. They never required it in the past."

Barney: "Whoa. Let's think about that. A spirit or a thought can travel free between universes. Maybe that's what returned saints always were—visions, not solid bodies."

Karlslund: "Some were positively substantial."

Nobu: "I would guess that a saint can utilize any mass to form a body. Air, for instance, and a few pounds of dust for minerals, would provide the necessary atoms. Don't forget what he or she is, as far as we know: a soul in Heaven, which is to say one near God. How can he fail to gain remarkable abilities as well as spiritual eminence—from the Source of power and creativity?"

Charles: "What ails these characters, then?"

"Messieurs," my body said, stepping toward them, "I beg your indulgence. As yet I have not entirely accustomed myself to thinking

in this corporeal manifold. Do me the honor to remember that it is unlike the one I originally inhabited. Nor have I assimilated the details of the problem which led to your request for help. Finally, while confined to human form, I have no better means than you for discovering the identity of the gentleman in the cat. I do believe I know his purpose, but let us wait, if you will, for more exact knowledge before drawing conclusions."

"Wow," Barney breathed. "How's it feel, Steve?"

"Not bad," I said. "Better by the minute." That was an ultimate understatement. As Lobachevsky and I got acquainted, I felt in myself, coexistent with my own thoughts and emotions, those of a being grown good and wise beyond imagining.

Of course, I couldn't share his afterlife, nor the holiness thereof. My mortal brain and grimy soul didn't reach to it. At most, there sang at the edge of perception a peace and joy which were not static but a high eternal adventure. I did, though, have the presence of Lobachevsky the man to savor. Think of your oldest and best friend and you'll have a rough idea what that was like.

"We should be ready now," Ginny said.

She and Griswold had set a Ouija board on a bench, the easiest implement for a paw to operate. She perched herself on the edge, swinging legs whose shapeliness my associate noticed too, though mainly he worked out in my head the equation describing them. Svartalf took position at the gadget while I leaned across the opposite side to interrogate.

The planchette moved in a silence broken only by breathing. It was sympathetic with a piece of chalk under a broomstick spell, that wrote large on a blackboard where everyone could see.

ICH BIN JANOS BOLYAI VON UNGARN

"Bolyai!" gasped Falkenberg. "God, I forgot about him! No wonder he—but how—"

*"Enchanté, Monsieur,"* Lobachevsky said with a low bow. *"Dies ist für mich eine grosse Ehre. Ihrer Werke sint eine Inspiration für alles."* He meant it.

Neither Bolyai nor Svartalf were to be outdone in courtliness. They stood up on his hind legs, made a reverence with paw on heart, followed with a military salute, took the planchette again and launched into a string of flowery French compliments.

"Who is he, anyhow?" Charles hissed behind me.

"I . . . I don't know his biography," Falkenberg answered likewise. "But I recall now, he was the morning star of the new geometry."

"I'll check the library," Griswold offered. "These courtesies look as if they'll go on for some time."

"Yes," Ginny said in my ear, "can't you hurry things along a bit? We're way overdue at home, you and I. And that phone call could be trouble."

I put it to Lobachevsky, who put it to Bolyai, who wrote ABER NATUERLICH for the lack of an umlaut and gave us his assurances—at considerable length—that as an Imperial officer he had learned how to act with the decisiveness that became a soldier when need existed, as it clearly did in the present instance, especially when two such charming young ladies in distress laid claim upon his honor, which honor he would maintain upon any field without flinching, as he trusted he had done in life. . . .

I don't intend to mock a great man. Among us, he was a soul trying to think with the brain and feel with the nerves and glands of a tomcat. It magnified human failings and made well-nigh impossible the expression of his intellect and knightliness. We found these hinted at in the notes on him that Griswold located in encyclopedias and mathematical histories, which we read while he did his gallant best to communicate with Lobachevsky.

János Bolyai was born in Hungary in 1802, when it was hardly more than a province of the Austrian Empire. His father, a noted mathematician who was a close friend of Gauss, taught him calculus and analytical mechanics before he was thirteen and enrolled him in the Royal Engineering College in Vienna at fifteen. Twenty years old, he became an officer of engineers, well-known as a violinist and a swordsman dangerous to meet in a duel. In 1823 he sent to his father a draft of his *Absolute Science of Space.* While Gauss had anticipated some of its ideas in a general, philosophical way—unknown at the time to Bolyai—the young Hungarian had here done the first rigorous treatment of a non-Euclidean geometry, the first solid proof that space doesn't logically need to obey axioms like the one about parallel lines.

Unfortunately, it wasn't published till 1833, and just as an appendix to a two-volume work of his father's which, being in Latin, bore the gorgeous title *Tentatem juventutem studiosam in elementa matheseos purae introducendi.* By then Lobachevsky had independently announced similar results. Bolyai remained obscure.

It seemed to have discouraged him. He settled down in the same place as his father, who taught at the Reformed College of Maros-Vásáhely, and died there in 1860. His lifetime covered a rising Hungarian nationalism, Kossuth's rebellion in 1848, its failure and the

reactionary oppression that followed; but the articles said nothing about his conduct or opinions. He did see the end of martial law in 1857 and the increasing liberalization afterward: though his land did not achieve full national status under the dual monarchy till seven years past his death. I wondered if his ghost had hung around that long, waiting, before it departed for wider universes.

We found more on Lobachevsky. He was born in 1793, in Nizhni Novgorod. His mother was widowed when he was seven. She moved to Kazan and raised her boys in genteel but often desperate poverty. They won scholarships to the Gymnasium, Nikolai at the age of eight. He entered the local university at fourteen, got his master's degree at eighteen, was appointed assistant professor at twenty-one and full professor at twenty-three. Presently he had charge of the library and the museum. It was a tough distinction—both were neglected, disordered, so short of funds that he had to do most of the sheer physical labor himself—but over the years he made them a pride of Russia. In addition, while Czar Alexander lived, he was supposed to keep tabs on student politics. He managed to satisfy the government without finking; the kids adored him.

In 1827 he became rector, head of the university. He built it up in every way, including literally; he learned architecture so he could design proper structures. In 1830, when cholera struck, he pulled the academic community through with scant mortality, by enforcing sanitation as opposed to the medieval measures taken elsewhere in Kazan. Another time a fire totalled half the town. His new observatory, his best buildings went. But he rescued the instruments and books, and two years later had restored what was lost.

As early as 1826, he'd discussed non-Euclidean geometry. He might as well have done it in Kansas as Kazan. Word spread to western Europe with a slowness that would have driven a less patient, unegotistical man up the wall. But it did travel. When Gauss heard, he was impressed enough to get Lobachevsky elected to the Royal Society of Göttingen in 1842.

Maybe that—xenophobia, or simple spiteful jealousy—was what prompted the Czarist regime in 1846 to bounce him as rector. They let him keep his study at the university, but scant else. Heartbroken, he withdrew to his mathematical work. His eyesight failed. His son died. He thought on, dictating the *Pangeometry* that crowned his life. In 1856, shortly after he finished the book, that life ended.

Of course he was a saint!

—No, Steven Pavlovitch, you should not raise me above my worth.

I stumbled and sinned more than most, I am sure. But the mercy of God has no bounds. I have been . . . it is impossible to explain. Let us say I have been allowed to progress.

The blackboard filled. Janice wielded an eraser and the chalk squeaked on. To those who knew French—which the Russian and the Hungarian had switched to as being more elegant than German—it gradually became clear what had happened. But I alone shared Lobachevsky's degree of comprehension. As this grew, I fretted over ways to convey it in American. Time was shrinking on us fast.

—Indeed, Lobachevsky answered. Brusque though contemporary manners have become (*pardonnez-moi, je vous en prie*), haste is needed, for I agree that the hour is late and the peril dire.

Therefore I called the group to me when at last the questioning was done. Except for Ginny, who couldn't help being spectacular, and Svartalf, who sat at her feet with a human soul in his eyes, they were an unimpressive lot to see, tired, sweaty, haggard, neckties loosened or discarded, hair unkempt, cigarets in most hands. I was probably less glamorous, perched on a stool facing them. My voice grated and I'd developed a tic in one cheek. The fact that a blessed spirit had joint tenancy of my body didn't much affect plain, scared, fallible me.

"Things have got straightened out," I said. "We made a mistake. God doesn't issue personal orders to His angels and saints, at least not on our behalf. It appears, Pastor, from the form of your invocation, you understood that. But consciously or not, the rest of us assumed we're more important than we are." Lobachevsky corrected me. "No, everybody's important to Him. But there must be freedom, even for evil. And furthermore, there are considerations of—well, I guess you can't say *Realpolitik.* I don't know if it has earthly analogues. Roughly speaking, though, neither God nor the Adversary wants to provoke an early Armageddon. For two thousand years, they've avoided direct incursions into each other's, uh, home territories, Heaven or hell. That policy's not about to be changed.

"Our appeal was heard. Lobachevsky's a full-fledged saint. He couldn't resist coming down, and he wasn't forbidden to. But he's not allowed to aid us in hell. If he goes along, it has to be strictly as an observer, inside a mortal frame. He's sorry, but that's the way the elixir elides. If we get scragged there, he can't help our souls escape. Every spirit has to make its own way— No matter. The result was, he entered this continuum, with me as his logical target.

"Bolyai's different. He heard too, especially since the prayer was so loosely phrased it could well have referred to him. Now, he hasn't

made sainthood. He says he's been in Purgatory. I suspect most of us'd think of it as a condition where you haven't got what it takes to know God directly but you can improve yourself. At any rate, while he wasn't in Heaven, he wasn't damned either. And so he's under no prohibition as regards taking an active part in a fight. This looked like a chance to do a good deed. He assessed the content of our appeal, including the parts we didn't speak, and likewise chose me. Lobachevsky, who's more powerful by virtue of sanctity, and wasn't aware of his intent, arrived a split second ahead of him."

I stopped to bum a cigaret. What I really wanted was a gallon of hard cider. My throat felt like a washboard road in summer. "Evidently these cases are governed by rules," I said. "Don't ask me why; I'm sure the reasons are valid if we could know them; in part, I guess, it's to protect mortal flesh from undue shock and strain. Only one extra identity per customer. Bolyai hasn't the capability of a saint, to create a temporary real body out of whatever's handy, as you suggested a while back, Dr. Nobu. In fact, he probably couldn't have used organized material if we'd prepared some. His way to manifest himself was to enter a live corpus. Another rule: the returned soul can't switch from person to person. It must stay with whom it's at for the duration of the affair.

"Bolyai had to make a snap decision. I was preempted. His sense of propriety wouldn't let him, uh, enter a woman. It wouldn't do a lot of good if he hooked up with one of you others, who aren't going. Though our prayer hadn't mentioned it, he'd gathered from the overtones that the expedition did have a third member who was male. He willed himself there. He always was rash. Too late, he discovered he'd landed in Svartalf."

Barney's brick-house shoulders drooped. "Our project's gone for nothing?"

"No," I said. "With Ginny's witchcraft to help—boost his feline brain power—Bolyai thinks he can operate. He's spent a sizable chunk of afterlife studying the geometry of the continua, exploring planes of existence too weird for him to hint at. He loves the idea of a filibuster into hell."

Svartalf's tail swung, his ears stood erect, his whiskers dithered.

"Then it worked!" Ginny shouted. "Whoopee!"

"So far and to this extent, yeah." My determination was unchanged but my enthusiasm less. Lobachevsky's knowledge darkened me: —I sense a crisis. The Adversary can ill afford to let you succeed. His mightiest and subtlest forces will be arrayed against you.

"Well," Karlslund said blankly. "Well, well."

Ginny stopped her war dance when I said: "Maybe you better make that phone call, Dr. Griswold."

The little scientist nodded. "I'll do it from my office. We can plug in an extension here, audio-visual reception." We were far too groggy to give a curse about the lawfulness of that, though I do believe it's permissible, not being an actual scryertap.

We had a few minutes' wait. I held Ginny close by my side. Our troops muttered aimlessly or slumped exhausted. Bolyai was alone in his cheerfulness. He used Svartalf to tour the lab with eager curiosity. By now he knew more math and science than living men will acquire before world's end; but it intrigued him to see how we were going about things. He was ecstatic when Janice found him a copy of the *National Geographic.*

The phone awoke. We saw what Griswold did. The breath sucked in between my teeth. Shining Knife was indeed back.

"I'm sorry to keep you waiting," the professor said. "It was impossible for me to come earlier. What can I do for you?"

The G-man identified himself and showed his sigil. "I'm trying to get in touch with Mr. and Mrs. Steven Matuchek. You know them, don't you?"

"Well, ah, yes . . . haven't seen them lately—" Griswold was a lousy liar.

Shining Knife's countenance hardened. "Please listen, sir. I returned this afternoon from a trip to Washington on their account. The matter they're involved in is that big. I checked with my subordinates. Mrs. Matuchek had disappeared. Her husband had spent time in a spyproof conference room. He'd not been seen to leave his place of work at quitting time. I sent a man in to ask for him, and he wasn't to be found. Our people had taken pictures of those who went into the plant. A crime lab worker here recognized you among the members of the conference. Are you sure the Matucheks aren't with you?"

"Y-yes. Yes. What do you want with them? Not a criminal charge?"

"No, unless they misbehave. I've a special order enjoining them from certain actions they may undertake. Whoever abetted them would be equally subject to arrest."

Griswold was game. He overcame his shyness and sputtered: "Frankly, sir, I resent your implication. And in any event, the writ must be served to have force. Until such time, they are not bound by it, nor are their associates."

"True. Mind if I come look around your place? They might happen to be there . . . without your knowledge."

"Yes, sir, I do mind. You may not."

"Be reasonable, Dr. Griswold. Among other things, the purpose is to protect them from themselves."

"That attitude is a major part of what I dislike about the present Administration. Good day to you, sir."

"Uh, hold." Shining Knife's tone remained soft, but nobody could mistake his expression. "You don't own the building you're in."

"I'm responsible for it. Trismegistus is a private foundation. I can exercise discretionary authority and forbid access to your . . . your myrmidons."

"Not when they arrive with a warrant, Professor."

"Then I suggest you obtain one." Griswold broke the spell.

In the lab, we regarded each other. "How long?" I asked.

Barney shrugged. "Under thirty minutes. The FBI has ways."

"Can we scram out of here?" Ginny inquired of him.

"I wouldn't try it. The area probably went under surveillance before Shining Knife tried to call. I expect he stayed his hand simply because he doesn't know what we're doing and his orders are to proceed with extreme caution."

She straightened. "Okay. Then we go to hell." Her mouth twitched faintly upward. "Go directly to hell. Do not pass Go. Do not collect two hundred dollars."

"Huh?" Barney grunted, as if he'd been kicked in the stomach. "No! You're as crazy as the Feds think you are! No preparation, no proper equipment—"

"We can cobble together a lot with what's around here," Ginny said. "Bolyai can advise us, and Lobachevsky till we leave. We'll win an advantage of surprise. The demonic forces won't have had time to organize against our foray. Once we're out of American jurisdiction, can Shining Knife legally recall us? And he won't keep you from operating our lifeline. That'd be murder. Besides, I suspect he's on our side, not glad of his duty. He may well offer you help." She went to Barney, took one of his hands between both of hers, and looked up into his craggy face. "Don't hinder us, old friend," she pleaded. "We've got to have you on our side."

His torment was hurtful to see. But he started ripping out commands. Our team plunged into work.

Griswold entered. "Did you— Oh. You can't leave now."

"We can't not," I said.

"But you haven't . . . haven't had dinner! You'll be weak and— Well, I know I can't stop you. We keep a fridge with food in the research lab, for when a project runs late. I'll see what it holds."

So that's how we went to storm the fastness of hell: Janice's borrowed shoulder purse on Ginny, and the pockets of Barney's outsize jacket (sleeves haggled short) on me, abulge with peanut butter sandwiches, tinned kipper for Svartalf-Bolyai, and four cans of beer.

# XXXI

We had some equipment, notably Ginny's kit. This included Valeria's primary birth certificate, which Ashman had brought. The directions he could give us for using it were the main reason he'd been recruited. She put it in her own bag, clipped to her waist, for the time being.

Nobody, including our geometers, knew exactly what would and would not work in hell. Lobachevsky was able to tell us that high-religious symbols had no power there as they do here. Their virtue comes from their orientation to the Highest, and the fundamental thing about hell is that no dweller in it can love. However, we might gain something from paganism. Its element of honor and justice meant nothing where we were bound, but its element of power and propitiation did, and although centuries have passed since anyone served those gods, the mana has not wholly vanished from their emblems.

Ginny habitually wore on her dress the owl pin that showed she was a licensed witch. Griswold found a miniature jade plaque, Aztec, carved with a grotesque grinning feathered serpent, that could be secured to the wereflash beneath my shirt. A bit sheepish under Pastor Karlslund's eye, Barney fished out a silver hammer pendant, copy of a Viking era original. It belonged to his wife, but he'd carried it himself "for a rabbit's foot" since this trouble broke, and now passed the chain around Svartalf's neck.

Projectile weapons weren't apt to be worth lugging. Ginny and I are pretty good shots in the nearly Euclidean space of this plenum. But when the trajectory is through unpredictable distortions that affect the very gravity, forget it, chum. We buckled on swords. She had a slender modern Solingen blade, meant for ritual use but whetted to a

sharp point and edge. Mine was heavier and older, likewise kept for its goetic potency, but that stemmed from its being a cutlass which had once sailed with Decatur.

Air might be a problem. Hell was notoriously foul. Scuba rigs were in stock, being used for underwater investigations. When this gets you involved with nixies or other tricky creatures, you need a wizard or witch along, whose familiar won't be a convenient beast like a seal unless you have the luck to engage one of the few specialists. Accordingly there are miniature oxygen bottles and adjustable masks for a wide variety of animals. We could outfit Svartalf, and I tied another pint-size unit to the tank on my back—for Val, in case.

That completed the list. Given time, we could have done better. We could have ridden a dragon instead of two brooms, with an extra beast packing several tons of stuff against every contingency that a strategic analysis team might propose. Still, the Army had used that approach and failed. We had fresh knowledge and a unique scout. Maybe those would serve.

While we busked ourselves with several helpers, Barney and Nobu made the final preparations to transmit us. Or almost final. At the last minute I asked them to do an additional job as soon as might be.

At the center of the Nexus drawn on the floor, whose shape I won't reveal, they'd put a regular confining pentacle set about with blessed candles. A giant bell jar hung from a block and tackle above, ready to be lowered. This was for the counter-mass from the hell universe, which might be alive, gaseous, or otherwise troublesome. "After we've gone," I said, "lay a few hundred extra pounds of material in there, if the area's not too dangerous to enter.

"What?" Barney said, astonished. "But that'd allow, uh, anything—a pursuer—to make the transition with no difficulty."

"Having arrived here, it can't leave the diagram," I pointed out. "We can and will, in a mighty quick jump. Have spells ready to prevent its return home. Thing is, I don't know what we'll find. Could be an item, oh, of scientific value; and the race needs more data about hell. Probably we won't collect any loot. But let's keep the option."

"Okay. Sound thinking, for a lunatic." Barney wiped his eyes. "Damn, I must be allergic to something here."

Janice didn't weep alone when we bade good-bye. And within me paced the grave thought:

—No more may I aid you, Steven Pavlovitch, Virginia Williamovna, Janos Fárkasovitch, and cat who surely has a soul of his own. Now must I become a mere watcher and recorder, for the sake

of nothing except my curiosity. I will not burden you with the grief this causes me. You will not be further aware of my presence. May you fare with God's blessing.

I felt him depart from the conscious part of my mind like a dream that fades as you wake and try to remember. Soon he was only something good that had happened to me for a couple of hours. Or no, not entirely. I suspect what calm I kept in the time that followed was due to his unsensed companionship. He couldn't help being what he was.

Holding our brooms, Ginny and I walked hand in hand to the Nexus. Svartalf paced ahead. At the midpoint of the figure, we halted for a kiss and a whisper before we slipped the masks on. Our people cast the spell. Again the chamber filled with night. Energies gathered. Thunder and earthquake brawled. I hung onto my fellows lest we get separated. Through the rising racket, I heard my witch read from the parchment whereon stood the name Victrix, urging us toward her through diabolic space-time.

The room, the world, the stars, and universes began to rotate about the storm's eye where we stood. Swifter and swifter they turned until they were sheer spinning, the Grotte quern itself. Then was only a roar as of great waters. We were drawn down the maelstrom. The final glimpse of light dwindled with horrible speed; and when we reached infinity, it was snuffed out. Afterward came such twistings and terrors that nothing would have sent us through them except our Valeria Victrix.

I must have blanked out for a minute or a millennium. At least, I became aware with ax-chop abruptness that the passage was over and we had arrived.

Wherever it was.

I clutched Ginny to me. We searched each other with a touch that quivered and found no injuries. Svartalf was hale too. He didn't insist on attention as he normally would. Bolyai made him pad in widening spirals, feeling out our environment.

With caution I slipped off my mask and tried the air. It was bitterly cold, driving in a wind that sought to the bones, but seemed clean—sterile, in fact.

Sterility. That was the whole of this place. The sky was absolute and endless black, though in some fashion we could see stars and ugly cindered planets, visibly moving in chaotic paths; they were pieces of still deeper darkness, not an absence but a negation of light. We stood on a bare plain, hard and gray and flat as concrete, relieved by nothing except scattered boulders whose shapes were never alike and always hideous. The illumination came from the ground, wan, shadowless, colorless. Vision faded at last into utter distance. For that plain had no horizon, no interruptions; it went on. The sole direction, sound, movement, came from the drearily whistling wind.

I've seen some abominations in my time, I thought, but none to beat this. . . . No. The worst is forever a changeling in my daughter's crib.

Ginny removed her mask too, letting it hang over the closed bottle like mine. She shuddered and hugged herself. The dress whipped around her. "I w-w-was ready to guard against flames," she said. It

was as appropriate a remark as most that are made on historic occasions.

"Dante described the seventh circle of the Inferno as frozen," I answered slowly. "There's reason to believe he knew something. Where are we?"

"I can't tell. If the name spell worked, along with the rest, we're on the same planet—if 'planet' means a lot here—as Val will be, and not too far away." We'd naturally tried for a beforehand arrival.

"This isn't like what the previous expeditions reported."

"No. Nor was our transition. We used different rituals, and slanted across time to boot. Return should be easier."

Svartalf disappeared behind a rock. I didn't approve of that. "*Kommen Sie zurück!*" I shouted into the wind. "*Retournez-vous!*" I realized that, without making a fuss about it, Lobachevsky had prior to our departure impressed on me fluent French and German. By golly, Russian too!

"Mneowr-r," blew back. I turned. The cat was headed our way from opposite to where he'd been. "What the dickens?" I exclaimed.

"Warped space," Ginny said. "Look." While he trotted steadily, Svartalf's path wove as if he were drunk. "A line where he is must answer to a curve elsewhere. And he's within a few yards. What about miles off?"

I squinted around. "Everything appears straight."

"It would, while you're stationary. Br-r-r! We've got to get warmer."

She drew the telescoping wand from her purse. The star at its tip didn't coruscate here; it was an ember. But it made a lighted match held under our signatures and Svartalf's pawprint generate welcome heat in our bodies. A bit too much, to be frank; we started sweating. I decided the hell universe was at such high entropy—so deep into thermodynamic decay—that a little potential went very far.

Svartalf arrived. Staring uneasily over the plain, I muttered, "We haven't met enough troubles. What're we being set up for?"

"We've two items in our favor," Ginny said. "First, a really effective transfer spell. Its influence is still perceptible here, warding us, tending to smooth out fluctuations and similarize nature to home. Second, the demons must have known well in advance where and when the earlier expeditions would come through. They'd ample time to fix up some nasty tricks. We, though, we've stolen a march." She brushed an elflock from her brow and added starkly: "I expect we'll get our fill of problems as we travel."

"We have to?"

"Yes. Why should the kidnaper make re-entry at this desert spot? We can't have landed at the exact point we want. Be quiet while I get a bearing."

Held over the Victrix parchment, the proper words sung, her dowser pointed out an unequivocal direction. The scryer globe remained cloudy, giving us no hint of distance or look at what lay ahead. Space-time in between was too alien.

We ate, drank, rested what minutes we dared, and took off. Ginny had the lead with Svartalf on her saddlebow, I flew on her right in echelon. The sticks were cranky and sluggish, the screenfields kaput, leaving us exposed to the wind from starboard. But we did loft and level off before the going got tough.

At first it was visual distortion. What I saw—my grasp on the controls, Svartalf, Ginny's splendid figure, the stones underneath—rippled, wavered, widened, narrowed, flowed from one obscene caricature of itself to a worse. Gobs of flesh seemed to slough off, hang in drops, stretch thin, break free and disappear. Sound altered too; the skirl turned into a cacophony of yells, buzzes, drones, fleetingly like words almost understandable and threatening, pulses too deep to hear except with the body's automatic terror reaction. "Don't pay heed!" I called. "Optical effects, Doppler—" but no message could get through that gibbering.

Suddenly my love receded. She whirled from me like a blown leaf. I tried to follow, straight into the blast that lashed tears from my eyes. The more rudder I gave the broom, the faster our courses split apart. "Bolyai, help!" I cried into the aloneness. It swallowed me.

I slid down a long wild curve. The stick would not pull out of it. Well, flashed through my fear, I'm not in a crash dive, it'll flatten a short ways above—

And the line of rocks athwart my path were not rocks, they were a mountain range toward which I catapulted. The gale laughed in my skull and shivered the broom beneath me. I hauled on controls, I bellowed the spells, but any change I could make would dash me on the ground before I hit those cliffs.

Somehow I'd traveled thousands of miles—had to be that much, or I'd have seen these peaks on the limitless plain, wouldn't I have?—and Ginny was lost, Val was lost, I could brace myself for death but not for the end of hope.

"Yeee-ow-w-w!" cut through the clamor. I twisted in my seat. And there came Ginny. Her hair blew in fire. The star on her wand burned

anew like Sirius. Bolyai was using Svartalf's paws to steer; yellow eyes and white fangs flared in the panther countenance.

They pulled alongside. Ginny leaned over till our fingers met. Her sensations ran down the circuit to me. I saw with her what the cat was doing. I imitated. It would have wrecked us at home. But here we slewed sideways and started gaining altitude.

How to explain? Suppose you were a Flatlander, a mythical creature (if any creature is mythical) of two space dimensions, no more. You live in a surface. That's right, *in.* If this is a plane, its geometry obeys the Euclidean rules we learn in high school: parallel lines don't meet, the shortest distance between two points is a straight line, the angles of a triangle total 180 degrees, et cetera. But now imagine that some three-dimensional giant plucks you out and drops you into a surface of different shape. It might be a sphere, for example. You'll find space fantastically changed. In a sphere, you must think of lines in terms of meridians and parallels, which means they have finite length; in general, distance between points is minimized by following a great circle; triangles have a variable number of degrees, but always more than 180— You might well go mad. Now imagine cones, hyperboloids, rotated trigonometric and logarithmic curves, Möbius bands, whatever you can.

And now imagine a planet which is all water, churned by storms and not constrained by the ordinary laws of physics. At any point its surface can have any form, which won't even stay constant in time. Expand the two dimensions into three; make it four for the temporal axis, unless this requires more than one, as many philosophers believe; add the hyperspace in which paranatural forces act; put it under the rule of chaos and hatred: and you've got some analogy to the hell universe.

We'd hit a saddle point back yonder, Ginny passing to one side of it, I to the other. Our courses diverged because the curvatures of space did. My attempt to intercept her was worse than useless; in the region where I found myself, a line aimed her way quickly bent in a different direction. I blundered from geometry to geometry, through a tuck in space that bypassed enormous reaches, toward my doom.

No mortal could have avoided it. But Bolyai was mortal no longer. To his genius had been added the knowledge and skill of more than a century's liberation from the dear but confining flesh. Svartalf's body had changed from a trap to a tool, once his rapport with Ginny enabled the mathematician to draw on her resources also. He could make lightning-quick observations of a domain, mentally write and solve the

equations that described it, calculate what its properties would be, get an excellent notion of what the contour would shade into next—in fractional seconds. He wove through the dimensional storms of hell like a quarterback bound for a touchdown.

He gloried. For lack of other voice, he sang the songs of a black tomcat out after fornication and battle. We clawed over the mountains and streaked toward our goal.

It was no milk run. We must keep aware and reacting each instant. Often we made an error that well-nigh brought us to grief. I'd lose contact with Ginny and wander off again; or a lurch would nearly make us collide; or the intense gravitational field where space was sharply warped hurled our sticks groundward and tried to yank out guts and eyeballs; or a quick drop in weight sent us spinning; or we shot through folds in space instead of going around and were immediately elsewhere; or we passed into volumes where hyperspace was so flat that our broomspells didn't work and we must get through on momentum and aerodynamics—I don't recall every incident. I was too busy to notice a lot of them.

We traveled, though, and faster than we'd hoped, once Bolyai discovered what tricks we could play when the time dimension was buckled. The deafening racket and disgusting illusions plagued us less as we got the hang of passing smoothly from metric to metric. Moreover, the world around us grew steadier. Somebody or something wanted to lair in a region where disturbances tended to cancel out.

At last we could study the landscape. Hitherto we'd simply kept flying. We'd noted the plain had given way to crags, to miles of jumbled bones, to a pit that seemed without bottom, to a lava sea across which sleeted flames and from which rose fumes that made us don our masks before the lungs were corroded within us. But such glimpses were remote, things to stay well above while we fought to make distance. Now progress was, by comparison, easy. We could spare a little attention. And we'd better. When Ginny lifted out her globe, a pale but waxing glow from inside it showed we were approaching the goal.

I released her hand, not because I wanted to but because our arms ached from straining across the gap. We flew quietly for a while, observing.

Quietly. . . . The wind had fallen behind; nothing blew around us but a murmur of cloven air. It bore a graveyard stench, we gasped in its warmth and slimy humidity, but it could be breathed. The sky remained black, with its more-than-black crawling orbs. Sometimes a huge pitted meteoroid passed close overhead, hardly faster than we,

following a track above shallow atmosphere to vanishment over the horizonless world. Sometimes corposants blossomed and bobbed in the nether gloom.

The mournful phosphorescence of the ground remained our chief illumination. We were on the fringes of a swamp as vast as every other piece of country we'd seen here. Pools, bayous, lakes stretched beyond sight, dimly glimmering where they were not scummed with decayed matter. Trees stood thick and gnarled, branches tangled together, cypress knees thrust above water and floating logs; but not one of them was alive. Reeds choked the shorelines, dense and dead. Yellow mists stole through the murk between boles: tendrils of a fogbank that hid the inner reaches of marsh in a slow dirty seething.

Immensely far ahead, light reflected ruddy and restless off low clouds. Without warning, a slip or convulsion in space brought us on top of it.

Sound assailed us, drums, pipings, screeches. At the middle of a cleared island, a fire burned, high as a steeple, heat striking from it like a flayer's knife. Past its white heart, where things writhed and screamed that were not clear to the eye, I glimpsed the shapes that danced around it, black, naked, thin as mantises. When they saw us, their shrieks pierced the surf roar of the flames, and the tom-toms went *Boom-ba-da-boom, boom-ba-da-boom.* A dozen birds labored from the leafless trees. They were the size and color of vultures, but with no flesh on their skulls and cruel claws.

Svartalf spat defiance. Our sticks accelerated and left the flock behind. I don't think it was alive either. From miles in front we heard new drums commence, and after them, a whisper across the leagues, again *Boom-ba-da-boom, boom-ba-da-boom.*

Ginny beckoned me and I edged close. She looked grim. "If I don't miss my guess," she said, "we're over Diddy-Wah-Diddy and the word's being passed on."

My left hand dropped to my cutlass hilt. "What should we do?"

"Veer. Try for a different approach. But fast."

The wind of our speed felt nearly good after that blistering calor; and presently it cooled and lost its stench. When we'd passed a line of dolmens, the air was again wintry for a while. Beneath us lay a barren moor. Two armies fought. They must have been doing it for centuries, because many wore chain mail and peaked helmets, the rest were in skins and rough cloth, the weapons were sword, spear, ax. We heard the iron clamor, the shuffling, slipping feet, the butcher sound of blows

driven home: but no cries, no trumpets, no rasp of breath. Wearily, hopelessly, the dead men fought their war that had no end.

Beyond them we turned and made once more for our destination. We crossed a forest of gallows and a river that flowed with a noise like sobbing and whose spray, cast up by a gust, tasted warm and salt. We suffered the heat and poisonous vapors from a system of roads where motor vehicles of some kind crawled nose to tail, a network miles wide and I know not how long, nor can I guess its purpose. We traversed hills gouged with trenches and the craters of explosions, rusted cannon the last sign of life except for one flag, raised as in victory, whose colors had faded to gray. The hills climbed till we met another range so high we needed our masks; flitting through its canyons, we dodged stones that fell upward.

But past those mountains the land swooped down anew. Another plain of boulders reached beyond sight. Far off upon it, toylike at their remove, we spied gaunt black towers. The globe flared brilliant, the wand leaped to point in Ginny's fingers. "By Hecate," she cried, "that's it!"

I drew alongside. The air was still cold and blowing, a wail in our ears, a streaming past our ribs, a smell akin to burning sulfur and wet iron. At hover, the broomsticks rocked and pitched. Her foot against mine was a very precious contact.

We peered into the globe she held. Svartalf-Bolyai craned around her arm to see. This close, the intervening space not too different from home geometry, the scrying functioned well. Ginny zoomed in on the castle. It was sable in hue, monstrous in size and shape. Or had it a shape? It sprawled, it soared, it burrowed with no unity except ugliness. Here a thin spire lifted crookedly from a cubical donjon, there a dome swelled pustular, yonder a stone beard overhung a misproportioned gate . . . square miles of planless deformity, aswarm with the maggoty traffic of devils.

We tried to look through the walls, but didn't penetrate far. Behind and beneath the cavernous chambers and twisted labyrinths that we discerned, too much evil force roiled. It was as well, considering what we did vaguely make out. At the limit, a thought came from just beyond, for an instant—no, not a thought, a wave of such agony that Ginny cried aloud and I bit blood out of my lip. We blanked the globe and embraced till we could stop shuddering.

"Can't afford this," she said, drawing free. "Time's gotten in short supply."

She reactivated the scryer, with a foreseer spell. Those rarely work in our universe, but Lobachevsky had theorized the fluid dimensions of the Low Continuum might give us a better chance. The view in the globe panned, steadied on one spot, and moved close. Slablike buildings and contorted towers enclosed a certain courtyard in an irregular sep-

tagon. At the middle of this was a small, lumpy stone house, windowless and with a single doorway. A steeple climbed from it, suggestive of a malformed ebon toadstool, that over-topped the surrounding structures and overshadowed the pavement.

We couldn't view the inside of this either, for the same reason as before. It seemed to be untenanted, though. I had the creepy feeling that it corresponded in some perverted way to a chapel.

"Unambiguous and sharp," Ginny said. "That means she'll arrive there, and soon. We'll have to lay our plans fast."

"And move fast, too," I said. "Give me an overall scan, will you, with spot close-ups?"

She nodded. The scene changed to one from on high. I noted afresh how it pullulated in the crowds. Were they always this frantic? Not quite, surely. We focused on a single band of demons. No two looked alike; vanity runs high in hell. A body covered with spines, a tentacled dinosaur, a fat slattern whose nipples were tiny grinning heads, a flying swine, a changeable blob, a nude man with a snake for a phallus, a face in a belly, a dwarf on ten-foot pencil-thin legs, and less describable sights— What held my attention was that most of them were armed. They didn't go for projectiles either, evidently. However, those medievalish weapons would be bad to encounter.

Sweeping around, our vision caught similar groups. The confusion was unbelievable. There was no discipline, no consideration, everybody dashed about like a decapitated chicken yelling at everybody else, they jostled and snarled and broke into fights. But more arms were being fetched each minute from inside, more grotesque flyers lumbered into the air and circled.

"They've been alerted, all right," I said. "The drums—"

"I don't suppose they know what to expect," Ginny said in a low tight voice. "They aren't especially guarding the site we're after. Didn't the Adversary pass word about us?"

"He seems to be debarred from taking a personal hand in this matter, same as Lobachevsky and for analogous reasons, I guess. At most, he may've tipped his underlings to watch out for trouble from us. But they can't know we've acquired the capability to do what we did. Especially since we've made an end run in time."

"And the diabolic forces are stupid," Ginny said. "Evil is never intelligent or creative. They receive word a raid is possible, and look at that mess!"

"Don't underrate them. An idiot can kill you just as dead." I pondered. "Here's what we'll do, if you agree. Rush straight in. We can't

prevent them seeing us, so we have to be quick. Good thing our sticks function close to normal in this neighborhood. We won't make directly for the yard or they might block us off. See that palace, I assume it is, over to the left—the one with the columns in front that look like bowels? Must belong to the big cheese, which makes it a logical spot for enemies to drop a bomb on. At the last moment we'll swerve toward our real mark. You get inside, establish our paranatural defenses, and ready the return spell. I'll keep the door. The instant Val appears, you skewer the kidnaper and grab her. Got it?"

"Yes. Oh, Steve." The tears ran silently from her eyes. "I love you."

We kissed a final time, there in the sky of hell. Then we attacked.

The wind of our passage shouted around us. The drear landscape reeled away beneath. I heard Svartalf's challenge and answered with my own whoop. Fear blew out of me. Gangway, you legions of darkness, we're coming to fetch our girl!

They began to see us. Croaks and yammers reached our ears, answered by shrieks from below. The flying devils milled in the air. Others joined them till several hundred wings beat in a swarm across the sooty stars. They couldn't make up the minds they scarcely had what to do about us. Nearer we came and nearer. The castle rose in our vision like the ranges we had crossed.

Ginny must spend her entire force warding off sorceries. Lightning bolts spattered blue on the shieldfield, yards off, followed by thunder and ozone. Lethal clouds boiled from smokestacks, englobed our volume of air and dissipated. I had no doubt that, unperceived by us, curses, hoodoos, illusions, temptations, and screaming meemies rained upward and rebounded.

The effort was draining her. I glimpsed the white, strained countenance, hair plastered to brow and cheeks by sweat, wand darting while the free hand gestured and the lips talked spells. Svartalf snarled in front of her; Bolyai piloted the broom. None of them could keep it up for many minutes.

But that conjure wave made it impossible for anything to get at us physically. The creature in charge must have realized this at the end, for the assault stopped. An eagle the size of a horse, wearing a crocodile's head, stooped upon us.

My cutlass was drawn. I rose in the stirrups. "Not one cent for tribute!" I bayed, and struck. The old power awoke in the blade. It smote home with a force I felt through my bones. Blood spurted from a sheared-off wing. The devil bawled and dropped.

A batsnake threw a loop around my right arm. I grabbed its neck with my left hand before it could sink fangs in me. Human, I remain wolf; I bit its head off. Barely in time, I cut at a twin-tailed manta coming for Ginny. It fell aft, spilling guts. An aerial hound sought to intercept us. I held my weapon straight and got him with the point.

Horns hooted their discord. The flapping, cawing, stinking flock retreated in its regular disorder. Our stratagem had worked. Their entire outfit, infantry, air corps, and all, was being summoned to defend the palace.

We pursued to within a hundred yards. The manor was no longer visible for wings and feculent bodies. I lifted my blade as signal. We swung right and whizzed downward. Babel erupted behind us.

We landed jarringly hard. Surrounded by walls, brooded over by the cap of its tower, the building huddled in twilight. I bounced from my seat to the door and tried its ill-feeling handle. It creaked open and we ran in.

A single room, dank jagged stone, lay before us. It wasn't large in area, but opened above on the measureless dark of the tower. The room was bare except for an altar where a Glory Hand cast dull blue light. The arrangement of objects and the pattern on the floor were similar to those we'd employed for transit.

The heart cracked in me. "Val!" I sobbed. Ginny wrestled me to a halt. She couldn't have done so without Svartalf getting between my ankles.

"Hold it," she gasped. "Don't move. That's the changeling."

I drew a lungful of air and regained my sanity. Of course, of course. But it was more than I could endure to look at that chubby shape before the altar, gold curls and empty, empty eyes. Strange, also, to see next to the half-alive thing the mass already exchanged from our house: dust, sandbox contents, coffee grounds, soggy paper towels, a Campbell's Soup can—

The devil garrison was boiling over the walls and through the portals into this courtyard. I slammed the door and dropped the bolt. It was good and heavy: might buy us a few minutes.

How many did we need? I tried to reconstruct events. The kidnaper was doubtless moronic even by hell's standards. He'd heard Marmiadon's curse. A lot of them must have, but didn't see anything they could do to fulfill it. This one noticed our vulnerability. "Duh," he said, and flashed off to collect some kudos, without consulting any of the few demons that are able to think. Such a higher-up could have told him to lay off. His action would give a clue to the link between

hell and the Johannine Church, and thus imperil the whole scheme for the sabotage of religion and society that the Adversary had been working on since he deluded the first of the neo-Gnostics.

Being the dimbulb he was, this creature could not solve the momentum problem of transferring a body other than his own between universes, unless the exchange mass was nearly identical in configuration. His plan would have been to appear in our home, scan Valeria as she slept, return here, 'chant a hunk of meat into her semblance, and go back after her. The first part would only have taken seconds, though it got the wind up Svartalf. The snatch ought to have gone quickly too, but the cat was waiting and attacked.

At this moment, if simultaneity had meaning between universes, the fight ramped and Svartalf's blood was riven from him. My throat tightened. I stooped over him. "We'd've arrived too late here except for you," I whispered. "They don't make thanks for that sort of help." Infinitely gently, I stroked the sleek head. He twitched his ears, annoyed. In these surroundings, he'd no patience with fine sentiments. Besides, currently they were János Bolyai's ears too.

Ginny was chalking a diagram around the room for a passive defense against demonurgy. It took care, because she mustn't disturb altar, emblem, or objects elsewhere. They were the fiend's return ticket. Given them, he need simply cast the appropriate spell in our cosmos, just as we'd use the things and symbols in Griswold's lab for a lifeline. If the kidnaper found himself unable to make it back with his victim, God alone knew what would happen. They'd certainly both leave our home and a changeling replace them. But we'd have no inkling of how this came about or where they'd gone. It might provide the exact chance the enemy needed to get his project back on the rails.

Outside, noise swelled—stamp, hop, clang, howl, whistle, grunt, gibber, bubble, hiss, yelp, whine, squawk, moan, bellow. The door reverberated under fists, feet, hoofs. I might well have to transform. I dropped the scuba gear and my outer garments, except for wrapping Barney's jacket around my left forearm.

A mouth, six feet wide and full of clashing teeth, floated through a wall. I yelled, Svartalf spat. Ginny grabbed her wand and cried dismissal. The thing vanished. But thereafter she was continually interrupted to fight off such attacks.

She had to erect fortifications against them before she could begin the spell that would send us home. The latter ritual must not be broken off till at least a weak field had been established between this point and the lab on earth, or it became worthless. Having made initial con-

tact, Ginny could feel out at leisure what balance of forces was required, and bring them up to the strength necessary for carrying us. Now she wasn't getting leisure. In consequence, her defensive construction went jaggedly and slowly.

The hullabaloo outside dwindled somewhat. I heard orders barked. Thuds and yammers suggested they were enforced with clubs. A galloping grew. The door rocked under a battering ram.

I stood aside. At the third blow, the door splintered and its hinges tore loose. The lead devil on the log stumbled through. He was rather like a man-sized cockroach. I cut him apart with a brisk sweep. The halves threshed and clawed for a while after they fell. They entangled the stag-horned being that came next, enabling me to take him with ease.

The others hauled back the log, which blocked the narrow entrance. But my kills remained as a partial barrier in front of me. The murk outside turned most of the garrison into shadows, though their noise stayed deafening and their odors revolting.

One trod forward in the shape of a gorilla on man's legs. He wielded an ax in proportion to his size. It hewed. Poised in karate stance, I shifted to let it go by. Chips sleeted where it hit stone. My cutlass sang. Fingers came off him. He dropped the ax. Bawling his pain, he cuffed at me. I did the fastest squat on record. While that skull-cracker of a hand boomed above, I got an Achilles tendon. He fell. I didn't try for a death, because he barred access while he dragged himself away. My pulse seethed in my ears.

A thing with sword and shield was next. We traded blows for a couple of minutes. He was good. I parried, except for slashes that the jacket absorbed; but I could not get past that shield. Metal clashed above the bedlam, sparks showered in twilight. My breath started coming hard. He pressed close. A notion flashed in me. As he cut over the top of his shield, I dropped down again. My weapon turned his, barely. My left hand grabbed the ax, stuck the helve between his legs, and shoved. He toppled, exposing his neck. I smote.

Rising, I threw the ax at the monster behind, who reeled back. A spear wielder poked at me. I got hold of the shaft and chopped it over.

No further candidates advanced right away. The mass churned around, arguing with itself. Through the hammering of my heart, I realized I couldn't hold out much longer. As human, that is. Here was a chance to assume the less vulnerable lyco state. I tossed my blade aside and turned the flash on myself.

At once I discovered that transformation was slow and agonizing

amidst these influences. For a space I writhed helpless between shapes. A rooster-headed fiend cackled his glee and rushed forward, snickersnee on high. Were or no, I couldn't survive bisection. Svartalf bolted past me, walked up the enemy's abdomen, and clawed his eyes out.

Wolf, I resumed my post. The cat went back inside. We were just in time. The garrison finally got the idea of throwing stuff. Space grew thick with rocks, weapons, and assorted impedimenta. Most missed. Hell is no place to develop your throwing arm. Those that hit knocked me about, briefly in pain, but couldn't do any real damage.

The barrage ended when, in sheer hysteria, they tried to storm us. That was turmoil, slice, hack, rip, tumbling about in their vile welter. They might have overrun me by numbers had Ginny not finished her paranatural defenses and come to my aid. Her weapon disposed of the demons that crawled over the pile of struggling bodies.

When at last they withdrew, their dead and wounded were heaped high. I sat down amidst the ichor, the fragments, the lamentations, unreeled my tongue and gulped air. Ginny rumpled my fur, half laughing, half crying. Some claws had reached her; blood trickled from scratches and her dress was tattered into battle banners. Svartalf's aid had prevented her opponents from inflicting serious wounds, though. I glanced within and saw him playing mousey with a devil's tail.

More important was the soft luminosity from the lines woven across the floor. We were accessible as ever to physical force, but goetics couldn't touch us now. To break down her impalpable walls would take longer than we'd possibly stay.

"Steve, Steve, Steve—" Ginny straightened. "I'd better prepare for our return."

*"Halt!"* called a voice from the dusk. It was hoarse, with an eerie hypnotic rhythm, not calming, but, rather, invoking wrath and blind energy. *"Waffenstillstand. Parlementieren Sie mit uns."*

The devils, even the strewn wounded, fell quiet. Their noise sibilated away until the silence was nearly total, and those who could, withdrew until they merged in vision with the blackness behind them. I knew their master had spoken, the lord of this castle . . . who stood high in the Adversary's councils, if he commanded obedience from these mad creatures.

Boots clacked over flagstones. The demon chief came before us. The shape he had adopted startled me. Like his voice, it was human; but it was completely unmemorable. He was of medium height or less, narrow-shouldered, face homely and a bit puffy, ornamented with nothing but a small toothbrush mustache and a lock of dark hair slanting

across the brow. He wore some kind of plain brown military uniform. But why did he add a red armband with the ancient and honorable sign of the fylfot?

Svartalf quit his game and bristled. Through diabolic stench, I caught the smell of Ginny's fear. When you looked into the eyes in that face, it stopped being ordinary. She braced herself, made a point of staring down along the couple of inches she overtopped him, and sa*id in her haughtiest tone, "Was willst du?"*

It was the *du* of insult. Her personal German was limited, but while Bolyai was in Svartalf she could tap his fluency by rapport with her familiar. (Why did the devil prince insist on German? There's a mystery here that I've never solved.) I retained sufficient human-type capabilities to follow along.

"I ask you the same," the enemy replied. Though he kept to the formal pronoun, his manner was peremptory. "You have encroached on our fatherland. You have flouted our laws. You have killed and maimed our gallant warriors when they sought to defend themselves. You desecrate our House of Sendings with your odious presence. What is your excuse?"

"We have come to gain back what is ours."

"Well? Say on."

I growled a warning, which Ginny didn't need. "If I told you, you might find ways to thwart us," she said. "Be assured, however, we don't intend to stay. We'll soon have completed our mission." Sweat glistened forth on her brow. "I . . . I suggest it will be to the advantage of both parties if you let us alone meanwhile."

He stamped a boot. "I must know! I demand to know! It is my right!"

"Diseases have no rights," Ginny said. "Think. You cannot pierce our spell-wall nor break through by violence in the time that is left. You can only lose troops. I do not believe your ultimate master would be pleased at such squandering of resources."

He waved his arms. His tone loudened. "I do not admit defeat. For me, defeat has no existence. If I suffer a reverse, it is because I have been stabbed in the back by traitors." He was heading off into half a trance. His words became a harsh, compelling chant. "We shall break the iron ring. We shall crush the vermin that infest the universes. We shall go on to victory. No surrender! No compromise! Destiny calls us onward!"

The mob of monsters picked up a cue and cried hail to him. Ginny

said: "If you want to make an offer, make it. Otherwise go away. I've work to do."

His features writhed, but he got back the self-control to say: "I prefer not to demolish the building. Much effort and wizardry is in these stones. Yield yourselves and I promise fair treatment."

"What are your promises worth?"

"We might discuss, for example, the worldly gains rewarding those who serve the cause of the rightful—"

Svartalf mewed. Ginny spun about. I threw a look behind, as a new odor came to me. The kidnaper had materialized. Valeria lay in his grasp.

She was just coming awake, lashes aflutter, head turning, one fist to her lips. "Daddy?" the sleepy little voice murmured. "Mothuh?"

The thing that held her was actually of less weight. It wore an armor-plated spiky-backed body on two clawed feet, a pair of gibbon-like arms ending in similarly murderous talons, and a tiny head with blob features. Blood dripped off it here and there. The loose lips bubbled with an imbecilic grin, till it saw what was waiting.

It yowled an English, "Boss, help!" as it let Val go and tried to scuttle aside. Svartalf blocked the way. It raked at him. He dodged. Ginny got there. She stamped down. I heard a crunch. The demon ululated.

I'd stuck at my post. The lord of the castle tried to get past me. I removed a chunk of his calf. It tasted human, too, sort of. He retreated, into the shadow chaos of his appalled followers. Through their din I followed his screams: "I shall have revenge for this! I shall unleash a secret weapon! Let the House be destroyed! Our pride demands satisfaction! *My patience is exhausted!*"

I braced myself for a fresh combat. For a minute, I almost got one. But the baron managed to control his horde; the haranguing voice overrode theirs. As Ginny said, he couldn't afford more futile casualties.

I thought, as well as a wolf can: Good thing he doesn't know they might not have been futile this time.

For Ginny could not have aided me. After the briefest possible enfolding of her daughter, she'd given the kid to Svartalf. The familiar—and no doubt the mathematician—busied himself with dances, pounces, patty-cake and wurrawurra, to keep her out of her mother's hair. I heard the delighted laughter, like silver bells and springtime rain. But I heard, likewise, Ginny's incantation.

She must have about five unbroken minutes to establish initial contact with home, before she could stop and rest. Then she'd need an

additional period to determine the precise configuration of vectors and gather the required paranatural energies. And then we'd go!

It clamored in the dark. An occasional missile flew at me, for no reason except hatred. I stood in the door and wondered if we had time.

A rumbling went through the air. The ground shuddered underfoot. The devils keened among shadows. I heard them retreating. Fear gripped me by the gullet. I have never done anything harder than to keep that guardian post.

The castle groaned at its foundations. Dislodged blocks slid from the battlements and crashed. Flamelight flickered out of cracks opened in gates and shutters. Smoke tried to strangle me. It passed, and was followed by the smell of ancient mold.

"*. . . in nomine Potestatis, fiat janua . . . ,*" the witch's hurried verses ran at my back.

The giant upheaved himself.

Higher he stood than the highest spire of this stronghold beside which he had lain buried. The blackness of him blotted out the stars of hell. His tottering feet knocked a curtain wall down in a grinding roar; dust whirled up, earthquake ran. Nearly as loud was the rain of dirt, mud gravel from the wrinkled skin. Fungi grew there, pallidly phosphorescent, and worms dripped from his eye sockets. The corruption of him seized the breath. The heat of his decay smoldered and radiated. He was dead; but the power of the demon was in him.

"*. . . saeculi aeternitatis.*" Ginny had kept going till she could pause without danger to the spell. She was that kind of girl. But now she came to kneel by me. "Oh, darling," she wept, "we almost won through!"

I fumbled at my flash. The giant wove his head from side to side as if he still had vision. The faceless visage came to a stop, pointed our way. I shoved the switch and underwent the Skin-turning back to human. The giant raised a foot. He who operated him was trying to minimize damage to the castle. Slowly, carefully, he set it down inside the fortifications.

I held my girl to me. My other girl laughed and romped with the cat. Why trouble them? "We've no chance?"

"I . . . no time . . . first-stage field ready, b-b-but flesh can't cross before I . . . complete— I love you, I love you."

I reached for Decatur's sword where it gleamed in the Handlight. We've come to the end of creation, I thought, and we'll die here. Let's go out fighting. Maybe our souls can escape.

Souls!

I grabbed Ginny by the shoulder and thrust her back to look at. "We can send for help," burst from me. "Not mortals, and angels're forbidden, but, but you do have contact established and . . . the energy state of this universe—it doesn't take a lot to— There's bound to be many c-creatures, not of Heaven but still no friends of hell—"

Her eyes kindled. She sprang erect, seized wand and sword, swung them aloft and shouted.

The giant stepped into our courtyard. The crippled devils gibbered their terror, those he did not crush underfoot. His fingers closed around the tower.

I couldn't tell what language Ginny's formula was in, but she ended her cry in English: "Ye who knew man and were enemies of Chaos, by the mana of the signs we bear I call on you and tell you that the way from earth stands open!"

The chapel rocked. Stones fell, inside and outside. The tower came off. It broke apart in the giant's clutch, a torrent that buried the last of hell's wounded. We looked into lightless constellations. The giant groped to scoop us out.

Our rescuers arrived.

I don't know who or what they were. Perhaps their looks were illusion. I'll admit that the quarters of the compass were from which they came, because these are nonsense in hell. Perhaps what answered Ginny's call was simply a group of beings, from our universe or yet another, who were glad of a chance to raid the realm of the Adversary that is theirs too. She had built a bridge that was, as yet, too frail to bear mortal bodies. However, as I'd guessed, the entropy of the Low Continuum made paranatural forces able to accomplish what was impossible elsewhere.

Explain it as you like. This is what I saw:

From the west, the figure of a woman, queenly in blue-bordered white robe. Her eyes were gray, her features of icicle beauty. The dark tresses bore a crested helmet. Her right hand carried a spear whose head shimmered midnight azure with glitters as of earthly stars; and upon that shoulder sat an owl. On her left arm was a long shield, which for boss had the agonized face of another woman whose locks were serpents.

From the south, the greatest serpent of them all. His orbs were like suns, his teeth like white knives. Plumes of rainbow color grew on his head, nodding in the wind he brought with him, shining with droplets of the rain that walked beneath. More feathers made a glory

down his back. His scales were coral, the scutes upon his belly shone golden. The coils of him lashed about as does the lightning.

From the north, a man in a chariot drawn by two goats. He stood burly, red-bearded, clad in helmet and ringmail, iron gloves and an iron belt. Driving with his left hand, he gripped a short-handled hammer in his right. The cloak blew behind him on mighty gales. The rumble of his car wheels went down and down the sky. He laughed, swung the hammer and threw it. Where it struck, fire blasted and the air roared; it returned to him.

Each of these loomed so tall that the firmament would hardly contain them. Hell trembled at their passage. The devils fled in a cloud. When his master left, the giant's animation ceased. He fell with an impact that knocked me off my feet. It demolished a large part of the castle. The newcomers didn't stop to level the rest right away, but took off after the fiends. I don't imagine that many escaped.

We didn't watch. Ginny completed the transfer spell and seized Valeria in both her arms. I tucked Decatur's sword under one of mine—damn if it'd be left here!—and offered Svartalf the crook of that elbow. From the floor I plucked up the kidnaper demon. It had a broken leg. "Boss, don't hurt me, I'll be good, I'll talk, I'll tell ya ever't'ing ya want," it kept whining. Evil has no honor.

Ginny spoke the final word, made the final pass. We crossed.

# XXXIV

That was nothing like the outbound trip. We were headed back where we belonged. The cosmic forces didn't buck us, they worked for us. We knew a moment of whirling, and were there.

Barney's gang waited in the lab. They sprang back with a cry, a sob, a prayer of thanks as we whoofed into sight under the bell jar. It turned out that we'd only been absent a couple of hours from this continuum. And maybe no more in hell? We couldn't be sure, our watches having stopped during the first transition. It felt like centuries. I looked upon Valeria and Ginny, and it felt like no time.

The child was blinking those big heaven-colored eyes around in astonishment. It struck me that the terrible things she'd witnessed might have scarred her for life. Shakily, I bent over her. "Are you okay, sweetheart?"

"Ooh, Daddy," she beamed. " 'At was fun. Do it again?"

Ginny set her down. I bent and swept the little one to me. She was restless. "I'm hungry," she complained.

I'd let the prisoner go. After the bell jar was raised, it tried to creep off. But it couldn't leave the pentacle, and Barney had laid the spell I asked for that prevented it from returning to the Low Continuum without our leave. Shining Knife had gotten his warrant. He waited too, with a number of his men. He strode in among us and lifted the demon by its sound leg. The grotesque figure sprattled in his grasp. "Boss, gimme a break, boss," it begged. "I'll squeal."

We found out later that the diabolic mass exchanged for us was a heap of rocks, dirt, and similar material. It happened to include a considerable amount of elemental sulfur, pitch, and light hydrocarbons. Hardy and Griswold had passed some time rearranging this into an ex-

plosive-incendiary configuration. Following my request, they mixed in some earthly stuff as well. It had to be safe for us, in case little or none of it got swapped (and in fact, as you see, only a few pounds did). The team scurried around collecting bottles of strong acid, shotgun shells, razor blades, and whatnot. Barney then rigged a photocell-controlled gizmo that would ignite the whole mess the exact instant that it left our universe. I don't suppose that whatever part of hell it materialized in was done any good.

The changeling, of course, vanished from the juvenile home when Valeria was restored. Poor flesh, I hope it was allowed to die.

I didn't think of these matters immediately. Being sure our daughter was well, Ginny and I sought each other. What broke our kiss was a joy greater yet, a happiness whose echo will never stop chiming in us: *"Free! O Father!"* And when we could look at this world again, Svartalf was only Svartalf.

The gracious presence within me said: —Yes, for this deed János Bolyai is made a saint and admitted to the nearness of God. How glad I am. And how glad you won your cause, dear friends, and Valeria Stevenovna is safe and the enemies of the Highest confounded! (Shyly) I have a selfish reason for additional pleasure, be it confessed. What I observed on this journey has given me some fascinating new ideas. A rigorous theoretical treatment—

I sensed the wish that Lobachevsky could not bring himself to think overtly, and uttered it for him: You'd like to stick around awhile?

—Frankly, yes. A few days, after which I must indeed return. It would be marvelous to explore these discoveries, not as a soul, but once again as a mortal. It is like a game, Steven Pavlovitch. One would like to see how far it is possible to go within the constraints of humanity. (In haste) But I beg you, esteemed friend, do not consider this a request. Your lady and yourself have endured perils, hardships, and fear of losing more than your lives. You wish to celebrate your triumph. Believe me, I would never be so indelicate as to—

I looked fondly, a trifle wistfully at Ginny and thought back: I know what you mean, Nick, and I've every intention of celebrating with her, at frequent intervals, till we reach an implausibly ripe old age. But you've forgotten that the flesh has physical as well as mental limits. She needs a good rest. I need a better one. You might as well stay for a bit. Besides, I want to see that what you write goes to the proper journals. It'll be quite a boost for our side.

And this is how it happened that, although Bolyai led our expedition, Lobachevsky published first.

There's no such thing as living happily ever after.

You'd like to be famous? You can have it, buster: every last reporter, crystal interview, daily ton of mail, pitch for Worthy Causes, autograph hound, belligerent drunk, crank phone call, uninvited visitor, sycophant, and you name it. Luckily, we followed sound advice and played loose. I ended up with a better position than I probably rate, Ginny with the freelance studio she'd always wanted, and we're no longer especially newsworthy. Meanwhile Valeria's gotten to the boyfriend stage, and none of them seem worthy of her. They tell me every father of a girl goes through that. The other children keep me too busy to fret much.

It *was* quite a story. The demon's public confession brought the Johannine Church down in spectacular style. We've got its diehards around yet, but they're harmless. Then there's the reformed sect of it—where my old sparring partner Marmiadon is prominent—that tries to promulgate the Gospel of Love as merely another creed. Since the Gnosticism and the secret diabolism are out, I don't expect that either St. Peter or gentle St. John greatly mind.

Before he left me for Heaven, Lobachevsky proved some theorems I don't understand. I'm told they've doubled the effectiveness of the spells that Barney's people worked out in those long-ago terrible hours. Our buddy Bob Shining Knife had a lot to do with arranging sensible dissemination of the new knowledge. It has to be classified; you can't trust any old nut with the capabilities conferred. However, the United States government is not the only one that knows how to invade hell if provoked. The armies of Earth couldn't hope to conquer it, but they could make big trouble, and Heaven would probably intervene. As a result, we've no cause to fear other direct assaults from the Adversary's

dominion. From men, yes—because he still tempts, corrupts, seduces, tricks, and betrays. But I think if we keep our honor clean and our powder dry we won't suffer more than we can bear.

Looking back, I often can't believe it happened: that this was done by a red-haired witch, a bobtailed werewolf, and a snooty black tomcat. Then I remember it's the Adversary who is humorless. I'm sure God likes to laugh.

# Operation Luna

*To Janet, Jeff, and Kathy,*
*who in their different ways are all magicians*

# ACKNOWLEDGMENTS

As always, Karen Anderson has been first and foremost among those who helped me, in her case with ideas, research, criticism, encouragement, and companionship.

We thank Steve and Jan Stirling for kindness and hospitality; Laura Frankos for admission to the church in her novel *St. Oswald's Niche*; David Eck, Jim Moore, and Ken Seowtewa for guidance and information. None of these people is in any way responsible for any errors of fact, mistaken interpretations, important omissions, and other infelicities that may remain, but without them there would have been many more.

The verses quoted in Chapters XL and XLI are from "The Childish Edda," which was largely composed by Ron Ellik and me on an overnight drive long years ago. He was a great guy. It's been a pleasure to bring back this memory of him.

# I

Witchlights glowed blue along the fence, outlining Cardinal Point against night. Earth lay darker than heaven. There stars gleamed and the Milky Way glimmered. A moon one day past full, climbing out of the east, veiled many of them behind its own brightness. It cast pallor and long shadows across the malpais. Northward, Mount Taylor bulked ghost gray.

When Ginny and I looked ahead and down, the glare near the middle of the great pentacle, searchbeams focused on the spacecraft, drove most of this from our eyes. My heart jumped to see that splendor.

Somewhere inside me I felt something different stir. The shiver strengthened as we drew closer. It wasn't happening for the first time. Earlier, though, it had been rare, faint and fleeting, no more than the uneasiness everybody gets once in a while for no good reason. You don't rub an amulet or make a religious sign or ask whatever witch or warlock may be nearby if it means anything. No, you shrug it off as a passing nerve-twitch. You're modern, scientific, free of superstitions. Aren't you?

What touched me now was stronger, too vague to be a foreboding but not just a collywobble. I'd had enough experience to know that. A hunch? I turned my head to and fro. All I saw besides sky was the headlights of a few other broomsticks, belated like ours. I took a long, slow breath. Even in human shape, my nose is pretty keen. The air that flowed in was pure and chill; temperature in New Mexico generally drops fast after sunset. I did catch a slight ozonelike tang of goetic forces at work, but that was to be expected hereabouts, especially to-night.

Wait, wait—a bare hint of strangeness, outsideness such as I couldn't put a name to? Wolf, I might have been more nearly sure.

My look went back to Ginny. Since it would be only us two, we'd taken her Jaguar instead of the family Ford. We'd left the windfield off except in front, and breeze got by to flutter the skirt she'd chosen to wear for this occasion. It was pressed around the downcurve of the shaft and across a pair of long, trim legs. The sweater above hugged a figure as good at age forty-two as it'd been when we met.

My attention stayed above the neck. Moonlight made her aristocratic features into an ivory carving. It whitened and rippled the shoulder-length hair. On her left breast, the silver owl emblem of her order seemed icily afire. I saw not only her usual alertness upon her, but a sudden wariness.

My voice sounded loud through the air whispering past us. "You feel a spooky whiff too?"

She nodded. Her contralto had gone metallic. "Uncanny might be a better word. Or—" I couldn't make out the rest. As a licensed witch, she has a wide vocabulary from exotic languages. I guessed this was Zuni. "Powers are abroad. Coyote is certainly on the prowl."

"And nearby, watching for a chance?"

"Of course. He always is."

"Oh, well, then." I didn't intend bravado. The Trickster is a bad enemy, and not exactly a reliable friend. He'd wrought havoc in the early days here, like when one test vehicle, a flying wing, molted in midair, or when moths got at a still more expensive experimental model, a supercarpet, and ate it full of holes.

However, I recalled, before there was any actual fatality, the National Astral Spellcraft Administration had grown smart for the nonce and consulted the local Indians. They informed it that Coyote had declared feud on it. He didn't like this invasion of his stamping grounds, not to speak of stunts more spectacular than any of his. The medicine men weren't very happy about it either.

So NASA's chief had a talk with President Lambert in Washington. Project Selene had been Lambert's way of pulling his political chestnuts out of the fire after the Brazilian crisis, when he'd fearlessly told the people of Rio de Janeiro he was one of them—*"¡Yo soy un carioca!"*—in Spanish. Also, it would mean considerable pork for his Southwestern power base. Therefore he twisted arms, and possibly other body parts, in Congress, and the Indians got a more decent deal from the givernment than they'd had before, and the priests invoked their gods and kachinas to protect Cardinal Point. . . .

I hauled my mind back. Had the outlaw influences caused it to wander? Those things had happened seven or eight years ago. My family and I had been here for only two. Ginny was correcting me: "Not him alone, though I do feel he's more . . . eager . . . than anytime I've known since I first learned a little about such things. Something else also."

"Like the Blue Flint Boys?" I ventured. I'd picked up odds and ends of lore, nothing like the education she'd set herself to acquire. Mischievous but not malignant spirits shouldn't be cause for worry.

She dashed my hopes. "Something much more powerful, something I—" She seldom hesitated. "—I can half guess at, though not really—"

If I'd been wolf, I'd have bristled. As it was, chill tiptoed along my spine and out to my nerve ends. "Can you discover what?"

"Maybe. But not without cantrips, and we aren't allowed any tonight. This is just sensitivity," like mine, but way sharper.

She shook herself, always an interesting sight, straightened in her seat, and, slowly, smiled. "Well, it's probably nothing to fear. The 'chantments stand strong. I'd know if they didn't. Quite likely a troop of Beings have simply come to watch, same as us."

She gestured downward. Our broom was descending. We could see hundreds of others below, across the landscape, and their dismounted riders, saintelmos shining on the ground or bobbing in hands, people talking or snacking or smoking or tilting a bottle or staring, staring at the vision. They'd come from Grants, Gallup, the pueblos, farms, ranches, as far as Albuquerque and Santa Fe, maybe farther. Sure, they could've stayed home and watched on the farseer, but this was history happening, the first real flight of the beast that should eventually land humans on yonder moon.

"If the Beings aren't friendly to what we're doing, why, neither are a lot of our fellow Americans," Ginny went on. "In either case, they can't help being fascinated." Her laughter chimed. "After all, what a show!"

That whipped my dim dreads off me. The crowd below was heartening, too. They weren't ideologues yammering about Tower-of-Babel technoarrogance, or demagogues whining about money that ought to be spent on their own admirers, or intellectuals oh, so superior to everything less than the critical deconstruction of James Joyce's *Odysseus*. They were ordinary, working men and women, along with kids, students, dreamers— and quite a few tribesfolk, I saw—here because they'd decided for themselves that going to the stars was a great idea.

In a way, too many had. Ruefulness quirked my lips. At the *n*th hour, Ginny and I found that no babysitters would be available, not for any price, not even her housecleaner, Audrey Becker, or Audrey's elderly mother. Once we might have entrusted the job to her familiar, but Svartalf was old and dozy, Edgar's sense of responsibility still unproven.

So Valeria got stuck with riding herd on Ben and Chryssa. She'd looked forward to witnessing the launch in person, with a fourteen-year-old's intensity, and didn't take kindly to the change in plans. What we offered in return hardly appeased her. We tried to be fair, but didn't believe in begging or bribing children to do their duty. Not that Val exploded, much. It wasn't her style. She'd brood, I knew. What would come of that, I didn't know.

Our broom stopped in midair. After a moment the air said, "Pass" and we continued. The checkspell had verified that we were entitled to go within the perimeter. Its effectiveness was reassuring. In fact, I lost my sense of outside presences, and soon more or less forgot about them. My wife told me later that she did likewise, though I suspect she never really became quite unaware of anything that ever come to her attention.

As late as our frantic search had made us, we were lucky to find a place at the edge of the employees' parking lot. It was jammed. Besides their vehicles, we spied those of journalists, VIPs, and Lord knows who else had wangled admission. We barely eased in between a chrome-plated Cadillac and an old Honda with a sweep of withered but real straw. As we settled it into the rack and got off, our Jaguar waggled its shaft. The sprite in it never had liked close quarters. Ginny bent over to stroke the spotty-furry rear end and make soothing noises. It calmed down. We hiked off fast across the paving, through the cold. Our footfalls clattered beneath the Swan, the Dragon, and the ascending moon.

As we neared the gate, illumination took most night away from us. The chain-link fence stretched right and left for a mile or more, its witchlights dwindling off into darkness. Here the edisons glared. Though the physical barrier was just fifteen feet high, I winded a little of the forces that charged it and warded the compound on every quarter, zenith and nadir included.

Since we already wore badges spelled to our identities, we had no rigmarole to go through. They were special, of course. I didn't draw my pay from NASA but from Nornwell Scryotronics back in the Midwest, which had a contract to develop space communication

systems. It had gotten me seconded to Cardinal Point as an engineer. My boss, Barney Sturlason, knew well that my lifelong dream had been to work on celestonautics. He also knew that a happy man is a productive man. As for Ginny, who ran her Artemis Consultancy out of our home, we'd more than once had occasion to sic her onto some other weird problem.

One of the guards knew us. "Why, hello, Mr. and Mrs.—uh, Dr. Matuchek," he greeted. "I was getting afraid you wouldn't make it. You're barely in time, unless they put a hold on the countdown."

"I know," I said.

"Wasn't your daughter coming along? And what about Dr. Graylock, ma'am?"

"We had babysitter woes," Ginny explained, "and my brother isn't feeling well."

"Too bad. Sure wish I could watch from where you're going to. A medicine man from Acoma Pueblo who's here, I heard him mention sensing how even spirits have come to see, heap big spirits."

"Leave that to the professionals," I snapped, "and let us by, for God's sake."

Immediately I regretted my impatience. He'd intended friendliness. Hurt, he retorted, "Well, Mr. Matuchek, you remember the rules. The moon *is* up, but nobody's supposed to change shape."

Ginny laid a cautionary hand on mine and a smile on the janus. "Of course," she murmured. "No offense. Excuse us if we're in a hurry, Mr. Gitling. Actually, once the beast rises, what you see ought to be better than the mere liftoff." He dissolved into amiability and waved us through.

The paths beyond lay dim, almost deserted. Everybody not in Mission Control wanted to be at a viewing station. Buildings enclosed us, murky against the sky-sheen from the launch paddock ahead. Off on the left, rising above roofs, the great onion dome of the VAB caught some of that light. The moon barely cleared the walls opposite; its cold, blue-blazoned shield still looked huge.

I did not plan on skinturning. In fact, I seldom transformed at all anymore, aside from an occasional romp out in the desert or, once in a while, to amuse little Chryssa. Her siblings had long since taken Daddy's trick for granted. Nevertheless, as the moonbeams caught me, I felt a strong urge. Excitement, no doubt, weakening inhibitions, stirring ancient instincts.

I quelled the lust by asking, quite sincerely, "What is the trouble

with Will, anyway? In the hullabaloo, I didn't get a chance to find out."

"I'm not sure either," Ginny replied. "Nor is he, I suppose. He phoned to say he felt terrible and would stay home and try to sleep off whatever it is."

"A dirty shame. He's probably as responsible for getting a space program started as any man alive."

"Yes, and has it as dear to his heart." Hearing the trouble in Ginny's tone, I glanced at her and saw how she bit her lip. "Steve, I've been worried about him."

"Um-m, yeah, he has seemed a bit odd lately, now and then. Sort of . . . absent. But I figured he was preoccupied."

"No, it's not his research, his instruments. He's hardly said a word about them, which in itself is peculiar. I have an impression he's actually neglecting them, or at best tinkering without making progress. But he doesn't volunteer any information, he's dodged my few questions—"

*If anyone would have sound intuitions about Will Graylock,* I thought, *it'd be his sister.* She was nine years old, he twenty-one when an accident orphaned them. Circumstances then kept them more apart than together, but he was always kind and caring, the closest figure to a father she had. We'd been delighted when he resigned from Flagstaff and moved out here shortly after we did, with a National Parascience Foundation grant to concentrate on his lunar studies. Soon our kids also were.

Her inner steeliness came back to Ginny. "And I won't pry," she finished. "He'll tell me what and when he chooses."

"Maybe a love affair isn't going so well," I suggested.

"At his age?"

"Hell, I don't expect to be a dodderer when I get there. You'd better keep me satisfied, woman."

She grinned. "Same to you, man." Seriously again: "Okay, I've been assuming it's a personal matter. After all, it doesn't often show; mostly he's his usual self. Simply short bouts of moodiness and—and maybe, now, a touch of flu."

"Still, a pity."

"Yes, but this isn't the big event." Merely the first piloted test of the type of vessel meant to land the first humans on the moon. Seven orbits around Earth, if everything went well, mainly to try out the control spells and life-support systems. Will would have plenty more

launches to behold, each different, more venturesome, inching toward yonder globe and the mysteries on it that he himself had revealed.

I didn't remark on how unnecessarily complicated and expensive a way to go I thought this was. Ginny had heard her fill of me on that subject. Besides, she'd repeatedly given the little Operation Luna Company help more valuable than it could have paid for.

And meanwhile, maybe forever, NASA's was the only game in town.

And— We came out onto open ground. Ahead of us a viewing stand raised white bleachers into black night. Beyond stretched half a mile of lava. Short paved roads cut through that jumble, converging on a central spot. There loomed the beast, waiting to leap, ablaze with the light upon it, a magnificence that my humble dream could never match.

# II

We'd had a few qualms about making for the journalistic observation area. Employees not on duty generally did so, because the site was better than that given the VIPs. We, though, had been famous ourselves for a while, headline material. That was eleven years ago. The sensation had ebbed like a sticky tide, till for the most part we were again contentedly obscure. Nevertheless, once in a while some complete and usually boring stranger or some interviewer desperate for copy hunted us down.

We couldn't readily disappear into the crowd that seethed along the benches and spilled out onto the rocks. My six-foot height and football shoulders are nothing unusual, nor does a wide Slavic face with snub nose, blue eyes, and hair-colored hair stand out especially. But Ginny needs a Tarnkappe, if not a transformation spell, to pass unnoticed by men; and right now any goetics not required for the project or for communications was, naturally, forbidden. We didn't want a farseer bezel and a string of banal questions thrust at us. We wanted to enjoy the event, unpestered.

Well, the press would also swarm thick at the other grandstand, where politicians, pundits, movie stars, self-appointed leaders of this or that self-defined underclass, corporate executives, evangelists, et cetera really did hope to grandstand. Our chances were better among people interested in the adventure for its own sake. In fact, we wouldn't mind encountering certain of the science writers and reporters. We liked and trusted them. But probably they'd be too busy doing their jobs to chat.

Chance favored us, or else we'd overestimated what notoriety remained ours. As we squirmed up the aisles between the tiers of

benches, a few friends saw us and waved—maybe they hollered hello through the babble—and male gazes tracked Ginny, but nothing else occurred. We spied what seemed to be a vacant spot in a good location next to a couple of artificers from the project, Miguel Santos and Jim Franklin. Jim's glance met mine. His chocolate-hued phiz split in a wide grin as he gestured. Ginny and I started that way.

Our course took us past a knot of newsies. There our luck nearly broke down. Haris ed-Din al-Bunni himself had chosen to watch from here. Of course they came at him in a feeding frenzy. He didn't care. No, he basked.

Don't get me wrong. He was a good man who'd done tremendous work. Without his vision, genius, and drive, NASA would be mucking around yet with whiskbrooms and muttering about maybe trying for the moon in fifty or a hundred years. He convinced Lambert and the public that it could be done in our own lifetimes. Now his leadership was making it happen.

If some of us believed it could be done smaller, faster, and cheaper, none of us denied that Project Selene's pioneering had brought us knowledge, technology and paratechnology, vital to any space venture. If he courted personal publicity, I'm sure that was mainly for the sake of his program, keeping Congress and the taxpayers happy; his pleasure in it was incidental. To him, everything was incidental to the goal.

Oh, sure, he worked for the Caliphate during the war, when his flying bronze horses gave us a lot of grief. But he didn't subscribe to its fanatical heresy. He'd have been among our orthodox Muslim allies if he'd been born in the right country—though space was his true religion, and he liked his beer and Scotch as well as I did. He actually got into trouble in those days by remarking that his horses were galloping above the wrong planet. At the end of hostilities, the United States Army fell over itself recruiting him for defense research, and later was mighty reluctant about releasing him to the civilian agency where he really wanted to be.

Besides, hell, the war ended twenty years ago.

Big and beefy as he was, he glimpsed us across the heads and lifted a hand. "Ah, Virginia Matuchek!" he boomed. "The beauty titer and charm quotient have risen to where they should be. And Steven, fortunate man, hail also to you." His gallantries were well-meant, though I'd gathered they often got results.

Stares flew at us. Al-Bunni immediately went on with what he'd been saying. Nobody left that. I couldn't hear what it was. Probably a

variation on his favorite theme of how the marriage of Eastern and Western Art was bearing fruit that would seed the stars.

Relieved, we pushed on and took our seats. "Hi. Welcome," greeted Miguel through the hubbub, and Jim: "Howdy. Had trouble? Glad you made it, even if just barely."

I told them what had happened. "Improvident, man," said Jim with a bachelor's smugness. "But it's nice that people are this interested, huh?"

"My Juanita is," Miguel put in, half defensively. "She does not like crowds. And if the children are too little to be allowed in, she wants to be in front of the farseer, sharing with them." In haste: "Not that you do wrong, Dr. Matuchek. Each family has its style, no?" She gave him a gracious nod and smile.

"Everything seems Aleph-OK," Jim said. "What you've lost is just time for admiring."

Our gazes locked onto the beast.

Beautiful it was indeed. The paddock stood emerald green, its low fence golden, above the jumbled dark rock. Broad though it was, it barely accommodated the hundred-foot length of the great bronze stallion. Seen at such distance, the figure revealed itself as the work of art, as well as Art, that it was. The head lifted high and proud, eyes turned heavenward, nostrils dilated to drink ethereal winds, and it was as if those winds tossed the streaming mane and tail, as if muscles tautened and quivered beneath the ruddy-sheening coat. The four giant broomstick strap-ons were no disfigurement; they belonged, the way a lance belongs with a knight's destrier. Likewise did the crew capsule on the back, a saddle of domed crystal.

"Here," Jim offered, handed me a pair of binoculars, and got busy with his camera. Witch-sight was permitted none but the tracking team. Ginny already had our glasses up. I focused Jim's.

They were powerful. Through the clear capsule shell, I could pick out accommodations, equipment, and stores for an intended crew of three. The pilot went alone this trip. I saw that she had taken her post at the front, buckled into her seat, and gripped the two pegs that jutted out of the neck, ready to ride.

"*Por Dios,* I envy her," Miguel muttered.

Ginny grinned. "A good masculinist like you?" she gently gibed.

"Well, there should be more men in the celestonaut corps. It is only prejudice that says women fly better."

"No, tradition, I think," I put in. "European. Countless old stories

about witches. In other cultures, before the thing started truly happening, it was mostly men, warlocks, and to this day—"

"Captain Newton is where she is because she earned it," Ginny clipped. "You'll see equal numbers of men when they have qualified."

"Hey, I was just talking academese, honey," I said. "You know I respect Curtice." She'd become a pretty good friend of ours, ever since she sought out my wife for extracurricular lessons in dealing with Others. Not that anybody knew anything for certain except that *something* haunted the moon. Yet Ginny had had closer experience than most, clear to Hell and back. Me too; but mainly, I sort of got dragged along, without her education or intuition to enlighten me.

"Oh, *asimismo,*" Miguel added. "I envy, but I am not jealous." Mexican-born or no, he understood the difference, which few native English speakers do anymore in these days of progressive education. "I marvel, like the whole world."

Now clear of the buildings, the moon no longer appeared swollen. It was small, cold, and beckoning. I realized what shrewd public relations al-Bunni exercised in scheduling the launch for tonight. Since Luna was the ultimate destination, the sympathetics would always work best—the piece of lunar meteorite in the horse's head would influence most efficiently—if the moon was in the sky. For this short trial run, any phase, any hour would serve about as well. But how dramatic a scene!

A male voice tolled through the noise, which died away beneath it. "All systems are do. Repeat, all systems are do. Final countdown is about to commence."

A kind of gasp went over the tiers and lost itself in the dark. The binoculars fell to Ginny's and my laps. Nor did we bother with cameras. This was a thing to see directly and engrave in living memory. I heard myself whisper, "Do, yes, do. Go with God."

"*Decem,*" boomed forth.

"*Novem. Octo.*" I wondered momentarily if Arabic wouldn't have been better. But no, it was al-Bunni's mother tongue. His being in charge made Latin more esoteric, more powerful, than it would otherwise have been in a Western undertaking. *"Septem."* Navajo, Shoshonean, Zuni? No, they hadn't been well studied—by whites—and our team might have lost some measure of control. *"Sex."*

*Right now?* I thought crazily.

Ginny's fingers clamped on my arm. "Steve," she hissed, "something's wrong, terribly wrong."

"*Quinque.*" I turned my head and saw her face bloodless, the green eyes wide.

"*Quattuor.*" The sense of it came on me, not as keenly as to her, but like a barely captured smell. The odor wasn't foul, it was sweet and sharp, dizzying. Nobody else in the crowd or in Mission Control seemed aware. None had had the experiences that sensitized us beyond the normal threshold of perception. "*Tria.*" If anyone did feel a touch of alienness, he or she ignored it, lost in the sight of the moon horse.

"*Duo.*" The stallion trembled.

"*Unum.*" The bronze rolled and rippled, like muscles beneath skin.

"*Nihil!*"

The beast reared. His neigh clanged from horizon to horizon. He sprang toward the sky.

He screamed. The booster brooms uncoupled. They fell to earth and started sweeping. The sound crackled and swished, monstrous. Clouds of grit whirled gray-black aloft from their titanium straws. They knocked over the searchlights. Night clamped down on the field.

I scarcely noticed. The stallion held my horror. Moonbeams bounced off him where he bucked like a bronco, two or three hundred feet in the air. Then he fell.

The crash belled and thundered. A huge, twisted, broken wreck sprawled near the paddock, among the berserk brooms. Not pausing to think, I raised Jim's binoculars. The lenses gave me sight of the shattered capsule. I saw nothing of the pilot. She couldn't have gotten to her ejection system, or she'd have ridden the brass eagle down to earth by now.

"Oh, no, no," I heard Jim groan. "The energy—"

Yes, the energy that was to have carried our beast on high and home again was goetically evoked and stored, but that made no difference. The conservation laws of physics said it had to escape somewhere. Yonder metal would soon be incandescent.

Ginny grabbed my arm once more—not in alarm, in command. "Steve," she yelled through the uproar around us, "go get her!"

My wits came awake. Christ, I should have been on my way already. Moonlight poured icy over the screaming, surging, clawing mob on the benches. As I kicked off my shoes and peeled off my clothes, my body drank the radiance down. Flesh and bone went fluid, awareness whirled, soul rejoiced in the pangs that were half ecstasy, the old carnivore came to life and I howled aloud.

I was animal.

Being a fairly big man, I'm quite a big wolf; and the were condition

gives added strength. I went through the crowd like a buzzsaw through a bowl of Jell-O. If I knocked down whoever didn't move aside fast enough, too bad. Several times I leaped, to arc over heads and land on a lower tier. I felt some blows—yes, a heavy camera on a tripod—but vaguely. The were condition also means near-instant recovery from injuries that don't outright maim or kill. Nobody was packing a firearm loaded with silver bullets.

I hit the ground and sped on over the lava. A wolf's brain, even a werewolf's, isn't very bright by human standards, but I kept sufficient knowledge of who I was and what I meant to try. And, though I was now nearsighted and colorblind, my nose gave me a worldful of smells, my ears captured sounds a man never hears, every hair on my pelt was a feeler feeding into my nerves.

So rich were my senses that I even noticed I was naked. Not expecting this, I hadn't worn the knitsuit under my clothes that lets me run free as a wolf without embarrassment when I turn back to human. I had thought to leave my shorts on. They fitted reasonably well, since a war wound has left me bobtailed. But somehow they'd gotten torn off in the ruckus.

To hell with that. *Aou-ow-w!* Gangway!

Dust grated my nostrils, plastered my tongue, stung my eyes. A broom forty feet high came at me. The metal rattled horribly. I dodged past, right into another. It sent me flying. I thumped down, recovered, and loped on. The fallen beast loomed ahead. The heat in it billowed over me.

This would be no fun at all. Well, I'd encountered Fire in a worse form before. What was human in me grabbed hold of the lupine. Up over the alloy I bounded. Fur scorched, pads blistered. I howled for pain, yet I kept going. My body drew on its reserves to repair itself almost as fast as the harm was done. Almost.

There were limits—dehydration, if nothing else. I had to be quick. Across a flank I went, along the crumpled mass, to the forequarters and the capsule.

Through dust and smoke off my fur I peered past the crystal. It had shattered when the strength spell on it was annulled, or perverted, or whatever had been done. Yes, Curtice Newton crouched under the touchstone panel. The cabin deck, oak from Dodona, protected her for this while. But if she tried to climb over the sharded crystal, it would slash her like swords, while the metal outside was by now as hot as a medieval heretic's pyre.

But if she didn't escape pronto, she'd bake. Rearward I saw the

door of the toilet compartment, burst open. The little Hydro there had collapsed into a puddle of plain water, steaming away beneath the Kheper mural.

No time to waste. I sprang over the rim, onto those blessed hardwood boards. The cuts I'd taken as I crossed knitted before I really felt them.

The pilot stared dazedly at me. Blood ran copious from a scalp wound. The damage seemed worse than that. Crumpling, the horse's mass had absorbed most of the impact, but something had torn loose and hit her. She'd recovered enough to unbuckle and creep out of her seat, then slumped to the deck. I saw that the eagle which could have swung her free hung in its brackets with one wing broken.

I licked her hand. My muzzle jerked sideways. She pounced on the idea, stunned though she was. "Steve Matuchek?" I heard through the racket, a faltering note of amazed hope. I nodded and braced myself. She straddled my back, clutched my shaggy neck, and held her legs close against my flanks.

The expectation of more pain was harder to take than the pain itself. I mastered it somehow and bore her away, out of the capsule and down off the wreck. I don't much remember this.

I do remember us reaching the ground, and a broom bound for us, and how I stumbled beneath my burden. All at once the sticks fell. With a last huge clatter, they bounced across the rocks and lay inert.

The ruin behind us started to glow, but we were well clear of it. I felt only a dull warmth. Mainly, I felt the agony leave me as I healed, and an awful thirst and hunger after what the healing had demanded, and utter exhaustion. I collapsed. Curtice got off and sat down at my side. A shaky hand stroked my head.

The rescue squad arrived. They were a good outfit. They simply hadn't been supplied or trained to cope with anything as grotesque as this. Their warlock had handily exorcised whatever possessed the brooms, considering that he had no idea what it was. It had already left the horse. Its mission of ruin was accomplished.

The team carried Curtice and me off to the infirmary. Unfortunately, it was as fully equipped as most hospitals. Turning back to human, I demanded a pair of pants and immediate release. What I got was one of those silly gowns and a lot of medics giving me every test known to man and some that I think man was never meant to know.

Eventually Ginny arrived and sprung me. I'd never seen a more glorious sight than her when she entered, the telescoping wand from her purse star-gleaming at the tip. (Well, there had been times to match

this, also involving her, but they're none of your business.) She'd promptly offered her services to al-Bunni, and, before he could reply more than, "Yes," headed off in search of clues to what had happened.

"I'll tell you later," she said. A weariness greater than mine loaded her shoulders and voice. "Not that I've really discovered anything. Let's go home." We arrived as dawn was silvering the eastern sky.

We woke at mid-morning. Sunlight filtered softly past venetian blinds, touching bedroom furniture, Hiroshige and Charlie Russell reproductions framed on the walls, assorted oddments and souvenirs from our years together. It made flame of Ginny's hair over her pillow. We'd showered before we turned in, of course, and she smelled all fresh and—

"Not so fast, wolfie," she murmured with a wry grin.

Her hand stroked my cheek. I felt the stubble stir. "Yeah, I ought to shave."

"Later. You've got a great idea, but the kids are up and about, along with everything else."

I sighed and stretched. In spite of what we'd been through and the short rest afterward, we felt reasonably lively. Lycanthropes generally recover fast from stress, and Ginny had laid a quick fettling spell on herself. She'd have to pay nature's price, but ten or twelve hours' sleep tonight should do that, and meanwhile this day bade fair to be hectic.

"Speak of the devil," she added as a knock sounded on the door. "Come in," she called. We sat up against the headboard.

Valeria appeared. "Hi, reverend ancestors," she greeted. "I've been crouching for you to come a-conscious."

No surprise. Officially our older daughter had no more goetic skills than the schools had taught her so far, mild stuff proper to her age. But it was plain she had a Gift at least equal to her mother's. She won every spelling bee hands down, and a couple of her experiments in alchemy lab had alarmed the teacher. She was also smart, observant, and more self-guided than was entirely safe. We knew darn well she'd sneaked looks at advanced textbooks—easily wheedled from a boy-

friend—and the part of Ginny's library that wasn't under seal. Since Ginny hadn't set any geas on the house last night, it was no trick for Val to play peekaboo with an incantation and a mirror.

Ordinarily we'd have administered a stern lecture about respect for privacy and set some dull chore as a penance. But under these circumstances, chaos at Cardinal Point and, I did believe, anxiety on our account, her surveillance was pardonable, even touching. Besides, she was turning on the charm—the real charm, not a mere cantrip—at full dazzlement.

There she stood, not in the usual grubby sweater, faded jeans, and torn sneakers of vacation time: no, in frilly white blouse and wide plaid skirt. They were exactly right for a figure withy-slim, not yet as tall as Ginny's but stacked like two state capitols. The eyes shone huge and turquoise in a pert, tip-tilted face. With the rest of her female cohort, she wore her hair long, but today the ruddy-brown locks weren't coiled against her head in the currently *de rigueur* Hopi style, like two pieces of Danish pastry. They fell straight down to her waist. She knew my weakness for that Alice in Wonderland look, the minx.

This was our little Valeria, our first-born, whom we'd snatched back from Hell itself when she was only three, and watched grow into an active, happy child with a wacky sense of humor. How suddenly and well I remembered one early morning when she was five: Ginny happened to be away, I was making breakfast for the two of us and dropped an egg on the kitchen floor—how she looked at me struggling to curb my tongue, and murmured in a tone of infinite compassion, "Daddy, don't you want to say, 'Shit!'?"

Then she turned twelve, and the boys were buzzing around her. She enjoyed it but, from all I could gather, she kept them—including those several years older—from going off the reservation, with the same cool competence she'd shown for horses, canyon hikes, and dry camping since we moved to these parts.

Not that she didn't carry high explosive in her spirit— Enough for now.

She beamed. "I've been fixing your breakfast," she said. "I'll bring it." She slipped out the door.

Ginny and I exchanged a look. We both considered breakfast in bed a much overrated pleasure. However, this time we had no choice. I brought my lips close to ear. Stray hairs tickled. "Quick," I whispered, "what's the real situation and the official story? Why aren't reporters trampling our grass flat?"

"I saw to that before I fetched you," she said as fast and low. "The

management agreed a hundred percent. The project's suffered a catastrophe nobody understands. The witches and warlocks who cast about for clues along with me found nothing except what's so obvious it may as well be made public today. Oh, traces, suggestions— But you know the basic law of military intelligence as well as I do, Steve. You don't let the enemy know what you know about him, nor what your own capabilities are. Your rescue of Curtice may or may not have strategic implications. Sure, it's a story the agency's image boys would dearly love to build up, but it's being kept from them. The word is, she got away on her own before the metal was too hot, but then had to keep clear of the brooms till they'd been dischanted. The rescue squad's under strict security gag too. The FBI will take over the investigation. We'll hear from them."

"Good work, sweetheart!" I patted her hip.

"You did mighty well yourself, lover." She patted back.

Valeria returned with a tray.

Ben followed, carrying the other. At ten, he'd outgrown a lot of rambunctiousness—or rather, I suspected, figured out that it didn't pay. These days he was a quiet, well-mannered, somewhat studious boy, though he liked exploring our new environs as well as the rest of us. Slender, dark blond, he was a ferocious basketball player at school, made excellent grades, and got along well with his fellow kids. His main interest was dinosaurs. If he stayed by his wish to become a paleontologist, he'd have to master some spooky thaumaturgics, but I felt confident it wouldn't faze him.

Chryssa stumped behind. Four, she was chubby but starting to lengthen out: with her features and curly yellow hair, much like Val at that same age. Where her brother looked serious and her sister blazingly eager, she was quite simply glad to see Mommy and Daddy home. About the single break in her sunny disposition had been a year or so back, when for some reason she'd developed a hatred of baths. She'd submit, but only under protest.

This family reunion, after the savagery last night, roused more and more irrelevant memories in me. Like Val, assigned once to bathe the little one, and the song that floated out of the bathroom to the tune of "Yankee Doodle."

> *"Chryssa's hair is moldy green.*
> *Her skin is gray and awful.*
> *She has toadstools in her scalp.*
> *Her ears are full of fungus.*

*We will make our Chryssa clean,*
*We will scrub our Chryssa,*
*We will polish Chryssa up*
*Until she shines like onions!"*

Though the phase was past and we'd had no more such trouble, sometimes I still heard Val refer to her sister as "Moldylocks." Both of them thought it was funny.

Edgar, Ginny's new familiar, had ridden in on Val's shoulder. The big black raven hopped off onto the bed and walked to his witch. "Gruk," he croaked, half uneasily, half indignantly. He'd missed out on all the hijinks.

Ginny stroked him under his beak and down his shimmery back. "I'm sorry, Edgar," she said. "They wouldn't have let you in. You'll get plenty of action, believe me."

"Gronk," he answered, flapped up onto the headboard, and perched. The knowledge that looked out of his beady eyes was benign—toward us—but somehow, indescribably, colder than what had ever been in tomcat Svartalf's. Well, Ben had told me that birds are the last surviving dinosaurs.

Val plunked her tray down in front of me. I saw coffee, ham, hash browns, buttered toast, marmalade, tomato juice, and a shot of chilled vodka. "Thanks, pony," I mumbled. My girl was reaching womanhood fast. In some respects, anyhow.

She settled down on the edge of the bed. "You're welcome. When you're *quite* ready, Padrito, we'd like to hear what actually happened. We really-o truly-o would."

Ben gave Ginny her tray and took a chair. Chryssa climbed up and snuggled next to her, spilling some juice. Edgar rocked forward and reached for her toast. She glared. He sat back. "Who, me?" he croaked. After she'd had a few sips of coffee, she was able to smile and give him a hash brown.

As the life-giving alkaloid soothed me, too, I could ask Val, "What do you know? What did you kids see on the crystal?"

"First a lot of views," she sneered. "A *scabrous* lot of reporters talking to anybody they could catch, or to each other." She wrinkled her nose. " 'This is a historic occasion, isn't it, Sam?' 'Yes, it sure is historic, Connie. Our first step toward the moon and those mysterious Beings on it.' 'Do you think they're omegans, souls who've achieved perfect clarity, like the Psychontologists claim, Sam?' 'I don't know, Connie. Who does? But we'll be back in a moment after this message.'

Meaning commercials for HP dowsers, and Elfland tours, and Audhumla Cream Cheese—'the food of the gods'—as if we hadn't heard all that blat a *million* times before."

I squeezed a small hand. "I am sorry you got stuck here, princess. Though I'm also glad. It became a tad dangerous out there. What did you see and hear right after the launch?"

"Well, how the horse rose and bucked and nosedived, and the brooms went wild, and then just all sorts of chatter and patter and shots of the wreckage, till I plain old *had* to go to bed. Ben and Moldylocks caved in way before." She looked hard into my eyes. "What were you and Mother up to?"

"Uh, helping where we could. Wasn't much."

"I heard mention of some people who claimed they'd seen a wolf run across the ground."

"Rumors, rumors."

"NASA isn't saying anything except that somehow the guard spells got broken and something came in and viked the launch. 'The proper authorities will investigate and report their findings in due course.' Yee-ork!"

"You and Mother didn't sit still, did you, Dad?" Ben asked quietly.

I collected what *gravitas* was available to me. "No, of course not. We aren't at liberty to discuss it yet, though. All we can say is that for us it was no big deal, and we're home safe, and nobody got seriously hurt." Other than Haris ed-Din al-Bunni and all of us who'd longed beyond the sky. "Let's give thanks for this and get on with our work. When we have a real story to tell, you'll hear it." If the government permitted.

"Will we?" Val challenged.

"When it's possible, yes, you will," I promised, regardless of what the goddamn government permitted.

"This isn't the end of the world, you know," Ginny said. "A setback, but we can hope the project will recover."

"Or Operation Luna will take over," Ben said, as softly as before.

Val raised her arms. "Yay for Operation Luna!" she cried.

"Operation Loony, Operation Loony," Chryssa chortled.

"Hey, hold on, kids," I protested. "It's only a sideline, don't forget. A kind of hobby. What we need is to set Project Selene back on its feet."

"What we need immediately," Ginny declared, "is to finish this nice meal you made before it gets soggy and hard to light."

That quieted conversation down to what she and I could more

easily handle. We were finishing when the telephone spoiled our carefully rebuilt family harmony. Telephones have a way of doing such things.

The partial animation meant well, of course—especially when the sympathetic vibrations were to be between *simpático* persons. For an instant I was even pleased. The phone flitted to the open door, hung there, and said, "A call from Dr. Graylock."

"Whee, Unca Will!" Chryssa exulted, bouncing on the mattress. To her he meant fun, jokes, comic songs, stories, maybe a toy or a treat. Val and Ben brightened too. He talked and played games with them, always interestingly, never the least condescendingly. Ginny sounded less joyful. "Well, come on," she said. The phone floated to the bed and settled between us. She gestured acceptance.

Her brother's face showed wan in the screen. *Aged,* I thought. *Overnight?* His voice dragged. "Ginny, Steve, you're all right, aren't you? I've just heard the news. Terrible. But it said there were no casualties."

"You've slept this late?" she asked. "What's wrong? You look like clabbered oatmeal."

"Bad night. Could I come see you? I've a notion, maybe clear off orbit, but a notion my trouble might tie in with what's happened at the Point."

A shiver passed through my skin. Considering what Will Graylock's work meant to the whole undertaking— And furthermore— "In any case, the investigation can use your advice and ideas," I blurted.

Ginny made a shushing motion at me. "We're barely back in action ourselves," she said. "How about eleven o'clock? Try to arrive inconspicuously. Currently we need the attentions of the press as much as we need cholla in the toilet paper." He nodded agreement. She disempathed.

I glanced around at our offspring. "Hear that, kids?" I said. "I'm afraid you'll have to be elsewhere while he's here."

Chryssa clouded up. "Poor Unca Will, he's sick? I c'd pick him some flowers."

"No, thank you, darling," Ginny told her. "He has to talk about something private. You know, like when you whisper a secret to Daddy or me."

"He wasn't at the launch last night?" Ben inquired sharply. "Hey, what *is* the matter, anyway?"

"That's what we're trying to find out," I replied. "Secret and Urgent." That farseer show about spies was among his favorites. I plagiarized from it: "What you don't know can't be wrung out of you."

*You can't innocently blab* would doubtless be more accurate, but counterproductive.

"Hoy, there, don't scare them," Ginny said. "It's nothing to be frightened of, dears."

Ben rose, stiff-backed. "I know my duty," he said, wounded in his machismo.

"Uh, Val, maybe the three of you could go to the park," I suggested.

Our oldest was also on her feet. The veneer of sweetness had cracked apart. I damn near heard the pieces of it tinkle to the floor. "You mean I get to babysit *again?*" she exclaimed, fire-faced. "While everything interesting happens? Nixway!"

"But—"

"You promised last night! You promised I wouldn't get stuck like that again! This is unseelie! It's scabrous!" She clenched her fists. She clenched her fists. "You're a, a, a wereliar!"

In our theory, we should have disciplined her for disrespect. But, well, she'd been so hopeful of getting the exciting truth straight from us, and instead we'd pussyfooted like NASA itself—no, we'd heard her refer to NASA's public relations as "cowfoot"—and now we not only wanted her out of the way as if she were an infant, we proposed to saddle her once more with that same infant.

"Okay, okay, it was a passing notion," I said. "Not compulsory. Why don't you give Larry Weller a call and maybe go have a hamburger or see a movie?" The last I'd heard, he was the closest to a steady boyfriend she'd yet acquired. The competition seemed to be fierce.

"Him?" she yelled. "That mudhead?" She collected her dignity. "No, thank you very much," she said, hailstone by slowly pattering hailstone. "I'll stay in my room, if you please." The way she stalked out, all she needed to be Svartalf in his heyday was a tail straight up in the air.

"Women," said Ben with the loftiness of ten-year-old masculinity.

"I'm one," Ginny pointed out mildly.

"Well, girls. Raging hormones."

*Wait till yours kick in,* I thought, *and God help us, every one.*

"I'll take care of Chryssa," Ben offered. "How 'bout it, sis? We'll go down to the rumpus room and animate my model Cretaceous."

That was manfully done of him. "Jolly shrewd," I said, also out of *Secret and Urgent.* "You may have to keep her amused for two or three hours, though."

"Aw, I can always play a Howleglass show on the farseer. She can't see those often enough, can you, sis? And me, I've got this neat new reckoner game."

"Splendid," Ginny said. "I'll arrange snacks and stuff for you, and lunch if necessary." And for Valeria if possible. "You don't have to disappear before, oh, quarter to eleven, you know—unless we have another emergency," she added, probably to liven things up for him. "Meanwhile, we two had better make ourselves presentable. We'll join you shortly."

"I wanna see the t'rannosaur attack the tri*cera*tops right now," Chryssa said. "Please?"

"Okay," Ben agreed. She jumped off the bed and took his hand. They left. Good kids, both of them.

Val, though, she wasn't only good—at heart—but remarkable. "Hey, what's this problem with Larry?" I demanded.

"I shouldn't tell you," Ginny answered low. "She confided in me, with tears, the other evening. But under the circumstances— His hands got too busy. She had to cast a minor geas to make him stop. I'm glad I taught her how."

It was knowledge legally reserved for older, more responsible children. But Val blossomed early.

"He brought her straight home, but didn't deign to speak a word," Ginny finished. "You were out playing poker."

Rage erupted. "That whelp! That swine! Why didn't you tell me before?"

"I wasn't supposed to. But this is an uncanny situation all around, and you may need to understand everything—"

"When I catch him, by Loki—"

"—understand everything, so you can see what's not important and dismiss it. Steve, hark back. Moonlight on the desert, stars, and a pretty and full-blooded girl—what would you have tried for? I gather Larry had plenty of encouragement, up to a point. By then he wasn't exactly a pointillist. Valeria curbed her own emotions suddenly, violently. It amounted to reacting against him. She hasn't gotten over it yet. I'll bet he's hurting worse."

"Um, well, yeah, maybe," I grumbled as I subsided. True, nothing irrevocable had happened. None of those louts who hung around my daughter were worthy of her anyway. Larry was among the less obnoxious. And, yes, I remembered my own teens. Wretched time of life, especially since it tends to turn off all compassion for it from those of us who've served our sentences.

"Take pride in her," Ginny said. "It's more than—than not being cheap. It's looking ahead and hewing to a purpose."

I nodded, a little jerkily. If Val was to fully master the female side of the Art like her mother, as her genes and her dreams alike called for, she must stay virgin till she had her magistra's degree. "Not easy," Ginny ended. "I know."

In one supple movement, she left the bed and stood beside it. "Well, c'mon, lazybones," she urged.

I followed along. Her familiar followed us. My shaving, dressing, and so forth were mechanical. The raven brooded over them. He didn't mean to be sinister; mostly he was a rather genial sort. But though he could more or less pronounce a number of human words, he hadn't said, "Howdy" this morning, only croaked. Now he sat on the shower curtain rod, limned against luminous blinds, like a piece of night, reminding me that he was in rapport with strange things. What was due to hit us next?

And—a silly question maybe, but very natural for a father—how might a young girl, witchy-gifted and in turmoil, bollix everything up for everybody, wizards and demons and angels alike?

# IV

The second day of August was getting down to business when we reached the living room. Svartalf sprawled on a broad windowsill. Sunlight flooded his blackness. He absorbed it like a rug.

Ginny went over to give him his due fondling around the throat and ears. He opened an indolent yellow eye and half purred. Edgar, back on her shoulder, leaned over and said quite distinctly, "Greetings, old garbage diver."

"Mind your manners, bird!" Ginny snapped. She swatted the raven, not hard but with plenty of meaning. Svartalf bared a worn-down fang and snarled a bit. Fortunately, he didn't otherwise react. Maybe, being a little hard of hearing these days, he hadn't actually caught the insult; or maybe he didn't feel like leaving his comfortable location. Ginny's Art kept him healthy, but she couldn't turn time backward. Though not senile, he was venerable for a cat, or would have been had anybody venerated him. If he still domineered in the feline neighborhood, it was more by bluff and cunning than prowess. Certainly he was too stiff of joints and short of wind to go on any serious witch-venture—or so she deemed, and gave him honorable retirement.

I don't say he and his successor hated one another. Call it professional jealousy, which now and then led to a squabble. Early on, Edgar had laid a dropping on Svartalf's head. I don't say, either, that was deliberate, though it sure was precise. The tom gathered his muscles to leap and do murder. Ginny intervened. Svartalf stalked off. He returned with a medal in his mouth, one of the several he'd received for his share in past exploits from such outfits as the United States Army, Trismegistus University, the Evangelical Lutheran Church, and the American Mathematical Society. He put it down on the floor by Edgar's

perch. When the raven had had a good look at the shiny object, such as his breed love to collect, Svartalf bore it away and came back with the next. And the next and the next and the next. Edgar was fairly subdued for a while afterward.

I went to another window and glanced out. Our back yard had a big old cottonwood to shade it, together with a garden, but in front a patch of brownish grass ran along a sidewalk and a street whose asphalt would beget heat shimmers this afternoon. The houses beyond huddled close, fake ranch style, devoid of trees, under a stark blue sky. The Eskimo dolls in them must already be hard at work cooling them off.

We'd been lucky when we moved here. The place we acquired had stood for a long while on the edge of town, red-tiled, tawny-walled, spacious, honestly built. The suburb was mushrooming around it, if mushroom growth is accompanied by the sound of hammers and cement mixers.

Grants was booming worse, being near Cardinal Point—employees, tourists, and everything that that implied. We'd chosen to settle in Gallup, some fifty miles west. I didn't mind the commute. Flying along, you saw awesome scenery, in spite of what people were doing to it. Gallup kept part of the genuine Southwest, offered the kids a wholesome environment for school and play, and gave Ginny an excellent base in which to reestablish her consulting service. It's the rendezvous for the annual ceremonial gathering of the Indian tribes. That meant paranatural phenomena to observe and goetic work to do, even for a female paleface if she had the skill. Also, what had become more important yet, not far south lay the Zuni pueblo.

"Peaceful scene," I said, for lack of any inspired remark. "Last night hardly seems real."

"You have the order of things reversed," Ginny replied. "Peace is not a natural condition. Your own body is a battleground, every moment of your life. How can you expect the world or any of the universes except Heaven—if Heaven is another continuum, which I doubt—any of them to be different? I should think you'd learned better."

It wasn't like her to lecture me. "You're pretty worried, aren't you?" I said.

"Are you shrugging this off?"

"No, no, of course not. But looking back, I wonder if we're up against any force more formidable than old man Coyote. The business had a certain humor to it—brutal, yes, but not completely malign." As I spoke, I wished I hadn't. My careless words recalled to me the absolute evil we did once confront.

Ginny saw me shiver and came to stand beside me. "Coyote alone would be trouble enough. But he couldn't have gotten in and done his mischief by himself. If it was he, somebody or something else aided and abetted him. How? Who? Why? That last is probably the most basic question of the three." The cheerfulness she'd maintained began to waver. Her voice thinned. "What's been plaguing Will?"

I laid an arm about her waist. We stood silent. Occasional wains trundled down the street or broomsticks slid above; pedestrians and dogs passed along the sidewalk. Then a Völve, staid and sturdy, descended to our parking rack. "There he is!" Ginny cried. She ran to open the front door.

I kept aside and studied my brother-in-law more narrowly than ever before. He stood a couple of inches shorter than me, had grown portly in his fifties, but remained light on his feet. Today the shoulders slumped and he moved heavily. The normal liveliness was likewise gone from the roundish, hooknosed face. Suddenly I noticed more white than gray in the brush-cut hair and Vandyke beard.

Yet when he shook my hand the clasp was firm, the eyes behind their steel-rimmed glasses as bright a green as his sister's. Above the Southwest's ubiquitous jeans, his shirt of yellow silk shantung and Longevity pendant bespoke a sort of defiance. China and its culture were among his many interests. He knew the history and the Mandarin language, had visited the country several times both as guest astronomer and tourist in spite of its current turmoil, and maintained connections with friends and colleagues over there.

"Welcome," I said. "Sit down. Coffee, lemonade, beer? We hope you can stay for lunch."

"Nothing now, thanks." His tone was leaden. "Except, mind if I smoke?"

"Not at all," we told him, routine response to routine courtesy. An ashtray waited. Ginny and I quit years ago, but we don't take the Christer attitude of too many ex-puffers. Just don't blow it straight at us, or most particularly at our children.

He settled into an armchair, took out pipe and tobacco pouch, and lit up. To tell the truth, I kind of liked the aroma of the Russell's Mixture he used. "Is this an inconvenient time for you?" he asked. "I imagine you're both overwhelmed."

"On the contrary," Ginny said. "Before turning in last night, or rather this morning, I gave every client scheduled for today a message on the phone canceling the appointment. Three or four, none of them

anything big." In order that she could help my work in its hour of need.

"And, obviously, engineering-type operations are suspended till further notice," I put in. "We're both at your service, Will."

"You're very kind." He sighed. "I feel presumptuous, shoving my petty woes forward."

"Nonsense," said Ginny. "They aren't, and you should have earlier."

"Besides," I added, "you think they may be related to ours."

He frowned through a blue cloud. "That may be the most ridiculous presumption of the lot." After a pause: "However, my physician has checked me over and found nothing, nor did the warlock I consulted."

"I might have," said Ginny a trifle stiffly.

"My dear, in the first place, I knew you wouldn't charge me, and we Graylocks don't freeload unless we get desperate—do we? In the second and more obvious place, Hosteen Yazzie *is* a Navajo Singer, and I thought I might have run afoul of some local influence."

"Ah, Yazzie. A good man, yes. I'd be the first to admit I'm no expert on Southwestern paranature, after only two years. I have learned a little something from the Zuni, but not enough, I'm afraid, to give you much more than a referral."

"And there're a lot more Navajo and Hopi hereabouts, with their assorted gods, ghosts, and goblins," was my banal contribution.

Will couldn't help correcting me: "In spite of their linguistic differences, I've gathered that those peoples have remarkably similar beliefs. Which, in this day and age, means 'measure of understanding.' But since I happened to be on the Navajo reservation south of Ramah when . . . it . . . may have happened . . . it was natural, later on, to check with a shaman of that background."

Ginny leaned forward. "You haven't told us anything about the matter."

"I didn't know it was relevant to you. I still don't. Merely a guess, *faute de mieux*. But, well, you may remember my mentioning to you last year that I'd begun to get some peculiar and . . . somewhat disturbing . . . data in my observations."

I nodded. "That was after you'd made the improvements on your instrument, wasn't it?" I meant the specterscope, his invention, which ten years ago shook the science of astronomy and broomboosted public interest in spaceflight when it found spoor of invisible creatures alive on the moon.

"Not quite. Even before then, I'd caught indications that, whatever they are, those Beings are not all benign, as they'd appeared at first. Several fellow researchers in various countries reported similar results. None of us published, we kept it confidential between us, because the traces were so slight, so ambiguous. Variations in the polarization of moonlight are damnably hard to measure, point by point, let alone their changes with time and the interpretation of the figures." Will's pipe trembled in his hand. "But you've heard this from me before, and seen it amply in magazines like *Goetic American* and *Paranatural History.* What you haven't heard is how the variations went chaotic, and fractal analysis seemed, *seemed,* to show that the attractors may be of the diabolical sort."

I caught my breath. Ginny sat glacier-calm. "This caused you to try for a 'scope with more sensitivity?" she prompted.

"Yes. Well, of course I wanted one anyway. Larger aperture and, for the spectral part, a dragonskin diffraction grating—"

She quelled the professional enthusiasm that had for a moment made him happy again. "Skip the details. Why didn't you give me a look at those patterns? I've acquired more sense for deviltry that I ever really wanted to."

"I told you, they're too vague. The data points wander over the chart, the probable error is absurdly large, the whole thing could as easily be used to prove that the lunar Beings have established a casino or a stock market. I had little more than a hunch that something yonder had gone seriously wrong. Some of my colleagues agreed this is possible, some didn't. Everybody agreed we need better data.

"I had funds at my disposal, and ideas. So I worked, alone and uncommunicative because you know how easily any fool can disrupt such delicate spells. By June this year, I had my new instrument built, rebuilt, and calibrated against the Ankh, the Tetragrammaton, and the Pentacle Reversed. Obviously, it'd require tinkering to get the kobolds out. On the full moon nearest the equinox, I took it into the desert for some preliminary tests."

Will stopped. His pipe smoked like Siegfried's funeral pyre. Ginny gauged when he had mustered strength to continue. "What exactly happened?" she asked low.

He sighed once more. "I don't know. Maybe a, uh, a blob of undigested mustard, or whatever Scrooge said Marley's ghost might be. It wasn't like that first time—" His voice broke. "You know, Virginia. It wasn't like that at all."

"Tell us, though," his sister prompted softly. "You need to."

"I can't very well, because I don't understand it. Perhaps—oh, I'd been brooding somewhat over Princess Tamako of Japan. Who didn't, back at that time?"

Me, for one. I'd thought those several days of global grief and display were mainly hysteria. True, so violent an end to so stormy and embittered a life was tragic; but tragedy happens somewhere along the line to all of us.

Will hauled himself back to the subject. "In any case, I did my early observations, then got into my sleeping bag for a nap before resuming toward moonset. The moonlight lay like ice over the sage and sand and rock; the stars seemed oddly cold and strange, far away—Never mind. I drowsed off. Into nightmares. I must have threshed and struggled, because when I finally lurched back to consciousness, I'd rolled clear off my air mattress. I wasn't in fit shape to carry on; tried, but kept fumbling, making gross errors. And since then, this past couple of months, well, nothing has gone right for me in my research. I can't get up any energy, I can't come up with any ideas, I klutz up every experiment or observation I attempt—"

He shrugged. "The doctor thinks it's depression, and wrote me a prescription. It hasn't helped. The Singer said it might be a curse or some other malign influence, and tried Enemy Way, but that didn't help either, so now he's baffled too."

"Beauty Way would have to wait for winter," Ginny said. "Too long, and maybe just as futile." She narrowed her eyes. "Do you recall those nightmares?"

"Not well. Terrible, hostile shapes and . . . and Chinese writing that crawled like nests of snakes. . . . But the, the thing that came at me screamed in a different language. It was like a woman, sort of, in a wide-sleeved robe, her hair blowing wild, her mouth stretched open and full of teeth—" Will shuddered. "That's about all. Hosteen Yazzie could make nothing of it."

"Maybe not quite his department. . . . Okay, what about last night?"

Will frowned. I could well-nigh feel how he picked his way through a minefield of confusion and of terrors he was trying to deny. "I told you, I'd felt wretched the whole day. Finally I crept into bed and fell asleep. Fever dreams? I can't say. But they went on and on and on, and the same grisly woman was in them. Somehow she . . . rode me, like a horse—"

I tried to show I had some knowledge too by asking, "The way a Haitian obeah rides a worshipper?"

"No, no," Ginny said, "that's possession, not being literally saddled. And the obeah means well."

"My metaphor wasn't right anyhow," Will continued. "And as for worship, no, this wasn't benign or ecstatic or anything. It was grave-cold, and as if a wind blew and blew while I stumbled along under her lash— It becomes a kind of jagged blur."

He straightened. His tone steadied. "Enough. I do *not* feel sorry for myself. If enemy influences were on the loose last night, as they obviously were, it's no wonder they troubled me. I am associated with the project."

"In a very basic way," I murmured.

"But you suspect the involvement goes deeper than that," Ginny said.

"Well," he replied, "when at last I woke, got out of bed, went to the bathroom—besides feeling beaten down, I noticed dust on my feet. And, when I squinted closer, traces of it in the rug. I'm not that sloppy a housekeeper, Virginia. True, I'd flitted out to the desert yesterday afternoon and taken a walk in hopes of making my blood circulate better. Probably, as miserable as I was, I didn't notice what I brought back. But— Well, I simply don't know. Since we did have a disaster, I thought I'd give you what information I have. It may well be totally worthless."

"Don't you scientists say there's no such thing as too much data?" She smiled the best way she could under the circumstances. "You did completely right to bring this forward. The clues we have are so slight—"

The phone interrupted. "A confidential call for Dr. Matuchek from a person known to her," it announced.

"Oh, damn. Excuse me." Ginny got up and went to its corner. Naturally, she kept the scryer blank and held the audio disc to her ear. Will and I weren't nosy, but the matter seemed to be for her only. We sat where we were, unable to think of anything conversational.

I heard: "Yes. . . . Really? You're okay otherwise? . . . I understand, dear, believe me, I do. . . . The pestilential press, camped everywhere around your house. . . . Here's how we'll work it. You come out, telling them, 'No comment.' Of course they'll trail you, but . . . You know the Sipapu Saloon on Shoshone Street? . . . Okay. Get a taxi there. Arrive about, oh, 12:15. Order a beer or whatever, take a few sips, and go to the ladies' room. I don't expect even a female reporter will be prepared to follow you. I'll be waiting inside with Tarnkappen for both of us. We'll slip out and come here, where I should

be able to take care of the problem. Afterward we'll call another cab to take you home. . . . Glad to help. Gives me a feeling of accomplishment, in this general mess. . . . Okay, quarter past twelve in the Sipapu."

She disempathed and turned to us. "Sorry, guys, I'll have to abandon you for a bit," she said, "and trust you not to be curious or gossipy about the one who comes back with me. Now I'd better get my apparatus together."

Edgar flapped from her chair to her shoulder. She left the room. Soon she left the house. Svartalf dozed, Valeria sulked, Ben and Chryssa were occupied downstairs. I sat alone with my troubled kinsman.

# V

The silence dragged on. "Hey," I said after a minute, "how about I build us a pot of coffee? Uh, no, you prefer China tea, don't you? We've got the Lapsang Soochong you like so much."

"Thank you. That would indeed go well." He trailed me into the kitchen. His wonted, sometimes professorish humor flickered. "I'll have done best, unlike Keats, if I've 'stayed upon the green shore, and piped a silly pipe, and took tea and comfortable advice.' "

I had no idea where he found that quote, and didn't inquire. I'm a small-town boy whom a Hollywood talent scout brought to roles in such things as *The Call of the Wild* and *Silver Chief,* till the Caliph's War hit us and the Army had other uses for my talents. Afterward I studied engineering on my GI Bill, and then worked directly for Nornwell in the Midwest, and now indirectly here in the Southwest. I suppose the things that happened to me along the way made me a bit more thoughtful than would otherwise have been the case, though my wife's influence may well have been stronger toward that. Certainly she led me to read a lot of books, history and world literature and such. But I still liked coming back to my parents' home for Thanksgiving, along with the rest of the clan, and swapping small-town small talk. Ginny was always gracious and charming there, and always denied to me that she was bored like a naval gun. I kept my suspicions to myself and loved her for them.

Undeniably, the Graylocks of Stony Brook, New York had a more intellectual tradition than the Matucheks of Watsonville, California.

We entered the kitchen. "I wish this were mine," Will remarked. He occupied a little house in the older part of Gallup, adequate for a single man, aside from books overflowing it, but limited in facilities.

Since he enjoyed cooking and was good at it, he'd come here several times to make dinner for the bunch of us.

His words showed me how perturbed he was, because he'd spoken them before and self-repetition wasn't a habit of his. Looking around the broad expanse of Spanish tile, polished enamel, and timber beams, I groped for something consoling or distracting to say. "Yeah, it's nice. But, you know, I kind of miss the brownie back in our old digs."

"You told me he made mischief," Will said, likewise trying to keep the tone light.

"Not much, and mainly with provocation, like before we broke Svartalf of chasing him. Sometimes he'd play with Val, and later Ben, when they were little. They were the envy of other kids whose house didn't harbor any such Being. I'm sorry Chryssa won't have the experience. Now and then, here, I start to put out a bowl of milk for the brownie before turning in, and bring myself up short."

Will smiled. "Ah, yes, I remember ours on Long Island. But don't the Indians have Good Folk?"

"Not that I've heard of. Bad Folk, yes. Ginny can tell you more. In this regard, the Europeans are lucky."

I've heard of schemes to import Little People. Lord knows they're plentiful overseas. Trouble is, hardly any are interested. Our American fays, leprechauns, nisser, domovoi, and whatnot mostly came over early in this century, shortly after the Awakening. It was a bewildering new world to them, and if a human family to which one had attached himself or herself decided to try their luck overseas, often the Being tagged along. Meanwhile, though, the majority adapted to present-day conditions in their old countries. Many of the dwarves, for instance, began making a good thing of the industrial age.

Similarly for half-world animals, or more so. The useful types such as unicorns are everywhere, of course, but what you may encounter in the Canadian woods will be a wendigo, not a leshy; the few surviving firedrakes are now banned from military use—never very practical anyway—and safely in European zoos; et cetera.

I realized I'd fallen into my bad habit of mentally rehashing the obvious. To avoid thinking about the immediate and unobvious? I got busy with pot, kettle, and canister. Behind me, I heard Will's voice bleaken: "Well, yes, the wee folk are generally cute. But not everything is that Awoke, by a long shot."

Was he remembering his and Ginny's brilliant, prosperous parents, killed on vacation abroad when a griffin, newly aroused, ravenous, and surely confused, flew up from a Balkan peak and tangled with their

broomstick? I didn't know how to respond to so old a grief. But it became clear he had wider concerns on his mind: "Oh, the ferocious creatures weren't ever that much of a problem, and we put them in their place fast, the same as we'd done with tigers and wolves." Somberness stumbled over embarrassment. "Er, no offense, Steve. You know what I mean. However, malevolent intelligences—including humans, now that they have their ancient powers back—"

I set the water over the fire and turned around. Clearly, I thought, his nightmare was haunting him. It shouldn't, not a sensible, easygoing guy like this. To be sure, if he believed there might be some connection to the disaster at the Point, that would reinforce the bad feeling; and he had already spent a couple of months in the dumps.

Maybe some common sense would brighten his mood. "Look," I said, "we know the Adversary's active in every universe, or at least in every one where fallen humans live. If these days his agents, demons and such, can operate more openly than they were able to for a long time, why, then we're better able to spot them at it and outwit them. Not to mention the technologies we can bring to bear, everything from exorcism to clean thaumaturgics. As for human baddies, yeah, they've gained some capabilities they didn't used to have, but they don't have others they might have gotten. For instance, suppose those Tibetan prayer wheels turning to keep nuclear weapons from ever becoming functional—suppose they didn't work."

"Um-m, yes," he conceded.

"And what about science and industry?" I pursued. "Where'd your career have been without goetics?"

"Oh, I could have become an astronomer nevertheless." He hesitated. "But maybe I wouldn't have."

That puzzled me a mite. As far as I knew, his fascination with the heavens was lifelong. He married fairly late on account of it, and when his wife died childless he never seemed to consider remarrying, though he kept an appreciative eye for pretty women. His research claimed too much of him. He took out parental urges in being Uncle Will to our kids.

Or so I'd supposed. I'd begun to wonder some.

I didn't want to pry, but I did hope to jockey him into a better frame of mind. "And what about Ginny? Granted, she'd've gone far in any universe that didn't kill her outright, but I don't see how she could've had the meteoric career she did if witchcraft hadn't been available."

Meteoric indeed. After they were orphaned, he hired lawyers to

pull wires and get him custody of her. Studying at Harvard, though, he couldn't do much more than put her in the best available boarding school. Driven by loneliness as well as creativity and ambition, she sailed through it and through college, taking her magistra's at age sixteen. Weary of academe, she had him pull more legal wires and went to work the next year for a New York advertising agency, mostly handling elementals and other paranormals in displays. The war interrupted. It determined her to become independent. Therefore, after the war, she went back to school and got her Ph.D. Marriage and kids interrupted, but I wonder how many long-established pros could have survived our raid into Hell, let alone come home victorious. Now she was herself established, solving all sorts of problems for people, her fees each year totalling more than my salary. I didn't care, I gloried. She said once, with a laugh, that male wolves have no doubts about their masculinity.

"Quite a girl," Will agreed. "If any devils cross her path, God help them."

He didn't attempt more jokes. Still, I'd lifted his spirits enough that he at least turned philosophical. "Yes, critical points," he mused. "I've often speculated. What if James Watt, say, had never lived? And there are countless Earths where he didn't."

The kettle whistled and puffed. I filled the teapot. "By then the Industrial Revolution was inevitable—under way, in fact, with primitive steam engines pumping water out of mines," said the engineer part of me. "Carnot's work on thermodynamics and Maxwell's analysis of how a governor operates made the really big difference. Though you also have to count in Faraday and Kelvin and Herz and . . . a long list."

"But you know history branches and rebranches, a quasi-infinity of coexisting, equally real universes. You've been in another one yourself."

I grimaced. "The Low Continuum isn't the same thing. The geometry, the very laws of what passes for nature, they're different from ours." Ugly. Evil.

"Yes, right; I misspoke myself. What I'm thinking of are worlds that are *almost* like this."

"Which Ginny thinks is the reason we've not been able to make contact with any. The differences are too subtle." I'd been involved in such an effort. Waste of time. We never got an answer to the telepathic messages we tried to send. Well, maybe nobody who received them could figure out how to respond.

The teapot was heated. I emptied it, put in the leaves, and added fresh boiling water.

"I've tried to imagine what they could be like," Will said.

"Lots of people have." I should encourage him to talk. "What have you thought about particularly?"

"Oh, suppose—and there must be worlds where it went this way—suppose Einstein and Planck did not get together in 1901. They could have tried to explain the paradoxical findings of late nineteenth-century physics separately. Instead of rheatics, we might have gotten distinct theories of relativity and quantum mechanics, hard to reconcile. Or suppose Moseley, a few years later, had not applied the new equations in his laboratory, had not discovered he could degauss the effects of cold iron and release the goetic forces— We'd have a world dominated by fossil fuels and electricity. The railroads might run the same as here, but personal transportation would be mostly horseless carriages and air travel by dirigibles."

"And you'd have been analyzing spectra, not specters."

"If I went into astronomy at all," he muttered. Quickly, louder: "I doubt anything would have been alive on the moon to detect. What was left of paranature would have stayed Asleep, hidden away. And witches and warlocks wouldn't be respected professionals, they'd be cranks and charlatans."

"And the biologists would be trying to figure out what a certain part of the DNA of people like me was for. Yeah." I took down a tray and set pot, cups, saucers, and a plate of almond cookies on it. He drank his tea Chinese style, no milk or sugar, even when it wasn't Chinese.

"The political, historical consequences are still more interesting to wonder about," Will said. "I guess by 1900 a general European war was inevitable, but the course it took, and what came afterward—"

"Hm, yes." I hadn't ever considered this much, and found myself intrigued. "Like, on our time line, suddenly those folk who'd maintained some tradition of, uh, magic it was called—suddenly it was really working. They had a head start, in the practical if not the theoretical areas. Africans, Australians, our own Indians, especially hereabouts—something to bargain with and wangle a better deal from the white man— It's one of those things I've always kind of taken for granted. Might have been very different." I picked up the tray. "C'mon, let's shift."

We moved back to the living room. I poured; we sipped and got

into a bull session we both enjoyed. How good to see Will's heart returning to him.

Ginny interrupted when she opened the door. He and I rose to our feet, for another woman was with her: Curtice Newton.

She looked fine. No doubt her head was bandaged, but she covered that with a turban. She went straight over to me and took my hand in both hers. "I haven't had a chance to thank you properly for saving my life, Steve," she said in her direct fashion, "and never will be able to. But thank you."

"Aw, nothing heroic, not for the likes of me," I answered. "Mighty glad to've been of help."

I'd always felt a tad awkward with her—a big, comely woman, red-haired like Ginny though she kept hers bobbed short. Probably all I'd ever do about spaceflight was some of the engineering, with help from my wife on some of the artificing. Curtice Newton was among those who were going to *go.*

If we could salvage Project Selene—or maybe, just maybe, get somewhere real with Operation Luna—or whatever. If, if, if.

The four of us chatted for a few minutes, politely, carefully. I sensed a certain constraint and was not surprised when Ginny said, "If you two will pardon us, Curtice and I have business. It shouldn't take too long, and afterward we can think about lunch."

They went off to her arcanum. Will and I sat back down. His gaze followed them out of sight. "A dream walking," he breathed; I barely heard.

*Oh-ho!* "Well, you can try," I said, "but I understand quite a few young bucks have the same idea."

He blinked, then chuckled. "And an excellent idea it is, but not mine. I know my limitations."

He turned solemn again, though not gloomy. I realized he couldn't have rid himself this fast of the darkness in him; but it had retreated to the depths, leaving his normal personality in charge of surface thoughts and emotions. "I meant that Captain Newton can hope to meet, to experience in full, what to me has been . . . a midsummer night's dream," he said low.

"Huh? I call it hard, cutting-edge science, what you've done."

"But the beginning—" I saw him come to a resolution. His eyes met mine straight on. "Steve, I've never told this to anyone but Ginny, under pledge of secrecy. I'd like to share it now with you. Whatever the present trouble is, we seem to be in it together, and your knowing

may conceivably make a difference. Besides, you . . . you're a fine fellow. My sister could not have done better."

"Oh, hey, sure she could have," I mumbled, blushing. "I was lucky, that's all. But if you want to tell me something private, I promise it'll stay private unless and until you release me."

He nodded. "I knew you'd say that, and say it truly." After a pause: "You may speak of it if, somehow, dire necessity requires, or in case of my death or permanent disability. This isn't a thing I'm ashamed of. On the contrary. It was . . . intimate, in a way nothing else has ever since been for me. It shaped my whole life. That alone makes it hard to talk about. And it was indescribable. By anybody. I'm no poet. But I don't believe Sappho or Shakespeare could have found words for it."

"Well, I've never seen a good description of lycanthropy, what it actually feels like, even by two or three fine writers who've been there. Why don't you give me the dry facts and let my imagination do what it can?"

He leaned back in his chair, crossed his legs, bridged his fingers, and spoke very quietly.

"I was fifteen years old. Interested in astronomy, yes, but equally interested in baseball, sailing, handicrafts, travel, literature—in spite of what the English teachers did to it—and still more in girls. You may remember we lived on the outskirts of Stony Brook. One summer evening a full eclipse of the moon was due. I thought I'd like to watch it from start to finish, unpestered by hoi polloi. There's no snob like an adolescent with intellectual pretensions. My mother packed me some sandwiches, I put them and my Newtonian telescope on my bicycle luggage rack, and pedaled off into the countryside—a dozen miles or so, to a meadow I knew in the Brookhaven area.

"I arrived after sunset and settled myself in tall grass where daisies glimmered and crickets chirped. Trees stood scattered, with night already underneath them but their crowns faintly aglow. One house was in sight, well away, its windows like stars fallen to earth. The earliest real stars were blinking forth in a sky that slowly went from deep blue to violet. The air lay quiet, cool but with a sort of ghost in it from the day's warmth and green smells. And then the eastern horizon lightened and the full moon rose, huge and pale gold, with marks across it the color of the dusk that had met me before deepening away. . . . I'm not trying for fancy language, Steve. I'm trying to give you an idea of a place that was suddenly no longer just an open spot but—that line from Dunsany—'beyond the fields we know.'

"The eclipse had begun, dimming an edge of the disc. My telescope showed me how sharp-edged the boundary of that shadow was, and somehow this made everything else the more mysterious, but I don't know whether I spent more time peering through the eyepiece or with my own eyes on the vision. I was utterly lost in it. I do remember how I wondered, fleetingly, why that should be—here was a commonplace astronomical phenomenon, right?—but I soon forgot everything other than the night and the moon.

"To this day I'm not sure what brought on the trance, though I can guess. What I can't guess is why it should have come over me, a kid, a prosaic, loutish beast of a boy. Older, wiser, better people must have been watching too, around this whole half of the planet. Why didn't the, the influence touch one of them? Well, maybe I simply happened to be the only human at a site that . . . they . . . wanted to seek out. It was so beautiful, after all."

A small chill tingled through me. I'm an ordinary kind of guy myself, but great Powers once gathered around me, because they foreknew that the future would turn on what my wife and I did or did not survive to do. And Will was her brother. I doubted that what he told me of had been entirely accidental. If nothing else, his latent abilities—I kept silent.

"As the shadow crept onward, I felt more and more taken out of my flesh," he went on. "A strangeness was everywhere around me, in the air, in the earth, in the starlight that strengthened as the moonlight waned, a strangeness wild and sweet, like the happiness I'd felt when a girl I was in love with smiled at me, or like—oh, I can't describe it, except that alongside was also a hint of anxiousness, even fear—

"The eclipse totalled. The moon stood dark, tarnished red, while early dew on the grass caught the glint of stars. And there *they* were, flying, whirling, dancing, through the air, over the ground, come down from the sky to their great mother, who was my mother too, and everybody's—"

Will gasped, the way a man does when memory hits hard. I left him in peace.

Soon he could go on: "I barely saw them, understand. Glimpses, hints, a highlight, a translucency, a tracing of shadow. . . . Think of starlit mists in a mild whirlwind, while somewhere, softly, something sings what could be by Bach or Mozart at their dearest and loveliest. . . . Half-seen, slender female figures, if that wasn't simply the way my imagination was bound to render them. Long, flowing hair, long flow-

ing draperies, wings, maybe, a face that was—oh, elfin or, or I don't know—"

He stopped again. When he hadn't spoken for a minute or two, I ventured, "They sound to me like traditional—you know, medieval—ideas of the Fair Folk. Not the sort that name was a euphemism for, who lived in Elf Hill or a sidhe mound or a dolmen and could bring mortals to grief. No, innocent spirits of the woodlands and waterfalls, who came out after dark to rejoice. I recall a picture I saw as a child, in a fairy tale book—a log laid over a stone, and half a dozen of them playing teeter-totter with a nisse but not weighing enough to counterbalance him. Like airy, free-wandering nymphs, with no power to talk of, but also without sin, maybe a free gift of God to put some extra happiness and beauty into the world."

Will nodded. He grew fairly matter-of-fact: "That's what I've since thought is likeliest. It fits with the folklore I've studied and with what the specterscope has revealed, though as you know, there are nine-and-ninety contending notions about what *that* is. If they were what you and I suspect, then the implications—

"Look." He leaned forward, his gaze searching mine. "Imagine these harmless, once gladsome Beings as they came Awake when the electromagnetic inhibition of rheatic forces dwindled to an end. It was to a transformed world, a world of railroads, steamships, machine shops, huge cities, farmlands across hundreds of square miles, glaring lights, wilderness reduced to a few enclaves. Above all, perhaps, a world where the dominant culture was pragmatic, capitalistic, scientific-minded, where goetics was essentially a new set of technologies, where the different kinds of Awakened creatures had to seek and struggle for whatever niches they could find— What might spirits as gentle as these do? Try to become pets, playthings, tourist attractions? Or try for freedom?

"I think they fled to the moon."

The idea that the lunar population consisted of refugees wasn't altogether new to me. It'd been kicked around a little ever since Will reported his first discoveries. However, I hadn't heard it in just this form before. Also, he needed to talk. "Uh-huh," I said.

"Probably they'd always gone to and fro. The folk tales suggest as much. They're ethereal; they can fly on the changeable streams of gravity, of space-time. But if they can't endure direct sunlight, they can only take that route through shadow—that is, during a lunar or solar eclipse. I think they got together and made the great migration, oh, decades ago. They don't mind vacuum. They can take shelter from day,

whether by going underground or by flitting around as the moon rotates—and a night there is two weeks long, you know. They can create their own insubstantial, invisible-to-us dwellings, gardens, pools, fountains, shrines. . . . But I think they always long back to their old haunts. Or they have unfinished business here, or contacts they want to keep up, or— Anyhow, whenever they can, some of them return, and stay on Earth till the next opportunity to cross space. One of those visitations came on me."

"And?" I asked after a while, softly.

He shrugged and half smiled. "The eclipse ended, the moon brightened. I was lost in their nearness. Toward dawn they left for woodlands or caves that would hide them from the sun. Perhaps they laid sleep on me, or perhaps I collapsed, exhausted. When I woke and crawled home, hours later, my parents gave me billy hell. I didn't want to talk about what had happened. How could I, really? The folks may or may not have believed the story I cobbled together. They were wise and didn't pursue the matter. But from then on, my course in life was set."

*The faerie touch.* "Could they have had that in mind when they appeared to you?" I wondered.

"Well, naturally, I've considered the possibility. If they'd spoken directly to me or anyone—assuming they are able to—we'd only have had that person's word for it, soon forgotten. But scientific evidence— Humans were bound to reach the moon someday. Given foreknowledge, maybe they wouldn't ruthlessly set about industrializing it. Maybe, having had time to think, they'd . . . show mercy. . . . I don't know. There's so much I don't know."

Will scowled. His tone harshened. "Except that the specterscope does seem to have begun giving indications of evil already up there. And lately I've had that experience in the desert that I told you about. In the light of what's happened it looked like a perverted version of my first, but merely a horrible dream—until yesterday when the moon flight program crashed—"

The telephone chose this instant to break in, as telephones are apt to. "A confidential call to Mr. and Dr. Matuchek from a person known to them, who claims urgency," it said in its tapioca-bland fashion.

"Rats! Sorry, Will." I went over to the foul thing and snugged the audio close. "Steven Matuchek here."

"Federal Bureau of Investigation," came the mandated identification, followed by a voice I hadn't heard for years. "Steve? This is Bob Shining Knife, calling from Washington."

"Hm? Oh. Hi. How are you?"

"Okay personally, wife and kids too, hope the same for you. Listen, the Bureau's taking over the investigation of what happened last night." No surprise. "When I heard, I remembered you and Ginny are involved."

"Um, we're not what I'd call involved," I said cautiously. "We're just on the scene."

"Considering the Johannine case, I'm not so sure about that. But in any event, Steve, we know each other, and I hope we still like each other. I've a notion you and Ginny—" a brief laugh "—or Ginny and you can be of real help. If you'll, uh, go more by the rule book this time. As soon as I got the news, I put in for assignment. Catching a redeye, arriving in Albuquerque tomorrow, going on to Grants, can I see you two in our office at ten A.M.?"

"I didn't know you had an office there."

"It's been arranged, and personnel are being flown in." He gave me the address.

This was his style, and certainly we could have done a lot worse. Nevertheless— But that could wait. "Why Grants?" I asked automatically. "The Federal Building's here in Gallup."

"Yes, but what with Grants being close to the NASA site, we can operate better. You'll be there?"

"I think so," I said. "Ginny's busy right now. I'll tell her, though, and call you back if we have any problem. By the way, her brother happens to be here, Dr. Graylock, who first discovered Beings on the moon. He may have useful information. Shall we bring him along, if we can?" Not that I meant Will should be pumped for more than he cared to let out.

I'd seldom heard Shining Knife hesitate. "Um-m, well, I think not. We'll want to talk with him, of course, but I've run a quick background check and . . . I don't think he can contribute at this stage."

What the devil?

We exchanged a few politenesses. I disempathed and returned to Will. "Sorry about that" was the best I could say. The mood between us had evaporated. We sipped tea and voiced banalities.

Ginny and Curtice arrived to break the dismal spell. They were radiant. "All done," Ginny told us. "I'll throw together a belated lunch. The kids will be overjoyed at the company."

"Thank you," said the celestonaut. "I hate to decline, especially when you've been so kind already. But could I take a rain check? They badly want me back at the Point, to tell them and tell them and tell

them what little I can. It was plenty hard getting leave to go home and rest for a short time."

Will had risen, like me. The liveliness had drained from him; again he seemed gaunt and aged. "And I," he said. "I thank you too, for much more than this invitation, but last night is catching up with me and I'd be a pretty ramshackle skeleton at the feast. What I'd better do is go back home myself, snatch a bite of any old thing, and try for some honest sleep."

Curtice gave him a sharp glance—she'd doubtless heard rumors—but stayed by the decencies and only said, "I s'pose everybody's fairly well outgewashed. Have a thorough nap, Dr. Graylock."

Thus we bade them both good-bye and found ourselves alone. Though a disappointment, it had its advantages. Ginny made sandwiches and took them with some milk down to Ben and Chryssa, who were still absorbed in their own interests. Meanwhile I got out cold stuff, including two beers, for her and me. Val would probably sulk for a couple of hours yet, then descend on the kitchen like a devouring flame.

Ginny and I sat down to our food. Edgar croaked on the back of her chair, Svartalf ambled over and mneowrred. She gave them both their treats. I told her what had passed between Will and me, and about Bob Shining Knife's call. She nodded and said, "All right, we'll do what we can for him." After a moment: "But I'm doubtful what use it'll be. I want to meet with Balawahdiwa as soon as possible."

I figured she must be right about that, and didn't ask for details. Instead: "What was Curtice's problem, anyway? Is it confidential?"

Ginny laughed. "Yes, sort of. But I imagine you can guess, and I know you won't blab, so best you have the truth. They were to take the sanitation spell off her after the mission, of course, and somebody tried, last night at the infirmary. Given the confusion, and maybe whatever curse is lingering, he failed, as she found out this morning. Rather than make a fuss at NASA—poor girl, she has enough henhouse to cope with there as is—she came to me. I fixed her up."

"Oh. Yeah, I would've guessed."

After all, nothing about the life-support systems for spaceflight was supposed to be secret. We'd been exposed to ample, if coy publicity about hygiene in microgravity. A water elemental, a minihydro, was to float around the toilet cubicle and absorb urine. I'd seen the embodiment being reduced to steam. As for solid wastes, a cantrip recovered from ancient Egyptian papyruses was to turn them instantly into stone

scarabs, the sale of which as collectibles ought to help the NASA budget.

"She's back to normal?" I said. "Okay, DNQ. You know I'm good at keeping my mouth shut."

"Unless for food or beer or— Well," Ginny murmured, "I trust we can relax now till tomorrow morning, and even manage a smidgen of fun. We have a busy time ahead."

That was the understatement of the year, if not the century.

# VI

The temporary FBI station in Grants occupied several rooms on the ground floor of a commercial building in what had once passed for downtown. A window above proclaimed a dentist. The agents flown in crammed the quarters and spilled over the sidewalk. More, I knew from having called my lab, were at Cardinal Point, grilling everybody, peering everywhere after clues, and in general tangling Project Selene up worse than Coyote himself could have hoped to. These here were mostly bound for the field, therefore not wearing their usual business suits. They seemed ill at ease in broad-brimmed hats, open-necked shirts, stiff new Levi's, and stiff new boots—though some had shod themselves in canvas, which I knew they'd regret by day's end. They stood around waiting for their transportation like a tour group. Real tourists who came by gave them quizzical stares. Locals, Indians especially, cast glances sharper and colder.

They weren't stumblebums, understand. They'd simply been thrown overnight into a land and a situation foreign enough to bewilder anybody. I saw a few comfortable in well-worn outfits, faces tanned and creased by the sun that already hammered us. They'd been working hereabouts, out of Gallup, a fairly long time. Plain to see, each would guide a party around some predetermined section of the malpais. Though tenderfeet, the newcomers did have skills and equipment that might spot something significant.

Among them, posed as masterfully as each could manage under the circumstances, were half a dozen really high-powered thaumaturges. Their particular working garbs identified them as such. I saw a white beard spilling down a purple robe embroidered with stars; ostrich plumes, a necklace of leopard's teeth, and a grass kilt over a black

skin; a grandmotherly type with a ferret peeking from her big apron pocket, who passed the time knitting a scarf of interlocked Möbius strips; and—yes, yonder, unmistakable, Bob Shining Knife.

He and another man kept slightly aside. The sight of his tall, rangy form bright with painted patterns where breechclout or medicine blanket did not cover him, the craggy features surmounted by a bonnet of eagle feathers, brought memories of last time to me across the years like a fist. I caught my breath. Ginny clutched my arm. She too remembered. Then I glimpsed her smile, followed her look, and half grinned too. Though practical for this day's work, Bob's desert boots took the edge off the dramatic effect.

We approached. He blinked at sight of Edgar, big and glossy-black on Ginny's left shoulder. He controlled his face immediately and trod forward to give her and me his firm, quick handshake. "Good to see you," he said. The tone was as brisk as the gesture. Nevertheless, we knew he spoke sincerely. It was just that he was so much the honor-duty-country type. "Been a long while. Thanks for coming." He turned his head. "Steven and Virginia Matuchek, I'd like you to meet—"

"Gruk," interrupted the raven. He ruffled his feathers in a marked manner.

"Oh. Your new familiar?" Not wanting a scene, the agent bowed. "I'm sorry, sir. May I present myself? Robert Shining Knife, Federal Bureau of Investigation."

"Edgar," croaked Edgar, more or less mollified.

"How is old Svartalf?" Shining Knife inquired.

"Still with us," Ginny replied, "but, yes, old."

Shining Knife gestured to his companion. "Now let me introduce Jack Moy, of our San Francisco office."

This was a compact young man, whose clothes and bearing suggested he spent vacations in places like the Sierra and the Mojave. Though the round face was Chinese, his English was straight Californian. "Glad to meet you. I've heard a lot about you lately." He seemed amiable. Seemed.

"From the files?" Ginny asked in her most guileless fashion.

"Well, yes, mainly. Your, uh, episode was before my time." Moy whistled. "But what an episode it was."

"I take it you had Mr. Moy look it up when you co-opted him, Bob," Ginny said to Shining Knife with the same mildness.

He nodded, imperturbable. "Yes and yes. Let's get started. Okay?"

"Only us four—us five?" I wondered.

"Today, at least." Shining Knife strode off. We could either come

along or stand where we were and waste our sweatiness on the desert air. Behind us, a bus carpet pulled alongside the curb to take on the first bunch of agents. Ginny nudged me and inclined her head. I glanced that way. A pair of teenage boys—Navajo, I guessed—lounged against a wall across the street. They snickered to one another and sneered, obviously at Shining Knife. If he noticed, he ignored them.

Our destination was the parking lot of the large new Flying Horse Broomotel. He led us to a rugged twin-sprite four-seat carpet with an outsize coffer at the rear. The Landlouper's well-worn condition and New Mexico license plates showed that it doubtless belonged to the Gallup office and he'd wangled or commandeered use of it.

"Where are we bound, anyway?" I asked.

"I hope you can tell us," he answered. "We'll talk as we go."

He took the key from somewhere inside his breechclout—the gourd shoved there rattled—and made the sign that released the warder charm too deftly for me to follow. I suspect Ginny did. We boarded. Taking the driver's seat, he spelled a windfield around us and a cloudlet overhead for shade. Ginny sat beside him, Moy and I behind. Edgar hopped off her and perched ahead, one foot clasping either of the two power control globes. They flushed angry red for a moment, but regained proper crystal clarity. Shining Knife gestured. The rug lifted and wove its way south through traffic.

The town fell away beneath us. From above, you could practically read its history. It had been a thin sprawl around a railway depot till Project Selene settled nearby. The resulting inburst of people and associated industries filled every vacant space and continued the sprawl farther. It was now bigger than Gallup, without having gained any of Gallup's charm. Mount Taylor loomed in the distance like a rampart that might someday, somehow stop the onrushing tide of losangelesation.

"For a guy who's barely arrived, you sure swing mucho weight, Bob," I said. "Are you in charge of the case?"

"Oh, no." He barked a laugh. "God forbid! I report directly to Mrs. Gutierrez Padilla in Albuquerque. But what with past experience—not only with you two—I've gotten a roving commission. I can act fairly independently.

"Carry on," he ordered the sprites. They obeyed, though they clearly didn't appreciate a bird on their balls. He looked first at Ginny, then me. "The fact that you're here, and we've been involved before, helped decide that."

Tactful of him to use a neutral word, "involved." Last time around,

Ginny and I hadn't exactly—what you might call—cooperated with the government. However, we didn't—exactly—oppose it either. Let's say that it and we had the same general objectives, but didn't see eye to eye on policy or procedure.

"May I ask why you've brought Mr. Moy in, evidently carrying a similar status?" Ginny inserted, tigress polite. "Amazing, how fast you've both moved." A touch of lightness: "A vigil spell, or gallons of coffee?"

"As for me," Moy said in candid California style, "I majored in Asian history, with an idea of going into the Foreign Service. When I got more interested in detective work, I went back to school, concentrating on Far Eastern talismanics and geomancy." The FBI requires every agent to have a degree in either sorcery or accounting.

"We've reason to suspect Asian complicity," Shining Knife added. "Jack came straightaway to my mind, and I called him."

Moy frowned. "Hey, easy, there. If you please, Mr. and Mrs. Matuchek, this is mighty delicate stuff. A false accusation, or a true one if it's not handled right, could upset a lot of applecarts."

"Such as those pushed by gentlemen in striped pants," Ginny said tartly.

She followed the news closer than I did, but I got her drift. The Chinese Revolution, the new Soong Dynasty a figurehead for a Taoist junta, the ruthless drives not only to put down the last bandits and warlords but to purge the country of alien influences, regain lost territories, make China once again a world power— They weren't necessarily pushing cookies in our State Department; over there, they were treading on eggshells. The situation wasn't just explosive, it was as scrambled as my metaphors.

Ginny acknowledged the fact. "All right, we'll stay discreet. But if we're to be of any service, we'll need to know what the reasons are for your suspicions."

"And for openers," I said, "the reasons for your bringing us in. Look, we're as surprised and ignorant as anybody. All I've ever done at the Point is communications R and D, straightforward scryotronics. And Ginny's an independent witch. We've consulted her a few times, but on strictly technical problems."

For instance, an experimental relay satellite that suddenly changed test messages into Breton obscenities. It turned out that when the bronze parrot was cast, the contractor had used an old, broken church bell from Quimper. That was no bad idea, lingering sanctity of St. Corentin and so forth, but the thaumaturgic tests were sloppily done

and nobody spotted a korrigan trapped in the metal. Cosmic rays broke down the quantum-resonance charm that bound it, and naturally it cut loose. Having identified the trouble, Ginny recalled the Being to Earth and set it happily free in the Forest of Broceliande.

"I've a hunch you don't simply happen to be on the spot," Shining Knife replied. He kept his gaze forward. City was giving way to sage, gray-blue under the sun and the depths of heaven. The air whispered hot around our passage. Its dryness made my nostrils tingle. He lifted a hand. "No offense, friends. I only mean that you may, entirely innocently, tend to be nexuses—uh—nexi?—"

"Nexuses," Ginny told him.

"—when major powers of darkness are afoot. Because you have unusual powers of your own. Though you use them for good, of course."

She tensed. "You don't mean the Adversary in person? Do you?"

"Can't say, at this stage. Most likely, Beings who're on his side but acting by and for themselves. That's plenty bad enough."

She scowled. "Coyote's hostile, no doubt, and not a very nice fellow anytime. But I don't believe we've a right to call him satanic."

"No judgments yet. We've barely begun collecting information. My hope is that you can help us gather more. If nothing else, you have your particular abilities, both of you. You know the territory and the people."

"Not intimately," I warned, "after two years."

"But I've gathered you, Virginia, have made friends among the Indians and learned quite a lot. That alone may make a difference. I know too damn well that the FBI isn't popular on reservations."

"Hereabouts they call you Fibbies," I stated bluntly.

He sighed. "I've heard. Unavoidable, I guess. When we, as federal agents, have to come in on certain crime scenes, we're apt to interfere with the tribal police, who often know better how the matter should be handled. Though I did think that I, being an Indian myself—"

"Sorry, Bob." Ginny patted his hand. Her voice had softened. "Locally, they look on outside Indians the way, oh, a Frenchman might look on a visiting German."

I saw his rueful grin. "And me an Oglala Sioux. Can you mediate?"

"I can try, but the connections I've developed are mainly Zuni." She paused. "Are the Hopi and Navajo shamans being stiff-necked?"

"I've been told they are. Of course, it's early in the game. Still,

I've heard that those of them who've been questioned have clammed up."

Her red head nodded. "What did you expect? The shamans made an agreement with NASA. In exchange for various benefits to their people, they'd see to it that Coyote and other Beings they knew about would be kept out of Cardinal Point. Now *something* has broken or wormed past the spells. By implication, at least, they're accused of either incompetence or conspiracy. Not only their pride, but the honor of their tribes is at stake."

"Yes, well, yes, but I should think if they opened up to us—"

"That's more complex than it sounds, as well you know, Robert Shining Knife."

He bit his lip. "Um-m, yeah. Possibly our operatives were kind of hamhanded yesterday. Is that unforgivable? The situation came at them in a rush, out of nowhere. Can you help us make amends?"

Ginny shrugged. "Maybe I can refer you to someone who may be able to." Sharply: "You've something more specific in mind for Steve and me. Otherwise you wouldn't flit us off like this. What do you think we can do that your thaumaturges can't?"

He sighed again. "I'm not too sure. Put us onto a spoor they might not scent?"

"Where? Obviously you've gridded the locality, and each of your teams will go over its assigned square with magnifying glasses and dowsers."

"They could miss traces you and Steve wouldn't. That's why I was anxious to get us in the field ahead of them."

"You're talking about a lot of acreage," I put in. "No way can we cover it all. Where should we head?"

"I hoped you'd have an intuition. As a medicine man myself, I knew from the first this isn't a routine case." Shining Knife's shoulders slumped. "It was worth a try."

"Hold on, man," Moy said. "We haven't provided the Matucheks near enough information. Like, we're asking them to make straw without bricks, right?" To us: "Okay, let me fill you in a little bit, like on the Asian angle."

Ginny twisted around to look straight at him. Edgar peered from the globes. It was easier for me. He leaned back in his seat, making a relaxed, open-handed gesture. "You see," he related, "we know—Military Intelligence and everybody else concerned does—the Chinese are hot to get into space and would dearly love to be first. Prestige, seizing the high ground, et geopolitical cetera. They can't do that unless

they stymie our effort, right? Also the Europeans', but it's way behind ours, and as for the Russians, with that huge religious revival of theirs they'll be content to orbit a few ikons. Now, the FBI keeps liaison with Scotland Yard, so we know Fu Ch'ing is currently in England."

"Fu who?" I blurted.

Moy gave me a capitalized Look. "You've never heard of the insidious Dr. Fu Ch'ing?"

Under the cloudlet, against the sun-glare beyond, the bones stood forth in Ginny's abruptly pale face. "I have," she said.

Moy nodded, more calm because he'd dealt with this more. "Sure, you would have, Mrs. Matuchek." To me: "It isn't publicized. The evidence has to stay confidential—protection of sources and so forth. Beside . . . hm-m . . . any journalists who've picked up some hints, either they came to bad ends, quick-like, or they've been smart and kept quiet. He's the top thaumaturge in China, and also its top secret agent."

"Not that he acts under orders," Shining Knife observed. "There are times when he *is* the Chinese government."

The small hairs rose across my body. Wolf, I'd have given a better display. "If he's that big, why isn't he under constant surveillance?" I demanded.

"Impossible," Moy explained. "It was indirectly, through their own spies, that the British Secret Service learned he's come to England. Applying their resources, they might find out where he's headquartered—maybe they have, a time or two—but what use is that? If they tried to raid the place, he'd be gone, taking everything important with him."

"Does the Yard have any idea what his purpose is?" Ginny asked.

"They and the Foreign Office can guess. Make trouble wherever he can. But mainly, insert some bad luck into the European Conference on Activity in Space. It's meeting in London this year, you may know, and has hopes of actually accomplishing something. But meanwhile, we Americans were ready for a major launch—and there Fu Ch'ing is, better connected to us across the Atlantic than across the Pacific. Wouldn't he try to take advantage of that?" Moy shrugged. "It's a thought. One of the many we need to pursue."

"My brother has Chinese connections," Ginny murmured. "Possibly that has sympathetic, sensitizing effects on me—" She stiffened. "Why didn't you invite him along today?"

As seldom before, Shining Knife sounded awkward. "He's a, a

scientist, isn't he? Not a practical goeticist. I don't think this is in his area of competence."

Ginny clenched her jaw. "So you say. I thought jargon was beneath you, Robert."

I saw him wounded. He masked it fast.

She relented for the time being. "However, what we want is the truth. All right, after what you two have told us, plus whatever knowledge we two have, I can try."

She stood up on the carpet. The cloudlet hazed her head; stray locks fluttered like flame. She took her wand from her belt pouch and extended it. The star-point at the tip burst into brilliance, even in this light. It lay loosely in her right hand while the green eyes half closed. The raven jumped to her shoulder and spread his wings straight aloft, like pieces of night. When she reached behind her and touched her left fingers to my head, tiny lightnings went through me.

I heard her murmur and sensed her think.

The wand swung about of itself to point southeast. "Go yonder," she said.

# VII

We landed in a gaunt part of the Malpais, beyond sight of anything human, and got off.

Mostly that great volcanic basin is rather beautiful. Grass, brush, and small evergreen trees cover it more fully than you might expect in so arid a land. Sandstone cliffs, like pale gold, rim it on the east, mesas and ridges on the west, beneath the royally blue sky of high altitude. But Ginny's wand had led us to the edge of a lava outcrop. Black, ropy masses lay tumbled before us, hot and hard; sharp shards waited underfoot for us to stumble on and slash ourselves if we fell. The sun savaged them.

Even here life kept a hold, a thin growth of stuff like saltbush, snakeweed, and bunchgrass, gray spatters of lichen, now and then a tiny flower. However, this was not a friendly place.

"I think you'd better go wolf, Steve," Ginny said into the quietness. "We'll need every capability we have."

"Yeah." Having expected that, I'd prepared. I went to the rear of the rug. The G-men had opened the coffer and were taking out their apparatus. "If you'll make room for me, I'll transform," I offered. "Provide you a better nose, if nothing else."

"Uh, won't the ultraviolet be dangerous for you?" asked Moy as he buttered sunblock over his exposed skin.

Evidently he wasn't too familiar with the subject. Nobody can know everything. "Not in itself, except for inhibiting the change in either direction," I said. "In my movie days, we often shot a scene under pretty fierce edisons." To make conversation while they emptied the coffer: "The reason werecritters were traditionally believed to be nightgangers was that in nature only a full or nearly full moon gives

the combination of polarizations, strong enough, necessary to trigger the hormones and such. Getting caught in animal shape by dawn could mean you were in big trouble. You might have to do desperate things, trying to stay alive through the month. It helped give our kind a bad name—which, in turn, helped sour their dispositions and make outlawry look not so bad."

"Ah, yes, it comes back to me now. The Bureau does employ a few therianthropes, you know." A few; we tend not to be organization persons, what with the wild instincts latent in us. "I never chanced to meet any till you, Mr. Matuchek, either professionally or socially." Moy smiled. "At least, that I'm aware of."

I nodded. "We're fairly scarce to start with. And there isn't a lot of demand for the ability anymore. Trite in show biz. These days Incantational Light and Technics can provide way fancier special effects. We do some police work, as you say; some military; and the Park Service would like to have more of us as rangers than it's got, but the pay's lousy. So, often, to avoid prejudice or cranks or inane questions, weres keep their nature to themselves and only change privately, for fun."

"They have semi-secret social groups," Shining Knife said. "*Not* the Lions, Elks, or Moose."

"It's hardly a Chinese thing at all," Moy observed. "Last I heard, the scientists hadn't agreed yet on how much that's due to culture, how much to genetics. Genetics mostly is my personal guess, because Japan's different."

I registered my surprise. "But aren't the Japanese and Chinese people close kin?"

"Not really. The distant ancestors of the Japanese came mainly from Southeast Asia. I'm told that weretigers are well-known down there."

I'd tangled with one once, Near Eastern. "Notorious, but rare. A man's got to be monstrous tall and heavy to have the mass of a respectable tiger. Wereleopards, now, or weredeer—" My mind wandered irresponsibly off to a silly old college song, tune of "Auld Lang Syne."

*We're deer because weredeer because we're dear—*

"Okay, Steve, the space is yours," Shining Knife said. Sweat blotted his blanket and shimmered across the thunderbirds, solar discs, and whatnot else painted on his body. I was pleased to see that among the objects removed were a cooler and four thermoses, plainly containing lunch. No doubt the bottles were full of lemonade or iced tea, but I imagined a few cans of beer in the box.

I took off my boots and clothes, down to the knitsuit underneath. Tossing them at a seat, I climbed into the coffer. Shining Knife closed the lid. Cramped in darkness, I fumbled after the Polaroid projector hung on my breast, aimed it, and thumbed the switch.

Transformation roiled me.

Wolf, I rapped with a paw. Shining Knife let me out. I sprang forth. Unshod, I felt the harshness of the terrain; but though I was a timber wolf, not a coyote, my pads were tough as leather. The heat was harder to take. Only my feet and black nose could sweat. I lolled my tongue. The steamoff from it sent a measure of—no proper human word available—relief down to the end of my abbreviated tail. The glare hurt worse. My eyes were nearsighted but sensitive. Ginny hurried over with a pair of dark glasses from her pouch and slipped them onto my muzzle. They were prescription, too; I saw almost as well as before.

This meant less than you might suppose. The dimwitted human aspect of me appreciated it, but I was largely lupine, my brain attuned to scents, sounds, breezelets that stirred the fine hairs in my ears and ghosted along my pelt, the *taste* of that air— Again, I haven't words. No language does. A lizard scuttered between stalks of grass. My nose told me how cool-sweet its flesh would be and I resisted the temptation to snap it up like a canapé off a tray. Somewhere nearby a rattlesnake lay coiled in the shade of a rock, a thicker, sharper smell: *touch me not.* The sun baked fragrances out of weeds and a faint memory of ancient brimstone out of the lava. . . .

"All set?" Shining Knife called. "Let's get going."

I don't remember the next few hours very clearly. As said, while in some ways I was smarter and more aware than ever in human shape, I didn't have my normal IQ by a long shot. Besides, I never was a warlock. I knew the everyday cantrips and such, plus those needed for my engineering work, plus oddments acquired here and there, but the Art of my companions went leagues beyond that, and on three separate roads.

Ginny, her own glasses on her like a mask, set Edgar aflight as she might have loosed a hawk. The wand quivered in her grasp, seeking to and fro; the star-point now blazed, now dimmed to a coal; she uttered words in tongues unknown to me.

Shining Knife danced. The eagle bonnet shivered, the blanket tossed, as if borne on unfelt winds. His voice keened high. The gourd rattled in his hand. Sometimes he'd pause and stride across yards of desolation, to hunker down and peer, take a pinch of soil and sniff,

ponder on what he had found. And sometimes he'd sit cross-legged, stare straight out over immensity, lose himself altogether from us.

Moy walked around slowly, also often stopping. In his left hand, supported on the arm, he carried a clipboard holding several sheets of paper. Some were covered with Chinese characters, some were blank. A container at the top held small implements. He'd take sightings with compass, goniometer, and plumb bob. He'd consult his texts. With a calligraphic fountain brush he'd make notes, which included vivid sketches of the scenery. Other writings were calculations or spells.

Me, I coursed to and fro, snuffing the earth and the air, hunting for spoor. Beetles, ground squirrel scat, packrat burrow, stray feather, forsaken bone. . . . For a while a stand of rabbitbrush threw me off. Its smell has been variously compared to dog piss and to a blend of thyme and skunk. Pretty overwhelming.

I worked my way around it and happened to come on the first clue. But that was when I saw Edgar descend for a close peek. Nor would either of us have found anything if the party as a whole hadn't charmed—intuited, reasoned, made—progress forward in the right general direction.

Traces, weathered but too strong to be quite gone, a reek that raised the lips off my fangs and my muzzle on high. . . . The howl rang lonesome through the noonday silence.

The others joined me as fast as the terrain allowed. I vaguely followed their excited voices: "—demonic. . . . Nothing I've ever met before. . . . Or I, unless— Mr. Moy? . . . Let me examine this more closely. If Mr. Matuchek will please outline the scented area—" My nose scuffed the dirt and got dust up it. I sneezed. That was okay; it blew out the odor.

"Shen—I think," Moy said low. "Could be something else—not clear enough to tell—but, yes, the geomantic alignment—"

We pressed our search harder. The trail, dim, repeatedly lost and regained, led toward unseen Cardinal Point. Once I heard Moy mutter, "Possibly accompanied by some kind of o-bake," and didn't understand.

What I did know, when I came on it, was the remnant of a big fat male stench not unlike what I might have left, except for overtones that made my tail-stump try to tuck itself between my hind legs. I mastered the fear but didn't quite dare make a noise. Instead, I lolloped back and tugged at Ginny's jeans.

She and the agents squatted to exercise their particular Gifts. Edgar

flapped to perch on her shoulder and croak in her ear. She nodded grimly.

"Out of my department, I'm afraid," Moy said after a few minutes.

"In mine, I think," Shining Knife answered. "We've had word on the Plains—" He glanced at Ginny. "Coyote, right?"

"Yes, I'm sure." Her tone was flat. "He met the other or the others, whoever or whatever they were—he met them here. But first, in his insolent fashion, he signed the territory."

To me, at the moment, that seemed a fairly natural thing to do.

"Rendezvous arranged by Fu Ch'ing?" Shining Knife wondered.

"I can't say," Moy replied. "Let's push on."

We did. The dome of the VAB at the Point hove above the horizon, wavery in heat-shimmers. We glimpsed distance-dwarfed figures scrambling about, FBI personnel. Probably we were near the end of our own usefulness.

No. Shining Knife spotted the last indications we found—crushed stems, scuffed soil—and pointed me at them. Human smells barely lingered. A few feet away, Coyote's and his cronies' drowned them. However, the physical marks were plain. I heard Shining Knife interpret them: "Somebody landed a broomstick, and walked around in company with the Beings. A man, not a woman, to judge from the footprints, blurry though they are. Steve, do you by any chance recognize a scent?"

I shook my long head. After two days in this weather, what individually identifiable mortal odor could remain? Inwardly, I shivered, and I choked off a growl. A hint, a tinge? No. Impossible. Besides, we canines don't rat on our friends.

Our party searched a bit more but found little or nothing. Also, by then we were exhausted and starved, and had emptied our canteens. We trudged back to the carpet. Edgar flew, and sat there when we arrived. "Lunch!" he demanded hoarsely.

My companions set it out. Meanwhile I crawled into the coffer and rechanged. That takes practice when you're an animal. The confined space didn't make it easier. First I squirmed around to lie on my back, so that the flash, hung from its cord, rested flat on me. Holding it down with my right paw, I used my left to press the switch. After that I worked it around, caught it under my jaw, and let it shine over my belly, hind legs, and tail. Not a dignified procedure, but sufficient for transformation.

When I came out, Shining Knife had evoked local HQ on the annular phone and was reporting in Middle Sumerian. It's been recon-

structed by tablet animation techniques, but is still obscure enough that hardly anybody knows it—not even thaumaturges wanting yet another exotic language for spellcasting—except in places like MI and the FBI, where they worry about eavesdroppers a lot.

By the time he was finished and I was dressed, the sandwiches, potato salad, and drinks had been set out. No beer, damn it. When he's on the job, Shining Knife is such a Boy Scout. Well, thirsty as I was, iced tea went down fine. We reversed the front seat of the Landlouper and sat face to face under the cloudlet, eating off our laps. Edgar stuck his beak in and nipped as he pleased. He figured he'd earned it.

Being newly human-intelligent, I needed explanations. "What did we actually find?" I asked.

"Plenty," Shining Knife said. "I doubt we could have without your help and Ginny's." The raven's beady eyes ransacked him. "And Edgar's, of course. Before the assigned search teams got this far, nature would have wiped out every helpful sign." Nature, always seeking for balance, blurring tracks to oblivion, evaporating volatiles, annulling memorials and memories. "Your country thanks you." He could say things like that without running for office. I liked him anyway. Too bad we kept clashing.

"As of now," he went on, "the teams have only gotten evidence of Coyote's nearness on the night of the disaster. Probably the, hm, the demons didn't need to approach any closer than we did today. From that distance, they could weaken the guardian spells."

"How?"

"Subtly, so that nothing visibly changed, no alarms went off, no warning was given," Moy said. "Cardinal Point was protected against Western goetics, white, Indian, and paranatural. It was not protected against influences more exotic. Nobody expected attack from that quarter. Also, to this day there's a great deal we don't know about the fine points of Far Eastern thaumaturgics. I'd guess that these Beings opened a way for Coyote to play his tricks."

*Yeah,* I thought, *real Asian.*

Moy brought me up short: "But I know enough about the subject that I can tell you they couldn't have done this without guidance, information, supplied by someone reasonably familiar with the layout and the goetics. Obviously, I'd say, the man who met them."

Ginny's voice leaped: "You keep saying 'they.' Who or what, besides Coyote, do you mean?"

"I'm sorry, but that's still obscure to me."

"More so to me. I trained at schools like Harvard and Trismegistus,

not Berkeley. You mentioned shen, Mr. Moy. As I understand it, those are Chinese Beings, related to the elements but not really as Western ones are. Could you clarify?"

Her intensity spoiled his enjoyment of his ham sandwich. Shining Knife and I tautened likewise.

"Not in any nutshell," Moy said. " 'Shen' in Chinese is about as catchall a word as 'spirit' is in English or 'daimon' and 'genius' were in Classical civilization. Some shen may, as you put it, be elementals of a sort, but not conjured up by humans the way we conjure up things like Hydros and salamanders. Others may be . . . not exactly ghosts, but a certain part or aspect of a human that stays around after the body dies. If that person is then paid honors and looked to for help for a long time—sort of like a medieval European saint—well, unlike the saint, the spirit's powers will grow. Some at last become very strong." He sighed. "I could spend the rest of the afternoon and not cover the nuances. Try the article in the *Encyclopaedia Sinica.*"

Ginny frowned. "Also unlike a local saint, a shen isn't necessarily benign, am I right?"

"True. Most are, some aren't. It's similar in Japan, with different names. The malignant kind feed on the fear they inspire and the sacrifices people make trying to appease them. They become roughly analogous to Western devils. But it's not a purely spiritual thing. Evil shen can do physical as well as moral harm."

"So can devils," I said, remembering. *Which means, on the plus side, they can be killed.*

"Did the shen all fall Asleep as the Iron Age advanced?" Ginny persisted.

"Apparently, except maybe for isolated localities," Moy answered. "When finally they Awoke, the evil shen saw what arrears of mischief waited for them. The chaos after the Manchu Dynasty fell gave them a field day. After the Mandate of Heaven came to the Soong, the Taoists, above all, got organized, and have been mounting a campaign to quell them."

"I know that. Who doesn't? Please go on."

"The question hasn't been properly addressed, I think—if the wicked ones escape the mages and priests, where shall they go, what shall they do? We have a few hints. The business on hand provides more."

"M'm. You're guessing, then, that for whatever reason, perhaps inspired by Dr. Fu, they want to sabotage the space program. Somehow they got together with Coyote, who wants the same—"

As Ginny's words trailed off, Shining Knife said, "Yes, they met mainly through the man who joined them that night to see the job got done. A reasonable hypothesis, anyhow."

My belly muscles tightened. I made a mental note that our Operation Luna needed better security, insignificant though it might be.

"You mentioned another kind of Being too, when we were out hunting," Ginny said. "I got indications myself, but couldn't name them. Something—" She hesitated. "—more eerie. Did I hear you use a Japanese word?"

"I don't know a lot about Japanese spirits—kami, o-bake, whatever," Moy admitted. "There are important differences from the Chinese. The oni might correspond to Scandinavian trolls, sort of. But you're aware the Shinto authorities in Japan, same as the Taoists in China, are trying to purge all the shrines of what they call unauthorized Beings. You may not like every current policy of those two governments—I don't myself—but both countries are going to be cleaner."

"And so the . . . demons . . . look for new strongholds? It'd be logical for the Chinese and Japanese ones to make alliance. But you gentlemen think they need the help of humans. What humans?"

"Dr. Fu, maybe," Shining Knife said fast. "But, hey, we've done a good day's work here. Let's finish our meal and scoot back to where we can relax."

Ginny and I swapped a glance. Edgar joined in. We realized our leader didn't want to pursue the topic. We weren't sure why, but knew the matter was settled.

Therefore we soon flew back to Grants, making small talk when we weren't silent. The silences felt companionable. There's nothing like a worthwhile undertaking to forge bonds. Whatever our disagreements, now or in the future, I was glad to have seen Bob Shining Knife again and met Jack Moy.

We shook hands in the parking lot. "I'll be in touch," Shining Knife said, as ambiguously as we knew he must. Ginny, Edgar, and I returned to our broom.

"What do you think about this?" I asked as we flitted.

"I'd rather not, yet," she sighed.

Poor girl, she'd laid out far more effort than me, even if it showed less. I stroked her mane. "Okay, then what's your opinion of a tall, cool drink?"

"Best offer I've had all day." She laughed.

Of course it wasn't that simple. Ben had gone on a campout with the family of his best friend. Val, whom we'd persuaded to look after

Chryssa, didn't mope at us. Instead, as agreed beforehand, she took off to meet a giggle of girls her age at a shishkebab parlor.

Well, Ginny and I only meant to throw something together, whatever it might be, when we felt the need. Meanwhile our youngest wanted stories and jokes and love. Svartalf graciously accepted some of the attention.

Thus an hour or more passed before I got around to the mail. Ginny came back from settling the kid down with a Wanda Witch show to hear me mumble, "Uh-oh," not precisely in those words.

"What's gone wrong now?" she asked.

"See for yourself." I handed her the letter.

The heading was federal, Inquisition for Revenue Securement. Operation Luna generally and we specifically were under income tax audit. Since we claimed part of our home costs as office expenses, the examiner wanted to meet us here. Sincerely, et cetera.

"Coincidence?" I speculated. "Or the Enemy at work?"

"I don't know." Ginny's features stood keenly against white walls and sun-yellowed blinds. "Maybe coincidence."

"You'll need time to collect our records, won't you?" God be praised, she took such horrors off my shoulders.

"That's no problem. But—" Her eyes sought mine. "Steve, the more I think about today, the more certain I feel that we must see Balawahdiwa. Soonest. Tomorrow, if possible. While I try to arrange that, suppose you check with Barney Sturlason."

She went out. I got onto the phone. It was past quitting time in the Midwest, but I caught him at the plant.

His image well-nigh filled the scryer. "*Ja,*" he rumbled. The blocky, crew-cut gray head wove back and forth, like a lion's when it's set on by a pack of jackals. "They're already infesting Nornwell. I didn't want to worry you about it, especially after the blowup, but— Well, carry on, and don't forget, we keep a pretty good tax diabolist on retainer."

That eased me. Neither Ginny and I nor Nornwell had attempted any kind of fraud. Bloody nuisance, of course, but— I called the local IRS and made an appointment for day after tomorrow. Ginny returned and told me Balawahdiwa would receive us in the morning. I wondered if she'd cast a minor spell to make events mesh this efficiently. She mixed a gin and tonic, I poured a beer, and we retired to the patio, beneath the trellis and its honeysuckle. Best to take what pleasure we could while we could.

# VIII

Zuni lies about thirty miles south of Gallup. We went there leisurely, starting while the day was still cool and skirting the eastern border of the reservation for the sake of the views. First the sunbeams turned the Wingate rock fiery for us. As we swung south, the Zuni Mountains ran along to our left, on the edge of the Continental Divide. In itself that mass wasn't too impressive, mostly a rounded ridge crowned by pines. But time and weather had done their own sorceries at the bases. Even with the sun low behind, the sandstone glowed tawny, red, white, often in bands like the stripes of Old Glory; and shadows brought out the relief of cliffs, crags, crevices, outthrusts and upthrusts, changing moment by moment as the light did, so that it was almost as if that banner rippled in a geological wind.

When we bore west, away from Ramah, we passed over valleys and low mesas begrown with piñon and juniper. Where two summer-dwindled streams flowed together to make the Zuni River, the land wrinkled upward again and we flew above the Gates of Zuni, the notch that the water had cut. Beyond, we found another valley, more broad and open, guarded on three sides by colorful steeps. Conifers and cropland greened it, though sparingly, for here was a parched country. The river always ran small; at this season the bed was nearly dry, though full of reeds.

The pueblo had in the course of time spread to both sides of it. Three miles off, Corn Mountain dominated the southeast, a giant, banded mesa rising sculptured, nearly sheer, to its own forest—Dowa Yalanne, as sacred to the people and central to their history as the Acropolis once was to Athens.

Courtesy, if not law, demanded we come down and fly in at man

height above the rutted dirt road from Gallup. That wasn't much altitude. Indians in these parts are mostly short and sturdy. Shining Knife stood forth among them like a Swede in Istanbul. The languages and cultures were about as different too, or more so.

A few dwellers were out tending patches of corns, beans, squash, chilis, peach trees, and occasional sheepfolds. They mostly wore faded denims, sometimes a headband instead of a hat. More often than not, men's hair fell to the shoulders. They used hand tools, and I glimpsed a cart drawn by a burro.

This was choice rather than poverty: a ceremonious, deeply religious folk keeping to their traditions as much as possible. They weren't fanatical about it; fanaticism wasn't in their nature. There were enough brooms, truckrugs, phones, crystals, and other such stuff in the pueblo to serve their modest needs. Their children attended a good school elsewhere on the reservation. They were strict about sanitation, and had modified their ancient healing practices to accommodate medical spells, antibiotics, and I know not what else. In fact, Ginny had told me that clinical practice in the outside world had learned things from them.

Several of the workers saw us go by and waved greetings. Given their history, the Zunis nurse prejudices against Spaniards—who also managed to garble their name, Ashiwi, and throw a tilde on top of the mistaken *n*—as well as Mexicans and Apaches. However, their relationship these days with the Navajos was fairly cordial, and of course they'd always had fellowship with the Hopis. On the whole, they'd gotten along comparatively well with Americans, ill-treated though they often were till lately. It stirred my heart to hear one man cry, "Hello, there, Dr. Matuchek!" Ginny waved back.

Well, from the beginning of our New Mexico stay she'd taken a special interest in them. Maybe it was happenstance, her meeting Balawahdiwa in Gallup and falling into shop talk. Or maybe, once more, it was something subtler. Anyhow, she'd become popular in the pueblo—her respectful questions, her study of the unique language, her helpfulness with minor problems. And though as a woman she was debarred from some things, I don't suppose her looks did any harm, no matter how foreign.

For a passing moment, my mind going grasshopper, I wondered how the tribe would have fared—did fare—in another history. Say the one that Will had speculated about, where science didn't find rheatics and therefore goetics didn't develop, so that machines more and more dominated technology. Would this road have been paved? Would these

plots exist along it, or would there have been a concentration on sheep farming for the market, or what? . . . No matter. We were here and now. But I did get a sense of strength, an idea that the Zuni soul would not easily surrender anywhere or anywhen.

We entered the town—or village, which is just as inaccurate—and landed at a parking site by the church. Lately restored, its simple squareness and the cross on top of a belfry arch loomed above a weed-begrown cemetery and a couple of *hornos,* round clay ovens. The interior was currently being decorated with vivid murals of native religious motifs. Though Catholicism had had considerable influence, the local faith was so firmly rooted that missionary efforts to replace it had, shall I say, petered out.

Otherwise little that was old remained. Homes were mostly one-family, low and small but modern, generally well apart on the dusty ground. There were a couple of stores and cafes. Aside from the mountain, sacred sites weren't in plain view, unless you counted the open areas where ceremonies took place in season. No visitors except us had yet appeared. The dwellers were going about their business, much of it indoors. School hadn't yet begun and children romped around. We'd arrived at a pause in the year's round of dances and other rites.

We picked our way beneath the sun, through the mounting warmth, to Balawahdiwa's house. Maybe because of his status, he'd chosen to renovate one of the surviving earlier buildings. It stood foursquare, dry-laid stone chinked with adobe, ceiling beams projecting below the flat roof. However, the windows were aluminum-framed and the door plywood.

I knocked. His wife admitted us: a stout woman in embroidery-trimmed blue blouse and long, sashed skirt, a necklace of silver, turquoise, and shell across her bosom. *"Keshi,"* she said, and rendered it into uncertain English: "Welcome. Welcome. Please come."

"Thank you, Mrs. Adams," I replied. I never could wrap my tongue around her Indian name.

Ginny managed it, "Waiyautitsa," in the middle of a proper Zuni phrase. We went in.

A fairly spacious room lay beyond, cool, darkish, neatly white-plastered between stone flagging and massive timbers. On the mantel of a fireplace stood a bowl of sacred cornmeal, and beside the hearth an up-to-date pair of thermostatic dolls, Eskimo and African. Elsewhere lamps, a farseer and music runer, a well-filled bookcase, and austere furniture stood on handsome rugs. In one corner an upright loom with

a half-finished piece of weaving reminded us that ancientness was still very much alive.

I'd heard from Ginny that beyond the door at the rear lay a regular kitchen and bathroom, plus a pair of cubicles for beds. It was all unpretentious, not what a white man might want if he bore a name famous in the history of his people; but the Zunis didn't go in for personal display.

Balawahdiwa sat alone at the table. His children were long since in households of their own. He drank one of his countless daily mugs of coffee and watched a chessboard. Animated, the pieces fought the game out by themselves. The runer was tootling the Dixieland jazz he also liked. Aside from a massive signatory ring, he was dressed like a farmer. He still tended the family plot, though he also occasionally made jewelry that fetched good prices.

Mainly, however, he was the chief Priest of the Bow.

He rose for us, signaling the chessmen to truce and the music to silence. "Welcome, Steven and Virginia," he said. "I wish the reason for this visit were luckier, but we are always glad to see you. Sit happy."

Unlike Waiyautitsa's, his English was fluent. When he was a boy, his Deer clan saw the promise in him and pooled its resources for him to attend the state university. When the war reached these parts, he was among the guerrillas who made life miserable for the invaders. Afterward he returned home, to become increasingly a leader in his kiva and in pueblo affairs generally. Those invaders he'd put out of their misery had qualified him for his high religious rank.

Though he stood half a head shorter than me and his hair hung grizzled, his hand clasped mine with at least equal power. The wide, strong-boned face was deeply creased around the mouth but otherwise unwrinkled. The eyes shone like polished obsidian.

His wife gave us coffee, started more brewing, and settled back down at the loom—not self-effacement, simply carrying on what she'd been doing. I'd seen the pattern of what she wove at dances and realized that this would be a ceremonial kilt. *Who might she be making it for?* I wondered.

"The Zunis were sorry to learn of your trouble at Cardinal Point," Balawahdiwa said, "but thankful that nobody came to serious harm."

Ginny spoke in his language. He thought for a second, then turned to me.

"Your lady found a polite way of asking if I wasn't just being polite," he explained. His bit of a smile faded. "In a way, yes. We may as well talk frankly. In fact, we'd better. You probably know I was not

among those who blessed the NASA compound against hostile spirits. A couple of men from here joined in. I might have, if I'd known you folks at the time. But my feelings were so mixed I couldn't rightly take part. They still are, to a certain extent."

"Well, uh, some people do think the, the project will violate the, uh, sacredness of the moon," I said clumsily. "That's not the intent. With, with, uh, Beings already living there—"

He nodded. "As Virginia's brother first discovered. Yes, if we establish communion with them, that should be wonderful. Mainly, I've wished the facility were somewhere else. It's pulling in too much that's loud, garish, greedy—" He lifted a palm. "I'm not an enemy of your culture, Steven. All mankind owes it thanks for many gifts, not least the United States Constitution and Bill of Rights. But nobody's perfect, and this overgrowth doesn't belong here."

*No,* I thought, *not in the peace of the desert and the harmonies of its dwellers.*

Ginny broke in on my sentimentalism. "Sir, I've said this before and I'll say it again. You're human too. Your ancestors were. The Anasazi had to leave the north, long ago, because they'd wrecked their environment, farming it barren, stripping it for firewood. Wars, witch hunts, raids for loot and slaves, torture, battues to kill more game than could be eaten before it rotted—all went on as enthusiastically in America before the white man arrived as in Europe or Asia or Africa."

Balawahdiwa shrugged. "No argument. But I suppose you see what I mean."

"Yes indeed, and no argument about *that.*"

"Some of us hope spaceflight can be done a lot smaller and quieter," I ventured.

Balawahdiwa nodded. "Virginia's told me a little about your . . . Operation Luna, do you call it? How high are those hopes?"

"Not awfully," I admitted.

"This is beside the point," Ginny said. "You never wanted Coyote to run wild over Project Selene, did you?"

"No," Balawahdiwa said, almost too softly to be heard. "It could go to his head."

*A giddy head at best,* I thought; *but a demigod's.* Sometimes, when the mood hit him or the payoff looked right, he had helped mankind. Oftener he'd snared himself in his own mischief, even gotten killed, though after a while he came back to life. And what had he won, what knowledge had he brought back, from those journeys beyond death?

Always he was the Trickster. Tricks can get out of hand. The madcap can turn really vicious.

"And when he attacked, the other night," Ginny said, "it was with the help of foreign Beings."

The priest's features congealed. "I know. They stink of evil."

"You know?" I exclaimed. "How?"

Immediately I saw the question was stupid. He answered as if it were not. "Certain of us went up on Dowa Yalanne and made medicine. I myself scouted around in the malpais. We've learned a few things."

Ginny's fingers gripped the table edge. "I expected you would. That's why I asked to see you."

"To request Zuni help?"

"Before the government clumps in on elephant feet and tries demanding it," I said.

"That would be unwise of the government. Maybe you can warn it off." Balawahdiwa looked searchingly from one to the other of us. "You, my friends, I will give any help I am able. Not that I wish anyone else hurt, either. And, as I agreed, quite aside from projects and careers, we'd damn well better head Coyote off before he goes on a total rampage—if we can. Which we certainly can't with federal agents and bureaucrats and journalists and local pompasses on our backs. Will you drop a hint to the right people?"

"We'll do our best," Ginny promised.

Waiyautitsa came over, refilled our coffee mugs, and returned to her weaving. I wondered more and more about that kilt. Everyone sat mute for a while.

Balawahdiwa's gaze went to Ginny. She met it. The silence lengthened. Clatter and voices outside reached us faintly, as if from far away. The light in the windows waxed, the shadows on the floor contracted.

"You're not appealing on general principles alone, are you?" he murmured at last.

She shook her head. "No," she answered as quietly.

A chill walked my spine.

When the priest spoke again, his matter-of-fact tone came over us like a benediction. "At least we're lucky in the time of year. The big summer Rain Dance is behind us, and there's only minor stuff till the Doll Dance in October. Of course, already before then preparations will be under way in earnest for the Shalako." I'd heard that the Zunis took that midwinter festival as seriously as devout Christians do Easter or Jews Yom Kippur, and worked making ready for it as long and hard as New Orleans krewes do for Mardi Gras. "But I'll be fairly free this

next month or two." Since it wasn't like him not to mention others, I guessed that he figured most of the searching and . . . mysteries . . . would necessarily fall to him. As chief Priest of the Bow, he must command lore and powers nobody else did. "Let's start by comparing notes, and let's in the name of all that's holy be frank and honest. Later we can decide what to keep to ourselves."

The session lasted a couple of hours. Part of it went in his language. He and Ginny apologized, but English didn't have the proper words or concepts. Ah, well, when it came to describing what I'd found while wolf, they must be content with statements as bald as a basketball, no real explanation of how I knew what I knew.

In the end, grimly, Balawahdiwa summed up: "Coyote was somehow put in touch with alien Beings who want spaceflight killed, probably more than he does. Or else someone led them to him. I suspect he mainly resents the encroachment on his territory, although he rejoices at a whole new set of challenges and possibilities for havoc. The Beings could temporarily and unnoticed annul the charms that protected Cardinal Point, because those were charms against local spirits and European-tradition evildoers. Your Fibby is probably right about their being Chinese demons—most of them. We Zunis have no information there. But we do seem to know more where it comes to ghosts. Not that we can put a name to that which accompanied the . . . the shen. But the signs were clear to us, and damn scary." His fist clenched on the table. "I've never before winded cold malignancy like that."

I heard the pain in Ginny's voice and reached for her hand. She clasped mine tightly. "And the human who met them?"

"We don't know, any of us," Balawahdiwa replied, gone gentle. "The dreams we dreamt on the mountain say he *could* be someone close to you."

"And the smells I smelled— No!" I shook my head violently. "Too faint, too contaminated. Not to mention the chance of malicious witchcraft, to throw us off the scent."

Ginny locked glances with Balawahdiwa. "Probably I can best look into that angle," she said fast. "What about you, sir?"

"I believe my fellows and I have done everything we can by ourselves," he answered. "I shall have to seek further help elsewhere."

"Where?" she whispered. "From who?"

"Nebayatuma, perhaps. He ranges widely, he sees much, his flute can lure truth off of tongues." Balawahdiwa paused. "Or Water Strider? No, not yet. If ever I dare . . . I'll go out into the desert and seek, Virginia. That's all I can do right now, seek."

"We too." Hand linked to hand around the table.

"Okay." Balawahdiwa mustered a grin. "How about we put our feet up first? Care to stay for lunch?"

I wasn't sure whether lunch at home was a Zuni custom or a friendly idea of his. Ginny declined with thanks. Though she didn't say so, I knew what was too much on her mind. He didn't press us, but sent us off with a hearty good-bye and good wishes.

We took a straight path back toward Gallup. "Let's call on Will," Ginny said.

"What can we tell him?"

"Very little at this stage. Leave it to me. Mainly I want to see him, in the light of what the situation's become, and chat a while, and . . . let him sense he's not been forsaken."

I squeezed her arm. "He never will be, darling."

"You're the sort of guy who would say that, Steve."

"I mean it. Be God damned if I can believe he'd do evil."

"No, he wouldn't." She broke off. I knew when she didn't want to talk. We took what consolation we could from the views around us. Welcome white clouds were sailing out of the west.

Gallup appeared ahead, high above the valley beyond. She was one batwing flyer. Our stick went through traffic like a snake threading a picket fence, and still I felt safe. Will's place was in an oldish, tree-shaded section. We started downward.

Ginny snarled. She veered the Jaguar. I saw what stood parked outside the small house, and added coarse words. Among the brooms was a Landlouper carpet that we recognized.

The FBI was there.

"I guess it's an interview," I said inanely.

"In force like that?" she replied. "I'd say investigation."

"Well, but— Should we go in? Maybe we can give him moral support."

She slumped, ever so slightly. "No. That'd be worse than useless."

We flew on at random. She straightened and turned to me. "Steve," she said, "let's not go home right away. Not till we've put our faces straight for the kids to see."

Ben was still camping, Val again babysitting Chryssa. She'd protested too little, methought, and had accepted our wage offer without dickering. Had something happened, or been said, or whatever, down at the shishkebab parlor yesterday, to drive her back into herself? She'd certainly been glum at breakfast. But what does a father ever know?

"Okay," I agreed. "Are you ready for lunch by now? Someplace with beer."

She managed a smile. "Occasionally, my dear, you're a great man."

We headed for the city center and parked where we could. Being farther from Cardinal Point, Gallup hadn't exploded quite like Grants, but its downtown was badly congested, the sidewalks thronged. Boutiques were taking over from the original businesses. Walking along, we passed one new to us, the Cunning Cactus. Among other kitsch, the window displayed a floor lamp in the shape of a giant saguaro. Besides those upraised arms, it had enormous eyes, a pug nose, and a rosebud mouth open to register surprise. Sometimes I wished the Pueblo revolt of 1680 had succeeded permanently.

We'd decided we wanted an atmosphere loose, easy, even a touch raucous, rather than elegant. Distraction. Probably we didn't hit the same place as our daughter's gang, since this had an on-sale license. Lamb, eggplant, onion, and tomato, pulled off their skewers into pockets of pita bread, were mighty heartening. America has gotten several excellent ideas since the war from the former enemy—though some of the combos you see are pretty weird. Frosty steins of Brockenbräu went better yet.

Unfortunately, not only did a farseer infest the joint, the volume was high. We could have ignored slush serials, fashion parades, and commercials in which the announcers sounded as though they were having orgasms. This, however, happened to be a news commentary, and Serious about the space program.

Congressman Blather declared that our disaster revealed it for the boondoggle it was, consuming tax money that ought to subsidize inefficient Wisconsin dairies, mismanaged New York banks, obsolete Texas oil refineries, foreign tobacco sales, and military bases in his district. Having presidential ambitions, he cast his net wide.

The Reverend Blither did also. Besides his declaration that a landing on the moon would corrupt its pure and innocent natives, as Western civilization had corrupted everything it ever touched, the project flaunted our utter lack of compassion for panhandlers, drug dealers, muggers, burglars, prostitutes, pimps, and, above all, his admirers.

A comedian made much of al-Bunni's having served the Caliphate. "He wants to put horses in the sky. Never mind whose heads the manure lands on." A cartoon showed our chief artificer as a crazed rabbit with ears that stretched to the moon and bounced it between them like a ping-pong ball. The fact that "bunni" means "brown" in Arabic was ignored.

I could go on, but why? "The project seems to be deep in political muck," Ginny said.

"It's often been," I reminded her. "This situation is desperate. Project Selene's got to concentrate on justifying its existence, which means the real work will be stalled indefinitely. NASA may knuckle under and cancel it."

"Operation Luna, then?" she breathed through the noise.

"Maybe. Maybe. Though how we can get over the threshold— Oh, hell, love, let's concentrate on our lunch, shall we?"

"And one another." Her smile was a kind of bugle call.

So, worried and tired but somewhat refreshed, we came home. The house seemed alarmingly quiet. Edgar dozed on his perch. But where was Svartalf? Why wasn't Chryssa racketing around with her usual liveliness? Heading rearward to check, I caught a voice. Relieved but curious, I continued.

Along the way I passed Valeria's room. The door stood open. As always, it showed a total hellhole. At her age, tidiness offers no obvious rewards. She did keep herself clean, and about as neat as an adolescent's peers will allow her to be. And she did make good grades in school, no matter how uppity she got. A real teacher *likes* awkward questions. Maybe inspired by her mother, though we didn't try to force interests on our kids, she'd become fascinated by Southwestern Indian lore. I glimpsed several books on the subject from the public library, on a shelf underneath a tacked-up Bat Man and Mina poster. She was also a great science fiction reader. Svartalf, who commonly shared her bed, sprawled there next to a copy of Lyle Monroe's latest Magister Lazarus novel, bought with her own money. *Ah-ha,* I thought, *when she's through with that I'm going to borrow it.*

I found her in Chryssa's room, telling a story. The infant sat enthralled. Apparently this was just beginning, and neither of them had heard us.

"Once upon a time there was a girl called Moldylocks. She had that name because she hated to bathe. It didn't matter to her that she drew flies and her bellybutton was full of moss. When she first saw a copy of Rodin's famous, brooding statue 'The Thinker,' she groaned, 'That poor man, he has to take a bath.'

"One day she went for a walk in the forest. It was a long, long walk, because she wanted to get as far away as possible from any soap. At last she came on a cottage. She didn't know it belonged to Papa Bear, Mama Bear, and Little Bear. Nor did she care. They'd trustingly

left the door unlocked. Moldylocks, being Moldylocks, went straight on in.

"She found a table with three chairs around it, and tried each of them. The big-sized chair was upholstered in ankylosaur skin and too knobbly. The middle-sized chair was so soft that she sank into it down to her guzzle and barely escaped with her life. The little-sized chair was just right. Moldylocks planked herself in it hard enough to splinter the cane bottom, but what the hell.

"There were three bowls of porridge on the table. She tried them each. The big bowl was too hot, and besides, it was half full of bourbon. Yuk! Moldylocks preferred single malt Scotch. The middle-sized bowl was fat-free, low-sodium, and totally organic. Yech! The little bowl was just right, and Moldylocks ate it all like a subduction zone eating a continent, only faster—"

I stole back to Ginny. Things were under control. Val was keeping her sister amused, if maybe a trifle bewildered. Still, plain to see and hear, plenty of devilment remained in her. I wondered what way it would strike next.

We called Will and invited him over for dinner. He accepted eagerly, but we were shocked at how haggard he looked when he arrived. "Rough day?" I asked after we'd sat down with drinks.

We'd mentioned knowing the feds had been at his place. He sighed. "Oh, they were polite. But very, very thorough. I wouldn't have believed so many questions were askable about my whereabouts and doings these past several years—as if anyone could remember in that kind of detail—not to mention my Chinese associates and, well, it seemed like nearly everything else. They even went over my poor old broomstick, whisking dust into envelopes."

Ginny scowled. "You shouldn't have permitted that. Nor should you have talked as freely as I'll bet you did."

"Why not?" He sounded surprised. "They're investigating a major crime."

"You needn't give them a free ride. They didn't bring a warrant, did they? You should have had an attorney on hand."

"Good Lord, why? Paying a fat fee in order to make it seem I've something to hide? I don't!"

Ginny and I exchanged a stare. She shook her head slightly. I nodded agreement and told him, "You never know how things will go when you deal with the government. Which is why no smart person does, more than he absolutely has to. Did they appear, um-m, satisfied?"

"Well, the gentleman in charge thanked me, but said they'd probably want to see me again, and requested me not to leave town."

"Requested," I muttered. "I want a talk of my own, with Shining Knife."

"You didn't plan to go anywhere soon anyway, did you, Will?" said Ginny. I knew she wanted to steer him from the idea that he might be under suspicion. Bad enough how it nagged us.

"Certainly not," replied the astronomer. "I learned from them that as far as they're concerned, the Point can resume work tomorrow. My moon studies—and I must get in touch with colleagues worldwide, to find out what they may have observed— Aren't you going back, Steve?"

"I'd like to, and they want me." I'd been on the phone to my department chief. "How communication systems were affected, or how they might even have been involved— Can't, though. Of all times in the history of the universe, an IRS auditor has chosen this one to come around and harass us."

The girls had sat quietly on the couch, Chryssa absorbed in a picture book, Val listening to the conversation while she sipped a Hepta-Up and stroked her buddy Svartalf. Now the older cried, "I didn't know that, Daddy!"

"No need for you to fret about it." I shrugged. "Like soldiering in wartime, financial management means long periods of boredom broken by moments of stark terror."

"He's joking," Ginny said. "We've nothing to fear except, true, the boredom."

"And the resentment," I added.

"Don't hang around, Val," Ginny went on. "You've accumulated good karma lately. Go enjoy yourself. Wasn't your circle planning a picnic?"

"Yeah. I won't be there." From the girl's tone, suddenly glacial after her cheerful rascality earlier, I could tell that the reminder had swung her mood back hellward. From the red that came and went across the clear face, I could guess she was still boycotting her boyfriend. Maybe he'd come to the shishkebab parlor yesterday evening, tried to mend fences, and clumsied it up. Remembering myself at that age, I felt a certain unwilling sympathy for him.

Ginny and I knew better than to inquire. "I'm sorry to hear that," she said, "but do as you want, go where you choose. Just be back by dinnertime."

"Do you expect the session will be difficult?" Will asked us.

"Well, our finances are rather complicated, you know. Steve's salary arrangement, my business, our investments, and, of course, Operation Luna."

He grunted and puffed hard on his pipe. "I'm involved in that myself." He sounded more anxious than he did about the FBI.

"Sit tight," Ginny advised, "carry on your daily life, and do not babble to anybody before you've consulted me. Let me decide what counsel you may need and see that you get it." She smiled rather bleakly. "Thank God, I am not one of His innocents like you."

I couldn't help wondering: *Like you, Will?* This nice, soft-spoken fellow with his gray beard and drawling humor—

Anger on his behalf, anger at the whole wretched mess, fueled what I already felt. "There will doubtless be a Black Plague's worth of snooping into every corner of our affairs, privacy be damned," I growled, "and tons of paper to find, and hours, days wasted that could have gone into something productive."

"Oh, it shouldn't be that bad," Ginny said. "I knew that someday the goblins would come, and prepared against them."

"Do you mean you understand the US Tax Code?" inquired Will, amazed.

"No, not really. I'm not a nigromancer."

"No mortal does," I declared. "Therefore they can always reach into their kettle and pull out an eye of newt or toe of frog you never imagined."

"Yes, I've heard of cases," Will said. "On the other hand, I've heard of taxpayers who, um-m, trumped this with a lizard's leg and howlet's wing."

"Their lawyers did, and battened off it," I grumbled, "A man is presumed guilty until he proves his innocence, at his own expense of money, energy, and lifespan. Is that what the Founding Fathers had in mind?"

Valeria had followed the talk with that intensity which could be hers. Whatever self-pity she felt got lost in youthful idealism. "If everybody hates the IRS, why do we have one?" she asked. "I thought this was a government of the people, by the people, and for the people."

"It is," I told her. "Unfortunately, these days the three classes of people aren't the same."

"Now, wait, Steve, you're too cynical," Will objected. He leaned back, regarded the girl, and smoked more like a philosopher than before. "Human affairs are always messy," he told her. "Whether that's because we're fallen angels or high-powered apes or both is a matter of opinion, but there the fact is. On the whole, our country copes with it better than most. Nearly everyone working for government agencies—" He threw me a look. "—like you, Steve—and I include tax

agencies, nearly everyone is a perfectly decent person, earning an honest living by making the laws work—laws enacted by our democratically elected representatives."

I might have gotten in a few licks about regulations, interpretations, and court decisions, but Ginny was ahead of me, doubtless for the best. "This is supposed to be happy hour," she decreed. "Let's discuss something cheerful, like funerals."

So Will told a story he'd lately heard, about two nuns driving a unicorn buggy through a moonlit night, on their way back to the convent from a church-sponsored fiesta. A huge bat flew down, landed on the whiffletree, and turned into a leering vampire. "Quick, sister," gasped the driver, "show him your cross!" The other nun pointed and snapped, "Young man, you get off that whiffletree this instant! I *mean* it." He got a laugh from Val, anyhow, which made Chryssa chime in.

I segued out of my bitterness with one about a general at the Pentacle who was going fishing and passed a bait shop that offered "All the worms you can use for a dollar." He went in and said, "Give me two dollars' worth."

Ginny supplied some real wit, and conversation improved. The mood grew outright blithe over dinner, and stayed like that till the last goodnight was said, and a while afterward.

This was just as well. We wouldn't have much fun again anytime soon.

Alger Sneep arrived promptly at 1 P.M. He was short and skinny but ramrod straight, with flat dark hair, cold brown eyes, and a nose that waggled at the tip when he spoke in his high voice. He marched directly in as I opened the door for him, though he did take off his hat and transfer it to the left hand that held his briefcase. The right hand flashed his identification card. The cartouche around the Anubis emblem showed that he ranked fairly high in the area office. He returned it to his wallet and extended the hand stiffly. Well, I'd doubtless shaken worse. I made this exchange quick.

"My wife Virginia," I said. She was pure cool graciousness. "Our daughters Valeria and Chryssa."

They didn't advance. Val stared as if at something loathsome. "Excuse me," she said to us, word by stony word. "I'll go and practice my goetics. *If* I may." She turned and stalked down the hall. Svartalf gave our visitor a yellow scrutiny, jerked his tail straight aloft, and followed her. "Guch," went Edgar from his perch, as though vomiting. Chryssa wailed and burst into tears. Sneep's mouth pinched together.

"I'm sorry," said my wife, hunkering down to embrace the little one. "I'm afraid she's tired and tense. There, there, darling, don't be afraid. Mommy and Daddy are right here. I'll tuck her in for an early nap. Suppose you show Mr. Sneep to the office, Steve, and fix him a cup of coffee if he wants."

Not too auspicious a start. "This way, please," I said. The examiner and I walked off. "Uh, if you'd come in the morning, the kids wouldn't have been a problem," and I wouldn't have had to spend those hours idled and fuming. Ginny, at least, could begin to pick up the threads of her consultation work.

"I expect a long session," he replied. "Best not to interrupt it for lunch." His tone implied we might well have used the break to destroy evidence.

I gave him a sideways look. Something odd— His clothes? The gray business suit, pinstriped shirt, navy blue necktie spotted with white gammadions, pointed black shoes, were straight establishment. Weren't they? The hat, while wider-brimmed than usual back east, was conservative in this land of the desert sun. It seemed new and expensive, but even civil servants are allowed a touch of vanity. Nevertheless, I wished I could go wolf and better smell the strangeness that barely touched my senses.

No, probably a bad idea. My animal impulses might get the better of me.

We went into the office. He peered around, finding mostly a large desk with ordinary equipment like a telephone and a reckoner, a couple of swivel chairs, and several filing cabinets. On one of these stood a plaster bust of Athene. A window revealed our garden. Ginny had painted and potentiated a defensive-cautionary sigil on a wall, an ankh with an eye in the loop above the incantation protege SEMPER NATES TUAS PAPYRO.

"This isn't Dr. Matuchek's studio, is it?" Sneep demanded.

"No, nor her interview room. Here's where we keep our records and do our clerical chores."

"I may want to inspect the rest, including your office, Mr. Matuchek. But this is the place to start."

I swallowed a nasty taste. "Haven't exactly got an office, myself. I do some work in my study, now and then." Anybody who calls it my den will get thrown to the cutesypoos. "But it's more for hobbies, reading, relaxation. We don't claim it as a business part of the house."

He settled at the desk, planking down his briefcase and hat. "There may be questions regarding it. Section 783(c)4. I'll decide later. Shall we begin?" He extracted a bulging manila folder.

"The accounts are my wife's department," I said. "I wouldn't know where to find what. She'll have the youngster asleep soon. Meanwhile, would you like that cup of coffee?"

"Not yet." He gestured. "Sit down, please." Maybe my ears were prejudiced, but the last word sounded grudging. "We'll discuss the situation informally, in a preliminary way. The big picture."

I took the other chair. "You mean you haven't got it already?"

"Only what you and your associates have reported on their returns and other legally required documents." What more was he after? And

why? We were *not* big game. "Certain things are unclear to us." *Yeah,* I thought, *you're tax collectors, not launch-and-dock-it scientists.* "Frankly, your public announcements have not been very forthcoming." *In other words, if we choose to play close to our vests, we're probably dealing from the bottom of the deck.* "We require further details."

Recalling Ginny's cautions to Will, I considered stalling till she arrived and decided whether to call for a lawyer. But no, that'd make the atmosphere really unpleasant. What incriminating thing could I say? I didn't know of any.

"You have Operation Luna in mind?" was my gambit.

He nodded. "In considerable part."

"Well, Mr. Sturlason tells me the IRS came at him several days ago. Hasn't it learned everything it needs to know?"

"That's back east. And the information transmitted to us here indicates Nornwell Scryotronics and Operation Luna have a tangled relationship, which even extends to NASA—and to you, your wife, and certain others. So your personal tax returns are involved too. Yes, we have heard explanations at Nornwell. We would like yours for comparison."

"It won't contradict theirs!" I flared.

"I didn't say it would, Mr. Matuchek. I only want to ask a few simple questions." Sneep gestured at his folder. "This is a substantial amount of material given me all at once. You can help me digest it."

*And what will the end product be?* I refrained from saying. Still, that glimpse of human limitations eased me slightly. Sneep had his job. Probably he had a wife and children. Probably he didn't beat them. I leaned back, folded my arms, and crossed my legs. "Okay, what can I tell you?"

I've seen pit bulls go less straight to the point. "Describe Operation Luna in your own words."

"Well," I said, inspecting each phrase before I turned it loose, "it's a small private corporation. Not a nonprofit, we hope, though so far it's always been in the red. Mr. Sturlason and a few old friends back there are shareholders." Old friends indeed, Ashman, Griswold, Wenzel, Nobu, Karlslund, Abrams, who'd stood by us in those long-ago terrible days when the portal opened between Earth and Hell. Except for Barney, none owned much stock. Their means were modest. It was their dream that was big. "And here in New Mexico there are Gi—Dr. Matuchek and me. As I suppose you know, we've been able to buy into a fair chunk of the outfit. Dr. Matuchek's brother, Dr. William

Graylock, has taken a few shares too, but just a token, just to get in on the action. Such as it is," I finished ruefully.

"What activities do you plan?"

"We don't plan, not at this early stage."

"Early? The corporation was formed five years ago."

*Oh, Christ, how can I make him see?* "Look, we were interested in space. Project Selene had lately been founded. I dearly wanted to work for it myself, but it was still a sprout, with as many engineers as it could use. Besides—" I braked my tongue. Why go into purely personal matters? Then, seeing those suspicious eyes on me, I figured I'd be smart to complete the sentence. "Besides, I hated the idea of leaving Nornwell. It's not located in my favorite part of the country, but otherwise it's a great outfit, a happy shop.

"Anyhow, our group focused on the commercial possibilities of spaceflight. If we could foresee them, organize ourselves to take advantage— among other things, by offering valuable advice—then when humans did get off Earth we'd be in on the ground floor, so to speak."

"What are those commercial possibilities?"

"Who can say? Energy's obvious—solar energy pouring onto the moon and through ambient space." I couldn't resist patronizing Sneep. "Brooms and carpets don't fly, saintelmos don't light up, industrial processes don't take place, for free, you know. Whether the energy comes from fuel or a waterfall or goetic quantum-wave transference across a potential difference, or whatever, it's conserved, same as mass is conserved in a transformation. Build collector pyramids on the moon, and we'll have power to do damn near anything. How'd you like to live in a flying house, or see a real Atlantis raised in midocean?"

Enthusiasm kept me talking. "Industry— Well, for instance, properly 'chanted moon rocks can draw water by tidal sympathy. Highly efficient pumps. You could make vitreous drops shine according to lunar phase—jewelry. What may be the medicinal value of a pinch of moondust in a glass of wine? The notions, the speculations— I could go on all day. Some doubtless won't work, but others ought to, and there're bound to be still others nobody will have thought of till we get there."

Sneep frowned. "Haven't you allowed for political opposition?"

"You mean international rivalries? I should think the gains will be ample for everybody." Given the likes of Fu Ch'ing, I didn't believe matters would be that simple, but neither did I care to get into side issues.

"First you'll have to meet objections within this country."

I grimaced. "Yeah. I'm no politician, though." For some reason I felt a need to justify my group morally. "Nor are we go-to-hell technoberserkers. Back then, hardly anything was known about the dwellers on the moon, other than that they exist. Now it seems they may be . . . vulnerable." Again I chose not to discuss the complications, the evil that might already lair yonder. "We absolutely would not hold with exploiting or distressing them. But who's to say at this point that a human presence will? They may be glad to have us. We may improve their condition."

Will thought otherwise: that they'd fled there to escape the industrial world, which we had then proposed to bring after them. I didn't want to concede Sneep anything, but I did feel bound to add: "However that may be, even if the only people we'll ever place on the moon are a few careful and considerate scientists who don't stay too long—even then, we've got the whole Solar System. What price the metals in an asteroid, or salt from a dead sea bottom on Mars to use sympathetically against floods, or a vial of Venusian atmosphere to repel insects and demons, or— No limits, once we get out yonder. Eventually, the stars."

That was what called us, I didn't say: called us, and surely millions more humans with wonder and adventure in their hearts. The Golcondas, industries, profits were really just ways to pay—by providing benefits, not extorting taxes—for the farings and discoveries. Sneep wouldn't understand.

"Operation Luna is a research organization," I ended flat-footedly.

"Your ambitions have expanded of late," he said.

"Why do you care?" I snapped, goaded. "Okay, OpLu has run at a loss till now, but it's collected enough to qualify as a business venture." That was mainly through the occasional consultation fee, selling our opinions on this and that to contractors working for NASA. There was also something Byzantine but, I was assured, legal about the arrangement whereby certain Nornwell people were lent to Project Selene. "We've reported every relevant transaction completely and accurately. If you mean to challenge that, talk with our lawyers, not me. I'm only an engineer."

Sneep made me sit while he riffled through his papers. At length he glanced up and said, "Your work on alternative vehicles is questionable."

I didn't know whether I wanted most to bare my teeth or lift my nose and howl. Having drawn three breaths, I retorted, "In what way? Look, we're not unique in thinking the government's approach is unnecessarily big, awkward, and expensive." After all, it was the govern-

ment's approach. "Sure, Project Selene has done brilliant things, blazed necessary trails, but since then— Blame Congress and media pressure and whatever else you want. But read some pro-space publications; talk with physicists and paraphysicists. You'll find out things like how much less the cost of launch could be—to start with, eliminate that standing army of paperpushers—and how much simpler life support could be, and— Oh, hell, just compare the costs and risks of a space mission to an ordinary transatlantic flight. They ought to be about the same. They aren't. And now that . . . that fiasco at the Point has shown how fragile the space program really is."

I found I'd uncrossed my legs, unfolded my arms, and gestured kind of wildly. With an effort, I settled back in the chair.

"Is Operation Luna, then, trying to undermine Project Selene?"

I blew up. "*No,* God damn it! Can't you by any stretch of your mind imagine us as anything but crooks? For your information, I don't cheat on my wife either."

"I did not imply that, Mr. Matuchek. No offense intended." His tone made clear that offense had been taken.

I swallowed hard. "All right," I grated. "I'd have thought you knew this already." Maybe he did, and was out to get my goat. "If not, please listen.

"In the last year or two, a few technically qualified members of Operation Luna, along with a few others, have been seriously investigating alternative ways of spaceflight. We do it on our own time, or on Nornwell's, with our organization's money, plus what we throw in out of our own pockets. We do it with the knowledge and approval of Project Selene, Dr. al-Bunni himself, who told us he'd cleared it with the bureaucracy. He doesn't mind. On the contrary. He does like grandiose stuff, which is also what the government and the media want. But mainly his goal is to put humans in space, by any means it takes. Why not encourage an alternative? He's even arranged for us to have a small piece of moon rock, along with meteorites we've acquired ourselves, for our experiments."

I sank back, half wrung out. In a moment's blessed silence, I stared out at the flowerbeds.

"Moon rocks?" Sneep seemed genuinely curious. "How do you get them?"

To talk straight science was like a drink from a mountain spring. "Meteorites are blasted off the moon—or Mars, or oftenest asteroids, maybe also Jovian satellites—by big impacts. After wandering around for thousands or millions of years, some hit Earth, survive the atmo-

spheric flameout, and strike ground. There are spectroscopic, alchemical, and symbolical techniques for identifying where one came from; I'm not too well up on that.

"The point is, since a piece of a heavenly body is in resonance with its source—law of contagion, you know—it gives impetus and direction to a spacecraft. I suppose we'll develop beyond the need for them," *if celestonautics doesn't die out in the near future,* "but at present they're pretty essential. Even if you don't intend to go the whole way—and so far, of course, we haven't—a chip off the ultimate goal helps like a, well, like a relic of a saint was once supposed to."

And maybe did, now and then. The original goetic power lasted well into the Iron Age, early medieval times, diminuendo. I'd seen arguments that a few creatures were around and a few minor spells effective as late as the eighteenth century. However, by then ferromagnetism was almost everywhere and had driven nearly all survivors into hiding places and the Long Sleep.

"I see. Interesting. Thank you," Sneep said, nearly like a human being. "You have given me angles to consider, Mr. Matuchek."

"While you do," I suggested, "how about I make you that cup of coffee?" A chance to be elsewhere!

"Well, yes, five or ten minutes for me to think before we attack the details. Skim milk, no sugar." Sneep returned to his papers. I rose and went out.

Along the way I heard a little *click-click,* looked behind me, and saw Edgar walking down the hall. Preoccupied, I gave it no further thought. He had the run of the house, and usually went on foot through narrowish spaces like this.

In the kitchen I started a potful, estimating we'd need that much in the course of the session, and brooded at it. The process was almost done when Ginny appeared. "I thought I heard you in here," she said. "Chryssa's lulled."

My heart rejoiced, not only because sunlight streamed through the window to make flame of her hair and caress her thinly gowned slenderness. "What a relief!" I answered. "I dreaded going back alone. In this kind of business, I'm a lamb to the slaughter."

"What exactly has happened?"

I told her. She scowled. "You shouldn't have barked at him, no matter what. One is exceedingly polite to such people. Amicable, if possible."

"Must one be? We haven't done anything wrong or failed to touch any required bases. Uh, haven't we?"

She shook her head, sighed, but gave me a smile. "My poor, dear naïf, that's entirely beside the point. Get an inquisitor personally mad at you, and he'll find ways to make you wish you'd never been born, whether or not he really hopes to make wages. We're guilty till proven innocent, remember?"

"Okay, I'll be good." I managed a grin. "And you'll be good-looking. Plus tactful, efficient, and generally irresistible." I paused. "There is something peculiar about him, though. I can only sense it vaguely, but—his clothes—"

"Oh, that. I felt it too, and ran a quick spell check after leaving Chryssa. It's simple enough. As I suspected, his outfit's been veracitized. When he hears a deliberate lie, it makes his skin tingle."

"Ugh! Is that constitutional?"

"Its evidence is not admissible in court, but—" She shrugged.

"At least he'll know we're on the level."

"Not necessarily. Any proficient witch or warlock could easily cast a counterspell."

"Why don't you, then?"

"Because he or somebody may have left a detector in range of us. If I did anything more potent than the check I mentioned, it'd register. It wouldn't reveal precisely what I did, but it'd probably turn his suspicions of us into convictions."

"Yeah, I forgot. Better we take no chances. We don't want to be convicted."

"Don't worry about it. I imagine all you have to avoid is saying how much you like and respect him."

"I'm safe, then."

"I need to be more careful."

I nodded. "A lightweight object with a rheatic charge reacts to any spell, however weak, that hits it, right? The results could be embarrassing. Though I don't expect any cantrip of yours would misfire."

"Thank you, dear. Let's proceed." Ginny arranged things on a tray. I moved to take it, but she did first. *Why, yes,* I realized, *part of the hostess image she means to project.* I stiffened my sinews, summoned up my blood, and followed her.

We came to the office. She nearly dropped the tray.

Sneep sat rigid, fingers clenched on the arms of his chair. He breathed hard as he glared at Edgar. Perched on the bust of Athene, the raven looked unblinkingly back at him.

"Good heavens," Ginny exclaimed, "what's this?"

Sneep swiveled around, white-faced. His voice trembled with in-

dignation. "Your . . . your familiar . . . flapped in and . . . *stares.* Do you think I have to be under surveillance, Dr. Matuchek? That I'm a, a robber?"

"Of course not!" Ginny replied, adding quickly, "You're an income tax collector."

*But Edgar thinks otherwise,* I realized. *He knows we don't want this intrusion, and he's gotten overzealous.*

"I'm so sorry. A dreadful misunderstanding, I'm sure." Ginny set the tray on the desk and turned to the bird. "What's the matter with you?" she shrilled. *Nice acting,* I thought. Her real angers were soft-spoken, ice-cold, and dangerous. Then I remembered Sneep's clothes and wondered what they'd hint at.

Well, she must in fact be annoyed with the featherbrain. He'd spoiled the atmosphere she wanted to create. She lowered her voice. "You apologize to Mr. Sneep right now."

"Nevermore," said the raven sullenly.

"Get out of here! Scram, you—you Edgar Allan Crow!"

He raised his hackles and hissed, but spread his wings, landed on the floor, and marched off. *Poor fellow, he's hurt,* I thought. *He meant well. I'll bet Ginny's unhappy at having to be so harsh. Which doesn't make him less mad.*

"We do regret this very much, Mr. Sneep," she said. That probably passed the truth test, since she didn't specify the reasons why we regretted it. "It's no way to treat a guest." Likewise true, including unwelcome ones. "Edgar's rather new on the job. Sometimes he behaves childishly. You do understand, don't you?"

"Yes," he clipped.

She returned a forty-kilowatt smile. "So you have children of your own?" She sat down and offered him a cup. I hung back, not to interfere with this charmcasting.

Sneep didn't actually thaw, but a few minutes of her chitchat and responses he couldn't escape making calmed him. "We'd better start work," he presently said.

"I'll fetch me a chair," I proposed.

Ginny's look mingled compassion and fortitude. "I don't think that'll be necessary," she said. "I am the family business manager. Just stay available in case we need you."

*Greater love hath no woman,* I thought, shaped a kiss, and retreated while the retreating was good.

It seemed wise to check on Edgar. A search of the house failed to locate him, though it was closed against the heat. The door to the

auxiliary workroom also stood shut. Val was in there with Svartalf, I knew, presumably going through witchy lore and exercises as she'd announced she would. The raven must have rapped with his beak and she'd let him in. Probably all three were taking out their assorted resentments in some double-double rite. Any IRS detector ought to identify it as very mild stuff and dismiss it. Every book and instrumentality in the house was sealed against outsiders—except as, bit by bit, Val mastered the responsible use of them. She'd progressed well beyond the ninth-grade level, but not far enough to be scary.

If she was angry, I could sympathize. Spirited and born with a tremendous aptitude, she naturally chafed at the restrictions on her. It was especially galling that she wouldn't get her flyer's license till she turned sixteen, when she could already damn well handle a stick. I'd taught her the basics and let her take over, safely off in the desert; she'd wanted it so much. And I had little doubt she'd cajoled two or three older boys into the same. It wasn't easy, being her age. I remembered.

Best I not interrupt. I went to fetch a beer from the fridge and took it into my study where nobody would disturb it. There I tried to lose myself in a mystery novel. But, excellent though *The Case of the Toxic Spell Dump* was, I failed. Sitting stalled like this when real work called me was too dismal. Of course, compared to what Ginny was going through—

A shout and clatter brought me to my feet. I sallied forth and saw Ben, sunburnt and dust-smeared, burst into the office. I dashed to the rescue.

The desk was strewn with documents. Sneep sat hunched over them. Ginny's expression told me that she'd stared out the window for an hour or worse while he wordlessly rummaged our files. "Mom, Mom!" our son yelled. "There you are! I'm back! I had a terrific time! Look!" He extended his hands. I glimpsed what they held. "I found this horny toad. Can I keep him, can I? Mr. Goldstein gave him a name. He's the IRS Monster—"

Somehow I brought the lad away, shoved him under the shower, gave him clean clothes, et cetera. Meanwhile Ginny performed what damage control she was able.

Afterward she told me that the ordeal had been harder than she expected. Mostly, as said, it amounted to waiting. Sneep maintained machinelike correctness. But when he had questions, they drilled deep. Witch or no, how the hell could she keep in mind every jot and niggle? She must trudge back through the records herself and reconstruct trivial

deals made two or three years ago. It could seldom be done on such short notice.

By about six o'clock he'd assembled a large stack of papers. "I'll take these along to the office and research them," he told her. "You'll hear from me."

"I can doppelgang copies for you," she proposed.

"If you please, Dr. Matuchek, we do that ourselves. Precaution against a possible hex. If we find no irregularity, the originals will be returned to you in due course."

"I set my teeth and made allowances," she told me. "He'd taken a couple of insults himself today, after all. Nevertheless—"

I've run ahead of myself. Ginny summoned me to say good-bye to Mr. Sneep. Chryssa was elsewhere with her dolls, pouring them pretend tea. Valeria, Svartalf, and Edgar sat in the living room. The girl's grim little grin worried me. But what could I do?

I opened the front door. Sneep stepped into the late afternoon blaze. Val sprang cat-silent to her feet. Maybe only I saw her gesture and mutter.

Sneep's expensive hat flapped its brim and rose off his head.

"What?" he yelped. "Hey, wait!"

Valeria sped to the door, Edgar on her wrist. "Go get it!" she shouted gleefully. The raven soared.

"Hold! Stop!" Ginny cried. She hurried outside too and raised her arms for a revocation.

Unfortunately, Edgar had overtaken the hat. It made a clumsy attempt to dodge. Not being a falcon, he grabbed it in his beak. It struggled. He let go and bashed it on the crown. It fluttered wounded down to the sidewalk.

"Svartalf," Val purred.

That old cat could still move like a streak when he chose to. He was onto the hat in an instant. It tried to escape. He batted, clawed, and bit at this marvelous prey.

Ginny's correction took hold. The hat, what was left of it, went lifeless. Svartalf took it between his teeth and trotted proudly back to us. Edgar flew to the rain gutter. "Kah, kah, kah," he exulted, "Billy Magee Magar."

I don't wish to recall what followed. We apologized and offered restitution, but be damned if we'd bellycrawl, or give our daughter more than a reprimand in front of a stranger. Sneep was icily polite. Watching him depart, I thought he figured he'd gained a certain moral ascendancy over us.

Once we were alone, it hurt to keelhaul Valeria. "But you hate him," she protested.

"We don't," I stated, more or less sincerely. "He may not be our favorite person on earth, but he's a man, doing his duty as he sees it," more or less, "and entitled to normal courtesy."

"Also," Ginny said, "you clearly haven't learned your social lessons. Ancient wisdom: It's stupid to make an enemy of someone whom you don't intend to kill."

Valeria tried to meet her eyes and couldn't.

"Furthermore," Ginny continued, "and more important, don't kid yourself that you were defending the family or any such idiotic thing. You're loaded with personal grudges, which you took out on him simply because he was a convenient target. You'll never get your witch's license if you don't show more self-control."

Hoo, am I glad she's never had to read me the riot act. Her occasional rebuke has been plenty enough.

The upshot was that we sent Val to bed without supper—which therefore became a cheerless meal, much to Ben's and Chryssa's distress—and confined her to the house for a week. She accepted the sentence as stonily as a soldier ought. I knew we'd all end up in mutual forgiveness.

Yet the consequences of this ill-omened day would be with us for we knew not how long or heavily. It was as if we'd fallen under a curse. Maybe to keep us entangled and helpless?

Though the next day was a Saturday, Ginny and I both went to work. Rather, she let her clients know she was again available and received a couple of them, while I flitted to Cardinal Point.

The place looked and felt forsaken. It had bustled the week around, but now little went on other than housekeeping and bookkeeping. Most staff were on leave, which they feared might turn into layoff. It certainly would if Project Selene didn't get an appropriation to pay for a second try. Congress was in adjournment, its members presumably back home taking the pulses of their constituents. They'd reconvene in September to take the purses. What news and commentary I'd followed thus far made it seem unlikely that much largesse would flow our way.

Even so, security was as tight as Torquemada. Four armed guards stood under improvised sunshelters around the three-quarters-empty parking lot. Maybe it was only a late arrival breaking their boredom that caused their gazes to stalk me, but I didn't appreciate being an instant suspect. At the gatehouse, where I'd hitherto simply picked up my badge, the man said, "I'm sorry, but we've got a new procedure. Please come in for identification."

"What?" I replied. "You know me, Gitling."

"Sure I do, Mr. Matuchek. But it's the rules. We, uh, have to make sure no Seeming or, uh, anything gets by."

"Good Lord, somebody disguised? Whatever *for?*"

"Sorry, sir. No exceptions. Orders from Washington, they tell me."

An offside room had been rigged as an inquisitory. A witch ran a dowser over me while chanting a disspell, took my thumbprint and did the same for it, had me sign my secret name and waved a doppel of it above till the paper flapped in response. (Not my real secret name,

of course; the one given me when I came to work here.) "How much blood do you need?" I snorted.

"None, sir, seeing you passed the prelims."

She was young and cute, which took the edge off my annoyance, and sounded very tired, which roused my sympathy. "Rough job, huh?" I asked.

"Not too bad anymore. But when the order first went into effect—employees, consultants, investigators, press, politicians—especially the press and the politicians."

"Yeah. Those'd scream to high heaven. At least they don't agree on which class of 'em owns the universe. But I suppose by now this bottleneck has reduced the flood a lot."

She nodded. "Essential people mainly, I guess."

"And *I* guess it hasn't helped the project's popularity one bit. Of all the officious official idiocies— What the devil is left to sabotage? I'd like to know what al-Bunni had to say about it."

Her lips twitched. "I heard tell of, er, 'grandfather of a thousand mangy camels.' "

"Which must have been in English. I understand Arabic gets more eloquent. Well, cheerio, sort of." I took my badge from her and left. She'd told me getting out was still uncomplicated.

The weather had mildened. Clouds moved stately over a sky from which spilled light that was merely radiant. A hedge of southernwood gave off a pungent scent as I brushed against it, like a friendly, hopeful message.

The next sight yanked my thoughts back and cast them down. I'd detoured to see how things were at the paddock. They were terrible. It was as if the bronze of the great proud horse was already tarnishing. Holes gaped where parts had been removed for study. Machinery, obviously brought here yesterday, hulked nearby, ready to complete the demolition on Monday. A breeze off the malpais sighed emptily past.

I zigged back to my proper goal, the building that held the communications lab. Hollowness greeted my entry. Upstairs, the lab itself was bright, equipment sparkled, something hummed, my werewolf senses caught a tingle of power, less clearly than my animal form would have but nevertheless heartening. However, nobody but Jim Franklin and a couple of assistants were on hand. The assistants nodded and continued their work. He came over to meet me and try to drive off the air of desolation with his big white smile.

"Welcome back, Steve," he said. "How've things gone?"

"Away, I hope." No such luck; but I didn't want to dump our tax

woes on him, and better not to mention the co-opting of Balawahdiwa to anyone just yet. "And here?"

"Well, we had a busy time for a while, studying what the event did to the com gear. Mostly not much—it withstood impact pretty well, the way it was made to—but some effects are sure goofball. Like a Doppler tracker gone into reverse. Red shift for approach, blue for recession. What this remnant of us is working on is a voice receiver that gives only yips and howls."

"Coyote's idea of a joke," I muttered.

"Could be. I've been wondering whether an incident my father told me about was a prank of his. At the time, it was taken to be a mistake in the spell."

"When was this?"

"Back during the war. Dad was working at the Dry Gulch proving grounds. They developed nasties there to send at the enemy, you may recall. Had a giant sidewinder airborne, putting it through its paces, when suddenly it turned into a rattlesnake the same size and fell down amongst them. Luckily, the range safety officer had a hyperborean charm primed and froze it before it bit somebody. They spent a few days respelling, and the next trial went okay. But maybe Coyote had passed by—southern California wasn't built up like it's become since—and gotten playful."

"Hm. And then afterward, seeing this really big installation sprout in the middle of his stamping grounds and attract thousands of people, he got more serious. Odd, though, that I've never heard of the business, and odder that Ginny hasn't. It's possibly relevant here."

"Dad told me confidentially. It was classified till last year. No reason that I can imagine."

"I can. Government."

"Uh-huh. They finally got around to releasing the file, along with a mess of other obsolete-looking stuff, but by then it wasn't newsworthy, even within the profession. I have gathered that the Smithsonian's acquired the snake, out of the Army's cold storage vault, and may put it on exhibit. That should rouse some public interest. The thing did nearly crottle their greeps that day. *Crotalus bunyani.*" Jim was an amateur naturalist.

I looked around. "Where's Helen?" I asked, meaning Krakowski, our section chief.

"Summoned to headquarters, like nearly everybody else important. Damn if I know what NASA thinks they can do there except answer

stupid questions, when they could be at something useful. Double damn if I know how al-Bunni's avoided it so far."

"Maybe he pulled wires. He does have friends high in the military. Or maybe he thundered the bureaucracy down. Or maybe he quick-like invented a religious occasion that forbids him to travel." I shrugged.

"Well, Helen told us to carry on as best we could, and when we ran out of work go home and stand by for a call . . . whenever it may come. We three are here today because I've got an experiment that won't keep. I expect in the course of next week more and more staff will phase themselves out and"—bitterly—"concentrate on angling for reassignment elsewhere, or whole new jobs."

"Ouch. What can I do?"

"I'm glad you showed. We can use your particular talents."

Jim's little team was trying to discover why the scryotronic communicator was making coyote noises. This might give a clue to the way the destructive force had operated, which would be mighty valuable knowledge at the next launch, if there was one. He knew the main crystal was somehow bollixed. He had an idea that it had gone into wave-mechanical oscillations, jumps to and fro between alternate histories, so to speak. The notion wasn't easy to test. The apparatus he'd rigged involved linked mandrake amplifiers. They're cantankerous buggers. If he left them untended longer than overnight, he might as well tear the whole thing down and start over.

Myself, I was more an engineer than an artificer. I knew just the elementary theory of rheatics. When forces transmit at infinite speed, such familiar concepts as frequency don't quite apply. But even in human form, I had a keen nose and a knack for handling wildlife. That included mandrakes, sort of.

Nobody has yet gotten any to breed true. Each is a law, or maybe I should say a caprice, unto itself. You'd better tickle it right, or it'll get into a snit and either give you no results at all or make you wish it had.

I sensed my way forward, carefully, carefully, tuning and retuning by fractional increments, through the next few hours. None of us went out for lunch. We snatched what we'd brownbagged while we worked on. The cafeteria would have been pretty depressing anyway. Here we cheered ourselves with progress.

"By God, Steve," Jim said at last. "I think we've done it. The plumbing is perking, and we ought to have our data in time to go home for dinner."

"Or first stop off for a beer." I rose, knuckled my bleary eyes, and

stretched cramped muscles. "Unless you've stashed an illicit six-pack in a fridge?"

" 'Fraid not," Jim replied. "But no sense in your hanging around here. Hoist one in the Mars for us on your way back." I wondered how long our favorite local bar would keep that name or even stay in business.

To this day I don't know whether it was coincidence or if the phone had been charmed to monitor us. Whichever, it said: "Mr. Steven Matuchek, please report to Dr. al-Bunni in Room Seventy-seven of the Suleiman Elaboratory."

We four gaped at each other. "Holy hoodoo," Jim breathed, "the big cheese's personal bell jar. What *you* done, man?"

*"Lapsituri te salutamus,"* I answered from the prayer to St. Ineptus, patron of klutzes, and went out.

# XII

The building was some distance off. It loomed at me as I approached. The onionoid cupola on top lent meaning to Jim's figure of speech. A text from the Qu'ran, flowing Arabic inset above the main entrance, added to the demonstration of how much al-Bunni was valued, how much was granted him. This had nourished not only jealousy but ethnic hatred, on which the likes of Blather and Blither were quick to batten.

President Lambert's influence and pork barrel politics countered them. Though he was now out of office, public interest, even enthusiasm, had done the same as mission after mission flew from Cardinal Point, each more spectacular than the last. But the modern American public is a fickle bitch. This gigantic failure of ours was provoking a reaction in proportion, which our opponents well knew how to make feed on itself.

I found al-Bunni alone in the workroom reserved for him and whomever he invited. After the glass eyes in the bronze door had scanned me, it swung aside and I stepped into a long chamber, greenishly lighted, handsomely but sparsely furnished except for the scientific apparatus. Sweet smoke wafted from a censer into cool air. A minor-key flute melody wove through it.

Al-Bunni advanced to meet me, which was courteous of one in his position. Usually he wore Western clothes, with a penchant for the gaudiest Hawaiian shirts he could buy in New Mexico, but today it was a white kaftan. It made him seem still bigger than before. The dark, crag-nosed face had none of its wonted joviality—and was the black beard suddenly more grizzled? His hand gripped hard, though, and his basso rumbled levelly. "How do you do, Mr. Matuchek. Thank you for coming this promptly."

"Glad to, sir," was my lame response, "though I'll be da—uh,

doggoned if I know why you called." My use of "doggoned" showed me how rattled and puzzled I was. We werewolves detest that word.

"You'll find out. The reason does you credit. But come." He took my elbow and guided me to an ebony-and-ivory table. "Please sit and let's talk. Coffee?" With his own hands he filled two cups from a silver pot above a flame. They were tiny, but the brew met the traditional specs: black as midnight, strong as death, sweet as love, and hot as the Pit.

He offered me a cigarillo too, and, when I declined, lit his own. "How goes it for you and your family?" he inquired.

"We're getting along." Again I had no wish to relate some details and knew better than to touch on others. I did describe our search through the malpais with the two feds.

He nodded. "Yes, I have had some report of this, under bonds of strict secrecy. Why not release the findings?"

"Well, sir, they might alert the enemy, and they aren't conclusive yet, and they'd be bound to make NASA look worse. Some people would say this proves our incompetence, that we didn't think to take those precautions. Others would say we're trying to cover up that incompetence by blindly accusing minority and foreign Beings."

"Ah, America," he said wryly. "I hesitate to tell even the FBI what I have found out for myself."

I almost spilled my coffee. "What? Sir."

His look riveted me. "I will tell you, and you may tell your wife. Need to know. But I put you on your sacred honor not to let it go further unless and until I allow. I have trouble enough already, thank you."

"Honor, sir. Yes."

"I called in a djinni from my homeland."

To my half horrified stare he responded: "Yes, I'm aware of the wartime encounter you two had with one. But take it easy. The djinn are as different from each other as humans are." *Uh-huh,* I recalled at the back of my mind, *"djinni" is singular, "djinn" plural.* "Some are evil, yes, virtual demons. Others are pious servants of God. Most are in between, same as us. I'd had dealings with this one in the past and found him reliable. At present he's taken a post as the tutelary spirit of Jebel Kharûf in the Negev of Palestine, right near the Egyptian border. So he hears news from the Powers of Air around the world.

"He confirmed for me what your FBI only suspects, that Asian Beings are in collaboration with at least one local godling and at least one local human to wreck our space program. Later they'll try to head

off the others. He knew no details, nor where to find any. It's as alien to him as it is to you. And when I asked if he and his kind could help us, he said no. They feel they'll have as much as they can handle, safeguarding their own territories."

Al-Bunni shrugged. "Hard to see how they could help, anyway, under your laws, no? In fact, if it came out that I had just consulted one, picture the conniptions at INS, NSA, ICC, FBI—"

"Yeah," I agreed. "And Congress, the White House, the Equal Opportunity League, the feminists, the American Legion, the media, and Chicken Little. As for co-opting any, forget it."

NASA wouldn't even engage native American or American-born Otherfolk. That wasn't entirely its fault. The question had come up early on, and several unions took a firm stand. If Cardinal Point hired so much as one leprechaun, the teamsters, the machinists, the electricians, and the geomancers would walk.

We sat for a while in silence. The incense curled, the music keened.

"You said, 'Need to know,' " I ventured at last. "Why Ginny and me in particular?"

"You have your Operation Luna," he answered. "You remember I have given it some trifling help."

"Yes, sir! Not that we've accomplished much. If we had more funding, more staff—" I bit my lip. "No, sorry, that sounds like whining and isn't what I meant. If *you'd* favored our approach, as a sideline, I can't help believing we'd've had people on the moon by now. And, uh, a small deal like that would be easier to guard, wouldn't it? Less vulnerable."

"Not only to sorceries, you are thinking."

"Well, uh, O'Brien's Law and— Never mind."

"I do mind. I am well aware of that law, like any other engineer or Artificer. 'Anything that can go wrong, will.' I agree. Project Selene and its constructs have inevitably been huge, complex, therefore full of the unforeseeable. Only God thinks of everything." I suspected the terminal sentence was more a sigh than a piety.

"If we are to be serious about a permanent human presence beyond Earth, we will eventually need large vessels with large, powerful boosters," he went on after a while. "But it does make sense to start small and learn as we go. True, each step would be riskier than any of NASA's. But there would also be much less to lose."

He drew heavily on his cigarillo. "I have done more than give your group what slight aid I was able to. I have checked into your concept personally. In fact, I've considered it ever since I was a boy,

looking up from the desert sands to the stars and dreaming. To ride my own horse, or just my own broomstick, wild and free—

"Well, but always the pressure was on for quick, splashy results. First the Caliphate, then the United States Army. I thought a civilian agency would be more patient. But no, NASA too must forever push the envelope, as the saying goes. I've learned what sort of political pressures drive this, and resigned myself to reality. At the same time, again for political reasons, NASA has a fear that borders on hysteria, fear of losing lives. Every imaginable precaution must be built into the system and procedures, no matter how complicated and expensive this makes them."

I nodded. Enough celestonauts had grumbled to me and others. They were willing to take chances for the sake of getting on with the job, the vision. Why didn't the bureaucrats let them?

"I have done the best I could under the conditions imposed on me." Al-Bunni's voice took on some briskness. "Nor do I complain. It is as God wills. Besides, I *like* big beasts. To work on one, give your heart and soul to the work, and then see it gloriously rise—ah, it's as well that such occasions come far apart, or space artificers would have no children."

He set down his demitasse and continued more slowly: "But meanwhile, whenever I found some time and resources lying loose, I investigated alternatives as thoroughly as I could without anyone but a few confidants knowing. I finally reached the point where I could write preliminary specifications and sketch a tentative design for a moonstick."

The blood racketed in my ears. I could barely whisper, "Sir, if you . . . you . . . have done this, can't you make a report, write a paper, let the world know?"

He shook his head. "Pointless. Unwise. You see, there is an element of risk that NASA would never accept. That's why I haven't solved the problem of life support for so bare-bones a spacecraft, among other things. I gave up, because it had become clear that the whole thing would be disallowed. I would merely find myself called a bad team player. That would damage Project Selene more than it would me."

"Why?" I floundered. "That is, of course you wouldn't claim you had a perfect solution. This would be a, a scientific paper, something published for discussion."

He lifted a finger. "Oh, but there are so many gaps in the concept that such a proposal would be scorned—laughed out of court, do you Americans say? So minimal a craft must omit material reinforcement,

shielding, nearly all redundancy. My research of the literature did not turn up any metals, spells, or other hardware and spookware that would suffice instead. Nor did I discover any American thaumaturges or Beings who might be able to provide it.

"Probably the Chinese have some on tap, but they will hardly tell us. The Russians and West Europeans are taking the same approach as we have taken in Selene. There may be some who could help us, quite likely there are, but they are not in the registries. Disreputable individualists, no doubt. In any event, *I* would never be authorized to engage any."

He gusted a real sigh. "I'll be entangled in hearings and infighting and God knows what till God knows when. We won't make another attempt like the last here at the Point for years, if ever we do. And then, as before, we'll be a conspicuous target, with more points of weakness than we can foresee or provide against. We'll be leashed by regulations, and everything we undertake will have to please Congress."

The old warrior resoluteness took over afresh. "But you—you and your wife are unfettered. You're tough, ingenious, discreet, and not afraid to break or bend a rule when necessary. It's worth a try, at least."

He surged to his feet and went to a filing cabinet. I rose too. His words trailed him: "I will give you the data I've compiled, the calculations I've done, and the designs I've drawn, for whatever your Operation Luna can make of them. You will share this with your associates, but try to make sure that my name does not go further than to those who can keep a secret. Perhaps you can accomplish something. Perhaps."

He took a stone from a drawer. It resembled a neolithic celt, as that make of lorestone generally does. Nothing but a code number in red paint indicated what kind of information the crystal structure and particle waves embedded. The numerals were the true Arabic, which don't have the same shape as ours. He laid it in my hand. It was dense, a weight that felt strong. I clutched it, dumbfounded, unable even to howl.

# XIII

Ginny and I weren't churchgoers. With all due respect, we'd never figured out which of the world's countless sets of rites and dogmas lead to the best relationship with God. To tell the truth, we hadn't tried very hard. Some people have a strong religious drive, others don't. We assumed that ordinary human decency, to the extent we could maintain it, met minimum requirements. We might have sent our children to Sunday school so they could learn something about that part of their heritage. However, these days they got plenty of it in their social studies and science classes.

So ordinarily our Sunday mornings were lazy. After coffee and a look at the paper, we'd rouse whatever youngsters weren't awake yet. While they made themselves sort of presentable, either Ginny or I would fix breakfast, depending on what was wanted. She had a Cordon Bleu touch with crepes, while I was proud of my flapjacks and, lately, huevos rancheros. Having told the dirty dishes to go wash, we'd all relax some more. Formerly Valeria, afterward Ben, would be down on the floor, bottom up, reading the funnies, but now they sat, or rather sprawled in unlikely configurations; and as yet Chryssa demanded we read to her. Oftener than not, the pack of us would then go out—for a picnic, a horseback ride, a show, a visit with friends who had children too, whatever—though in the past couple of years Val was apt to take off with her own bunch. American bourgeois.

Not today.

It had begun the evening before, when I took Ginny aside into my study, closed the door, told her what had happened, and showed her the lorestone. "It may mean we can *go!*" I exulted. "As soon as we've read it ourselves—you handle the spelling and unspelling, I'll translate the

engineerese—we'll get in touch with Barney Sturlason and—and—" My voice sputtered out. I saw how those green eyes regarded me.

The hand she laid on mine was cold. "In death's name, no," she whispered. "Not a word. Not a thought or a midnight dream if you can help it." She whirled, sprang to the window, and drew the shade down against the long, golden light outside. Her free hand made signs in the air.

I gaped. "Huh?"

She turned back to me. "You and al-Bunni, how could you be so careless? The enemy may be anywhere. I've warded this house, and I suppose he's arranged for some provision at his building, but you stuck that thing in your pocket, sauntered to your stick, stopped for a beer along the way, and now— Oh, yes, you're big and strong and always in full command, you two." The red head shook. "Men!"

"But, but, honey, I did stay alert, and I was never alone. Supposing somebody"—*something,* shivered through my bones—"was trying to keep a scry on me, why, all that traffic ought to've confused it hopelessly. Rheatic noise level—"

"It could still perceive an element of the unusual, and want to find out exactly what." She clenched a fist. "I don't think you appreciate the situation. You've met Powers of darkness before and you have some extrahuman abilities, but you are not a warlock. I wonder how clear the danger is to the Fibbies, in spite of the stuff they saw and took back to study. Out there in the malpais, those traces—the lingering spoor of evil— And since then I've been studying too and trying to augur, every chance I got."

She stepped closer. Her breath went quick and harsh. "We're not just up against a native godlet, angry or mischievous. Nor his demonic allies, though they're worse because we know so little about them and any friendly native Beings have no hold or influence on them. Al-Bunni said the djinn themselves are alarmed, didn't he? But there is at least one other as well, subtle, cold, like hate itself become a spirit."

Suddenly my tongue was parched, my tone hoarse. "What is it?"

"I don't know, only that it's terrifying." She paused. "I have a guess or two, but speaking aloud at this stage would disrupt the spells I'm trying to weave. Right now they're so vague, so fragile, that a clear name, whether correct or incorrect, would make them go wrong."

*Like letting a molten alloy congeal too fast, and getting fatal crystalline flaws,* I thought inadequately. Aloud: "I'm sorry. You're right, I didn't think. I was overjoyed at this gift and forgot what everything else might mean."

She set her fears aside and eased in the panther style I well knew. "Well, quite natural. I'm happy about it too, of course. In all probability, no harm was done. I simply want to make sure none will be. Then we'll rejoice."

Her smile flashed. "Here's a promissory note on that." She came into my arms.

After a minute, though, she disengaged, took the stone, and left for her workroom. When I knocked on the door later and inquired about dinner, she asked me to bring a couple of sandwiches and coffee. So I did, and cobbled together a meal for the rest of us. Luckily, a National Geographic special which we all wanted to see was on the farseer.

The kids were rapt, especially Val. She was still a bit stiff toward me, but not cruel as she could easily have been, nor often sulky. A week's house arrest even offered opportunities to an active mind like hers. She read a lot, practiced her goetics and piano, with a tendency to military marches and laments, played complicated reckoner games, and ran up considerable bills on the phone and the Mesh. Tonight's show could have been written for her.

It was about the Long Sleep and the Awakening. The scenes from the past were beautifully done. It was as if we saw the prehistoric world, mammoths and dragons, cave bears and centaurs, cave men and elves. One episode was funny at first, when a Cro-Magnon tried to make a spear point out of a unicorn's horn and it crumbled away. What with the effects of sunlight and other natural chemistry, even if half-world creatures or plants can endure these while alive, their remains after death can't without special treatment, which is why they have left no fossils. But the narration grew serious as it told how knowledge of such basic differences led to fear and abhorrence. That may be why Stone Age art shows little or nothing of them.

"No doubt hunters occasionally pursued the Other game, and sometimes came upon intelligent Beings," said a professor who was interviewed. "They may even have made friends—or deadly enemies. Folk tales of men or women who wandered into strange realms may well go this far back, to those eerie, evanescent elfin civilizations." A picture appeared of a rainbow-shimmering bubble village and soaring spires, more rheatic than substantial, at which a man in leather garments peered from forest cover, half lured, half frightened. "No doubt some shamans kept some regular contact. But the early warlocks and witches largely concerned themselves with trying to control the ele-

ments, the world, and fate. They groped and stumbled forward, but also sideways and backward, for they had no concept of scientific method."

*Are we today so very far ahead?* I wondered. Unwillingly, my mind drifted to Ginny, alone in her room waging her war against she knew not what.

"Magic, as protogoetics was called, suffered a setback in the Bronze Age. God-kings didn't like the idea of competition. Warrior aristocrats discouraged practices that might make the lower classes equal in strength to them. Magic began to get a bad name. Nevertheless, the human population was still small; there were still vast areas where paranature and its inhabitants flourished; diviners, healers, spaewives, and poets quietly carried out their arts. So too, we must admit, did evil sorcerers."

*Yep,* said my restless mind, *same as now. Give humans power, any kind of capability but especially power over other humans, and some will misuse it. And probably the rogues are less of a menace than the busybodies.*

"—the Iron Age, ferrous materials spreading across the planet, ferromagnetism canceling rheatic forces that natural magnetism had always kept unstable at best. . . . The withering of paranature, of its whole ecology—"

Pathetic scenes, a field of dead asphodel blowing away in dust, a dead mermaid on a beach drying to nothing faster than the jellyfish stranded beside her, vines grown over the lips of an image that once spoke oracles, a human mage desperately gesturing and chanting against the drought that seared his people's fields—"Some few held on a long while, in odd corners of the Old World or throughout the New World, the Arctic, the Pacific. But the remorseless advance of European civilization—"

*Remorselessness,* said my unruly mind. *Is that the inability or refusal to acquire more than one walrus?*

"Perhaps a few Beings survived on upper Earth—" Like maybe Coyote and—who were the rest? Balawahdiwa had spoken of somebody else, and there his voice held awe. . . . If they were resentful, could you blame them?

"—the European dwarves probably longest, because iron had never bothered them. In fact, they had become not only skillful smiths, but adept at infusing their works with goetic might. Stories of the things they forged, wondrous jewelry, golden steeds, enchanted weapons—"

*Hey,* I thought, *dwarves, sure, if anybody can make the special stuff al-Bunni says we'll need, it's the dwarves.*

"But otherwise, meanwhile, the last remnants, animal, vegetable, intelligent, had retreated. Their whole ecology destroyed, they could only withdraw far under earth and sea, cast the final spell, lie down to Sleep till a better day or till Judgment Day."

A wry scene showed a dwarf packing his blacksmith tools and climbing down into a mountain crevice. He could live in the world as it had become, except how could he keep eating? His trade with gods and Faerie was gone. How many humans would pay for his work, the more so when witchcraft and paganism were now abhorred?

Iron, steam, electricity ran rampant. . . .

All prologue. After touching on Planck, Einstein, Moseley, Maskelyne, and the discoveries following these pioneers, the show became mainly about how the Sleepers, one by one, two by two, bunch by timid little bunch, occasional wild firedrake or bumptious troll, Awoke, came forth, and found their way into the new Goetic Age. This was oftener scry than reconstruction. We got some piercingly lovely scenes, like nymphs with dew under their feet and dawnlight in their hair. Some were bleak, like the hunting down of a rusalka that murderously haunted Lake Ilmen. Some were a bit esoteric, like the synods of various churches debating whether Faerie folk could legitimately be godparents. Some were everyday, like arguments about whether or not a bowl of milk set out for a Scandinavian nisse who did housework after dark constituted minimum wage. . . . It went on. Worried, I didn't pay as much attention as it deserved.

And now came bedtime, kid after kid according to age, and finally me. I lay awake for what seemed a long while, but Ginny didn't join me till after I'd fallen into an uneasy sleep.

# XIV

So on Sunday we rose later than usual. We weren't discouraged or somber, but there was a lot to do and the need to get on with it was like rowels. Valeria came in, Svartalf at her heels. When she saw us brooding over our coffee, she stopped. The cat took the occasion to sneer at Edgar, who flicked his tailfeathers back at him.

"Good morning," said Ginny and I together.

Blue eyes regarded us for a second before the girl curtsied and replied in the manner of happier times, "Salutations, O Paterfamilias and Matriarch. What plan you for our sabbath delectation?"

"Nothing fancy, I'm afraid," Ginny told her. "Cereal, toast— We're very busy."

"Popsy Scrunchies with *milk?*" She raised her hands and gasped. "Maybe actual toast and *jelly* on the side? *Vive la gourmetise!*" Not sarcasm, I realized; a forlorn attempt to keep some cheerfulness alive. "Well, say," she proposed hurriedly, "how about I take over? My hash brown spatoonies and cetera the other day weren't too bad, were they? If you can stand a rerun?"

Ginny was able to say gravely and graciously, "Thank you, dear. That would be a help." Me, I could only nod, gulp, and blink to unblur my vision. My daughter knew perfectly well she couldn't bribe or wheedle us into shortening her sentence. She offered love anyway.

Ben had entered, more or less kempt, and heard. "Hey," he said, "if we haven't got anything planned, can I go over to Danny Goldstein's after breakfast? I could spend the day."

Ginny's smile faded. "You don't want to wear out your welcome there," she said slowly.

I followed her thought. The Goldsteins weren't Orthodox, but they

were fairly observant Conservative, which meant that ordinary goetic technology was allowable for them but not the invocation of unhumans. Our home had Ginny's two familiars for guardians, plus trigger spells to call on stronger help in emergency. Theirs didn't, nor did the streets between. Once, when we lay at strife with the Adversary, a demon had stolen Val—

"Aw, Mom, I won't," the boy said. "I'd've gone yesterday, except they had Temple and then a family dinner. Danny asked could I take along the IRS Monster. And he found a real Indian arrowhead, did I tell you?"

Ginny and I both drew breath. Teaching our children fear at so early an age and penning them in was no kindness. Besides, after the disaster that Val's kidnapping brought on the Powers of evil—without even doing her harm—they had probably put that tactic in the Terrible Mistakes file. At least, I suspect the smart ones among them are quicker studies than most generals and all politicians. While we figured our present enemies didn't come straight from the Low Continuum, word would have gotten around. The Adversary was certainly interested in this case, even if he kept himself in the background.

Ginny gave me a slight nod. "Okay," I said, "you can go, but not till after lunch, and be back here by dinnertime. We can't bum off friends too much." Though, damn, Martha Goldstein's sweet-and-sour salmon and cheese blintzes were to diet for.

Ben registered disappointment but accepted the compromise like the sensible guy he was.

"I'll rout the sprout first," Valeria volunteered, "and see to it she doesn't get her dress on backwards and her hair into elfknots like certain people I could name," which wasn't really fair to her brother. He shrugged it off with a resigned look at me that said, "Girls!"

Thus, after we were coffeed, Ginny led me to her arcanum and secured it. The room, darkened when needful, was light and airy this morning. Sigils, crystals, talismans sparkled. Scrolls on the walls glowed with the colors of hieroglyphs, archaic scripts, and illuminations. Sprigs of green-leaved oak, ash, and thorn sprang from a vase like a shout of life. The mother-of-pearl eyes of a small tiki seemed to twinkle. Even the old leather bookbindings took on a glow. She herself was the most vivid. I couldn't resist a grope and a nuzzle. Her hair smelled summery.

"Whoa, eight-limbed Sleipnir," she said, with a moment's grin. "We've got serious business here, I'm told."

"I was afraid of that." I let go and looked around. "Where's the wonderstone?"

She pointed to the safe in a corner. I knew it was warded forty ways from Wednesday; you'd need a powerful spell just to detect that there was anything remarkable inside. A chain went from its bottom through a hole in the floor, down to bedrock. The combination for the lock was a curse on any unauthorized person who twirled it out. Today I saw that she'd added a Seal of Solomon.

"Wow," I said. "But how can we use it?"

She opened a drawer in her desk. "I drew the contents forth through a translator from Arabic into English, as an imprint on this." She took a sheaf of papers and laid them on top.

"Wow to the *n*th. That's why you were awake half the night."

"Oh, it wouldn't have been too bad if al-Bunni had consistently used Arabic, with English loan words as necessary. But no, he kept throwing in German terms. Worse, trying to invent them. I think he wanted to show his command of the language off to himself. It's awful. You wouldn't believe what trouble things like *Besenstockstrohbinden-beschleunigungskraftwiderstehenzauberstoff* gave my sprite."

"Poor darling. We'd better suppress that detail. Germany might declare war," I muttered, my attention on the papers.

She laughed. "Stop slavering and give them a quick once-over. Don't worry. They'll crumble to ash if anybody but you or me touches them."

I flung myself into a chair, grabbed the stack, and plunged. Ginny settled too, fingers bridged, eyes closed. She wasn't dozing, I knew at the edge of awareness; she was devising.

Presently I emerged. Eagerness tingled in me. "This is True Cross, all right," I said. "I'll need to study it carefully, of course, over and over, but plain to see already, he's anticipated work OpLu couldn't have done for years, if ever. Well, he's a genius in his field, and had resources available to him that we don't."

The gaze on me grew hungry. "He has a design?"

"Um-m, not entirely. He has the basic layout and goetics for a broomstick that should be able to cruise from end to end of the Solar System. But his calculations show that some of the materials, especially in the shaft, require properties like none we've yet developed, or have much idea how to develop. Without that, the rheatics—got to hold off hard radiation, you know, as well as supply control and boost—so much force concentrated in so small a volume would shatter the whole works.

I noticed a notation, or should I say a query, about the metal of enchanted swords."

"Which may or may not be pure legend."

"Yeah, who'd try, when firearms were everywhere?" I did recall a blade I'd wielded once, and I'd heard of others, but what special strengths they had were from olden association; the steel was mundane.

Ginny's voice shivered. "Barney Sturlason could sic his artificers onto the problem."

Reality raised its ugly head. "Wait. Wait a minute, sweetheart. We can't bull forward like that. For openers, it'd be a breach of faith with al-Bunni. He kept it to himself because making it public would give too much mana to his and Project Selene's political enemies. In fact, he set it aside before he'd considered issues like life support, because he saw no possibility of anything like it being approved. All he felt he dared do was give our bunch a bit of quiet help, like releasing that chip of moon rock to us. Then NASA could tell the Republicans in Congress that it doesn't really stifle private research. But everybody looked on that as just a token."

"And now matters are desperate enough that he has passed the information on, under the rose." Ginny nodded. "Brave of him. And not only faithless, but foolish of us, if we let the world know. Our highly placed friend would be damaged, our enemies alerted. Still, he can't have meant we leave this lying idle."

"No, no. Suppose we give Barney the material, in strict confidence and without saying where we got it—though he'll doubtless guess—and then we all mull over what to do with it. If nothing else, he'll need some advance notice so he can shift money around and be ready to write OpLu a check for expenses."

"*If* we decide we can accomplish something. Yes, that makes sense." Ginny pondered. "We won't take chances with the mails or any direct transmission."

The morning felt abruptly less bright.

However, once we'd agreed on what to tell him, it was cheering to see Barney's homely phiz in the telephone. We caught him at home, a time zone east of us, shortly before he left for the golf course. After his surprised hello, Ginny said flat out, "We have an item for your eyes and no other. Can you send a trusty courier to fetch it?"

He reacted as I expected, fast and steadfast. "How trusty?"

"Ultra. Preferably inconspicuous. But, mainly, able to detect, and evade or defend against, possible attempts to waylay him. They could be subtle attempts, if you follow me."

"I believe I do. Let me think. . . . The best that comes to mind, I can't get hold of today. I'll try tomorrow, and hope he can reach you Tuesday. Will that do?"

"It will have to. Better safe than sorry. Can he come to our house?" Barney nodded. "Fine. When he's ready to take off, have him call and ask me for an appointment at his arrival hour, like anyone who'd like to consult a witch about something. He'll be a man, yes? Let him identify himself over the phone as Mr.—the gentleman you used to tell those stories about."

Barney couldn't avoid chuckling. His great-uncle had been a North Woods lumberjack, a fairly epic figure even in that era. Most of the stories were not fit for polite society. Like the one concerning him, Lena the camp cook, a gallon of moonshine, and a bear in the outhouse— Never mind.

Barney sobered. "You think you're under surveillance?"

"We don't know, nor how close it may be," Ginny answered. "We're hedging our bets."

"Right. I've had my hunches. God, I wish we could talk together at ease, like old days!"

"We will," I said. "Actually, what we've got for you is good news. We just want to keep it good."

After a little soothing gossipswap, we disempathed. "Okay," I said. "Now, what about Will?"

For an instant, I saw Ginny taken aback. That disturbed me. She recovered, but frowned. "What? When you promised al-Bunni secrecy?"

"I promised him discretion, and that we'd keep his name out of things. But in his own words, he gave the stuff to Operation Luna for whatever we can do with it. 'We' can't be you and me alone. We'll have to bring in others, carefully, but bring them in."

"Why Will, though, at this stage?"

"He knows more than anybody else we know of, about what's on the moon."

"However much that means."

I gave her a puzzled look. "And if we do start serious work, we'll certainly need an astronomer. Yes, I realize astronomers are specialists these days—uh, nights—but he's skilled in the fundamentals, and knows where to find what further information we may want, and— Well, damn it, Ginny, he's your brother. Don't you trust him?"

"Oh, yes, of course. But I am—frankly, I'm more worried about him than I've pretended. This off-and-on, undiagnosable condition of

his—" She reached a decision. "I've wanted to see him again anyway, to check up as best I can. I tried to call yesterday between clients, but no answer. Let's both try today, and play by ear." She rose, leaned over me, and hurriedly kissed my cheek. "Now run along. I'd like to straighten out a few things here before breakfast."

I wandered back to the kitchen, where Valeria was busy. The smells made my stomach bay. "Want some help, punkin?" I asked.

"No, thanks. It's almost done. I made Ben set the table." Her slim figure tensed in the blue jeans and GOBLIN MARKET/HALLOWEEN SALE T-shirt. She turned to me. Her voice nearly lost itself in the sizzle and sputter on the range. "Dad, what's happening? Really-o happening?"

"Why, uh, well, a situation we can't, uh, discuss for the time being," I stammered at the big eyes and intent little face. "Your mother and I are helping where we can, investigating what went wrong at the launch. But, but don't be afraid. Things are fairly well under control."

"Nixway," she said. "And not only your troubles with that scabrous tax man. Daddy, I *know* you and Mom. And Uncle Will. Something's awfully awry. Isn't it?"

"Well, we're pretty busy, sure, and troubles do come in bunches—"

"You're woolmouthing the news people too, aren't you? They blat about whether the crash was due to sabotage or stupidity. But it wasn't either, not really, was it? You and Mom, you come and go. Where? Why?"

Over the years we'd told her, oh, how cautiously, about her snatch to Hell and rescue. To her at the time—her time—it had been a quick, hilarious whirlaway. She had scarcely any conscious memory of it. But our account afterward must have touched depths. Besides, she always was unusually watchful and given to thinking for herself.

I accepted. "Okay, soldier," I said. "It is a dark business. Stay alert, and if you're ever in the least doubt, yell for help. I honestly don't think matters will come to that. But right now I can't say more. Your part is to stand by. Savvy?"

"Aye, aye, sir," she whispered, and went back to her cooking. How long her lashes were over her cheekbones, how delicate her hands on pan and spatula. Yet she played a mean game of volleyball and could make a horse do whatever she wanted.

"Great." I allowed myself to squeeze her shoulder for a second. "And we don't let on to Ben and Chryssa, right?"

"Posolutely and absitively not." Then she chirped as if this were any Sunday, "Stuff's ready. Want to go howl the pack together?"

Thanks largely to her, that meal became fairly happy. Even Ginny

and I managed a few jokes. When it was done, Ben went off to his books and games till he'd be free to visit his friend. Val winked at me and said to Chryssa, "Hey, small one, want we should put on our floppy hats and go in the garden like for an hour or so?" I'd rigged a swing, a slide, a sandbox, and a miniature merry-go-round out there. Since they hardly saw use anymore except when a playmate came around, Small One naturally squealed with delight.

After they were gone, I murmured, "Quite a girl, that first daughter of ours."

"Working on her karma," Ginny replied. "I wonder how long till she overdraws the account again."

"*I* think she's being a trouper."

"Well, we have an hour's privacy here. More would be above and beyond the call of duty, I agree. Let's use it."

# XV

Having discussed what we could say and how, same as for Barney, we resonated Will's phone. This time we got him. The image was pale, hollow-eyed, shockingly haggard. Beard or no, I saw the tic in his right cheek. Ginny hung onto an outward calm. "Hi," she greeted. "Where were you yesterday?"

"Business in Albuquerque." Dull-toned, he offered nothing further. I had a feeling it would be unwise to inquire.

Instead, I asked, "You free today? How about lunch or dinner? Or both, if you care to."

"No, thanks. I'm sorry, I can't."

"Busy?"

"Yes. I . . . may be onto something new in my research. Rather not talk about it till I have more data."

"Good. Listen, there's a possibility of Operation Luna making a serious start. We can't say more than that right now. We'd like to pick your brains for ideas, though. Sure you can't come over? If not today, soon."

The gray head shook. "I'm sorry," he repeated. "Later, yes, certainly, but I can't say when." The prospect I opened for him had put no life at all back into his voice.

"You've fallen sick again, haven't you?" Ginny challenged.

"Under the weather. I'll recover. Don't worry."

"I damn well do. None of those doctors and sages you've been spending money on has done you a mote of good. Have they? I want to check you over myself. If something paranatural is involved, I'll have a better chance of spotting it and doing something about it than any outsider. Kinship, DNA sympathetics—"

"No!" His cry jangled harsh and uneven. "I won't have it! You don't understand!"

What hideous shame did he carry inside him that his sister must never know about? I couldn't imagine.

He spoke more calmly, with a crooked half-grin. "You two really shouldn't be seen with me till this case is cleared up. I'm a prime suspect, you know."

"No, I don't know," Ginny snapped. "Whatever gave you that notion? Yes, you were interrogated at length a few days ago, like everybody else in sight. You cooperated fully, more than I think I would have without a lawyer standing by. What more can they want?"

"Two of them were waiting when I got home yesterday," he said. "They wanted to come in and talk. I was tired and in a bad mood, and remembered what you'd told me. We stood on the porch awhile. I declined to explain what I'd been doing out of town, except that it concerned my scientific work. They quizzed me about my Chinese connections—as if I hadn't been through hours of that earlier—and hinted heavily that I'd do best to notify their office before I left Gallup again. I'm no sleuth, but I'll wager that someone's keeping a watch over me and someone else is listening in on this conversation."

"They . . . they may only wonder if you . . . have information you don't recognize . . . that'd be a clue for them," I ventured lamely.

Ginny's lips tightened. "We'll do some investigation of our own," she said. Softly: "Carry on, old dear. And do think about letting me examine you."

After a few more words we disempathed and stared at one another. Her face wasn't simply redhead-fair, it was white. "Impossible," she breathed. "Will could no more do—any such things—than I could murder you."

"And you've had your provocations," I tried to jape.

"Some ghastly coincidence. Maybe I can 'chant forth a hint of it." She didn't sound hopeful. "I hate to pry, of course, but—"

I rallied my wits. "Meanwhile let's see what I can do with a professional pry bar."

"Hm?"

"Bob Shining Knife, who else?" As eagerness flared in her: "Wait, better I tackle this myself. Having you on hand could put him too much on his guard. I'm nothing but a big, dumb Bohunk werewolf."

A slow smile gave a glimpse of her teeth. "Ye-es. No smarter than Karel Capek, no more of a threat to the establishment than John Huss." Me, I'd rather have been compared to Thomas Masaryk, who broke

our people free of Austria-Hungary after the Kaiser's War, but I got her idea and was touched. "Also, you're his friend. You went hunting, fishing, poker playing, beer drinking together more than once, back in the Midwest. Male bonds. Go jerk them if you can."

When I called the broomotel in Grants, he'd just gotten back from a ten-mile run. "Kind of late in the day for that, wasn't it?" I asked.

"I slept late. Up half the night, working. The weather's slacked off. It wasn't too hot yet." He wiped a cloth over the sweat that polished his coppery countenance. "What can I do for you, Steve?"

"I need to talk with you. Privately."

"You know I can't discuss a case in progress." He tautened. "Unless you have something new to contribute."

"I might or might not. You be the judge. But it does involve personal matters."

He hesitated. "If it's about— You know I can't play favorites either. I meant to go around to headquarters this afternoon and see what the lab boys have made out of—what we found."

"Aw, c'mon, Bob, that can wait a few hours. Give me a break. I'll stand you lunch, if your bosses won't think it's bribery. Don Pedro's. Chili to make Lucifer flinch, and Dos Equis on tap to sanctify it."

"Um-m, thanks, I'm not sure about a heavy midday meal, but— Oh, all right, come here. We'll be alone. My roommate's already busy." He glanced at the image beside mine. "Hi, Ginny." Sympathy tinged his greeting. And maybe a touch of apprehension?

I spent the time en route arranging my thoughts and making a treaty with my conscience. Once in the past we'd defied him, his agency, the whole United States government, to go get our Valeria Victrix back. Only the spectacular outcome kept serious charges from being brought against us. But that had been an exceptional pickle. Neither Ginny nor I believed that, as a general rule, untrained, unorganized, unauthorized individuals could really fight crime, whether or not they wore silly comic-book costumes. That way lay lynch law. On the other hand, I was not about to mention our dealings with Balawahdiwa and al-Bunni, though they were certainly relevant and might contain important clues. Sometimes a person has to exercise personal judgment and take the chance of being mistaken, or stop calling himself or herself free. George Washington, for instance, or Sojourner Truth.

The unit where Shining Knife stayed was the usual, functional and characterless. His very presence, let alone his outfit hanging in the closet, overwhelmed it like a bagpipe at a tea party. "Have a seat," he

said as we shook hands. I took one of the two chairs. He chose to perch on one of the twin beds. His black eyes stabbed me, not quite the way Juliet's did Romeo. "What do you have to tell?"

"Sort of abrupt, aren't you?" I parried.

"We had our sociability over the phone. This is a major affair, and the more my associates and I look into it, the nastier it seems. Don't waste your time or mine, Steve."

"All right," I said just as coldly. "What do you guys have against Will Graylock?"

He went impassive. "I've explained before, I can't speak about that. Among other reasons, at this stage it wouldn't be fair to the subject. Not everybody investigated is necessarily a suspect. He might be a material witness, for instance, maybe without realizing it. What did you come here to say?"

"That my wife and I *know* him. Her brother, after all, who saw her through to adulthood when she was orphaned. Bob, you know us. Would we cover up for a criminal, in a crime that could have cost lives and did wreck my work of the past two years? We don't want you baying on a false scent. I tell you, and this is a question of fact, not family: Will Graylock is incapable of any such act."

When Shining Knife sat silent, he forced me to end awkwardly, "To start with, he's no warlock. And he's new to this area, and hasn't taken more than an ordinary benign interest in the Indians and their cultures. How the devil could he have any ties to Coyote?"

"Nobody claims he did," Shining Knife answered. "For that matter, nobody claims Coyote, or any local Power, is the mastermind behind the sabotage. Maybe so, maybe not. We do know, and that 'we' includes you, Asian Beings are involved. A human reasonably familiar with the Cardinal Point layout had to help them, advise them. Will Graylock's behaved pretty odd, hasn't he? Once alerted to that, we've, my team's begun to find how odd.

"I'm not telling tales out of school here, because you know more about this than we do, and I'd be glad to hear whatever you want to share. Meanwhile, he's had close Chinese contacts for a long time, friends, colleagues, correspondents; he's made several visits to the country, some extensive; he speaks the language and is well versed in the history, literature, and anthropology. And demonology?"

Shining Knife finished his hammerblow sentences in milder style: "I can say that much because it's obvious to you. Now, what can you say to me?"

"That, yes, he isn't well, and nobody's diagnosed the trouble, but

he has been going in for tests, examinations, and treatments. Do you suppose an invalid would traipse around the malpais after dark? Or a quiet, decent, rationalistic scientist would get involved in any kind of conspiracy? Why would the conspirators *want* him? Good Lord, there must be a couple dozen people at the Point with Chinese connections of one sort or another. A few Chinese journalists and diplomatic personnel and whatnot have been given the grand tour. Why aren't you investigating them and their guides?"

"Who says we're not?" he retorted.

I wasn't to be stopped in midcareer. "And what about this mysterious Dr. Fu Ch'ing? Your buddy Moy didn't exactly give him a clean bill of health last week. Why aren't you on his trail?"

Shining Knife fell silent a few seconds. "That's easier said than done," he replied at last.

"But you think he's currently in England. Well, don't you have liaison with Scotland Yard?"

Shining Knife smiled ruefully and spoke readily. I guessed he was glad to get off a topic painful to me, if only for a moment. "Sure we do. And the Yard has first-class thaumaturges, as well as operatives of every other kind. They did get word, through their own lines into China, that Fu was bound for England, with no good intentions toward Western civilization. They were even able to establish that he had arrived, shortly after the fact. But that's all. In spite of every effort, they still have no idea of his whereabouts."

I rubbed my chin, feeling likewise relieved by the change of pace. "Funny. If he's as great a warlock as Moy claims, I should think activity, forces, spirits at that level would be hard to screen off untraceably."

"True, sort of. But you see, he keeps conjuring up false traces of his presence everywhere around the country. The Yard, MI, everybody's run ragged chasing them down and drawing blank at the end. The latest site I heard of was Buckingham Palace." Shining Knife turned grim. "It's also all too possible that Fu's got double agents inside Scotland Yard and the British military. He thinks and acts in terms of decades. Nobody knows how old he is."

"So you fellows have to be wary," I murmured. "How certain are you of your FBI?"

"We're trying. Whoever or whatever is behind the trouble at Cardinal Point, a knowledgeable human agent on the spot was clearly required. We begin by finding who he is."

"And I tell you, Will Graylock—"

"There is such a thing as demonic possession," Shining Knife interrupted very quietly.

I sat as if he'd slapped a muzzle on me.

"I've given this a lot of thought, Steve," he went on. "I'm glad you came today, even if your idea was nothing but to be a character witness. Do you suppose you could persuade him to volunteer for a psychoscopy? I'll bend the rules and tell you, if he comes through clean, that'll revive a lot of questions that right now seem like they may have an answer."

"He can't be possessed," I gabbled. "How on Earth or Below could he have been?"

"If perchance he somehow is," Shining Knife said, unrelenting, "then, assuming he didn't invite it, he's legally innocent; and an exorcism will liberate him."

"But, but it's impossible."

"The possession, or his agreeing?"

*Both,* I thought. The lump in my throat blocked off speech. Will was such a private man. The days-long search for a demon didn't involve merely spells, though some of them would be uncomfortable enough, or medical procedures, though some of them would be undignified enough. It included sessions with—opening himself, his life and heart to—a psychic analyst.

"Fifth Amendment," I mumbled. Nobody has never broken an occasional law.

"Yes. It works to his advantage, Steve. Didn't you know? The Supreme Court's ruled that anything revealed under psychoscopy is immune to prosecution. I knew a man once who tried very hard to convince the police he needed one. He failed. Turned out he'd committed a murder. As for anything that a demon forced someone to do, I repeat, as long as he didn't invite it in, obviously he's innocent."

*But the intimacies,* I thought, *his wife, other women before her and maybe after, the mystic beauty that gave his life its direction, so strange and precious that he had told none but his sister about it, of all people now living, till at last his need and his trust brought him to share it with me—*

*And everything else that any man may damn well want to keep to himself.* "I wouldn't submit," I stated.

"He'll be safe, Steve. Home free, I'll bet, whatever the outcome. If it turns out he is afflicted, he'll be made well. Won't you at least propose it to him? Better from you, better yet from Ginny, than an outsider."

I thought of the tortured face and dragging voice. “Not today,” I said. “We need to think this over.”

The rest of our conversation was short and constrained. We did not go to lunch.

Flying back, I realized the clues pointing toward Will must be stronger that Shining Knife had admitted. A hell of a lot stronger. But what could they be? Dust and other traces, closely analyzed? Goetics partially reconstructing those blurred footprints?

Hey, a really gifted villain might arrange things to frame a guiltless party—and wasn’t Fu Ch’ing supposed to be the Genghis Khan of crime . . . ?

Ginny met me at our front door. She took both my hands in hers. I felt the tension, saw it on her, heard it in her. “We’d better catch a nap this afternoon, darling, if we can. We’ve gotten a note from Balawahdiwa. A son of his delivered it, and didn’t stay. It said only, ‘Come after sunset. Be ready for the mountains.’ As soon as I’d read it, it became ash.”

# XVI

Valeria, our built-in babysitter, struggled gallantly not to ask questions. After dinner she said she wanted to call a friend. I heard strangled tears. She vanished into her room. The conversation was interminable. However, I daresay she kept it light. "Arnie's broom? That old dustmop? Now, Larry's Fiat Lux, I mean when his elders let him have it, there's a swoopersweeper! . . . Saturday? Yes, I'll be out of durance vile by then. The Gustafsons' swimming pool? Magniff!" Or something like that. I don't eavesdrop, but occasionally I'd passed by her door when it was open and she a-chatter, on the bed with legs propped high on the headboard and likely as not Svartalf on her stomach.

Ginny and I outfitted ourselves. Besides rough-country garb, I wore my skinsuit and carried my wereflash. To her outfit she added a cloak, not only for warmth but as a minor talisman; Fritz Leiber had once played Prospero in it. The owl pin on her shirt was much more potent, a badge of her order that had been to Hell and back. She'd given her best wand a magnum charge. The raven perched black on her shoulder.

Our stick bore us south. The night was windless but already I felt glad of my jacket. Once we'd gone beyond city lights, the stars gleamed brilliant around an ice-clear galaxy, so many that I could hardly make out the constellations toward which we flew, the Archer, the Eagle, and over our heads the Lyre and the Swan. We spoke little; we felt too small.

Beneath that sky, we easily found the pueblo and our way through its almost empty lanes. A yellow glow spilled from the windows of Balawahdiwa's house, but he stood outside. *Must have scryed us coming, or whatever he does,* I thought. Unlike us, he wore no hat; the

grizzled hair looked ashen in the half-light. Otherwise his clothes resembled ours, except for a kilt and sash. They didn't look funny above his pants; we knew they were sacred.

"Greeting," he said without preamble. "I'm sorry not to invite you in, but we should take off at once."

"Far to go?" I asked inanely.

"Not in space," he answered. "In spirit, yes, very far."

"Shall we flit together?" Ginny suggested. It had been her idea to take our Ford. Three riders would have cramped the Jag.

Balawahdiwa nodded. We walked back to the parking space. Rather than rack the stick, we'd snapped its legs down, figuring it wouldn't stand there long.

"I sought to call on Nebayatuma," he told us. "He too has gone beyond death and returned. From him stem the Sacred Clowns. But—I don't know why, and maybe I never will—he who came to me was the other flute-player, the hunchbacked wanderer Owiwi. You're more familiar with his Hopi name, Kokopelli."

"He'll help us?" Ginny breathed.

"First he wants to know you, and of you."

*Well,* I thought in the cold and the silence, *that's reasonable, if reasonableness means anything where gods and spirits are concerned.*

We took our places, Ginny at the control crystal, Balawahdiwa beside her, me behind, and lifted. He pointed easterly. "We're bound for the Zuni Mountains," he said. "I'll guide you as we travel."

Air whispered around the windfield. The chill deepened. Ginny didn't cast any heat spell, and somehow I knew it wouldn't have been right. She wrapped the cloak close about her.

"I mustn't tell you much," Balawahdiwa went on after a while, in the same soft, even tone. "Sacred things, you understand?" We both nodded. "I purified myself and went out in the desert in search of a dream. The dream told me I should go to those mountains. There I made the medicine and waited." Fasting and thirsting, I expected. "He came at moonrise. We had talk. Tonight moonrise is later, but you need time to make your hearts ready."

"Gruk," said Edgar hoarsely, and stretched his cramped wings a bit.

Balawahdiwa smiled. "It is well that you have one with you who is of earth and the winds."

If he meant natural nature, I had my doubts. Edgar stole every coin and button he could, to hoard. He swiped Svartalf's kibble when he got a chance, and had to be forcibly restrained from raids on the

cat's twice-weekly treat of canned fish. I'd seen him eat a cigar butt. Once when we were hosting a cocktail party, he grabbed the olives out of three martinis before Ginny caged him. And we were lucky that Val didn't play much of that wretched excuse for music, sway 'n swivel. He loved it, he danced to it, he screeched right along with it.

"I know you don't lack courage, you two," Balawahdiwa said. "But you'll need all your resolution, all your honesty of purpose. Mostly Kokopelli is a friend to man. But he is ancient. He has his terrible side."

*Yes,* I thought, *the Anasazi knew him, and maybe peoples before them. Chiseled and painted rocks over the whole Southwest bear his image. As for terrible, what of Apollo and his deadly arrows, Odin and his Wild Hunt, Huitzilopochtli eater of hearts—what of Jehovah and his vengeances?*

We flew on over the miles. Now and then a few human lights twinkled lonely. They soon fell behind us.

"The Anasazi were not entirely peaceful farmers," Balawahdiwa said once, barely to be heard. "There were cannibals among them."

The mountains bulked ahead. I've said they aren't too impressive by day, except for the wonderful color-wild cliffs below. Still, in a few places they reach about nine thousand feet; and in this hush, starlit, the masses of them rolling downward into darknesses, I felt what mortality really means.

Balawahdiwa had been pointing the way for Ginny. His finger dipped. She made a tricky landing on a boulder-strewn slope. Bunch grass, silver-gray in the night, brushed my calves as I got off. I caught faint smells of the stunted evergreens that gloomed around the open area, but probably my companions could not.

"From here we walk," Balawahdiwa said. His breath smoked ghost white. "It's a sign of respect and a part of becoming ready."

He led the way, surefooted as a bobcat. Ginny and I followed. Often we groped and staggered. We hadn't given ourselves witch-sight; any spell cast in advance might prejudice our case. We both had good dark vision, and heaven out here was brighter than city dwellers ever know, but the murks were many.

Nonetheless we toiled on for a couple of hours or more. I didn't check my watch. This was not a place to chop time into numerals. The way led upward, now and then around a bluff or through a defile where stones rattled underfoot. Gloom lay thick in wooded stretches. Mostly, though, we were on bare mountainside, among rocks and sparse plants, outcrops and hollows. Sweat gathered under my clothes and felt

clammy on exposed skin. My nostrils dried out as I snatched after the thin air.

Finally Balawahdiwa raised his hand. "Here we stop," he said. Heard through the blood thudding in my ears, his voice sounded far-off and like a prophet's. "Here we wait, keep silent, and calm our souls."

We'd reached a flat spot atop a ridge, thinly begrown, roofed with sky and the Milky Way a tremendous, upholding arch. The least of winds had begun to rustle. We sat down cross-legged in a kind of circle, to abide.

I couldn't see the others well. Balawahdiwa was motionless, expressionless. Ginny's gaze reached into light-years. I did my best to become stoic or reverent or whatever was called for. After a while the ground beneath my bottom got flinking hard and frosty, while my thighs protested the position they were in. Edgar, who'd settled at Ginny's side, shifted from foot to foot till he resignedly tucked his head under a wing and went to sleep. But we'd tried, both of us.

A waning half moon climbed from the Continental Divide. Phantoms grew more solid, darknesses less heavy. The wind strengthened. I heard how it piped through the scattered trees, over the stones—

No, it was not the wind. It was music, an eerie, hiccoughy whistling in no key known to me—

He came before us out of the night, dancing to the tune of his cedar flute. We saw him the way we saw the land, strange, starlit, moonlit. He had chosen to be man-size. His face, bent over the flute, was obscure, but some kind of feather headdress plumed upward. His arms and legs were so skinny that he well-nigh seemed a huge insect. I never quite saw whether he was really hunchbacked or only wore a big pack full of who knows what. Leather clothes closely fitted him, but his equipment stuck out, erect, for horses to envy. The gods aren't bound by human etiquette.

We rose. Ginny and I bowed and I removed my hat, not knowing what else to do. Balawahdiwa made a more complex gesture and spoke in, I think, the Zuni language.

Kokopelli lowered his flute and looked at us. I felt myself searched from the inside out.

Otherwise, from then on, I was a spectator. I didn't understand what happened, nor did Ginny afterward tell me much. Edgar, too, kept his beak shut. Ginny joined the talk to the extent she was able. It was slow and careful talk, with long pauses in between.

And yet, more and more, Kokopelli grinned, finally laughed. The

moon rose higher, shrunken and pale. He edged near her and murmured like a brook through a flowerfield.

Though I was neither female nor wolf, the scent, the power flooded over me. It was like nothing I'd known since we long ago came up against a succubus-incubus down in Mexico. Stronger, maybe—here was a godling, at least—but then, I'm male and it wasn't meant for me. All I knew was such a rush of lust that if she and I had been alone—

And she admitted later she'd gone giddy and horny too. I can only guess how much more. Yet she held fast to herself, kept her stance, and declined Kokopelli's proposition, doubtless politely but maybe almost as calmly as I knew she'd declined others.

He appeared to take it amicably, which suggests to me the American gods are gentlemen in ways the Greek gods weren't. He made a gesture that might have corresponded to a shrug. The wildness blew away on the night wind. He addressed Balawahdiwa in straightforward fashion. After a minute or two Ginny regained enough balance to join in. Me, I stood dazed. Edgar slumped like a bag of black potatoes. I don't know what he'd experienced.

Kokopelli finished with us. He turned and danced off into the darkness. We heard his flute-song dwindle into silence.

For a span we stood unmoving. I felt wrung out. The wind poked fingers beneath my jacket.

At last Balawahdiwa said, word by word: "He likes you well enough. You are genuine. He's aware of the foreign Beings, and does not like them at all. I think they scare him too, but he'll never admit that."

He fell into bald practicality, as if in defiance: "However, they are allied with Coyote, and Kokopelli can't bad-mouth them to him without better evidence than we've offered. It'd be like somebody telling you not to trust a political ally, who's probably pleasant as well, and has buttered you up, and convinced you he's got the plan for reaching your goals. The native Powers do resent NASA's intrusion on their land and their people's lifeways."

"What can we do, then?" Ginny asked beneath the half moon and the wind.

"Prove that the aliens didn't wreck the space launch for sport, but have wider ambitions. Kokopelli frankly doesn't believe they're on the moon, and won't make a fool of himself by passing such stuff on to his fellows. You must also show you can do better for this land than you have been doing. Else, he says, they'd just as soon see your works

destroyed. You wouldn't be the first who've come and gone in this old, old country."

Balawahdiwa sighed. "I think I've done as much as I can, for now, anyway," he ended. "The next move is yours."

We started back down the mountainside.

# XVII

The carpet came over a height north of us like a flat stormcloud.

Our encounter had lasted longer than we realized. Wearied, we made a slow and stumblesome return. Dawn found us with, I guessed, a couple of miles yet to go. The sky behind us whitened and wan light sneaked over the world. Above us spooked the moon, ahead of us the last stars were dying out. Ruggedness and trees still hid our broomstick. We were on a broad open stretch, though, the nearest woods several hundred yards downward on the right, darkling against sallow clumps of grass and bleached rocks. The wind had stopped, but the night's cold filled air and earth.

I think Edgar saw the carpet first. He squawked from Ginny's shoulder. We humans stopped and peered the same way. Against the ever more luminous heavens, it was a foreshortened black rectangle, featureless. Ginny's voice shivered through the stillness: "Who in Hermes' name is cruising here at this hour on that?"

A flash in me remembered that Hermes isn't only the Messenger and the Thief, he's the Psychopomp, conductor of the dead to Hades. The prosaic part of me squinted and tried to identify the thing—a large family-type carryall, for passengers and groceries and lumber and whatnot else—a Plymouth Conestoga or a Baghdadi Caravaneer, I couldn't make out which—serviceable, but not what you'd ordinarily take far off the regular traffic lanes or attempt to land on rough terrain—

Balawahdiwa sensed the aura first. "Evil!" he shouted. "Beware!"

The carpet slithered to a halt and hung some fifty feet behind us and above the slope. Light gleamed off metal abruptly thrust out in front.

The war came back to me on a tide of instinct. "That's a rifle!" I cried. "Run! Zigzag!"

The first bullet spanged off a boulder close by. Chips flew. An instant afterward I heard the *crack.*

Ginny yelled and pointed. Edgar took off. She burst into speed along with us men. We bounded, we leaped, to and fro, down toward the concealment beneath the trees.

I cast a glance over my shoulder. The sun mounted the crest. It dazzled away all sight of enemy and familiar. Its afterimage burned in my vision. I tripped over a stone, rolled, lurched to my feet and onward.

Ravens are big birds. Could Edgar get past the gunfire, reach the gunman, and peck his eyes out?

The bullets whanged, right, left, ahead, behind. That bastard must have a surplus military weapon with an outsize clip, like an M-7 or a Swiss Schraubenzieher. They're legal, at least in this part of the country. He wasn't much of a marksman, but by sheer volume— Were those stupid trees an inch nearer?

Edgar flapped back out of the sun-glare. He staggered on his wings. A powerful warding spell must have smacked him off.

Spells!

I veered to catch Ginny. She'd lost her hat. Her locks rippled like flame. The cloak fluttered wildly behind her. "Give me that," I said. She caught on at once, undid it, passed it to me, and sped on. The bullets pursued her.

"Help her!" I shrieked to Balawahdiwa. "Shield her!"

I threw myself to the ground and pulled the cloak over me. In the sudden darkness I heard him: "You're too easy a target—"

"Run, God damn it!" One hand unzipped my jacket and ripped my shirt open, popping buttons, to get at the wereflash and uncover enough skin. The other fumbled around my drawn-up knees, undoing belt and fly, hauling my pants down in the darkness where I lay.

*Yes,* said a passionless voice at the back of my head, *he may very well guess what I'm at and concentrate on me. If he nails me before I've transformed, that's it. But I'll have bought time for Ginny to get to safety.*

The Polaroid glowed. Change writhed and churned.

Agony struck. For an instant I whirled away from myself.

I awoke. No more than a few seconds could have passed. The pain was gone. Another slug hit, and another, but like heavy blows with a soft hammer. I was wolf. My wounds, including the first one, healed nearly as fast as I took them.

I threw off the cloak and snarled at the sky.

My outer garments hampered me. Three more bullets smote. The impacts knocked me around. I tore off clothes with my teeth, except the skinsuit, stepped from the boots, and dodged away, unhumanly swift. My howl railed at the enemy.

Unless he got me right in the skull and spattered my brains—not bloody likely—I was safe from him. Unless his ammo included some silvernosed rounds. But those *are* illegal for civilians.

Wolf, I savagely exulted. I wanted his throat between my jaws. Canine, I wanted to dash downhill and catch up with my beloved. Human, partly, I knew I should keep springing about in the area where he was and draw his fire.

He did keep trying for me, forlorn though the chance was. Whether or not he killed my companions, I'd make my way home, turn into a man again, and bear witness. The bullets sleeted. I danced with them and jeered.

He got smart. The carpet slid forward, downhill, after the others. It dropped lower, too. Myopic though my lupine vision was, across this distance I spied an ordinary broomstick secured on top. The sight wasn't clear, barely a clue to what the thing was. Just as vaguely, I spied the one who lay prone on the leading edge, rifle to shoulder. Did he wear a ski mask? I couldn't tell.

I bayed and gave futile chase.

But now Ginny and Balawahdiwa were under the trees. The woodlet engulfed them in branches, needles, shadows. The carpet veered, hung for a moment, and began to withdraw.

Ginny trod forth. She had taken her wand from the sheath. Its star flared scarlet. Beside her, Balawahdiwa raised his arms. I heard him chant, a sound that raised every hair on my hide.

They could duck back under cover if they had to. They didn't. The forces they flung cast blue fire around the carpet. Suddenly the air reeked of lightning.

The carpet wavered. Smoke trailed its unsteady flight. It disappeared behind the summit over which it had attacked, wobbling more and more.

I reached Ginny and dropped on my haunches, tongue unreeled, lungs pumping. Her wand had faded to normal. She went on her knees. "Oh, Steve, Steve!" She threw her arms around my shaggy neck and kissed me right on my wet black nose. Then Edgar arrived and demanded his share of attention. He'd done his best, hadn't he?

Later I retransformed under the cloak. Balawahdiwa surveyed the

holes and bloodstains and shook his head. "This was historic, wasn't it?" he said. "Too bad. I hope you can get it repaired. If not, you'll give it honorable burning, won't you?"

The trace of wolf lingering in me exclaimed, "How about we take our stick and track that torpedo down? He can't get far."

"No," Ginny replied. "You told us he has auxiliary transportation. He'd scarcely hang around his grounded rug."

"Besides," Balawahdiwa pointed out, "he remains armed and dangerous. Best we go home. You'll have breakfast at my place, I hope? Later you can report this to the authorities." He paused. "We had better decide how much you should report."

# XVIII

We returned via Grants. Shining Knife's investigations had taken him elsewhere for the nonce, but we had the luck to catch Jack Moy. While not auld acquaintance, he was intelligent, and as *simpático* as his job allowed him to be. He found a tiny room among the crowded offices where we could talk by ourselves.

I let Ginny handle most of that and worked at maintaining my poker face. She told no lies, not really. She being friends with Balawahdiwa, we'd asked if his wisdom could help. He'd led us into the mountains for some night hours of meditation and communion. Indian medicine didn't take the headlong, linearly logical, impersonal course of Western goetics. It was indirect and patient. You began by preparing your own spirit.

Moy nodded. "Yes, I've heard something about that since I came here," he said. "I think a Taoist would understand."

"Are you of that faith, if I may ask?"

"Well, a civil servant with a wife, two children, and a mortgage gets to be more of a Confucianist, I guess. Go on, please."

The rest of the account was straightforward. His questions went to the point, a few of them at me. Once he said, "That was heroic of you, Mr. Matuchek."

"Naw," I said, "desperate," and meant it. Ginny's look and the brief touch of her hand on mine were worth more than medals.

At the end, Moy formed a soundless whistle. "A wicked business for certain. Have you any idea who it may have been or why he assaulted you?"

"None," Ginny answered, "except that I suppose he fears what we might accomplish. That implies he knows the situation well."

Moy's almond eyes drew into slits. "Someone close to you, then?" he said very quietly.

Ginny sat straighter. Her words crackled. "Not necessarily, sir, not necessarily at all. Project Selene could have been infiltrated years ago. As for my husband and me, we were public figures once. Anyone could look up the stories about us. Since then I have become well-known in my profession." And formidable, she needn't add. "We have not spoken to anybody else of what we found in the malpais with you and Shining Knife, but this kind of opponent could readily learn that the four of us were out there together. Meanwhile the findings have been disseminated widely through the Bureau, correct? Let me suggest you check up on some of your own personnel."

"No offense, Dr. Matuchek," Moy said hastily.

"You might also set diplomatic pussyfooting aside and look into the possibility of foreign agents more thoroughly than I suspect you have. But I can't run your shop for you. We have told you as much as we can," whether or not that was precisely as much as we knew, "for whatever use it may be to you. You have our address and phone glyphs. Now, if you will excuse us, we're tired and had better go home to rest."

And *that* was the absolute truth. I didn't see how Ginny managed it, poised there as if her begrimed outdoor garb were a freshly cleaned business suit and speaking the way an old-time schoolteacher would have to a slightly difficult pupil. Me, I ached and prickled, my eyeballs smoldered, and my head was full of sand. It's only comic-book heroes and their ilk who bounce directly from one brush with death to the next, wisecracking along the way. Real humans react to such things.

"Certainly," Moy agreed. I can't say whether he, like Britannia, waived the rules. "You've given us something enormously valuable, I'm sure—" He could not altogether quell a grin. "—even if it wasn't quite your intention. On behalf of the Bureau and the nation, I thank you. Do you want an escort back to Gallup and a guard for a few days? . . . No? . . . Well, then, good-bye, and do get a good rest."

We shook hands and left.

Westbound, I said once, "My brain's dragging in the dirt behind me. I wonder if we shouldn't've accepted that offer of protection. The kids—"

Ginny bit her lip. "No. The danger's not likely any worse than before, and probably less, since the enemy showed his hand."

"And had to fold it. Yeah. But there'll be a new deal soon."

"Scarcely the same. We, the Fibbies, the Zunis, we've been fully

alerted. And he's left a trail for our sleuth hounds to follow." Her laugh rattled. "Oh, my, I'm worn out myself, scrambling metaphors like this. But all in all, I wouldn't expect fresh violence, at least in the near future. As for goetic attempts, our house is well warded. Let's not have any more government agents around than we can avoid."

"Always a good idea in principle. In this case, you also think they'd cramp our style?"

"They could." I hadn't the energy to ask further.

Somehow we made it home. I called in sick at the lab, not that that made any real difference. Meanwhile Ginny gave Valeria furlough if she'd take Chryssa over to a neighbor who had a contemporary little girl. Val had already seen Ben off, lunch packed, to play softball with some other boys. Edgar lumbered to his perch and slept. Svartalf lay cat-flat in the sunlight. Ginny and I fumbled our way to bed.

I've gathered that most people who've been through mortal danger are apt to have nightmares afterward. I don't claim to be any tougher. In the lycanthrope strain it may be nature's way of healing the trauma; or maybe I'm just lucky. My dreams go erotic.

However, it was hunger that roused us about four hours later. We still had the house to ourselves. Having showered and changed clothes, we went into the kitchen. "The nap helped," I mumbled, "but I sure hope to turn in early tonight," and yawned.

"Fenris would be proud of that gape," Ginny said. "Yes, me too." She had her own way of taking off the psychological effects of stress. It involved mentally reciting a mantra while visualizing a fractal mandala. Beyond my abilities.

Fenris couldn't have tackled my roast beef sandwich, piled high with horseradish, onion, and tomato, more gluttonously. Coffee worked its fragrant miracle. I gave her a suggestive leer across the table. The smile I got back, through a mouthful of her tuna salad, was responsive but wry. "The younger generation will start returning any minute," she reminded me when she'd swallowed.

The phone called. "And that stinkful nuisance always does," I growled.

Yet we'd told the sprite to repel subscription pitchmen, self-styled worthy causes, and other such infestations. They usually pick dinner-time anyway. "Come on in," Ginny cried. I gollopped my food, an electric chill forcing itself into my skin past every skepticism, while the instrument floated to us and settled down.

Shining Knife's image looked out of it. "How're you doing?" he asked.

"Fairly well," Ginny replied. "What are you up to?"

"I thought you'd like to hear. I reached the office shortly after you'd left and helped organize an immediate set of searches."

*"Set,"* I thought. *He takes—they take—this matter tombstone-seriously. I doubt he'll describe what every one of those parties is in search of.*

"I'm all ears," Ginny said. I guess she calculated the cliché would lighten the atmosphere a trifle, because she had features more prominent.

Indeed, his expression became a tad less official. He stayed with his account, though, like a hunter on a spoor. "We found the carpet in the general area you told about. We don't know whether the flyer brought it down on its last gasp or abandoned it for the broomstick Steve saw. Either way, he and the stick are gone, no footprints or other traces in the vicinity. No sign of that rifle, either. But where you were we collected plenty of spent rounds and may be able to trace them."

I'd come entirely wakeful. "If I were the gunman," I suggested, "I'd've taken that weapon someplace else in the desert and buried it."

"Yeah, we've got hoardfinders going back and forth within a large perimeter," Shining Knife answered. "Meanwhile, the registry on the carpet has identified it for us. It belongs to a family in the older part of Gallup. They'd reported it as stolen this morning. They have a broomport, not a garage, and left it rolled up there and locked as usual yesterday evening. That's a peaceful neighborhood. Somebody hot-spelled the talisman during the night and made off."

"Hm," Ginny said. "Have you any idea who?"

"No, except that the thief is obviously at least a fairly competent thaumaturge, or possesses equivalent powers. He, she, or it needn't be identical with your would-be murderer. I'd guess so, but they could be in cahoots." Shining Knife inserted a pause. "We'd really like a talk with your friend, the Zuni gentleman. I haven't got the hang of his name yet."

"Matthew Adams, more properly called Balawahdiwa." He and Ginny had agreed she couldn't evade naming him to the FBI.

"We sent a team there, but he seems to have walked out."

"He has a right."

"Material witness."

"He was being shot at too!" Ginny flared. "Get your damn warrant if you must, but I assure you nobody in the pueblo will betray him, and Steve and I certainly don't know where he's chosen to seek."

Shining Knife raised a palm. "Hey, wait a minute, Ginny—"

"If anyone has a chance of getting at the root of this evil, it's Balawahdiwa. If you bureaucrats will *give* him the chance."

"All right, all right! Look, we don't want to arrest him or anything. We'd simply like to know what he may have discovered or deduced, and work together with him."

"Yeah, sure," I said under my breath, although I did believe my quondam pal was sincere, sort of.

"That will be for him, a Priest of the Bow, to decide," Ginny said more clearly and a lot more coldly.

Before Shining Knife had time to resent this, I put in: "If nothing else, Will Graylock should now be off the hook."

A few clock ticks passed. "Oh?" he said neutrally.

"Think, man. Never mind anything else, like his having nothing against him unless it was overstaying a parking meter or two. Look at his whole life. He's never been involved with firearms in any way, shape, or form. Served during the war as a civilian intelligence analyst. Hasn't been a hunter, a target shooter, hell, even a fan of Western movies." I'd been slightly hurt when he admitted he hadn't seen me as Tom Spurr's faithful companion. He made it up by complimenting me on my role in *The Hound of the Baskervilles.*

"As for wizardry," I plodded on, "yes, he's had to be good in some lines, like what it's taken to invent and use his specterscope. But I tell you as an engineer what you ought to know better than I do, that sort of work is no more related to unbinding locks and stealing vehicles than a minestrone is to a manticore."

Shining Knife was silent for a longer while than before. I refilled our coffee cups. Through no fault of its own, the taste had gone bitter.

"Well," he said at last, slowly, "that's as may be. You have a point. I did mention the possibility of possession."

"And do you imagine I, his sister, a five-star witch, would have caught no hint of that?" Ginny interrupted like a pouncing lioness. "I've been more concerned than you are, going further back. He's not well, that's true, but suppose you leave him alone to recover!"

I'd rarely seen Shining Knife flounder. "Well, but, but if he'd consent to an examination—get rid of loose ends—"

"Would you kindly tell me what those may be?"

He couldn't, of course. Regulations bound him. They weren't unreasonable. If somebody is a suspect, in any degree, you don't tell his nearest and dearest what tracks he should cover. The knowledge made a hard lump in my throat.

"No accusations," Shining Knife finished. "No accusations what-

ever, yet. We have to look at every conceivable angle. You understand, don't you? You two've been through a rough go. Relax, don't worry, we'll keep in touch," et cetera, until finally: "So long."

Ginny and I stared at one another.

# XIX

Time stretched and snapped. “If only I didn’t feel so goddamn helpless!” broke from me.

She reached to squeeze my hand. “You were anything but, this morning.”

“Thanks, sweetheart. You and Balawahdiwa weren’t exactly freeloading. But that was when the enemy came out in the open—at last, after all these days when— Oh, hell, it’s still like groping around in a fog. Can’t see anything, can’t tell north from south, can’t even grab hold of the clammy faceless gray,” to slash and bite and feel blood spurt hot.

“Why, we helped the agents learn that foreign devils are involved, we brought Balawahdiwa into partnership, al-Bunni gave you his spacecraft plans, last night we met none less than Kokopelli—and if you don’t know how extraordinary that was for a white person, how many mages and anthropologists would give half their teeth and a left kidney for the experience, you haven’t really learned anything about this country—and then we frustrated a direct attack and have undoubtedly provided the FBI with a number of important clues.”

Ginny had spoken fast, but somehow her tone rang leaden.

“Yeah,” I said. “Except we’ve been barely on the fringe of the investigation, and I’ve a notion that from here on we’ll be eased out. We aren’t official, and we are related to Will Graylock, and in the past we didn’t stick meekly to our assigned parts as passive civilians. We’ve got those plans, but unless we can find some way to make hardware from them, plans is all they’ll be for a long while—maybe forever. Kokopelli doesn’t take us seriously enough to speak for us to his higher-ups, and I wonder if Balawahdiwa can approach them directly. We

escaped alive, but the enemy's not going to underestimate us again. No, he'll keep on with his dirty work, but quietly, while you and I sit idle and the G-men— Oh, they aren't fools, but I've got a hunch the enemy took their measure beforehand and made provision against their methods."

My witch laid fingers around chin and gazed out the window. "Yes, that may well be," she murmured. "Coyote could act on impulse, but those behind him, who urged him on and opened the way and then doubtless helped—yes, I believe they're thinking far ahead."

She looked back at me. It was as if a green fire flickered in her eyes. Now her voice took on a shivery kind of life. "If this is a plot by Fu Ch'ing, to wreck the American space program as part of gnawing away at the foundations of all the West— Perhaps it isn't. But our ignorance itself is a heavy handicap. I can imagine him snickering in his hideaway, at the middle of his web. One way or another, we need to know."

I couldn't respond in kind, not at once. "The British have been trying hard, and they aren't fools either."

"No, but— Steve, I've been thinking. The fact that they've failed thus far seems to show that he's taken their measure, in your words. And surely also of every thaumaturge they might reasonably consult, whether from other government agencies or independent operators. Nevertheless, Fu Ch'ing is mortal. And demons too have their limitations—in some ways narrower than the limits on humans. Nobody can think of everything."

Excitement rammed into me. It felt cold and smelled of thunderstorm. "Hey, you don't mean—"

"Cardinal Point was—is again, by now—well warded against every plausible kind of hostile spell and Power, whether American, European, or Indian. Nobody thought of Far Eastern forces. They aren't too well understood in the West anyway. Well, I've acquired some small amount of Zuni lore and skill. Would the enemy be prepared for that?"

"My God!" I leaped to my feet, shaking. "And you and I together, we'd be unexpected in ourselves, if we manage it right— The old firm!" I whooped. "Matuchek and Matuchek, confounders of the ungodly, rescuers of the afflicted, we also walk dogs! Yahoo!"

"Easy, wolf, easy," she cautioned. "So far it's just an idea. It may be worthless. We'd certainly need to plan and prepare, and we'd need somebody over there to help us, somebody strong who has never occurred to anyone, and—" She broke off. "And that's enough for the time being. Put on your cheerful mask. We have company."

I calmed myself, sort of. Ben came dustily into the kitchen, where he'd heard us, and stopped at the breakfast nook. His feet plodded, his head drooped. "Hi, scout," I greeted. "How was the game?"

"All right," he mumbled.

"Your team lost, huh?"

"Naw. We won."

"Well, good for you."

"Not me. I struck out every time at bat. In the outfield I missed two balls I should've got."

"Too bad. Well, everybody has an occasional off day," I said desperately. "I don't imagine your teammates hold it against you."

He looked up. "I wasn't thinking," he blurted. "I was scared. About you and Mom."

"What?" said Ginny. "Oh, my dear. We told you yesterday evening we had to go out and might not get back till this morning." She reached up to stroke the rumpled hair. "And here we are. What is there to be scared of?"

"N-nothin'. If you say so." His lip quivered. "I, uh, I better go wash and change." He hurried off.

"What the devil?" I muttered, dismayed. "Has Val been telling tales? And why? What about?"

"She hasn't, I'm certain. Children are more observant and smarter than their parents are apt to know," Ginny replied bleakly. "Ours have heard something of what happened in the past. It's natural for them to wonder if it could happen again. The Selene fiasco was bad enough. Now we come and go on mysterious errands, and we and Uncle Will are obviously worried, and we won't tell them what it's all about."

"Um-m, yeah. . . . But how can we?"

"We can *think.*"

Seizing after anything, I said, "You know, I'd guess Ben's more frightened on our account than on his own."

"I expect so. He's your son." *And yours,* I thought. Ginny's voice lost its momentary softness. "That is a horrible fear. I know."

Finishing our meal in an automatic way, we repaired to the living room. We hadn't long to brood till Val returned too, leading Chryssa by the hand. The little one ran straight to Ginny and buried her curly head in her mother's lap. She didn't cry, but she clung. Ginny hugged her and murmured.

Val regarded me. "How was your outing?" she asked. She didn't smile. "You look like the ants came at the picnic with machine guns and freight cars."

"Oh, it wasn't a picnic," I said. "You heard us explain we needed to do some nighttime research. It took all night, it was tiring, and afterward we had to be at a conference about it. How was your day?"

She shrugged. "It was a day. If you don't want me for anything, I'd like to relax a while." She stalked off to her room. There was no reason for her to slam the door. I know when I've been rebuffed.

Because she felt we'd rebuffed her. That hurt worse than fire ants.

Ginny got Chryssa more or less comforted and settled down in the game room. Ben was on hand there. She came back to me and said, "I told them we're going to call on Will, if he's receiving, but we'll soon be home again."

"We are?" I asked vaguely.

"If possible." She resonated the phone. To my surprise, her brother seemed much better, even at ease. "Sure," he said. "Come on over. Be happy to see you."

Ginny took her wand and summoned Edgar from his perch. I wondered why. We got on our Jag and skimmed the streets. Passersby gave us fleeting glances. Some waved. We'd become an ordinary sight hereabouts. It was as well they didn't see us closely. My emotions were a hash, glad, angry, fierce, eager, sad. Ginny, who steered, had taken on the look of a Valkyrie canvassing for candidates.

After a while she spoke, knifelike through the murmur of traffic and cleft warm air. "This trouble in the children settles the matter, doesn't it? We won't let things writhe on and on, not if we can do anything at all by ourselves."

My heart bumped. "Go after that highbinder in England?"

"I'll have to study the situation. It may not be feasible. But we can dare hope."

"Uh, this involves Will?"

"Inevitably, if we'll be away for any length of time. Of course, we'll make no mention of what we really have in mind."

I must force: "You don't trust him—entirely?"

Her fingers tightened around her knees. "That's beside the point. The idea is to take Fu Ch'ing by surprise. What Will, or anybody, doesn't know can't be . . . tricked . . . out of him." She was silent for a bit. "We can tell him about the al-Bunni plans in nonspecific terms. If something comes of that, it won't stay secret long."

We entered his neighborhood of old houses, old trees, old memories. She lifted us into the top traffic lane, which nobody else was using, and unsheathed her wand. "Edgar," she said to the bird on her

shoulder, "seek out any spy who lurks hereabouts," added several arcane words, and touched the star to his beak.

"Gruk," he croaked, "yoicks," and took off. We circled around several blocks while he disappeared beneath the sunlit green crowns.

He was soon back, flapped alongside, and pointed with his beak. We followed. When he landed on her shoulder again, she aimed the wand straight earthward. It flashed. She smiled as sweetly as any cat at a mouse, brought us to street level, and cruised past the spot. Two vehicles stood on their unfolded legs a couple of blocks diagonally from the rear of Will's house, barely in sight of it. Neither was noteworthy, a broom and a small carpet with its pavilion up and curtains drawn.

We passed on by. Ginny nodded. "Two men inside," she said, "doubtless Fibbies. They're employing a scryer and a spell checker. Whenever Will leaves, I daresay one trails him, on foot or on the stick."

"They'll note our arrival," I said unnecessarily.

"And why should we not visit my brother?"

"Hey," I cried, "if he's been under surveillance, then after that encounter we had, he's got to be in the clear!"

"A great enough, alien enough Power could deceive their eyes and blind their apparatus."

Her starkness shriveled my timbre. "You don't mean you really believe—"

"No. I don't. But it is a possibility that will have occurred to the agency. We need facts—positive, not negative evidence—who and what the enemy is, what he's been doing and why."

We settled in front of the little house. Sun-speckled shade cooled an outsize, not too well mowed lawn. A goldfinch chirped energetically, somewhere among leaves. Will met us at the door. His clothes were sloppy and comfortable, his handshake firm, his voice hearty. "Welcome. What's the occasion?"

"Oh, to say hello and, well, see how you're doing," I replied. "You're looking pretty good."

"Feeling it, too. Sorry I was such a moomph yesterday." *Was it only yesterday? Judas priest!* "In rotten shape. But now— Come in, come in."

Ginny had kept her wand loosely in her hand and stayed a bit aside. From the corner of an eye I saw her give the rod a casual half twirl that swept the star-point over his breast before she collapsed and sheathed it. Edgar leaned forward at the same instant, wings partly spread, beak aimed.

"Why, is anything wrong?" she said to the raven, quite lightly, and once more spoke a phrase unknown to me. He buzzed into her ear. She laughed. "Just fidgety." We went inside.

Crammed bookshelves fairly well lined the living room. Volumes spilled over onto worn carpet and shabby chairs. They included an *I Ching* and *Book of Songs* in the original—he'd identified them for us earlier—through scientific and historical tomes to literature from Shakespeare to Sherlock Holmes, with plenty of modern paperbacks in various languages. Some of the covers on those were gaudy. Two fine old Chinese scrolls found space on the walls. Something in the background, I guessed by Vivaldi, turned the tobacco-tainted air lyrical.

Will cleared seats for us. "Beer?" he offered. "I've made a discovery, a Dutch brew, worth sailing far for."

We said yes, please, and settled ourselves, Edgar on the mantel amidst a souvenir collection of Japanese figurines, dogs and badgers and whatnot. Will went off to the kitchen. Ginny leaned close to me. Her whole being glowed. "Steve," she whispered, "he's at peace."

"He does seem okay." It wasn't easy to keep my reply as low, the way her relief washed over me.

"Nothing bad registered. Nothing. Oh, it was a superficial scan, like the others I was able to make before. I couldn't be sure then and I can't be absolutely certain now. But there *is* a difference, not merely in his appearance and behavior."

"Uh-huh. Extracting information even when your data points are below noise level—"

"And I know him. He's himself again, completely himself."

*Let's hope he stays that way,* I thought, and kicked the thought downstairs.

Will returned carrying a tray loaded with crackers, cheese, glasses, and three frosty bottles of Vanderdecken. Having set it before us, he put a saucerful of the snacks on the mantel for Edgar. "What a change in you," his sister said frankly. "I'm so glad."

He chuckled. "Me too."

"How did it happen?"

He extracted pipe and pouch from assorted pockets. "Well, after we talked on the phone I heated some soup. Afterward I couldn't stay on my feet and went to bed. Slept the clock around and more; must've been ten A.M. at least when I woke. Ravenous, if your familiar will pardon the expression. Did horrid things to a steak and appurtenances, soon felt marvelous, got an idea, worked on it, and was relaxing for a bit when you called."

"But the cause?"

He shrugged. "Who knows? What caused the malaise in the first place?"

"Unless we learn that," said Ginny slowly, "we can't tell whether it will recur."

"Or, if it does, how to fix it," I added.

Will nodded. "I've been thinking about that." He stayed calm. "Off and on throughout, when I had a chance and was in shape to. Who wouldn't? Likewise today, till my idea seized me." He filled the pipe and tamped it with a thumb. "You're the expert, of course, Ginny. In this field, my notions are inevitably vague. But I wonder if my trouble hasn't been a simple matter of resonance."

"Hm." She frowned. "Naturally, that occurred to me, but since you wouldn't agree to a thorough examination—"

He darkened for a minute. "You know why. I told you. Privacy. I have not told you how much turmoil this has brought to my consciousness. Imagine, though. Would you have let me probe you, however lovingly, however confidentially, unless you'd become more desperate than I was?"

I, at least, could imagine; and Ginny was my wife, for Heaven's sake. After all, Will hadn't been continuously miserable. Those were episodes. In between them he was more or less okay.

"Resonances?" I asked.

He snapped fire from his ring. Ginny explained for him: "Goetic forces were surely striking at the project, like waves against a seawall, long before they broke through. Will was a large part of its original and continuing inspiration. By the law of sympathy, he may have responded to—shall I say backwashes of those thwarted tides. They could have produced depression, confusion, and psychosomatic illness."

"Why didn't it happen to anybody else?"

"His innate personality may make him unusually vulnerable. And then his early experience with the Fair Folk may have made him hypersensitive to such influences, almost like getting an allergy. In any event, now the wall has been breached, the damage has been done, the assault is in abeyance, the whole situation has changed."

She did not say it was less dangerous.

"I'd guess the aftereffects took this past week to wear off," Will proposed. "An optimistic diagnosis, perhaps, but why not accept it till further notice?" His cheer had revived. He sat down across the coffee table from us, filled pilsner glasses, and raised his. "To a better future.

*Kan bei.* Or *proost,* I believe, is the Dutch word. What's the Czech toast, Steve?"

"I dunno. I've heard my family doesn't even spell the name right any longer." We clinked rims. The drink was cool and tingly. "How about dinner with us again this evening?" I invited.

"Thanks, but sorry," he replied. "I told you I had a great idea today. I want to develop it further, turn in as early as possible, get up before moonrise, and take my portable specterscope into the desert."

*With the FBI tippytoeing behind,* I thought. *Oh well.* I wished them joy of it. Me, I find few things more exquisitely boring than standing by while somebody else tinkers with a piece of apparatus. "What is this idea?"

"Um-m, on the technical side, I'm afraid. A test of the hypothesis that the Fair Folk are indeed there. That implies that some are always moving away from the morning terminator, the sunrise line, to avoid direct sunlight. Since by the laws of thermodynamics they are at a temperature not identical with that of their immediate surroundings, a minuscule Doppler effect on the infrared radiation that their presence polarizes slightly but measurably—"

Ginny laughed. "Never mind. You *are* back to your own self."

"Well, fine," I said. "However, I expect you'll agree the real test is for somebody to land and meet them."

Will was not an unworldly academic. On Long Island he'd been a keen sailboat racer; here he went camping and backpacking; he'd taken more money from me in poker games than I had from him. He caught my drift, lowered his beer, and clamped his gaze upon me. "You have hopes beyond another Selene," he breathed.

We told him that we'd obtained certain calculations and preliminary plans that looked promising. He didn't inquire further. Nor did he jump up and dance, though we saw it in his eyes. "A possibility, you say? But to realize it—" He sighed. "That, the how of it, is out of my department."

"Not absolutely," Ginny said.

He jerked to attention. "What do you mean, please?"

"Steve and I may have to go back east in this connection." I sat in awe of her steadiness. "Back east" implied the Midwest, Nornwell; it did not actually say so. "A week, perhaps more. We aren't free to discuss details yet, and if we do leave we shall have to word our calls home carefully. The hostiles are still loose, you know."

He smoked like a steam locomotive. "Are you that worried about

Coyote or whoever? Parochial and unsophisticated Beings, I should think."

"Coyote—or whoever—apparently has allies." She could admit this because the press had already speculated about it, along with much wilder stories. My favorite rumor had to do with the moon inciting free love, which led to a plot against a lunar landing by the Pope and the Ku Klux Klan. "Let's play cautiously."

He nodded. "I see."

She caught me also by surprise: "If we do have to take off, would you come over and stay with the children?"

He barely grabbed his pipe before it dropped and ignited his pants. "What? Are you joking?"

"Some adult must. You're our best bet."

*The FBI surveillance will come along,* I thought. *Which in the present case is not a bad thing.*

"But," he protested, "but I don't know anything about—about child care."

"You know more than you think," she pursued. "Not that there would likely be much call on you. Valeria is quite mature for her age. Ben is a sensible and well-behaved boy. Between them they can mostly do for Chryssa whatever she can't do herself—except be the father stand-in and tell her bedtime stories and other such roles I know you enjoy. We'd arrange for our housecleaner and her mother to give extra help. They're kind and reliable people. As for your work, I'm hoping you can take it over there, and sleep there, and know where to call for help in any unlikely emergencies."

He bit his lip. "It's a considerable responsibility," he stalled.

She looked straight at him. "We trust you, Will."

On our way home, Ginny and I reached another agreement. When we arrived, I knocked on Valeria's door. She opened it and glowered. "We need to talk by ourselves," I said. "There's something important for you to know."

Her face came alive. "Yako," she replied, whatever that meant in her argot, and followed me to my study. Her mother felt that her father could best handle this, preferably in a masculine atmosphere. Well-worn leather chairs; a couple of ship models on shelves and a half-built one on the desk along with other clutter; a bookshelf whose contents ran to Mark Twain, Jack London, mystery novels, and stacked-up *Arizona Flyways* as well as engineering references; a bowling trophy; pictures on the walls that included me with my high school football team and me canoeing in the North Woods; also on the wall, a cutlass that sailed with Decatur and afterward went on a journey more long and strange; my pistol, which I still used for target shooting, locked away, but a faint fragrance of Hoppe's No. 9 in the air—

We took our seats, she on the edge of hers. My swivel chair creaked as I leaned back, crossed my legs, and bridged my fingers. Otherwise we kept silent maybe half a minute. The blue eyes were enormous. For the first time in years, I missed my pipe.

"Val," I said at last, "you probably think we owe you an apology and an explanation. In a way we do. Trouble is, right now it's impossible, and will be for some while to come. Back in the war, men got told to do this or not do that. Period. Usually the reason seemed plain. Like clearing the enemy off a hill that gave him too good a position for his artillery. Sometimes, though, we didn't know sh—diddly about why. And we never were briefed on the overall tactics. That'd have

been bound to leak to the enemy, and he'd know what to prepare for and where'd be the place to strike back at us. Nor were those tactics fair. Some units got thrown into a meat grinder, and their officers knew beforehand that would happen. Others stayed in reserve and mainly were bored to death. It was how things worked out.

"I know this is ancient history to you, buried in the books with Waterloo and Gettysburg. But plenty of guys are above ground yet to whom it was grunt reality. And it's still in the nature of conflict, of life itself. If you haven't read the Book of Job let me recommend it to you."

Val gulped and shivered.

"All right," I continued after another stillness, "that affair at the Point was, is, more than a malicious prank. It turns out to involve truly dark Powers. What they are, what they want, and how powerful they are, we can only guess. Your mother and I have taken part in trying to find out more and do something about it. We wanted to spare our children fear and nightmares. So we evaded questions. Maybe now and then we lied. It was well intentioned. But to suppose that you, at your age, with your intelligence, would not soon realize we weren't leveling with you—too late, I see that was an insult. For this we do most humbly apologize."

"Oh, Dad!" She half reached toward me. The hand dropped. But sudden tears glimmered on her lashes.

"We still can't tell you much," I said. "This *is* a sort of war situation. Not that we're high brass with any clear understanding. But we do need to keep certain things secret."

"Yes, it's a gitzy business," she whispered. "Scabrous, too."

I smiled. "What we can do, if you're willing, is enlist you."

She leaped to her feet. "What? Me? Yes, sir!" she whooped. "Molly O'Kay!"

"Whoa, pony, whoa down." I waved her back to her chair. "It'll be Home Guard duty, keeping alert, standing by, a lot of KP. Which is vital stuff. Your Uncle Will did as much toward winning the Caliph's War as most front-line soldiers. Likewise for military mechanics, quartermasters, and, yes, clerks. We'll *depend* on you."

Her lip quivered, the rest of her shuddered, then she sat quietly and replied, "Yes, I, I understand. If I can just have an idea of what it's all for."

"It seems the bad guys mean to sabotage the American space program—permanently," I said. "The FBI and other agencies are working on that. Your mother and I were able to contribute a little, and we've

called on the wisdom of her friend, the Zuni priest." This much I could tell her. Part of it was no more than common sense could deduce from available facts; part was by now known to both the Feds and the foe. "I can't go into detail. That'd endanger us. However, I can share something special, if you'll keep it to your absolute self."

Her forefinger drew a cross over her lips. "On my soul's honor." How utterly solemn she could be!

But when I spoke of the spacecraft plans we'd gotten from a source I must not name, of the possibility of Operation Luna making an end run around both the politicians and the enemy, she shouted and laughed and sprang into my lap to hug me. "Magniff! Like—like stars in the mashed potatoes! Oh, Daddy-man, you are a sly old woof!"

"Easy, there," I urged after she'd calmed slightly. "This is at the earliest stage, remember. Don't count your chickens when the rooster's barely been introduced to the hen. Probably your mother and I will have to go back east for a week or two and investigate further." That misdirection hadn't hurt me when we used it before. It did this time. "If so, Uncle Will will move in here, but most of the housekeeping responsibility will fall on you. He knows as much as you do about our new prospects, so you and he can discuss them if you want, but only when you're strictly alone. Mainly, though, what we need you for, starting this day, is to create a better atmosphere at home. Join with us in lifting Ben and, especially, Chryssa out of their fears. If they see you relaxed and cheerful—savvy?"

After she had swallowed hard, her answer came bravely. "*Sí, señor.* I feel a lot better already."

"Good. We can maybe figure out tactics, like jokes and games. But first— Well, no denying there'll be a load on you, and it may from time to time get heavy. Are you prepared to shoulder it?"

"I am."

"Okay. In return, your sentence of confinement to quarters is commuted as of tomorrow morning. Go out and have fun while you can, punkin."

"Th-th-thanks." The youthful earnestness remained. "I'll always be on call, sir. And if anything really bad happens while you're gone—" Fire blazed up. "God help the baddies!"

That alarmed me a bit as I recalled Sneep's visit, plus various earlier incidents. Feeling it would be unwise to spoil the present mood, I contented myself with a mild warning. Thereafter we plunged into plans for things to do.

The upshot was that dinner became a happy meal and the young-

sters quickly got back their merriment. Soon they looked forward to the change of pace while their parents were gone.

As for me, I returned to the lab. Thus Ginny, not I, received Barney's courier and gave him a copy of the documents. She told me that, as promised, he bore no resemblance to the colorful woodsman whose name he borrowed. He didn't even wear the winged Federal Express cap. Rather, he showed just enough individuality that he wasn't too conspicuously drab and anonymous. "Yeah," I said, recalling an incident once at Nornwell, "from a private detective firm. Watson and Goodwin, I'll bet. Their operatives are expert at self-effacement."

Otherwise Ginny was occupied most of her waking hours. That wasn't with her practice. Again she'd phased it out, canceling or postponing appointments, referring urgent cases elsewhere. I'd have worried about her future career if I didn't know her reputation had become proof against moth, rust, and disgruntlement.

In fact, this was part of her problem. Word would fly around that Dr. Matuchek must be up to something. The enemy's spies would scarcely buy the idea that it was a much-needed vacation. Well, let them share the impression that we planned a huddle with our partners at Nornwell. So far, we hoped, they wouldn't suspect why, but they could make several different plausible guesses, and if one of them happened to be the "real" reason, Operation Luna, it was a blind anyway.

Barney gave it substance when he called on Friday. That resonance was encrypted, but we couldn't be dead certain of security and he kept his language well guarded, like us. Still, that big, easygoing man had gotten as enthusiastic as a supernova. "It looks great," he boomed. "You'll want funds. Suppose I transfer fifty thousand dollars for startup expenses—to your personal account, to keep things simple. We'll worry about the bookkeeping later."

"First we'd better worry about the feasibility of the whole thing," I said, hedging the way any engineer had better.

"Sure, sure, but that's what you're going to investigate, isn't it?" The letter we sent along with the plans had made clear that he shouldn't confide in anyone else till further notice. "You can call on our facilities anytime, like a superreckoner to solve some complicated question. Its operators don't have to know what the calculation is for. And so forth. But mainly, I'll bet, you'll be working by yourselves, on the spot. R and D costs money. I don't mind this much risk. Looks to me like we've been dealt three of a kind. We might draw for a full house or a four."

"*Might,*" I said. "Oh, well, we'll keep reasonably good records here, and if the effort fails, it's deductible, isn't it?"

"We'll want a conference with you, *viva voce,* soon," Ginny added.

The letter had given a slight but sufficient hint that we didn't really. "Sure. Anytime. I'll see to it that you aren't pestered while you're hereabouts. Only give me a little advance notice, please. You remember the code message for that."

There wasn't any. Ginny caught on at once, I a second later. "We do," she said. "Meanwhile, carry on. Give everybody our best," by which she meant his family and our small gang of dreamers.

This was among the few interruptions in her labors. Mostly those were too esoteric to seem like the hard work they were. She ransacked arcane files, learning what she could about Fu Ch'ing, his cohorts, and possible allies for us in England. The last of these searches drew her into long comunications over channels known to few. She studied the goetics of our local Indians and, besides the books, passed considerable time down on the Zuni reservation, occasionally at peculiar hours. I gathered that Balawahdiwa wasn't the only adept she inquired of, learned from, and practiced with, but she didn't encourage questions about it. Having decided in due course that, yes, we should go, she slipped off to Albuquerque and made the travel arrangements. I didn't ask what precautions she took.

I myself had far less of a role. Three days passed at the Point, in the lab, more and more frustrated. We simply hadn't anything worthwhile to do. Then Helen Krakowski, newly back from Washington, sighed that I might as well take indefinite leave of absence. Project Selene appeared to have been decanted into a Klein bottle.

The next several days were *good.* Barney's call Friday morning began them. After that I didn't spend, I gained, many hours with the kids. Their mother being busy, I took them to shows and on excursions—not always all three, because Val had her own pleasures to pursue while she could, but generally she did come along—and once Ben and I went fishing, just the two us— Never mind. In between, I worked on my ship model, played a little poker, finally read *War and Peace* . . . No matter.

"I've found the man we want," Ginny whispered at last in our bed. The window stood open to a night not yet gone cold. A breeze lulled. She lay close beside me. I put a hand on her thigh and through the silky nightgown felt how the muscles stirred.

Nevertheless the news jarred me to hunter's attention. "You have? Who?"

"Nobody you ever heard of, though he knew my parents and once had a scientific collaboration with my father. Tobias Frogmorton of Cambridge University."

"Huh?"

"Professor emeritus of archaeology, Fellow of Trinity College. He's lived sedately, lifelong bachelor, except for field work in younger days. During the Kaiser's War he was a cryptographer. After taking a thaumaturgic degree with honors, he put that knowledge to use, notably in deciphering Mayan and Aztec inscriptions—animating copies, observing responses to experimental readings and enactments. It's become a standard technique, which has lately cracked Minoan Linear A. His skills were invaluable in the Caliph's War, reconstructing intelligence from fragments of information. But he's been retired and obscure for years—a large plus for our purposes. And he is willing to help."

"Well, if you say so," I muttered dubiously.

Her lecturer's tone livened. "Among other things, he may be able to provide us with a familiar."

"What? You're not taking Edgar along?"

"No. British quarantine regulations. I suppose we could get an exemption for him, I being a licensed witch, but that would mean the kind of attention-drawing paperwork we want to avoid."

"Good work, sweetheart." I pulled her to me.

Thus, two weeks and three days after the disaster, we kissed our kids goodbye very early in the morning. Will flitted us to Albuquerque flyport. We shook hands with him, ignored the tickets to the Midwest that we'd openly bought—maybe we could get a refund later—and used those Ginny had arranged.

The flight to New York was uneventful. We'd have liked to break the journey there, as sensible people do, but didn't really dare. Instead, we changed carpets at Idlewild for London. The transatlantic crossing wasn't bad. A Boeing 666 gives room to walk around in the pavilion, have a drink at the bar as well as a couple of meals in your seat, and try for a snooze. Just the same, six or seven hours aloft can get long, particularly after a hop across the continent, and half a hundred fellow travelers don't make for restful surroundings. We reached Heathrow pretty well wiped out and, having gone through passport control and customs, wanted nothing more than the nearest available hotel room.

Some hours of sleep and a big, fat English brunch restored us. Still trying not leave a trail, we didn't rent a broom but boarded a train for Cambridge. I like those puffy little locomotives, the genial conductors, the compartments where people mind their own business and read

their own newspapers unless perchance you fall into an interesting conversation, the beautiful countryside through which you steam, even the meat pies you can buy at the stops. Ginny does too, I think. In any case, we felt rather jolly as we chugged north to our meeting.

Cambridge gave us a proper English welcome, rain. Our glimpses of several lovely ancient buildings were blurred as we cabbed from the station to a hotel and, after unpacking and phoning, on to Frogmorton's house. The weather was soft, though, cool and silver-gray. When we stepped off the taxi and out of its field, Ginny stopped a moment. "After New Mexico," she sighed, "I have an impulse to stand here, staring up, with my mouth open."

"Like a turkey?" I answered.

"Have you no poetry in you?"

"Oh, sure. 'Rain, rain, go away. Come again another day.' " It's apt to give me a phantom ache in the tailtip I no longer have. Even so, I might have enjoyed it if we'd thought to buy an umbrella. Or if she'd spelled it off us; but that was more effort than it was worth.

We opened a garden gate and strode fast along a path lined with zinnias. Their colors flew gallant as battle flags. Everything else was green, vivid, intense, nearly arrogant when we remembered our Southwest. Through a line of willows behind the house, I spied the river. Our errand felt unreal amidst this peacefulness.

The Lindens probably took its name from trees long gone; an elm companioned it now. It was old enough—older than Albuquerque, not much younger than Santa Fe. Beneath a steep, tiled roof, most windows in the whitewashed walls had eighteenth-century casements with nineteenth-century glass, but the oaken, iron-bound front door must be original. I felt shy about wielding the knocker till I saw what a drunken brass face leered at me, right out of the Restoration.

A formidable-looking housekeeper let us in. When we explained who we were, she rustled ahead of us through a vestibule to the—sitting

room, is that the right word? It was rather dim today in spite of an edison shining inside a beaded lampshade. Furniture was antique, unmarked by children or cats. Books were as thick as Will's, but all neatly shelved. Between the cases, forebears stared from their sepia photographs. I couldn't help wondering if we'd come to the right place.

Frogmorton left an armchair to greet us. He was short, skinny, round-shouldered, in baggy tweeds with a drab tie. White thin hair, white toothbrush mustache, and horn-rimmed spectacles ornamented a beaky face as wrinkled as a washday bundle. "Ah, Mr. and Mrs. Matuchek!" His voice was high, almost squeaky. "No, I beg your pardon. Dr. and Mr. Matuchek, eh? How good to meet you." He shook my hand briefly—his felt birdlike—but clung to Ginny's. "I well remember your father, that great scholar, and your dear mother. Our acquaintance was before they were blessed with offspring. We lost touch, as one does. One intends to resume a relationship, but somehow time slips past until suddenly it is too late. *Fugaces labuntur anni.*"

"They do indeed," Giny murmured while I, fumbling with the remnants of my Latin, decided this was probably not obscene.

"Mrs. Turner, bring in the tea, if you please," Frogmorton said. "A bit early for tea, perhaps, but we should fortify ourselves for the work ahead, don't you agree? Do please be seated. Smoke if you wish. Until we are positioned for action, will you permit me a few inquiries as to how you have fared over the years? I have been aware of your past exploits, of course, and have examined the detailed record of them since you first called. However, I shall be grateful if you care to bring me up to date on the Graylock family. And the, ah, Matuchek family, needless to say."

Ginny talked for both of us. Frogmorton chattered and chattered. I didn't want to appear surly, but a word had to be honed mighty thin to slip in edgewise, so I concentrated on the tea, cucumber sandwiches, and seedcake, suppressing wistful thoughts about a pub.

It got more interesting after Ginny steered him onto his own subject. *Hey,* I thought, *if Ben does go into paleontology, he ought to hear about these techniques. I'll bet they can be adapted.* Unfortunately, however, Frogmorton tried to spice the conversation with jokes. They ran to stories like that of a medieval monk who had a pot of wine at his side as he copied a chronicle. The penmanship got wobblier and wobblier. At the end he wrote *"Male scripsi, bene bipsi."* Frogmorton laughed and laughed. Ginny and I did our best.

The housekeeper cleared away the clutter. "We shall be in my closet, Mrs. Turner," he informed her. *Huh?* I thought. "Do not allow

us to be disturbed by anyone on any account. If perchance the Last Trump sounds, I daresay we shall hear it ourselves. Otherwise dinner for three will be at eight o'clock."

"Have no fears," he added as he led us off through a series of rooms. "For evening meals I rely on my cook. He does an excellent leg of mutton, if I may say so. Your father, Dr. Matuchek, used to complain to me about the difficulty of obtaining mutton in America. And we shall have something a little choice in the way of claret."

To my relief, "closet" turned out to mean a large chamber at the back of the house. He unlocked the door and bowed us in. Floorboards creaked underfoot; wormholes peppered murky oak wainscot. Three windows had been left unchanged: small, leaded, with glass like the bottoms of beer bottles. We were in dusk till Frogmorton barred the door and touched an object. It was a bronze statue, Greek or Roman, of a torchbearer whose branch flared with sudden cold corposant fire. More light streamed from the eyes of a grinning Mayan jaguar or feathered serpent or whatever it was. More books lined the walls. Papers filled pigeonholes above a desk long enough to double as a workbench. A few pieces of goetic equipment rested on it. Otherwise a cabinet, a couch, and three Victorian office chairs were the only furniture. A fine layer of dust grayed everything and a spider had set up shop under the ceiling.

"Pray pardon the untidiness," said Frogmorton. He found a feather duster and scuttled about making random motions. "I am seldom here, now in my *otium,* and cannot entrust its maintenance to anyone else, not even Mrs. Turner. An honest, conscientious woman, granted, but if, for example, she took volumes off the shelves for cleaning, she might refile them alphabetically!" Horror shook his voice. "And, to be sure, certain articles should not be so much as touched by laymen." Again he attempted levity. "The wrong laying on of hands, heh, heh."

Ginny looked around. She had unfolded a wand from her purse. The star-point flickered, ice blue, bloodred. "You do have some powerful things here," she agreed. "Don't you worry about accidents, intruders, fire, whatever could happen in your absence?"

"I have spelled in an alarm." He nodded at the Mayan figure. "If untoward circumstances arise, it will call for assistance, loudly as well as goetically."

I decided that if it did cry, "Help! Help!" it must be a jaguar.

But why, why had Ginny settled on this old dodderer for our ally?

Then all at once he stood straight, looked squarely at us, and said in a voice no longer thin but blade-keen: "Very well, shall we to work?

We can speak freely. The house was warded during the war against espial human and nonhuman. I have kept its defenses active and up-to-date, for I always hoped they would never be needed again, and I always suspected they would."

We sat down and commenced. He and Ginny spoke, or queried, directly to the point. I put in what I was able, not much; but I wasn't bored, Lord, no.

More than an hour went to exchanging information. They'd have been unwise to communicate other than minimally before now, no matter how secure the channels seemed to be. She filled him in on the space project situation, the native Beings, the spoor of Asian demons, the potentials of Zuni lore, and the unpleasantness out in the mountains. For his part, he knew considerable about Fu Ch'ing, and since she contacted him had managed to learn more.

"Largely through professional connections, you know. He is enigmatic but not totally isolated. Published several brilliant papers in the past, *exempli gratia,* on modifications of Feng Shui, geomancy, required by the theory of plate tectonics. Poems too, esteemed by connoisseurs, also for their calligraphy. Various colleagues told me this or that about his actions, his movements, yes, a few of his idiosyncrasies. And I still have acquaintances in the Secret Service, who were willing to pass along in confidence what little they knew. . . .

"Yes, you are quite right, it would be futile for you to approach the Service, Scotland Yard, or any other official agency. They could only listen to you, and must needs forbid you to act. Moreover, while they have not been subverted, it is far too possible that they have been infiltrated to some unknown degree. Witness the failure of every attempt to track him down."

"I think a version of a Zuni finding spell that I've learned might do the trick," Ginny said. "He wouldn't have safeguarded against that, would he?"

Frogmorton raised his brows. "Eh, what? Surely useless in this clime, this cultural setting. If it functioned at all, it might well merely warn him."

"I know. But I said a version. An adaptation, which you and I will work out between us. Look, Southwestern procedures of that kind are basically shamanistic, musical. That's not in the English tradition, therefore it'll be unexpected. Yes, I realize it occurs in China and throughout Central Asia. But this will employ a different scale, plus British elements you will supply to create a unique hybrid. And the *use* of it, the

methods by which we bring the cantrip to bear, everything we'll employ will surely be unknown to Dr. Fu."

"By God, we blindside him!" I exclaimed.

That was about all I got to say for another hour. Ginny and Frogmorton were off into technicalities, nearly as incomprehensible to me as modern literary criticism. Yet they kept my attention, ransacking musty books, uttering strange words, and operating peculiar instrumentalities. I shared the excitement that grew in them. The air fairly crackled with it.

And finally my love turned to me, aglow, and said, "I think we've got our basic spell, Steve. You'll take part too."

I realized I'd grabbed at the lens under my shirt. "How?" I admit I barked.

She laughed. "For starters, any suggestions you can make about the principal song. It's the core of the spell, you see. Fu Ch'ing hides his whereabouts by generating false indications of other places while screening his own. We need a counterconfusion to annul this while a concurrent Finding exposes the reality."

I throttled back my emotions and nodded. "I think I see. Kind of like light waves interfering. They black each other out at some points and reinforce elsewhere."

"The analogy to particle wave interference in the famous two-slit experiment is perhaps closer," Frogmorton said. "By preventing ourselves from making observations, we establish—"

"Never mind," Ginny interrupted. He took it like a good sport. "The point is, we must tailor that song for the problem. It has to be British, using words powerful in their proper contexts, put together in such a way that they almost but not quite make sense. While you sing it, Steve, Professor Frogmorton and I will carry out the rest of the rite."

"An Irish melody, as old as possible," he urged. "The Druids employed music in their Art, and a little persisted until recent times among the peasantry of the remoter counties. Some force should remain."

"Irish, hm?" Ginny pondered. "O'Carolan? No, it would take time to look up a piece of his and longer for Steve to learn. . . . Wait. Everybody knows this one, and nobody knows how old it is, though apparently it goes well back." She hummed a few bars.

"Oh, no!" I groaned.

Don't get me wrong. My wife is half Irish and we're both proud of it. We've visited Eire twice on vacations and been delighted with the country and the people. We know that throughout their history the

Irish have contributed more than their share to world civilization. Nevertheless, when one of those fileted tenors launches into "Danny Boy" the devil in me mutters, "Oliver Cromwell, where are you now when we need you?"

Ginny caught my drift. "As a matter of fact, earlier words exist for the 'Londonderry Air.' A love song beginning, 'Would God I were the tender apple blossom—' "

"That will do for a first line," Frogmorton said eagerly. "Anchors text to music, don't you know. Thereafter the sense must drift free, while continuing to be poetic."

"Lines of great literature, you mean."

"Precisely. Blank verse until the last, which the melody requires be an Alexandrine."

Poetry and goetics are everywhere and forever intertwined. Besides, Frogmorton was the sort of chap who likes few things better than to relax with a refreshing verse play or sonnet sequence. The library in here was well stocked with stuff of that kind. I could help. We attacked the collection, riffling pages, strewing volumes, gabbling our discoveries.

"We want some Shakespeare for certain. *Macbeth,* the witchy one."

"Uh, this from Ben Jonson—"

"—a touch of earthy vigor. I remember during the last war, a song British soldiers often sang, rather vulgar—"

"Frankly, to me Pope is Dryden as dust, but now and then he does come up with a rock-solid line."

"—sensuality, opposing Fu's cold calculation. The *Rubaiyat*—"

"Hey, did Rupert Brooke himself write this? We've got to work it in somehow."

"Shelley, *The Revolt of Islam.* An added dimension for the continuum of cultural conflict. And it has the necessary scansion."

I'm being impressionistic. Actually we hopped to and fro among the texts like fleas on a griddle, we proposed and argued and struggled to fit pieces together and trashcanned most, for another hour or more. Eventually we had a scrawled thing that ought to serve.

Ginny made a fair copy, using an eagle quill pen on a sheet of wyvern-wing parchment. Frogmorton thrice dripped wax from the bees of Delphi on it, to stamp with the sigils of Thoth, Solomon, and St. George. Meanwhile I rehearsed. My partners didn't visibly wince. They only made me keep still while they readied the rest of the proceedings.

Outside, the rain had gone heavy, filling the windows with murk.

We heard it hammer on walls and roofs. Wind piped. Inside, lights dimmed to embers and dusk laid hold of us. Ginny and Frogmorton enacted their gestures, chanted their words. At their signal I took the parchment, though I couldn't read it in the gloom, cleared my throat, and strove to stay on key.

*"Would God I were the tender apple blossom*
*That struts and frets his hour upon the stage.*
*To be made honest by an act of Parliament*
*Call up the bloody Territorials.*
*Worth makes the man, and want of it the fellow*
*Beside me singing in the wilderness.*
*Now there's a choice—heartache or tortured liver!*
*A sweeter draught than ye will ever taste, I ween."*

I concluded with a wolf-howl and bowed off. Nobody applauded. Well, they were still busy. I barely saw them as deeper shadows, dancing and gesticulating. Sparks spat blue in midair. I caught a brimstone whiff.

A crystal globe on the desk came alight. Writing appeared in it. No, nothing alien, nothing ominous. Simply:

3, UPPER SWANDAM LANE
LONDON—

The globe blanked too fast for me to catch the postal zone.

Corposants brightened to normal. Ginny and Frogmorton let out shuddery breaths. Sweat glistened on their faces. They'd been through a mill.

"Did you get all of that?" I cried.

"Oh, yes," Ginny whispered. "How could I not?"

"And I," Frogmorton said, no louder.

He shook himself. Amazingly for an old geezer, he went directly back to the shelves, took down a huge atlas, spread it on the desk, consulted the index, and turned to a map of a city section. His finger traced over the page. Ginny bent close.

"Here," he said. "A sideway, virtually an alley, in Limehouse."

Her laugh rattled. "Limehouse? Isn't that ridiculously obvious?"

"Which may be why he chose it, Dr. Matuchek. I don't know what the building is like, although I would guess an abandoned warehouse or a dubious commercial establishment in that rather decayed district.

One can readily learn. At any rate, there he sits motionless, like a spider in the center of its web, but that web has a thousand radiations, and he knows well every quiver of each of them.

"Enough for the nonce." Frogmorton turned away. "I decree that we have earned a bit of ease."

From the cabinet he took glasses and a bottle of Ragganmore, bless his tasteful heart. His alembic furnished Highland spring water. We sat for a while in companionable silence. The weather wildened.

"Perhaps we should inform the authorities," Frogmorton ventured at length.

"No," Ginny answered. "You know perfectly well Fu would be gone before they got there. Later, okay, *pro forma,* we can if you like. But first Steve and I have to go."

"The dangers are incalculable."

Her tone went steely. "Sir, my brother's reputation and liberty are at stake."

And possibly all our hopes and ambitions, or Western civilization, or humanity's future in the cosmos, or something else that I didn't feel like windbagging about. Mainly, I was goddamn mad. Whoever or whatever the jackals were behind our troubles, I wanted at them.

"I know," Frogmorton said softly. "I raised the question from a sense of duty." His glance dropped. "I regret that age and infirmity make me useless in anything but an advisory capacity. *Morbi tristisque senectus.*"

Ginny reached over and patted his hand. "Do you really imagine we can manage without your counsel?"

"Yeah," I chimed in. "Unlike the young gaucho named Bruno, I say as a werewolf I do know that muscles are fine, sharp senses divine, but brains, they are *número uno.*"

Resolution rose afresh in him. "What do you mean to attempt?" he asked.

"That depends," I replied. "Basically, I guess, break in, confront him, and demand to know what the hell is going on."

Frogmorton frowned. "He is well guarded."

"Unless they keep silver bullets loaded, I've a notion I can handle his, uh, dacoits or whatever you call 'em."

Now Frogmorton winced. "We don't want violence, Mr. Matuchek, do we?" His tone steadied. "Indeed, I suspect Dr. Fu employs it—the physical kind—only as a last resort. You will be in much greater peril from things much more recondite."

"That's why I'll need a familiar," Ginny said.

There's a lot of misinformation around about familiars. They don't just run errands and such. They lend their thaumaturges psychic strength and, through whatever degree of rapport is possible, their non-human viewpoints, insights. They can serve as vessels of power or of spirit—they can be comrades in battle—how well we knew!

"Plus a weapon against Fu's critters," I added. "Can you help us with that too, sir?"

Frogmorton nodded. "Conceivably I can point you toward both, in a single embodiment," he said. "Conceivably. It may prove infeasible. I cannot promise more."

The wind skirled.

"Go on, please," Ginny begged.

He looked past us into the darknesses that, despite the lamps, laired in the corners under the ceiling. "I know of a sword."

Presently he went on, still staring elsewhere, speaking like one in a dream: "Long ago, as humans reckon time, a young man, during the Kaiser's War, I had occasion to visit York. That was the heart of the Danelaw, you may recall. I served as a cryptographer. Someone in the War Office got the idea that if we could turn up an inscription in an obscure runic alphabet—there were several, you know—it might be spelled into the basis of an unbreakable code. Balderdash, but orders were orders, and so I went sniffing with my goetic instruments all about the region.

"Exploring in the city itself, I came upon an object preserved in a minor church, a sword. It had been donated centuries before to the Abbey of St. Oswald's by a nobleman who had no further use for it. The type had gone out of style, you see. Besides, he meant to take vows and end his days as a monk. It has never drawn much notice. Apart from being in good condition, it does not appear unusual for its era, and any historical associations were already more or less forgotten. It was simply a curiosum, among numerous others.

"The abbey was razed after the Dissolution. Most of its treasures had been confiscated by the agents of Henry VIII. However, some had been ignored as being of no particular worth. There is a fugitive tradition that the monks hid certain especially valued and sacred objects behind brickwork. Be that as it may, pious hands did lay the pathetic remnants of movable property in the ancient undercroft.

"In the eighteenth century the buildings that had sprung up on the site were torn down and a new St. Oswald's erected, merely a parish church to help accommodate the rapidly growing city population. The known relics were brought forth for display, albeit down in the vaults,

since the Georgian era had little interest in them. Nor did the antiquarianism of the Romantic movement change this. The building was too recent and architecturally uninspired. Its medieval objects had lain too long alone to have any reputation left such as might attract the curious.

"A Victorian gentleman did impulsively pay for the sword's restoration. His diary records surprise that it had not rusted, but what with chemistry being then an infant science, he does not seem to have wondered why. Only the organic parts, grip and scabbard, had rotted away and needed replacement. Shortly thereafter he died, before he could publicize the matter.

"Thus the undercroft and its contents continued to have few visitors. Vergers, of course, occasional clergy, tourists more active than most, and chiefly, the guest book shows, military men. But their interest was in the small souvenirs that soldiers back from the Napoleonic and colonial wars had donated, as was not uncustomary. These too were mostly downstairs. Among them, the sword was only an archaeological token."

Frogmorton paused for a sip. Ginny leaned forward. Light slid flamelike across her mane. "And?" she prompted.

"And I discovered a tremendous latent power in that blade," Frogmorton told us. "I established that it was dwarf-forged and given a spirit, far back in heathen Norway. It came to England with the Vikings. It can think, it can speak, it can hew through stone, steel, and spells. But all this became as nothing. The sword fell into the Great Sleep generations before it ceased to be carried into battle. It was still dormant when it received its new scabbard, and its powers remain bound until it is unsheathed."

"You didn't?"

"Good heavens, no. I detected the potential, but why loose it? I could imagine no use for it in the ongoing affray—or, for that matter, afterward in the Caliph's War—considering how limited its range of action must be. Rather, I visualized impetuous young men seizing on it and causing nothing but mischief within our own ranks. I take my Hermetic Oath seriously. Ergo, I maintained discretion.

"But as for you—what slight and uncertain auguries I was able to obtain after hearing from you suggest that here may be a weapon proper to your hands."

Lightning flared. Thunder crashed.

# XXII

We slept late the next morning, and then had things to do. Among them was arranging accommodations in York. With August Bank Holiday approaching, that wasn't the easiest job in the world. We waved money at a travel agent and got a suite in a posh hotel. Besides the expense, this was showier than we wanted. On the other hand, we might well need more privacy than a single room in a B&B offered. We shopped for several items we'd need—better here than close to the scene of the crime—and caught a train that brought us there by mid-afternoon.

We'd seen it before on our travels. One time isn't enough. The world has some towns that compare with it for beauty and charm—not many—but none that surpass. Mellow gold-hued sandstone of ancient walls and towers, crooked narrow streets with names like Whip-Ma-Whop-Ma Gate, half-timbered houses whose arcades line them and galleries lean over them, pubs where the beer and the friendliness are as genuine as you'll ever find and you can still hear the broad dialect of yeomen come in to market, history reaching back beyond the Romans and not embalmed but alive, here all around you— As we passed by the Merchants' Guildhall after we'd checked in at our lodging, we swore we'd come back when this miserable business of ours was behind us, and bring the kids, and take a week or more.

We found St. Oswald's on Oglethorpe Street. For a while we stood and stared, letting pedestrians surge around us. Though I strained my senses, nothing came to me but voices, shoe-clack, odors of man and smoke faint in the sunny air. Ginny couldn't very well unlimber a wand and check for peculiarities. The building did for sure look unpromising, brick, squarish. "Failed neoclassical," she muttered. Maybe the dull

appearance wasn't entirely its fault. It lay almost in the shadow of the Minster. That most glorious of churches rose above roofs like God's personal benediction.

"Well," I said, "let's do it."

She nodded. We mounted the steps and entered. The interior was cool and somewhat dark. I don't know whether that was merciful to the altarpiece or made it still more rococo. Memorial tablets were sparse on the walls, under nineteenth-century stained glass that hadn't benefited from the Burne-Jones influence. A couple of bewigged busts in niches seemed to disapprove of us.

Nobody else was here but a little gray verger. We hadn't the heart not to let him show us around and tell us about the two gentlemen represented. Since one of them had fought in the American War of Independence and we were Americans, we heard about him at length. Finally we could drop some money in a collection box and ask to see the crypt.

"Certainly, certainly. Tickets are a shilling, if you please. Goes toward upkeep . . . Thank you very much. This way, if you please." He pottered to a door, unlocked it, switched on an edison, and led us down a flight of stairs. The first few were brick, evidently part of the rebuilding, but beyond that they were stone, deeply worn, hewn out in early Norman times. "The undercroft is quite small, you see. Undoubtedly it was much larger beneath the abbey, but earth and rubble have buried most. We believe proper excavation would uncover parts of the twelfth-century walls and foundation, as well as—who knows?—treasures the monks hid away from King Henry's expropriators. That would also mean a modern metal stairwell—do watch your step, please—but I am afraid our humble house of worship lacks glamour."

A lightbulb hung in a cramped vault. Flagstones lay damp underfoot. The walls were masonry. "Observe the herringbone pattern," the verger said with pride. "The work is timber grillage, but otherwise the materials are largely Roman." He gestured toward a flat brick wall at the far end. "Except for that, of course. The Georgian builders put it in to keep this remnant clear. Who knows what lies behind?"

Glass-topped exhibition cases filled most of what floor space there was. They looked kind of time-worn themselves: nineteenth century, if not older. Ginny's jaw clenched for a moment and a chill along my nerves stirred every hair on me. We had glimpsed the sword. It was all we could do not to barge straight over and peer.

Instead, we smoothed our faces and made interested noises while our guide pointed out this and that. "—medal bequeathed by Colonel

Horatio Bullivant, who distinguished himself in the Peninsular Campaign. . . . Ghazi musket from the fatal battle of Maiwand. . . . Rather more antique, this rosary, said to have belonged to the last Catholic bishop but one—"

—and so on, until I could say, "What about this sword?" and hope I just sounded inquisitive.

It rested in a case together with a handsome earthenware bowl, a corroded bronze crucifix, a couple of bone chessmen, and a few more objects from the Middle Ages. The weapon dominated. About three feet long, blade broad on top and not tapering much to a bluntish point, it had a short, straight iron guard and a wide, flat-bottomed pommel rounded like a scoop of ice cream. Both were inset with gold curlicues. The haft between was wrapped in shagreen, doubtless part of the restoration. The scabbard was leather-covered wood, set with polished garnets. Was I fooling myself, or did I catch a sense of ferocity ready to spring, like a lynx in a cage? The jewels glared under the light. . . .

"Ah, yes." The verger was less than fascinated. "A venerable piece, dating back to the Danish period. Perhaps it properly belongs in a museum, but here it has been for some seven hundred years. It is remarkable chiefly for its excellent state of preservation. Now the bowl you see, that is a rather fine example of local thirteenth-century pottery. It was a gift from Ulfrida, the wife of a prosperous dealer in salted fish. She acquired a posthumous reputation as a saint, although it never reached Rome—"

A card in the case read: *Sword donated about 1225 by Sir Ranulph Daunay of Thurshaw Manor as a sign of contrition for past bloodthirstiness before he took monastic vows. Style and workmanship date it to Scandinavia, approximately ninth century. Presumably it came to England with a Dane whose descendants married into the Norman house. Although the design grew obsolete, fragmentary chronicles suggest that scions of the family carried it into battle as late as Sir Ranulph's time, possibly under the impression that it was lucky. The reconstruction of hilt and sheath, the latter emplacing the stones that had been on its predecessor, was the gift of Mr. Humphrey Sedgworth, banker, in 1846.*

Real romantic.

Ginny and I had roughed out our plans beforehand. The conditions we found told us how to improvise. We made much of other relics, explaining that I was a military history buff and Ginny a fan of Regency romances. We fussed around till the verger gave up, pleaded that he must return to his duties elsewhere, and tottered upstairs.

At once we were at the sword. Ginny's wand came forth. When she'd whispered the right words, its star flared, blue-tinged white. She traced the latent powerfields like a hummingbird tracing flower scents; I remembered that the hummingbird was an incarnation of the Aztec war god. Me, I snapped any number of Polaroid photos and measured the dimensions of the sword as exactly as possible.

We dared not take too long. After about half an hour we tucked away our gear and left. The verger bade us a wistful good-bye. He didn't get many visitors who cared this much.

We returned in silence to our rooms. I slumped into a chair. Ginny began unpacking the stuff she'd require. "I don't feel right about this," I mumbled.

She frowned. "It is technically a theft. Of course, we'll return the thing when we're done with it."

"If we can. In any case, it's a violation of trust."

"Necessity knows no law. You didn't hesitate before."

"Not till I'd met that nice little guy."

"Whatever happens, shall we make a substantial donation to the church? I mean substantial. Anonymous, probably, but it's obvious their building fund or poor fund can use it."

*Unless the whatever that happens involves our getting killed or worse,* I thought.

But no, this approached self-pity. I think the British call it whinging. I myself had preached to my daughter that sometimes we humans have to break the rules, certain moral rules maybe included, and take the consequences—the blame, if our judgment turns out to have been wrong. I rallied my spirit, got up, and lent a hand.

I won't describe the work of the next hour or so. Some details are public knowledge, others are restricted to licensed operators, still others were proprietary, unique to Ginny. Goetics remains as much Art as technology. (Well, that's fairly true of mundane engineering too.) Basically, we used the data we'd acquired and my calculations from them to draw up specs for the sword and sheath—the material objects, that is. Then Ginny laid out the stock we'd brought from Cambridge according to Frogmorton's description. Mainly this was an iron bar, a couple of laths, a piece of leather, and a few pebbles. She put a Seeming on them. To every unaided sense they became identical with the exhibit. You'd have needed a vernier and a pretty accurate scale to tell the differences, short of a chemical analysis which nobody had ever done anyway. Oh, someone who cast a minor spell or simply had a

Gift would realize something was funny, but it was a safe bet that no such person would visit the crypt anytime soon.

Afterward we went downstairs. The hour was early for dinner. We had a high tea instead, to which I added a stiff drink. Returning to our suite, we drew the shades and tried to sleep. That took me a while, but there was ample time. Night comes late in the English summer.

Also, it's short. Our clock owlhooted us awake at 2 A.M. We scrambled into our clothes. Besides my skinsuit underneath the street garb, I wore a topcoat and Ginny a cloak, cover for what we carried along and hoped to carry back. A distinct advantage of staying at a first-class hotel was that we didn't have to ring anybody out of bed at odd hours. That annoyance could have stuck in the memory.

Ginny smiled at the drowsy porter. "We thought we'd enjoy a starlit stroll on the walls," she explained in a voice that would have turned Scrooge's heart to warm mush.

"Be careful of your steps," he cautioned like a benign uncle. "You have a torch, ma'am? Good. Have a nice walk." He stood sentimentally looking after us.

I laid an arm around Ginny's waist. "Too bad we aren't really going to," I sighed. "Saving the world sure does get in the way of enjoying it."

She leaned briefly against me. "That's another matter we'll have to make amends for." Then her stride turned brisk.

The air was cool, damp, very quiet. Larger streets were lighted but the old "gates" lay full of shadows and old dreams. Once a policeman passed. He gave us a quick, close look, nodded affably, and continued on his beat. Somehow that deepened our loneliness.

St. Oswald's had too damn much illumination on it. We'd expected this, however. After scanning the sidewalks right and left, we went fast up the stairs to the portico. Ginny drew a Hand of Glory from her purse. It was only a monkey's paw, a tiny withered thing that glowed faint blue when she touched it to a door. (The monkey had died at an advanced age of a surfeit of bananas.) Its powers were equally slight. But ordinary locks clicked open under those black fingers, and closed again behind us.

No candles burned inside. St. Oswald's wasn't High Church. We used our flashlight—no, here in England, torch—to make our way through the nave to the inner door and down to the crypt.

Those innocents had installed no alarm for us to nullify. The Hand undid the case. I swung the glass lid back and grasped the sword. It felt massive, though not heavy. Unlike too many heroes of fantasy

fiction, our forefathers were practical men who didn't wear themselves out swinging unnecessary mass. Even a battle ax ran to only about five pounds. Nevertheless, it seemed as if I gripped something *alive.*

Ginny freed me of my left coat sleeve and unslung the fake beneath. She laid it in the case, taking great care about its position, hung the real one from my shoulder, and dressed me again. She lowered the lid. I heard its lock, too long unoiled, grate back to closure. We retraced our thievish steps.

The street still stretched empty. I realized I was shivering a bit, the smell of my sweat sharp in my nostrils. "This was almost too easy," Ginny said.

"Y-you mean the enemy knows and—helped us along?"

"No, I mean if we went back to the hotel right away, the porter would wonder why." She laughed and tucked her arm under mine. "Guess we'll have to take that walk after all."

Unreasonable gladness jumped in me. Fears and tension fled. "By God, I get my wish!"

A staircase led onto the city wall. Most of the medieval circuit remains. The top has been paved for easy footing. We wandered hand in hand between the battlements. Beneath us slept the town. Opposite gleamed the river, and outlying homes gave way to broad countryside. Steeples, portals, the strong delicate towers of the Minster reached for the stars that glimmered overhead. Now, when traffic was hushed, we breathed stillness and ghostly fragrances from gardens. Often we stopped. The east had gone pale before we turned back.

The porter smiled as we came in. "I hope you enjoyed yourselves," he said, wearily amiable.

Suddenly noticing how rumpled my best girl's hair had gotten, I felt sheepish. She, though, returned his grin. "Oh, my, yes," she purred.

"You'll be having your breakfast late? Perhaps lunch?"

"No, likelier at the usual time," Ginny replied. "We aren't sleepy yet."

He tried not to grin wider. Reality, the weight beneath my coat, jabbed into me. Yes, we had something in mind that we just weren't able to put off. No, it wasn't what he thought. Damn! And yet, and yet—

In our suite, the door latched and the DO NOT DISTURB on its knob, I slipped my coat off, removed my burden, and shakily set it on a table. Ginny joined me. For a time that we didn't reckon, we looked. Day waxed beyond the shades. My nerves once more strung close to the snapping point, I caught sounds of people coming astir.

"All right, let's," she said very softly. She unshipped her wand and made other precautionary preparations. Standing back, alert, she nodded to me. "Draw it, Steve."

*And see what happens.*

I took the scabbard in my left hand and lifted the weapon. My right went around the haft. It could barely squeeze between guard and pommel. The idea was to provide a tight, secure fit, and men averaged smaller in the past than now. Slowly, I pulled.

The iron sheened darkly. A line in *Beowulf* came back to me, "the brown blade." But this one had a bluish overtone with a damascene ripple. Dwarf-forged to cut through steel and stone, monsters and magics—what alloy, what heating and quenching, hammering and grinding, runecraft and songcraft had gone into it? I swung it through an arc. In spite of my awkward grip, a beautiful balance made it move like my own arm. A feeling of savage life flowed into my marrow.

A sound like throat-clearing rasped across our silence. "Ahem!" The scabbard dropped from me and thudded on the carpet.

"Har d'je do, m'lady, m'lord," said a raspy, vigorous baritone. "Gad, how good to be free again! Deuced bore, lying there, unable to do a bloody thing—if you'll pardon the language, m'lady—nothing but listen, ever since I Awoke. Fifty years? A hundred? Felt like a thousand, I can tell you. Outrage. Calls for a letter to the *Times.* Yes, and questions in Parliament, egad. Heads will roll for this, or there's no discipline and justice left in England, by Jove!"

Repartee failed me. The blade wobbled in my clutch. "Uh, I, uh, p-pleased to meet you," I stammered. How did you shake hands with a sword? That edge could take my fingers right off.

Ginny recovered faster. She's more used to dealing with the eldritch. I'm only a werewolf. "We are honored, sir," she said. "Excuse me, but before we go further, how would you like to be positioned?" Obviously I couldn't keep hold of it indefinitely, and it might think that simply laying it down was undignified.

Obviously, too, the spirit 'chanted into it had an equivalent of vision as well as of voice box—and who knew what more senses? I imagined cold blue eyes under shaggy brows darting to and fro. "Over yonder," it said. "That thingummy in the corner, ha? Best place I see. Where are we, some petty nobleman's manor or what? Demmed sparse furnishings, I must say. Any tapestries on any wall in here?"

"An inn, sir," I explained as I parked the terrible Viking weapon in the umbrella stand. "Things have changed a lot since you, uh, since you were last active."

"Last Awake, you mean, young fella. I dozed off, um-m, let me see . . . last engagement I'm sure of was, um-m, Tenchebrai, yes, Tenchebrai. Reign of Henry, y' know. Not long after I'd come back from Constantinople. Tenchebrai, yes, we gave that scoundrel Robert a proper thrashing, we did, him and his Frogs. There we stood, a thin red line— No, I'm mixing my epochs, damme. Hard to keep sorted out, when all I could bloody well do after I Awoke was lie there and hear whatever happened to be in bloody earshot. Unbelievably boring, most of it. Clergy, demmed heretics, the lot of 'em, and la-de-da pilgrims. Now and then a proper milit'ry man, true, or better yet two or three together, who'd talk about something worthwhile like battles."

"Henry," Ginny whispered to me. "Must be Henry I. Early twelfth century, I think."

The sword had gone dormant with the waning of rheatic energy everywhere, I realized. For generations before then, no doubt Christian owners had kept its nature secret and persuaded it to talk to nobody but themselves. Afterward that knowledge was suppressed and died out. Nonetheless a tradition went on in the family, that here was a brand more often victorious than not. So, antiquated though it was, it continued in use for another hundred years. But by then it was just another chunk of shaped metal, remarkable in some ways such as the keen, enduring edge and the immunity to rust, otherwise obsolete. Finally it was handed over to the Church, along with its last wielder. . . .

"Ahem!" the sword interrupted itself. "Beg pardon. We've not been properly introduced. Nor is anyone about who can do the honors, what? Needs must. Soldierly straightforwardness. Allow me. Decent lineage, never fear. Forged by the dwarf Fjalar in Norway, the Dofra Fell, mountains, y'know. That was on commission from Egil Asmundsson, jarl in Raumsdal. Independent kingdom then, y'know, though already rather under the sway of Halfdan the Swart southwards. Not unlike a native state in India during the British Raj. Good warrior, Egil. The first man he killed with me—But later, later. He called me Brynjubítr. Meant 'Byrnie Biter' in the language. I've since borne a hodgepodge of different names, or none. No respect, those younger generations. You may call me Fotherwick-Botts."

"Huh?" I croaked.

"Adopted from Major-General Sir Steelman Fotherwick-Botts, O.B.E. After his retirement he came down to the crypt rather often. I'd hear him discuss the milit'ry relics, battles past, the arts of war, and other good stuff with young officers he'd brought along or else with

whomever was there." *And who couldn't escape,* I thought. "Admirable chap. Solid. If only I'd been with him at Bloemfontein—"

*So that's how this Being's picked up what he knows of the modern English language and style. No, Edwardian at best. And there's a lot of frustration here to work off.*

"Allow us to introduce ourselves," Ginny inserted into the monologue. She even managed a sketchy account of what we needed.

"Jolly good!" exulted the sword. "A Chinaman, eh? Crafty, they are. Not that I've encountered 'em m'self, y'know, but I've heard stories. As long ago as down in Byzantium— I'd better describe my career for you, what?"

Its voice shifted into recitation gear. "Briefly put, except for Viking expeditions I was in Norway until the battle of Hafrsfjord. There we stood, a thin mail-clad line— But that ruddy Harald Fairhair had the vict'ry. Not wishing to live under him, my then warrior—Trygvi Sveinsson, good man of his hands, they called him the Fierce, tell you about him later— joined a crew in Denmark and won a homestead in England. A generation or two afterward we were converted—fine white robes they gave the newly baptized; quality declined deplorably as time went by—and what is this bloody heresy these days?—but I kept up the side, ruthlessness and so forth, best's I could. Was at Stamford Bridge. Accounts of it absurd, dead wrong, near's I can gather. There we stood, a thin Anglo-Danish line—Ahem. A while after the Norman Conquest, my then wielder left the country, like many Englishmen, to join the Varangian Guard down in Constantinople. Jolly good engagements we had there, I can tell you. And I shall. He came back with quite a decent sum of money and reconciled himself with the Normans. His son—"

Fotherwick-Botts paused, as if to catch the breath he didn't need, before going relentlessly on: "But enough outline. You'll want the details. To go back to the beginning, when the dwarf delivered me to Egil Asmundsson and he went off to take vengeance—no, damme, justice it was, justice—on Herjolf the Pugnosed, they met in a meadow—"

"Oh, my God," I muttered to Ginny. "What've we let ourselves in for?"

She shuddered. "I'm afraid this is one of those ancient enchanted swords that, when they're drawn, tell of every battle they ever fought," she whispered back. "At least, *he* will, poor devil, after lying so long silenced. And before then, in the Christian period, he could only talk

a little bit, secretly, to such of them as wouldn't be horrified and throw him into the sea for a piece of pagan witchcraft. Suddenly, now, he can cut loose—I mean speak freely to us."

"—I hewed into Herjolf's shield," Fotherwick-Botts told us, "but Egil did not let him twist me aside in the cleft. Common trick back then—"

"Judas priest," I gasped, "three centuries' worth, or whatever it is? How'll we get any sleep?"

"We can sheathe him," Ginny replied. "With proper apologies, of course. He'll start where he left off when we draw him again. I hope we can persuade him to glide over most of it, but I'm afraid we'll hear a great deal before he'll give us any real help. We'd better keep this suite through tonight, at least, and not take the train but rent a broom to go to London. Slowly."

"I say, are you paying attention?" barked the sword.

I'd have groaned louder if I'd known of the more important disaster hitting us meanwhile at home.

# XXIII

And yet it was only an overture, a few pips and tweedles before the Devil's Band started to play for us in earnest. We heard of it together with what was much worse, when it barely registered on our awareness. Later we sorted out the facts as best we could, because this too we must deal with, but at the time it seemed almost incidental. Nobody imagined the eventual consequences. If we had—well, that's useless. If an elephant were little and round and white it would be an aspirin.

My reconstruction of events is partly guesswork. No matter. This whole account isn't for publication. Too explosive, as well as being often too personal. It's going under hundred-year seal. Maybe after that it can give some kind of unforeseeable help to somebody in the unforeseeable future. A warning, if nothing else.

Things began when Alger Sneep of the IRS called on Thursday and demanded to speak with us. Will, who'd established himself in our house, explained that we'd gone away. No, he didn't know where or for how long. "Ha," said Sneep. "This makes investigation urgent. Please prepare to receive me tomorrow morning at ten A.M."

"But I don't know anything," Will protested. "I'm merely here for the sake of the children. I expect Gin—Dr. and Mr. Matuchek will be back in a week or two."

"We may well have some questions for you too, Professor Graylock. Last time I met with mischievous obstructionism. You will find cooperation with us to your advantage, Professor Graylock."

Ginny or I would have stiffened our voices and replied that first we'd speak with Mr. Sneep's supervisor, whose name and phone glyphs he would provide at once. Soon we'd have checked with Barney, and

he'd doubtless have called one of the lawyers he kept on tap. American taxpayers do retain some rights. Not many, but some. Federal tax collectors seldom feel obliged to list those rights. Will was caught entirely off guard.

Just the same, he should have shown a bit of firmness. Later he admitted not quite knowing why he didn't, unless the fault lay in a combination of his troublesome health and a notion that we had nothing to fear because we'd done nothing wrong. Anyhow, he accepted the appointment.

When he told the kids at dinnertime, Valeria lifted hands and eyes dramatically ceilingward, looked back down, and curled her lip. Yes, she did, actually and literally. "What?" she shrilled. "That nastard again? Why can't we just have black plague?"

"We, er, we must be polite to him," Will said. "He does represent our government."

She nodded. "Dad agrees."

"No, er, tricks or anything. Do you hear me? Your parents were very displeased last time. Let us have no repetitions."

"No, we won't." She squinted into space. "I'll make the necessary arrangements." Catching his expression, she gave him a grim smile. "Not salt in the coffee or any such silly thing. I'll behave, and do my best to keep him out of trouble."

After the meal and cleanup she retired to her room with Svartalf. Will worried. However, he could not think of any objection when she explained she wanted to practice her spellcraft. Though precociously skilled, she was still capable only of minor, reasonably safe conjurations. The old black cat had by now become more her familiar than her mother's, but a stabilizer as much as an energizer.

It was she who admitted Sneep next morning when he rang. "How do you do," she said. Her cold graciousness, which would have done credit to Elizabeth Báthory, was not marred by pony tail, bare feet, faded blue jeans, and a T-shirt reading KILL THE FANATICS!

His lips compressed. "How do you do, Miss Matuchek," he said, clutching his briefcase tightly.

"Everything's in order, Mr. Sneep. I've left the younger children with a neighbor, where they'll be safe."

He gave her his gimlet look. "Do you mean there will be danger?"

She went totally bland. "Not from us. Please come in." As he did, she stepped aside, out of arm's reach.

They entered the living room. Edgar flapped his wings on his perch. "O villany!" he screamed. "Ho! Let the door be lock'd."

Will had risen from the chair where he'd sat attempting to read a scientific journal. "That's rude," he protested. "I'm sorry."

"I've been teaching him lines from Shakespeare," Val said, smiling. "Don't you think households should be cultured, Mr. Sneep?"

"Unfortunate," Will sputtered. "Indiscreet. We owe you an apology, sir."

"Bad bird." Val's tone wasn't even half-hearted.

"Well, uh, please sit down, Mr. Sneep," Will gulped. "Would you care for coffee? Valeria, will you fetch it?"

"Thank you, I believe I had better go straight to work," clipped the agent. "There's a great deal requiring explanation and substantiation. Perhaps you can help, Professor Graylock."

"That, er, that isn't my proper title. Never mind. I don't know what I can do in the absence of my sister and her husband."

"Can you tell me why they suddenly left—" Sneep paused, then pounced. "—right after a large sum of money had been transferred to their bank account?"

"Well, no, not really. That is, I understand it has to do with the Operation Luna enterprise. . . ."

Val widened her eyes. "How did you learn right away, Mr. Sneep?" she marveled. "You're real efficient, aren't you?"

He clenched a fist. "Banks are required to report such transactions, Miss Matuchek."

"I see. And I'm awful sorry. I *think* I paid $1.98 for these panties I'm wearing, but I could be wrong, I've lost the receipt. They'd know at the store, the Old Ranger Trading Post, and—"

"That will do, young lady!" her uncle yelled. In haste: "We all want to resolve this problem, whatever it is. Frankly, I should think it could wait till the Matucheks return, or that your Midwestern office can get a perfectly satisfactory accounting from the people at Nornwell. Meanwhile, I'm told you have taken a large selection of the Matucheks' records to study."

"Some questions call for immediate answers, here on the spot." Sneep's manner implied that otherwise we'd pull a fast one. "To start with, I need to see Mrs., ah, Dr. Matuchek's studio."

"Her arcanum?" Val cried. "You can't!"

"I beg your pardon?"

"Not while she's away—" At this point, if not before, Ginny or I would have been quoting the Fourth Amendment, possibly to good effect. Will was sort of numbed, though, and Val naive, as well as being only a young girl. (Maybe "only" isn't the word I want.) She blurted,

"Nobody can. It's warded. Against robbers and priers and—" She caught Will's eye. "And l-layfolk who might endanger themselves if they got in. You'll *have* to wait till my mother gets home and undoes the spell."

"Several official forms are missing from the documents we have seen," Sneep told her. "Perhaps they are in there. Certainly I must get the dimensions of this house to verify whether the office space claimed as deductible is correct."

Val bridled. "Are you calling my mother a liar?"

Will tried to intervene. "This is unfortunate, but, but surely understandable. Isn't it? I haven't had cause to visit the studio myself lately, but believe me, if my sister has warded it, any attempt—well, I warn you, I sincerely warn you."

"If the spell is hazardous to life or limb, it's highly illegal," Sneep reminded him. "I trust Dr. Matuchek knows better. We'll see. I too have resources available to me."

He reached into his briefcase and took out a box. Stooping to one knee, he released a tape worm. The creature inched along the baseboard, measuring and recording. Sneep rose. "Now, that studio. Down the hall yonder, isn't it?"

"No, don't, please don't," Valeria begged. He ignored her. She followed at a yard's distance.

As they advanced, the corridor went gloomy, and more gloomy, until it was coalsack dark. And it reached on, and on, and on. Echoes rang hollowly off unseen walls. Air turned freezingly cold. Will-o'-the wisps darted here and there, ghastly corpse blue. Something afar howled, something closer snickered.

"Illusions." Sneep lifted his ring finger. A beam of light sprang from the bezel. He trudged forward. "Ah, yes," he said after a while. "An asymptotic warp. Intruders would take an eternity to reach the end."

"It's easy going back," Val said from behind. Though Ginny had briefed her and would never set up anything that could harm her, the words wavered. This was an environment straight out of nightmare.

Sneep halted. "The spell is within the limits of the law," he acknowledged.

A glowing, blobby image appeared ahead of him, opened a fangful mouth, and gibbered.

"Accordingly," Sneep said, "it is annullable by the powers vested in me."

He fished a book out of his briefcase. As he held it in one hand,

it opened to the page he wanted, which shone bleak white. He read aloud:

"If the taxpayer's passive gross income from significant participation passive activities (within the meaning of section 1.469-2T (f) (2) (ii) for the taxable year (determined without regard to section 1.469-2T (f) (2) through (3)) exceeds the taxpayer's passive activity deductions from such activities for the taxable year, such activities shall be treated solely for purposes of applying this paragraph (f) (2) (i) for the taxable year, as a single activity that does not have a loss for such taxable year."

Before this fearsome cantrip, the phantoms quailed and dissolved, the blackness fled, space shrank back to normal, and Sneep stood triumphant in our ordinary home. The lock on Ginny's door opened of itself for him.

He peered around. His gaze fell on the studio couch. "Ha, a bed," he almost chortled. "Claimed office space must be used exclusively for business purposes."

Val had entered too. "Mom—my mother—sometimes she thinks best when she's lying down," she said. "Or I've seen her spread papers out on it for referring to."

"Can you swear that no one ever sleeps here? A guest, perhaps?"

"We've *got* a guest room." Val settled into a chair. "Go ahead. Do what you claim you have to."

Sneep frowned. "We don't appreciate interference with our duties, Miss Matuchek."

"Oh, I'll sit quiet, 'n case you need me." Will himself, when he arrived, couldn't move her. She sat. She said never a word, but she glowered. Teenagers are good at glowering. Our Valeria holds the championship.

Sneep was—I won't say vengeful—stalwart in his way. He scouted doggedly around the room, though he left cabinets and drawers alone. He took many notes, including about pictures and books and decorations. Do no other workplaces contain anything personal?

A raucous and rattling noise interrupted. Will came back in. "Oh, dear," he said, "I'm afraid the cat found your worm inching around and couldn't resist. I, er, I took it away from him, but the raven had already snatched a piece that was bitten off and flown out the window."

Sneep departed shortly afterward. He left ominous words behind him, to the effect that Ginny and I had better report in soon. We were out of touch, though, and hadn't gotten around to calling home.

* * *

Maybe that was just as well. Fotherwick-Botts droned on at us unceasingly except when he demanded, "What d'ye think of that, eh?" or when we mumbled with elaborate deference that we really must sheathe him and hide him away for a while. It lasted through Saturday in York and all the way to London on Sunday and in our hotel room there till nearly midnight.

Then finally he harrumphed and said, "And that was Tenchebrai. Jolly good scrap. Stout lads. Pity there's nothing more recent to tell you. I fell Asleep, y'know. Of course, I've passed over any number of lesser fights. You'll want to hear about those. But now we've work ahead of us, don't we?"

Eagerness rang in his voice. "Action again! Have at 'em! Thor help us—ahem!— Ha, ha among the trumpets, and all that sort of thing."

Fog smoked chill and wet, street lamps glowed blurrily through it, like skeleton trees from whose tops watched yellow-eyed goblins. Farther off they vanished into formlessness. My wolf nose drew in tides of smells, oily, chemical, rusty, rotted, sometimes a breath of something unknown to me. My pads and Ginny's sneakers whispered on pavement that stretched empty, gray where light fell, murkful elsewhere. Dreary brick walls hemmed it in on either side. Fresno, California, prosaic market town, felt a long ways from Fresno Street through Limehouse—on another world, maybe in another universe.

The district had been rehabilitated some since Victorian times, we'd learned. Businesses such as the Aberdeen Shipping Company were no longer islands of respectability in a swamp of squalor, vice, and crime. Others had moved into the old buildings that formerly housed slop shops, gin mills, cribs, and worse; the city had policed the area in both senses of the word. Still, at best it remained seedy, and reform hadn't taken any firm hold on this particular neighborhood along the docks east of London Bridge. When we'd walked through by day, we'd felt no urge to enter any pub.

For sure we wouldn't after dark, when the locals and the sailors had gotten thoroughly drunk—though a cafe would maybe pose deeper-going dangers. It would have been still more foolish for a woman to venture where everything was shut up and deserted for the night, even with a male escort. Unless, of course, he looked like a gigantic hound and was actually a timber wolf.

I'd better keep that shape till we got back to the railway station where she'd lockered my clothes for me after I changed in a gent's. Since my skinsuit might give my nature away to somebody who'd pass

the word on ahead of us, I wore only a collar with a leash that passed beneath her cloak. There also she kept my lens, just in case, her own gear, and Fotherwick-Botts.

We'd needed fewer precautions earlier, when I was human and we made like tourists seeking a quick, cheap thrill. Yet in a way we had had to take special care, because that was our scouting expedition. Who knew what watch-spells Dr. Fu had set?

We simply strolled by daylight through Upper Swandam Lane, past his hideout, and onto the high wharf beyond. Luckily, no ship was tied up there at this time. Ginny's looks had drawn attention enough elsewhere, leers and an occasional low whistle. I could imagine dock wallopers finding ways to keep her in sight. As it was, we took cover around the corner of a shed while she used her wand and skill to work what Art she dared. Carefully, carefully, feeling her way, alert to pull back at the slightest quiver of reaction— But the Sensitivities weren't primed against her hybrid Anglo-Zuni approach; and she didn't really try to probe, she simply skimmed off impressions of the layout and the general situation. Nor did we linger after she was done.

On the way back to our modest Whitechapel hotel, she walked like one in a dream. I didn't interrupt. She was in self-communion, evaluating what she'd discovered. Once we'd come to our room, she roused, took the sword from the suitcase where he'd lain wrapped in my bathrobe, and told us crisply:

"Two doors flank number 3, leading to what must have been small, probably disreputable shops but now stand empty except for some dusty stored things. The buildings on the opposite side have been converted to a warehouse, which turns a blank rear wall onto the alley and doesn't seem to be much used. The entrance to number 3 itself goes underground, into a long, low room and a couple of lesser ones behind. It contains the dingy remains of a low-class hotel lobby, a hotel which must have gone broke years ago and which Fu's agents could easily rent from the present owners. I caught ghostly traces—wasted lives leave residua that can hang on for a long time. They suggest that before it became a hotel this was an opium den. But no matter, I suppose. Number 3 includes the floors above the shops. Several rooms there have been refurnished in what seems to be high style, but I didn't check details."

"Any boltholes?" inquired Fotherwick-Botts. "Wouldn't be a proper Oriental lair without secret escape hatches, eh?"

"No, apparently not. The back of the house fronts on a narrow strip of ground between it and the wharf, mud at low tide, submerged

at high. Not suitable for a tunnel. I suppose you could jump out a window and flounder or swim away. Also at the back, where the top story projects a little, is a trapdoor, but I suspect that was for disposing of corpses and other inconvenient objects in old days. No, Fu Ch'ing must rely on secrecy, and on forewarning from his agents or guardian spells if the authorities do find where he is."

"And on fighting-type guardians if somebody unexpected breaks in?" Keeping my voice level was tough.

Ginny nodded. "Armed men and . . . potentials. It'd have been reckless of me to try counting or identifying them. But my Finding is pretty clear, they aren't a terribly strong force. One like that could too easily betray its presence, whether by numbers of foreigners suddenly in the area or by emanations from the Beings and the latencies. Scotland Yard will have scouted around, after all. I think the idea is merely to fight a delaying action while Fu and any top lieutenants of his make their escape."

"Fly out a window?"

"Hardly that simple. Raiders would be prepared for it. Plain Tarnkappen wouldn't work either, against modern police equipment. Something really powerful in the way of a transformation or a Seeming, maybe; but it would take time to prepare. We hope to surprise them, moving too fast for their getaway measures."

"Tally-ho!" the sword whooped. "Sweep 'em off their feet! St. George for merrie England, by Thor!"

"Sh, not so loud, please," Ginny hissed.

"Uh, maybe we should notify the police," I said. "You've done one hell of a job of tracking, sweetheart, but now—well, it's only the two of us, I mean the three of us, and—"

The red head shook. "You forget that Fu probably has spies in those forces. British lawmen aren't incompetent by any means, but they'd naturally need time to verify our rather peculiar story, get their warrants, and everything else. Ample time for Fu to be warned. Nothing useful to them would be left."

"Okay. Still, I don't think we should depend entirely on ourselves. If something does go badly wrong, we'll crap out knowing our efforts were worthless."

"Aye, hold cavalry in reserve behind the hill," agreed Fotherwick-Botts. "Besides, it lends tone to a battle."

Ginny went along with that. We worked out a scheme, which she implemented from our room. Remarkable what you can do these days if you know exactly what resonances to send where through the phones.

Thereafter we discussed our personal tactics. Not that that became elaborate or went on very long. We knew too little.

Besides, Ginny and I were aware of the military maxim that in any engagement the first casualty will be your own battle plan; while the sword harked back to eras when you might occasionally pull a smart trick like a feigned retreat, but mainly you just charged.

I always hated the idea of exposing Ginny to danger. And my personal hide counted for something too. Nevertheless I admit to a certain thrill rising in me. We had a hunt ahead of us.

First, once again, we gulped an early meal and went back to our room for a few hours' rest. This time, oddly enough, I dropped off almost at once, and enjoyed pleasant dreams. I loped on a slope in flowery Arcadia . . .

We went out before the last of the management had gone to bed. If later we rang somebody up in the small hours, what the hell. We'd either have succeeded or failed—or come to grief—in any case, blown our cover and have no further need of it.

And so we found ourselves walking down deserted Fresno Street to where Upper Swandam Lane ran off.

It opened before us like a gut, and nearly as black. Ginny had laid witch-sight on us both. Through fog-swirl, we made out the wharf as a block of blackness at the far end, and a sullen gleam off the river beyond. Mainly, though, I smelled, and felt every hair of my pelt stir to the slowly shifty airs. The alley slept. . . . No, not the thaumaturgic forces that barely rustled along my werewolf nerves. I glanced up at Ginny. Light from the nearest lamp touched the fog-drops in her hair. I tugged at my leash. She followed me.

Sometimes, in the gloom, we kicked aside litter, a bit of glass that clinked, crumpled paper that rustled, a bone that stank. Nothing awoke. We came to the entrance we wanted.

Even enhanced eyes could barely make out the flight of steps that plunged down to a door. The stairwell concentrated stenches—reptilian—at which I snarled and bristled. Ginny unclipped my leash. She knotted it about her waist. Throwing back her cloak, she took the scabbard from its awkward position beneath her left arm. Expanding the belt it hung from, she fastened it slantwise across her shoulders, where it wouldn't get in the way and might give a little protection. She reached into the pouch at her hip, snugged a silver and amethyst ring engraved with an Osiris eye against her wedding band, took forth her wand and extended it. Her right hand drew the sword. It sheened moon-wan in

the scanty light from the street. I heard her whisper to it: "For God's sake, *keep quiet.*"

She went down the stairs, I at her heels, to the landing.

One degree at a time, pauses between, during which the river flowed louder than our breaths, she turned the doorknob. Nothing happened. Well, we hadn't expected otherwise, simply felt obliged to try. Probably no Glory Hand, monkey or human, could open that lock. Probably the attempt would set off goetic alarms. Stealth had become pointless. She lifted the sword and swung.

A woman hasn't the upper-body strength of a man, but she was athletic and had deep resources to call on. Her weapon was dwarf-forged, enchanted, a sunderer of all things. I believe I heard "Yoicks!" ring from the blade. Then it crashed and clove.

Wood splintered. Sparks flew where metal sheared. The cut went nearly the length of the door, as though splitting a man from helmet to midriff. Any latches and deadbolts gave with the lock. Ginny pulled the sword free. That impetus dragged the door ajar. I slipped past her, wedged my snout in the crack, swung the barrier aside, and bounded in.

The old hotel lobby had been refurbished the way a landlord would expect a group to do who rented this El Cheapo for a co-op residence. A few second-hand armchairs sagged on a threadbare carpet. A discouraged aspidistra stood in a tarnished brass pot near the unused counter. A color print depicted a clipper ship in high seas under full sail, the way depicted square-riggers always seem to be in all weathers. An edison glowed dully from a dusty globe overhead. A flight of stairs curved aloft from the rear between two inner doors. Protective drabness for the dragon.

It didn't last. Half a dozen men swarmed from behind those doors. Two were white, two maybe Chinese, two smaller and darker, from southern Asia somewhere. All wore dingy street clothes. The night watch, no doubt. All were armed, long knives, a hatchet, a pistol. They didn't yell or anything. They ran directly at us.

I leaped for them. They couldn't hurt me, but Ginny— Behind me, she pointed her wand. The electric bulb exploded and darkness clapped down.

I hit the nearest of the thugs, dacoits, whatchacallems full tilt and bowled him over. Witch-sight gave shadowy vision. Mostly I went by my ears and nose—and, after a moment, my tongue. Snap, slash, hot blood, live bodies, and now they did cry out. It could have been a mixup back during the war. The wolf of me wildly rejoiced. The man

of me remembered, far back in my head, that I'd better not kill if I could avoid it. The modern English are stuffy about such things.

The modern English. Ginny had started up the stairs. Her wand cast fire-bright, frost-cold light before her. More men advanced downward, these in assorted sleeping garments but also armed. *"Yuk-hai-saa-saa!"* roared Fotherwick-Botts. "Haro! Have at 'em! Your widows will remember this night, you scurvy scoundrels!"

My playmates had scattered, such of them as were in shape to. I sprang to join my comrades—and on past them, before the gang could make the mistake of encountering that sword. Ginny got the idea straight off and doused her wand. Again it was strike and rip in the dark, foreign curses, screams of pain the same from any human throat, and a salt drunk-making taste of blood over my teeth.

A gong boomed. A pipe whistled on an eerie scale. Suddenly I panted and growled alone on the stairs. The opposition had fled. At a command?

Ginny joined me, a shadow, a touch, a oneness of woman-scents that poured through the reek and heat to call me back to sanity. The sword glimmered vague in her hand. "That was deuced selfish of you, Matuchek," he grumbled. "Not sporting at all. Not playing the game. When I haven't cloven a skull or even lopped off a leg in eight hundred years—"

The stairway shivered beneath us. I heard a dry rustle. The rank reptile stench flowed over me and into me. A deeper blackness unrolled. It hissed, geyserishly loud.

Ginny rekindled her star. Light glistened off the scales of a cobra. It poured down the steps, thick as two men, tail reaching behind the curve of the well, head well-nigh lost in the dark above us. Yet I saw the hood outspread, like monstrous blunt wings, the glitter of eyes, gleam of fangs, forked tongue that flickered in and out.

No therianthrope, I knew. A conjure. For an instant I cringed. From someplace unknown I rallied the will for a hopeless attack.

"No, Steve!" Ginny cried. "Back! This one is ours!"

I crouched stiff. "Down, Matuchek," Fotherwick-Botts ordered gleefully.

The nerve of him— Sheer resentment held me paralyzed while Ginny swept past.

The cobra struck. The sword whistled and thudded. The witch's wand flew back and forth in her left hand. Drops of venom bounced off it. Where they hit the steps, they left small pits.

Blood coursed from a wound in the cobra's nose. It gaped, as if

astounded. Again the sword bit, and again and again. A chunk fell off the hood. A gash opened in the belly scutes and gushed.

I howled my joy.

Abruptly the snake was gone, along with body parts and fluids. It had been plenty real. Air popped, rushing into the vacuum its mass left. Ginny and I stood alone in the star-glare of her wand.

"Well smitten, shield maiden," the sword said. "I must confess I didn't care for the notion of a woman wielding me, but you were a bally Brynhild, damme. My compliments."

"Thanks," she gasped. Sweat sheened on her face and darkened spots in her blouse. Both her weapons trembled slightly. Yet she stood fast, and added with a crooked grin, "I don't carry a shield, though, and as for the maiden part— Let's proceed."

We advanced to a corridor lined with doors. Abruptly it lay aglow in a mother-of-pearl softness which seemed to radiate from the air. The silence had become so absolute that we might have been the last creatures alive.

A tall, thin, stoop-shouldered man stood awaiting us. He had donned slippers, an embroidered robe, and a mandarin cap topped by a large spherical button. His hands were delicate, his fingernails very long, trimmed to points and polished. His head was bald or shaven. Despite the golden-hued skin and wispy white beard, the features beneath a brow like Shakespeare's, agelessly smooth, seemed almost too sharp to be Chinese. I know eyes don't really pierce, but damn if I didn't feel his.

"Good evening," he said, as quietly as a tiger might. His Oxford English bore the least, musical hint of another accent. "My apologies for this regrettable rowdiness. Had you notified me what caliber of opponents you are, your reception would have been properly dignified." *Yeah,* I thought, *and deadly. Unless you just decamped.* "However, as the learned Sun Tzu wrote, and later your Machiavelli, a test of strength is often the necessary prelude to meaningful negotiations. Shall we here call a truce?"

# XXV

Dr. Fu Ch'ing's private quarters were—well, it was as if the room where we talked reached impossibly vast, with lacquered pillars, gilt carvings, ivory-inlaid ebony furniture, silken hangings, scrolls of beautiful art inscribed with poems, and yet was a secret niche for gods and sorcerers to whisper in. He and Ginny sat in straight-backed chairs, a small table between them. The sword rested upright against a sculptured temple lion. I sprawled on a carpet whose rich hues my wolf eyes could not appreciate but whose texture caressed me. Incense wafted as faint and sweet as the twanging music, we knew not from whence.

After Ginny declined wine, mute servants brought tea and small cakes. She checked them with her wand, as unobtrusively as she could, before she took any; Fu smiled a tiny smile. I got mine in two bowls and lapped them up fast. Mainly I had a Sahara thirst, but the sugar took the blood taste out of my mouth and made me better able to listen to the conversation.

Elsewhere, no doubt, the highbinders were attending to each other's wounds. How many were they, anyway? No big number, surely; just enough to fight a holding action. Fu's operations extended across continents, but mostly they were subtle, a theft here, a spot of blackmail there, an occasional selective murder, a spell cast unbeknownst to the victim. We'd come this far by sheer bulling through.

He admitted as much. "I did not anticipate such a concentration of physical force in so small a band," he said impersonally, "and the goetics you employed is to a considerable extent, unfamiliar to me." He finished his tea and signaled for a refill. The barest pulsation went through his voice. "Fascinating. Might you possibly contemplate an alliance, or at least an exchange of information, honored colleague?"

"Sorry, I'm afraid not," Ginny replied.

"I should say not!" blustered Fotherwick-Botts. "With a Chinaman?"

"Down, boy," snapped Ginny. The sword gasped and gobbled but was too outraged to find words. "My apologies, Dr. Fu. What manners he didn't learn in the Middle Ages he acquired from leftover colonialists."

Fu sounded momentarily amused. "That is obvious, Dr. Matuchek." He went grim. "They are what I strive against, the hyenas and vultures preying on my poor China."

"Gad!" sputtered Fotherwick-Botts. "What's the world come to? Once upon a time, if anyone, let alone a native, used such language about Her Majesty's Empire, he'd've been horsewhipped on the steps of his club. Even nowadays—" He hesitated. "Er, do natives have clubs?"

"*Please* let me handle this," Ginny said. She made a small gesture at the sheath she'd removed, along with her cloak, which hung from a hook in the wall. It conveyed: If you don't, I'll shut you up good. He snorted but yielded. A sword can't turn purple and bulge the veins in its temples.

"Isn't your hostility a little obsolete, Dr. Fu?" she asked. "The Opium War and the Boxer Rebellion are long behind us. You have a native—um—all right, yes, a native dynasty back on the Imperial throne. Extraterritoriality has ended. The matter of treaty ports is being renegotiated. Why are you making such an effort?"

"China is still impoverished. Warlords, bandits, still run free in the hinterlands, aided by foreign adventurers and foreign gold. Trade with the outside is still through foreign ships, merchants, monopolies. Her voice still goes unheard in the councils of the world. My country, her ancient civilization, must become at least equal to the other great powers, Dr. Matuchek. At least equal."

My human part recalled vaguely that in its heyday the Middle Kingdom had regarded everybody else as barbarians, useless for anything except tribute. The Chinese were really no different from the rest of us.

"Can she only do this by undermining the West, Dr. Fu?" Ginny argued. "Frankly, I should think you'd better set your own house in order."

"The Emperor's government is going about that. But it is not enough." Fu's underplayed vehemence dropped down to a purr. "Did such rising nations as France in the Baroque period, Germany in the

modern era, or your United States in its expansion think in purely domestic terms? One cannot meaningfully bargain with a power greater than oneself; and no one willingly relinquishes power."

Ginny sighed. "As you like. Shall we leave the cosmic concerns and get down to business?"

He raised his brows and sipped his tea. "That is reasonable. I have only slight intimations of why you have broken in on us so unofficially."

She described the launch disaster and the traces of Asian demons at work. About Will she said nothing; that would have been to expose a hole card, not to mention a point of pain and vulnerability. "My husband and I learned you were in England, and thought we might find you when the regular forces couldn't. With the help of persons I won't name, other than our friend here—"

"Hrrumph," said Fotherwick-Botts.

"—we've come this far. What we'd like to know, Dr. Fu," said Ginny in a tone suggestive of a knife held to a throat, "is what you've been doing around Cardinal Point and what you propose to do in future. *If* you please."

Did that aristocratic face and mild voice faintly register surprise? "I regret that I cannot help you," he replied after a moment.

"Cannot, sir, or will not?"

Fotherwick-Botts made an ominous noise. I exposed a fang or two. "Like you, we would deplore any further violence," added Ginny butter-blandly. "Nor do we wish to take up more of your valuable time than we must."

Fu nodded. "I understand, Dr. Matuchek and gentlemen. But the fact is that I know nothing of this matter beyond what has appeared in the press. Indeed, since those discoveries that seem to indicate Eastern Beings have not been made public, you have given me my first news of them. Hence I am in no position to judge the validity of your inferences."

"Truly not?" Ginny persisted.

He shrugged. "I concede that doing your space program a mischief strikes me as an excellent idea. It is proper that China take leadership on the moon. But her own work will require several years more to reach fruition."

"You have a space program too?" she blurted. It had been a total secret.

"We propose to ride dragons. I would not reveal this now, save that the clues you deem you possess must have aroused suspicions and

your Centrum for Illicit Arcana will doubtless mount an intensive espionage operation, which will probably soon succeed. Clever, these Americans. But, no, my present venture into the Western world has had other purposes."

I saw and sensed the conflict within her. She didn't want to challenge his word outright. That would be useless, or worse. And yet—

He caught us off guard when he frowned, looked beyond her, ran fingernails through his beard, and whispered something. The implications of what she'd told him seemed to go further than he'd said.

However, he wouldn't readily yield. The razor gaze swung back to her. "Yes," he hissed, "you suspect me of a terminological inexactitude. How shall I persuade you otherwise? For my part, may I ask why I should make the attempt, why I should give you any cooperation whatsoever?"

Ginny tensed. "It will be to your advantage, Dr. Fu, very much to your advantage."

"Do you threaten my life, you three? I thought better of your intelligences." He glanced from her to me but, pointedly, not at Fotherwick-Botts. The sword harrumphed.

"No, sir," Ginny answered. "Your entire mission is spoiled. We offer you a chance to salvage what you can. But you've got to be quick."

"Ahhhh." He leaned back and stared impassively.

"I spelled a backup for us," Ginny explained. "If anything serious happens to me, phones will immediately scream at Scotland Yard, Military Intelligence, and the nearer police stations. They will anyway at a certain hour, which isn't far off now. With no advance warning, you and your gang might escape, barely, or might not. But I imagine it would be such a scramble that you'd leave the house loaded with leads to your whole organization. By speaking a certain word, I can postpone the moment."

That he showed no emotion was to be expected. Odd, though, how I could smell none of it from him. "My compliments, Dr. Matuchek," he murmured after a while, during which the music had only deepened the silence around us. "As the saying goes, you are a foe worthy of my steel."

Fotherwick-Botts harrumphed louder.

"Thank you," Ginny said. "You will understand, we can't in good conscience let you continue your subversions here. We shall have to bring in the authorities, and do so in time for them to find enough clues here to doom your mission."

The technicalities were beyond me, especially in my present form. But it should be obvious to any layman that removing every telltale object, smudge, and fluff of dust from the place, let alone every goetic trace, would take days.

"But I will give you a chance to escape with your men in an orderly way, taking along a few vital papers or whatever, and start for home, *if* you cooperate," Ginny finished.

I admired how quickly and calmly he came to decision. "Well done, madame. You have me in check. Best I resign before it is mate. There will be other games."

No American girl could forever match an unflappability that three thousand years of history had polished smooth. "You don't get out of this one unless you pay the fee," she snapped. "I want some proof that you aren't behind the Cardinal Point sabotage and, if you aren't, information about who or what is."

Again he sat silent. The music wailed low; the incense ghosted.

"Since time is limited, you must to a certain extent rely on my honor," he said at length. "I shall show you a synoptic record of my activities in England. It will argue that I and my followers were fully occupied. As for other knowledge—" Did I catch a hint of goodwill, however temporary? "It may be that, despite disagreements, we have a common interest, even a common cause."

I pricked up my ears. Ginny narrowed her eyes. "I had a hunch about that," she murmured. "If you've seen right away what it is, Dr. Fu, you're as brilliant as they say."

"They speak far too well of my humble abilities."

"They wish that were so." Ginny's slight smile faded. Her tone sharpened. "Your government is trying to expel the evil shen from your country."

" 'Kuei' is more correct, madame. The shen and kuei elements permeate the Wan Wu, or All. From the Jên part of the Wan Wu—one may say, very approximately, the human or conscious part—are derived, on the Yang side through the Three Spiritual Energies, the benign shen; on the Yin side, through the Seven Emotions, the kuei. The distinction resembles that between, on the one hand, fays, genii, angels, gods, and the like; on the other hand, devils, ghouls, goblins, vampires, and the like. I speak loosely, of course."

"I trust you do," said Ginny rather stiffly. In Chinese philosophy the Yang principle is male, the Yin female.

"Overlaps and interchanges occur. Is this not also true in your theology? Are not your devils angels who fell from grace, and do you

not speak of a person's evil genius? In like manner, sometimes 'shen' is used of all Beings derived from the Jên. But this is perhaps misleading."

"Thank you." Now Ginny sounded impatient. "Okay, your Taoist masters are exorcising or expelling—or whatever—the kuei throughout China. It's a long and difficult job—just hunting them down must be, and then overpowering them. But things can be made too uncomfortable and frustrating for them in their old haunts. Something similar is happening in Japan, right?

"Well, what are they to do? Where shall they go? No place else on Earth can they stay for long. They can't fit into the local paranature, which is as alien to them as a jungle and its animals would be to a polar bear. Modern, rationalistic, high-tech civilization is worse yet. What have you people expected would happen?"

"That those who were not soon destroyed by native Beings would seek wastelands, and gradually dwindle away to naught," Fu said. "What you have told me suggests that the masters have not thought these questions through to the end."

"Or else don't give a damn, as long as the demons are out of their hair," Ginny retorted. "In fact, some extra trouble wished onto us foreigners could give your government opportunities."

"It would not be altogether undesirable," admitted Fu.

"But it isn't working that way," Ginny said. "The shen—I mean the kuei, and the evil kami from Japan, and whatever else—they don't propose to perish slowly and piecemeal as your cat's-paws. If the Fair Folk can establish themselves on the moon, why not these too? That means keeping humans off it, out of space. In America the exiles have made a temporary alliance with some resident Beings who have it in for the white man. I suggest you look to your own space program. More may be going on in the background than you know."

"Oh, I shall," he replied most softly. "I shall."

"Doesn't this hypothesis fit the data?"

"Yes. It occurred to me when you had related your experiences."

"Then imagine the long-range consequences of the moon becoming a home, stronghold, and operating base of demons," Ginny hammered at him. "We want humans there, in strength, to head them off before they get well established. Does it really matter much which humans arrive first?"

"From a geopolitical viewpoint, it does."

I snarled. If we, the British, and the French had stood up to the Caliph at the outset, united, we could have squelched him then and

there. But no, we were each of us anxious to keep our particular trade concessions in the Near East, and to hell with anybody else's; while the Germans enjoyed seeing the bunch of us discomfited; and then suddenly it was too late, and people started getting killed.

"Yet some considerations are larger," Fu went on. "In what do you wish assistance, Dr. Matuchek?"

Ginny let out a breath. I lowered my head. This brought it near enough to the sword that he could mutter to me, "Bully for him. An Oriental, but a gentleman. I mind once in the Varangian Guard at Constantinople—" I raised a paw to shush him.

"You can tell me about the kuei," Ginny said.

"My dear lady," Fu protested, "you request the learning of half a lifetime's discipleship."

"You know what I mean. Practical, pertinent knowledge. I've been to the books. Now I need the kind of details that don't get into the books—everyday or everynight customs, habits, strengths, weaknesses, how to *fight* them."

Fu rose to his feet. "That is not really possible in completion. However, perhaps I can convey a few hints and ideas. This begins with proof of my bona fides." He nodded at me. "Will you . . . gentlemen excuse us for the nonce?"

They walked off together. Somehow, though I could not see an opening to any other room, they gradually vanished from sight and hearing.

"I say, aren't you going along?" asked the sword. I shook my head. They hadn't invited me.

"Well, I daresay milady can take care of herself," Fotherwick-Botts rumbled. "Still, I'd feel happier if you changed skin again. Old Norse term. Go human, d'you see? That Fu chap may or may not be trustworthy—mostly not—but what if his bloody henchmen take it into their dashed heads to set on us, eh? Can't very well wield me with paws and jaws."

I bared my teeth to indicate that I'd give an adequate account of myself.

"And leave me aside?" complained the sword. "Hogging all the sport, same's on the demmed ground floor? Not British, I must say. But then, you're a colonial, aren't you?

"Not your fault," he added after a minute. "Don't think I'm prejudiced. I mean, you didn't ask to be born overseas, did you? And what I hear about the American schools—never a caning— Well, I don't imagine the blighters will attack. Haven't the nerve. Reminds me of

when my then man, Thorgest Thorkelsson—Thorgest Mouth they called him, or sometimes Thorgest the Sleepmaker, because he would talk on and on—nevertheless a good man of his hands; once he and I made meat of ten Scots who thought they'd ambushed us; tell you about that later—he was off on a spot of raiding along the Irish coast, his ship and two others—"

I settled down. Listening was better than emptily waiting. A little bit better.

Afterward Ginny told me how Fu Ch'ing did indeed level with her, sort of. He didn't let her in on his schemes, of course, but the recording crystal that he activated for her showed enough rascalities that he could scarcely have had time for anything else. He went on to a hard, intense briefing on Far Eastern demonology. She would never become a Taoist or Shinto priest, with the associated knowledge and powers, but she acquired a lot of what she'd hoped for.

The time felt interminable, in spite of Fotherwick-Botts or because of him, before they returned. There was a remoteness in her expression; she had encountered a great deal of strangeness. Yet she spoke steadily: "You have done your share, Dr. Fu. Now I'll do mine." She waved her wand and uttered a word I didn't know. "I have postponed the message. You have three hours. I'm sorry to rush you, but I'm sure you understand."

He nodded, evidently recognizing the spell as valid. "It is sufficient. You are in the highest tradition of Machiavelli. Sun Tzu would also approve. Both men taught that one should always leave one's enemy a line of retreat."

She bowed. "You have been very helpful, learned sir."

He bowed back. "It has been a privilege and an honor, madame."

I thought of offering a paw to shake, but decided to sit on my haunches and dip my muzzle. "Pleased to've met you," rumbled Fotherwick-Botts. Ginny sheathed him and we departed. My final sight of Dr. Fu Ch'ing was as a silhouette, an outline of night, tall at the head of the stairs. Did *"Au revoir"* whisper around us as we descended?

The lobby lay deserted aside from bloodstains, tumbled furniture, and other signs of a fracas. We went forth into cold, dank air. Day was barely breaking, a paleness through the fog that dimmed the glimmer of the street lamps. We walked mute, Ginny lost in all that had been disclosed to her.

I turned human and got dressed at the railway station. The hotel porter whom we rang up to let us in gave us a surly glance. Bloody Yank toffs, carousing till dawn, he probably thought. But being English,

he reminded us of the hours when breakfast was served. We climbed the stairs to our room.

"Whoof!" gusted from me. I jerked open the drawer where we kept a bottle of Scotch. "To hell with breakfast. I'll settle for a stiff drink and sleeping till lunch."

Ginny had roused from her thoughts. "First we'll call home," she said. "We've been remiss about that."

I fetched two glasses, poured a hefty slug into each, and handed her one. "And then what?"

"Whatever moves fastest." She took a sip before she doffed her cloak and unslung the sword. "I'll tell you in detail later, as well as I can. Essentially, what I learned tonight shows that we can't put humans on the moon too soon."

"To croon a tune in June," I couldn't help throwing in. Seriously: "It won't happen through NASA."

"No. Especially since the . . . kuei and their allies aren't done with NASA by any means. Operation Luna— It wouldn't hurt to consult our friend." She drew the sword and laid him down on the bed.

"God's wounds and Satan's ballocks, what're you shilly-shallying about?" he rasped, going medieval again. "You want a simple broomstick that can make the crossing, what, what, what? I've gathered you're worried about wha'd'you-call-ems, Roentgen rays or something?"

"And stresses and a lot else," I said.

"Well, what you want is proper steel, by Jove, yes, proper steel, alloyed right and with the right spells on it, damme. Get the dwarves to forge it for you. Handy little beggars. Nobody does it like the dwarves. Made Sigurd's dragon-killer, they did, and Skofnung and Tyrfing—beastly ruffian, Tyrfing, but formidable—and others, including, ahem, m'self. Dwarves, yes, dwarves."

"We thought of that," I sighed. "Barney Sturlason, the big man behind Operation Luna—"

"*Hersir,* eh? Or baron, I s'pose. Damn these anachronisms! Too many centuries to keep track of."

"He made inquiries in Germany," I continued patiently. "It turns out that Nibelung Wunderwerke A/G has all the work it can handle. We'd have to wait a couple of years. Besides, there'd be no confidentiality with so large a company, and—"

"Yes, yes, yes! Do listen, will you? In my day, a subaltern who quacked such bally rot— Well. Hrrumph," said Fotherwick-Botts. "I forget you're colonials, and flinkin' civilians to boot. Also, I did misspeak myself. Admit it like a man. I did. 'Dwarves' was wrong. I meant

*a* dwarf, the dwarf who forged me, Fjalar. Excellent workman, as you can see."

My spine tingled. "He's . . . around? Available?"

"He Awoke some decades ago. Not doing much business. Doesn't want much. Independent chap. Select clientele. But I expect he'd be int'rested in your problem. I'll recommend it to him. Worth a try, any-how, eh?"

Ginny's voice throbbed. "How do you know?"

"Why, he's my maker, m'lady. How could I not?"

"Ah, yes," she breathed. "Sympathetic connection. You know, in-tuitively but surely—"

"I bloody *well* know. Same's I know that Gladstone scoundrel will be the ruin of England unless— No, he's been gone a while, hasn't he? I've only heard mention of him. But he seems to've inspired this upstart Labour Party—"

"Thank you," interrupted Ginny. "You've given us something im-portant to think about. Now we'd better call home and let them know we're all right, before they go to bed there."

"And we likewise here," I said through a mighty yawn.

Ginny resonated the phone. It came to life with Valeria's dear face. For an instant, she stared. Then tears burst forth. "Daddy, Mom, where've you been?" she cried. "Are you okay?"

My heart thuttered. "Sure, sweetheart. You see us, don't you? What's the trouble?"

"Th-they've arrested Uncle Will—they say he's behind th-the awful things—tried to *kill* you—and, and that grismal little Sneep, he— But Uncle Will! You've got to come back. Please!"

# XXVI

At this frantic end of the high season, every transatlantic flight was booked solid for days ahead. Ginny took a cab to Hampstead Heath, found a spot screened by bushes, and made heap big medicine. I don't know what it was, though since we'd packed light she remarked before leaving the hotel that it'd have to involve her owl pin, the sigil of Athene. When she came back to me and phoned the travel agency, there had been a last-minute cancellation—on Pan American, of course—and she got the seat. First class, expensive, but no matter. From New York it wouldn't be hard to reach Albuquerque and thence Gallup.

Two would have been a really tall order. Besides, I'd be more use overseas. I kissed her good-bye at the flyport that evening and returned to our quarters. On the way I read in a newspaper how an anonymous tip had sent the police to what seemed to have been the headquarters of a notorious international crime ring. The birds had flown, but left abundant clues and other evidence, including signs of a violent struggle. Chief Inspector MacDonald had told reporters only that the tip was of a nature to spur immediate action. He didn't know how much more he would become able to pass on; the government had quickly invoked the Official Secrets Act.

So far, so good. Lonely though the bed in the room felt, I damn near slept the clock around. When I unsheathed him to say good morning, Fotherwick-Botts declared he hadn't heard snoring like that since he fared with Eyvind Night-Thunder. One time in the Orkney Islands—

I headed off another war story: "We need to see this Fjalar guy pronto. How soon can you locate him?"

"Hard to tell. Sympathetic connection deuced vague, y'know.

Don't feel it at all unless I concentrate. Then, ha, hum, sense that he is alive, up and about, got a smithy somewhere in—in the high north, mountains, well offside. Beyond Nidaros, I'd say at a venture. Prob'ly Norway, unless they've tampered with the borders. Can't trust those shifty-eyed politicians, what? Not that those parts did much more than pay tribute to Harald Fairhair, when I left. Haven't been back since. Not up to date. Cruising to and fro on a silly broomstick, no, I'd never find him. On foot, come close enough, yes, I'll know. Wind him ten miles off at least. What we need to do, Matuchek, is get up a safari. Native bearers, beaters, guides, a shikari who knows the country. And gifts to hand out along the way. They used to like amber. Ivory not bad either, mostly walrus, some narwhal—"

"We haven't got a year!"

"No, we don't, do we? Snow falls early thereabouts, near's I recall. Hungry wolves a hazard and nuisance too— Ahem. Forgot you're a wolf. Sorry, old fella."

I was indeed a hungry wolf. "Let's let our brains do the walking," I said, suppressing the temptation to add: *Ahem. Forgot you haven't any. Sorry, old fella.* Yesterday, trying to be helpful while Ginny was out, I'd visited one of London's wonderful shops for such things and acquired a set of maps. She had laid a sensitizing spell on them. I unrolled a topographic of the upper Scandinavian peninsula and spread it on the floor, standing the sword against the wall nearby. "Suppose you study this while I eat breakfast. Work your, um, wits hard. See if any particular locale gives you a feeling." Before I babbled more or my stomach growled louder, I hurried off.

Bacon and eggs swimming in grease, cold dry toast with butter and marmalade, and a pot of coffee wrought their own miracle. The degree of optimism that arose in me strengthened as I reentered the room and Fotherwick-Botts bellowed, "I have it! Clear as a bell, by Jove! No, more like a hammer on a whacking great anvil. Haven't had so keen a Sense since the battle of—"

"Pianissimo, please." I shut the door. Excitement tingled through me. I squatted down by the map. As my finger tracked over it the sword directed me: "A bit to the right. . . . Up a quarter inch. . . . No, you bloody fool, too far."

As closely as we could identify it, Fjalar's workshop was in the Nordland of Norway north of Nidaros, which is Trondheim nowadays, somewhere in the unpeopled heights east of a village called Mo i Rana. *What and Frog?* I wondered fleetingly, then realized that the Spanish tags I'd collected in New Mexico had confused me.

The next several hours I spent making travel arrangements and shopping. I'd want suitable clothes and boots for a highland hike; to arrive as a wolf didn't seem practical. Besides, I couldn't carry a sword with me aboard a carpet, or even a ferry. Fotherwick-Botts must go as checked luggage, so I might as well pack him with the outdoor gear. A late flight to Oslo and a room there proved obtainable. I forfeited the day's rent in London and bused to Heathrow.

Seen from the air, the North Sea shimmered silver in a dusk that became night. Ships' running lights blinked forth against darkness like the stars overhead. The gibbous moon drew my thoughts to whatever unknown things were happening in yonder scarred badlands. I abandoned that for worry about my dear ones at home. It seemed nearly as distant.

But it still lay beneath daylight. I put a call through from the small, neat Norwegian hotel and got Ginny.

She looked worn-down, the cheekbones sharp in her face, eyes pale and shadowed. Regardless, she spoke crisply: "Will was arrested Monday morning. Val appealed to the Beckers and Hannah was kind enough to come stay here," our cleaning lady's mother, a fine person aside from spoiling the kids rotten whenever they got together. "I've just been through a sawtooth session with Bob Shining Knife. He doesn't like the situation either, but the evidence forced his hand. They checked gun dealers and learned Will bought a military rifle in Albuquerque the Saturday before the attack on us. The stolen carpet had been parked not far from his house, and analysis has identified spoor of him on it. They found the rifle shallowly buried in the desert—ballistic tests match it to the spent cartridges—and verified it was the one he'd bought. A mask and gloves were there too."

"Judas priest," I groaned. "What does he say?"

"Denies everything, Shining Knife tells me. I haven't seen him yet. Claims to have no recollection except that at those times he was on harmless errands or working with his lunar data or asleep. Feeling poorly, he slept a lot."

"How in the multiple names of God do they think he got past their surveillance or gimmicked that rug or shot so well or—the whole unholy mess? He's no wizard, mechanic, or marksman. And he wouldn't, for Christ's sake! You've known him all your life. I've known him for nigh on twenty years. This flat-out isn't *him*."

"Of course not," Ginny said slowly.

The notion I'd been evading these past three weeks circled behind me and slipped its cold knife into my spine. "Possession?"

"A demon could confer the abilities, falsify the memories, and . . . operate the machinery of him. He's agreed to a psychoscopy. Had to, under the circumstances. Otherwise they would have gotten a court order." Ginny's lips drew tight. "I don't know why I never caught so much as a hint of it when I tried. But anyhow, the process has started. It may take days."

Days of indignity, humiliation, sacrifice of privacy— Well, I'd been drafted into the Army during the war. "If he can be freed, cured, it's worth it," I said. "What more have you heard?"

"Barney's rallying his lawyers and whoever else might be useful."

"His Congressman?" I suggested.

"Not till we're desperate. We still have some hopes of keeping this from the media." She smiled starkly. "Although it is nice to know he's Barney's Congressman. At least, Barney owns about fifty percent of him."

That struck me as a little unfair to say of one of the few politicians whom I considered to be occasionally right-thinking. But underneath that armor of hers, Ginny needed every consolation possible. How I wanted to climb through the phone, crawl forth into our house, and hold her close!

I must settle for giving my love to the kids—Val and Ben were out at the moment, Chryssa still busy with her nap—and a progress report, such as it was. "We're off to Nordland in the morning," I finished. "I'll call again when I can, but if that isn't tomorrow, don't be afraid for me."

"I seldom am, Steve," Ginny said low. "Thank you for being what you are."

"Same to you in spades." Never mind the rest. In spite of everything, that night also I slept well.

Thursday's breakfast was infinitely superior to Wednesday's. None of your stingy Continental plates, either: a full smorgasbord, which would have filled Thor himself. Afterward, in the room, I called about a flight to Trondheim.

"I say," Fotherwick-Botts protested, "aren't we going to the museums here? Heard about 'em, I have. Not much for museums, unless milit'ry," as if he'd ever been in one, "but they've stuff from the old days before the Fairhair Raj, eh? Heard mention of a Gokstad ship. Think I may have known the very fella buried in her. Petty native king, Olaf, his name was. I'd be sure if I saw. Bring back memories, ha, jolly good battle at—"

"No time now," I interrupted hastily. "We're bound on safari, you know."

"Yes, yes. Track down old Fjalar. Won't we two have things to tell each other! Don't dawdle about like that, Matuchek. Get cracking."

A few hours later we were in Trondheim. It's a handsome provincial town on a large bay, surrounded by gently rolling countryside. The girl-watching is great, as it generally is in that part of the world. I only enjoyed those features incidentally, while buying more maps and renting a broom. Enough people knew English.

The land steepened fast as I flitted north. The way was long. The weather didn't help, low gray skies, chill headwinds, harsh rain showers. I got a bite to eat somewhere and arrived at Mo i Rana too exhausted to do more than register at the inn where I had a reservation and tumble into bed.

And when I woke, early though that was, the children were asleep at home. Very likely Ginny was too, after everything that yesterday had done to her. I had nothing to tell worth the risk of breaking her rest. Maybe by evening I would.

It shivered through me that today was the day of the hunt. I swung from underneath my comforter onto the wooden floor. Light streamed level through a window, bleak, broken by scudding clouds, but sunlight. Trees tossed their fading leaves in the wind. I heard the surflike rustle. It called me to be off, away, out of this vale and into those mountains.

# XXVII

The innkeeper spoke English after a fashion, but was of scant help. At first he didn't understand my inquiry, or pretended not to. When I pressed it, he mumbled, "Oh, yes. *Dvergen.*" My pocket dictionary had already told me this meant "the dwarf." Scandinavians tack the definite article onto the end of a noun. "Not Christian. Better keep avay." I pressed harder, until he waved a hand vaguely eastward. "Somevere t'at vay. *Hedensk troll,*" which I supposed meant "heathen troll."

He couldn't tell me of any actual harm Fjalar had done. Probably not everybody in town was as prejudiced. However, wandering the streets for a while, I saw nothing that looked like dwarf work, even in the tourist shops, just the usual cutesypoo wooden figures. To find a person willing and able to guide me might well take longer than my partner and I searching by ourselves. I loaded my luggage and the sword, well swaddled, onto the broom, hopped aboard, and took off for the general area.

It was rugged and steep, grass growing mostly in pale tufts and tussocks between lichenous rocks, dwarf birch and willow scattered around. Cloud shadows and sunlight raced over it on a chilly wind that smelled of moss and animal spoor. We were about twenty miles below the Arctic Circle. Footpaths twisted and hikers had left their traces, but I saw no one else. Vehicles were required to land only at designated spots. I obeyed, parking on the highest, because I had no wish to draw the attention of any ranger or whoever patrolled. A map in my pocket and compass in my left hand were plausible, but Fotherwick-Botts unsheathed in my right would have taken some explaining.

Clear to see, Fjalar didn't want casual visitors. I zigzagged for most of the long day, peering and sniffing, and still wouldn't have

found him without the sword's help. At first his intuition was pretty vague. We cast to and fro, trending aloft. I gasped and sweated and was damn glad to stop a while and eat the sandwich I'd brought. On the plus side, the effort and the pulse thudding in my ears muffled Fotherwick-Botts' reminiscences. Now and then he broke off to exclaim, "Ha, caught something there!" I'd relax my arm and let him be a dowsing rod. In this wise, we slowly narrowed down the direction—until he whooped, "Tally-ho!" and guided me along a faint and narrow trail. Presently I caught a whiff of sulfury smoke and the sound of iron clanging on iron.

Light streamed level from the west. The wind had stiffened and the chill deepened. I climbed onto a small, flat patch of grass and boulders. A spring bubbled. Ahead of us loomed a stony bluff. A cave gaped at the bottom. Above that mouth was chiseled a runic inscription. Not noticeably weathered, it couldn't be more than a few decades old. Pieces of slag, rusty scrap, and other junk littered the ground beneath. The smoke blew from over the top.

"Whe-ew!" I gusted. "At God damn last." My legs ached, my lungs heaved, my heart thuttered, visions of armchairs and fireplaces and hot toddies danced through my head.

"Hullo in there!" Fotherwick-Botts shouted. "I say!" He switched to Norwegian—no, not exactly Norwegian—*oh, sure,* I thought, *the Viking Age version.* He'd mentioned having learned Norman French between the Conquest and the time when he fell Asleep, but that wouldn't be any use here. Nor, apparently, was the English he'd acquired after he Awoke and lay sheathed with nothing to do but listen, year after year after year. It crossed my mind—I'd been too busy to think of it earlier—how cruel and ungrateful it would be to return him to that cabinet.

A figure appeared in the cave entrance and stepped forth. "Haa, Fjalar," my companion boomed.

The other halted warily. He was a dwarf, all right. I'd seen plenty of pictures of the German ones, who were getting rich and zipping around on their Mercedes and whooping it up on the Riviera in between jobs. This guy seemed more Nordic. He stood maybe four feet tall, but wider and thicker than me, sheer muscle and massive bone under the hairy hide. Below an unkempt blond mane and untrimmed hedgerow of brows squinted little blue eyes and jutted a majestic red cucumber of a nose. His ears were almost as big. Beard spilled down to his bellybutton. He wore a leather apron over coarse gray woolen tunic and britches, cross-garters on the stumpy calves, and wooden shoes.

Everything was sooty, spark-scorched in places. My own nose doubted that he ever bathed.

Old-fashioned, yeah. He didn't come outdoors unarmed. But not a stick-in-the-mud. Instead of a spear, he carried a sawed-off shotgun.

He lowered it. His voice rolled hoarse, deep as a bear's. Yet I heard surprise, and saw it on him. "Haa-hei. Brynjubítr?" The sword's original name, I recalled.

Suddenly those two were jabbering away in that archaic language. Wind whistled and bit, shadows lengthened, I visualized the hot toddy as being followed by a hot buttered rum.

In the end, Fjalar gestured with a powerful hand. "We're invited for tea," Fotherwick-Botts told me. "Rather an honor. He's not a very sociable bloke. Never was. But I am his handiwork, y'know. Old tool tie. Besides, you int'rest him. He wants to know more."

Weariness washed from me on a tide of hope.

I must hunch over to get through the cave entrance. A downward passage led to a big room. A fire leaped and crackled on a hearthstone at the middle, coals glowed near a forge at the far end, but the air, though warm and odorous, and the hewn-out stone walls were clean. Somehow smoke found its way straight up to exits overhead. Sand covered the floor. I couldn't see very well in the uneasy red light, but made out a table and several chests, beautifully carpentered and intricately carved. Slabs of dried meat, salt fish, and flatbread hung from hooks in the ceiling. More stuff filled the rear half of the room. Besides the forge, I recognized three large kettles, an upright loom, a stack of metal ingots, and a pile of firewood. Most, though, was lost to me among the unrestful shadows.

Fjalar pointed to a chest by the table, which obviously doubled as a bench. I sat down, my knees not far beneath my chin. He took Fotherwick-Botts—or Byrnie-biter, or whatever name suited best here—and drove his point into a chopping block, which he set on the table opposite me. "Positions for well-born guests," the sword explained. "A rough chap, Fjalar, but a pukka sahib at heart."

The dwarf brought refreshments. "Tea" turned out to be mead, poured from a clay jug into silver-rimmed horns. He raised his, sketched a T above it with his free forefinger, rumbled, "*Skaal,*" and tossed it off.

"Drink up," Fotherwick-Botts urged. "Mustn't insult his hospitality, y'know. I can't drink, but you will for both of us like a good fella, what?"

Dubiously, I swallowed, then wished I could have gone more

slowly. This was excellent, not the sticky-sweet muck I'd known under the name of mead but dry and pungently herb-flavored. Maybe the Vikings weren't quite such raving barbarians as I'd been taught. While Fjalar dragged another chest across for himself, I asked, "What was that sign he made over his glass—his horn?"

"The Hammer." Fotherwick-Botts sounded slightly embarrassed. "For Thor, y'know. His notion of saying grace. Always was a stubborn sort. Doubt he'll ever convert. But a heart of stout gold."

Seated, Fjalar refilled. This time gulping wasn't obligatory, which was a vast relief. The first draught had set the bees that made the honey buzzing through my brain in search of more clover. I was afraid they'd find some.

It didn't help much that I could catch hardly a word of the conversation. Those voices roared happily on while my glance went oftener and oftener toward the hanging meat. Its smell wafted strong, wild, delicious. I had my lens along, of course, and in this low illumination could easily become wolf, jump, and—

No, that'd probably seem ill-bred. As Fjalar was wetting his whistle for the sixth or seventh time I broke in: "Look, this is all very well and I realize you two have a lot to catch up on, but could we talk business for a while? Like maybe over a bite to eat?"

"Eh? Oh—oh, yes. Sorry," replied Fotherwick-Botts. "Got a bit carried away, I fear. Didn't even properly introduce you. These surroundings— Too easy to go native when one can't dress for dinner, what?"

He spoke to Fjalar, who nodded vigorously, belched a laugh, and smote the table so that the horns leaped and the jug nearly toppled. The dwarf tossed a sentence at me, which the sword rendered as: "Yes, he meant you no dishonor, and trusts you won't call him to *holmgang.*"

"To what?" I asked.

"Quaint custom in his day. Duel, y'know. Pref'rably fought on an islet, to get away from the hoi polloi. Ground's staked off with willow wands and the two chaps chop at each other by turns. If you're forced outside the bounds, you've lost. Or if you're killed, of course. Much better killed. Terrible disgrace, being forced out. But if you die with a quip on your lips, like, er, um—like 'Ax me no questions'—haw, pretty good, that, for a version in modern English, and no advance notice—may have a touch of skaldic talent m'self, who knows?—if you die well, you've not really lost, because men will remember you and quote you. Fjalar would be sorry to do you in. He's curious about what you have to say."

I considered those wide shoulders and long arms. "Oh, no," I answered. "No offense taken. None whatsoever. Especially from such a, uh, gracious host. And I really do want to talk with him."

The sword translated. I think the dwarf smiled, though it was hard to tell through that shrubbery. He spoke again, rose, and went off. "To fetch dinner," Fotherwick-Botts told me. "No wife, no servants. Crusty old bachelor sort. And a confirmed pagan. But a gentleman at heart."

Tableware proved to be wooden troughs. Dinner was meat hacked off and seared in the fire, together with plenty of hardtack and a fresh jug of mead. Fjalar cut his ration with a horn-handled knife. I unfolded my Swiss Army and went to work. It fascinated him. We spent minutes going over its features. I sensed him warming to me. When at the meal's end I gave it to him, he definitely beamed. By way of napkins, one licked one's fingers. By way of entertainment, the sword described a battle or two he'd seen. In Old Norse.

That became a long night, short though it still might be at this latitude. Yet I lost any wish for sleep. Detailing the discussion as it went through our interpreter would take a book by itself. Ignoring the asides, that-reminds-mes, crude jokes, and fumbles at understanding what a speaker had meant—and taking what I told for granted—here's the gist.

When Fjalar had first Woken it was tough for a while. He didn't know what to make of steamboats on the fjords, railroads down the valleys, broomsticks overhead, towns grown huge and built of peculiar materials, lights shining brilliantly at any hour, the whole country. However, you recall that the dwarves were better off than most Beings. Cold iron never bothered them, which means that electromagnetic fields never did. They went to Sleep simply because the paranatural ecology and dwellers were gone and contemporary humans seldom wanted their skills—rather, shunned them. Besides, having cold iron everywhere did interfere with those skills, for instance, the making of enchanted swords. The dwarves laid in supplies against the day when their dreams would inform them they once more had a chance of employment.

Earlier, they'd worked alone or in small groups, generally of brothers. Their wives stayed in the background, when they had any, and their children were few. That's usual among creatures that don't age beyond maturity but will live till they suffer a fatal accident, deadly violence, lethal sorcery, or the end of the world, whichever comes first. Now the German dwarves saw the situation was different. Being German, they studied it, incorporated, and were soon negotiating lucrative contracts.

Most of their Scandinavian kin moved south to join them. A handful of individualists hung on at home. Fjalar was one.

His wants were modest, whether or not he was. Mainly he liked practicing his craftsmanship in his own way at his own pace. The runes above the cave mouth translated, roughly, as

WEAPONS AND WONDERS TO ORDER
(IF I FEEL LIKE IT)
MAKE ME AN OFFER

His trade was therefore mostly with other Beings, who'd all Awakened to a need of things—fays; nisser; actual, roughneck trolls; an occasional *femme fatale* (not to him) huldre; the Wild Hunt, stopping by to get its horses reshod or a fresh stock of arrowheads—all one to him. None of them were menaces nowadays, not really, and the majority meant well. They paid him in kind or in gold or in services of their own.

Just the same, I could see why his reputation among local humans wasn't the best. They didn't advertise his presence, and they put on social pressure against visiting him. Some people did anyway. Since few of them knew Old Norse and he was apt to grump at those too, little business resulted. Oh, a certain amount; that was how he'd come by things like his shotgun, his hacksaw, his calipers, the tobacco pipe he lit after dinner, and a taste for Scotch whisky.

But he preferred to stay obscure. It helped that another dwarf, farther south, had set himself up to draw the tourist trade with demonstrations, a gift shop, a restaurant, and attractive young ladies who gave lectures on folklore.

Nevertheless Fjalar listened to me, ever more intently. The mead that gurgled down meanwhile blurs my memory a little. I do recollect him saying, earthquake-deep, and Fotherwick-Botts for once giving me a straightforward rendition: "Moon, you will not be seen from here tonight. But Garm shall not devour you, not yet."

The idea of space travel grabbed him like a lustful lover. "*To ride where Sleipnir runs—*" Also, it behooved any man of spirit to take arms against the hosts of Loki, unless he was on Loki's side. Stave off Ragnarok. . . . The theological technicalities escaped me. I could, though, describe the engineering difficulties. After that he was mine.

Yes, by Thor, he'd come to my homeland and work for me! I was a proper hero, I was, right out of the good old saga days, when many of the top warriors had been werewolves or werebears or wereseals or

whatever; and my wife, she sounded like a real Valkyrie, she did; and what I'd told about the worlds beyond Midgard, well, he realized he had much to learn, but he'd enjoy that—evidently the *Edda* hadn't gone into enough detail about what the gods fashioned from Ymir's body; and as for the broomstick we needed, yes, he'd have to think and tinker, but belike an alloy such as had gone into Brynjubítur, with maybe a pinch more dragon-bone charcoal and eagle dung, plus a spell such as had powered the spear Gungnir—

He hugged me. My ribs ached for three days.

Practicality reared its ugly head. "How're we going to bring him there without endless bureaucratic paperwork that's bound to alert the enemy?" I worried aloud.

"Fly him over the bally pond, what else?" Fotherwick-Botts replied.

"Not that simple. Since the war, the U.S. has maintained strict border controls. Watch-spells everywhere. Any transport approaching, air, water, or ground, gets challenged and has to identify itself and its passengers at a checkpoint. Fjalar's status, I guess you can't call it out-and-out treyf, but it's not strictly kosher either."

Since the matter doesn't often come to public attention, maybe I should explain that the Beings play billy hell with immigration laws. The ethereal types flit to and fro across frontiers as they please, seldom even aware of them. Besides, what is their legal standing? They're not human. Governments want them under a degree of control, including protection for them from evildoers. In the U.S., Congress settled on declaring them endangered species; and lawyers may file class action suits on their behalf, which lawyers have been doing with an enthusiasm that increases as they see how much money can be involved.

Dwarves, however, are as corporeal as you and me. Do they count as human? They have the same basic shape and psychology. It isn't their fault if they can't interbreed with us and don't grow old. The German dwarves quickly arranged to become subjects of the Kaiser, later citizens of the Republic, and our State Department perforce recognizes this. But Fjalar had never bothered to do anything similar. He wanted no part of the modern state.

"And we'd have to get him a green card before he could work for us," I muttered into the dregs of my last mead. Which one that was, I don't know. I'd lost count.

"Ridiculous," Fotherwick-Botts snorted. "No such thing in good King Edward VII's glorious days. Can't we smuggle him in? Good

cause, after all, trying to save the bloody colonials in spite of themselves."

"How? Oh, we can probably catch a flight from Oslo to New York or Los Angeles in a few days if we phone ahead, but—"

Fjalar interrupted, wanting to know what was going on. The sword explained. Fjalar sneered through his beard and said this was no problem. He'd built a ship that, frictionless, sailed as fast as the wind. She lay hidden in a cove of the nearest fjord.

"I'm afraid that to cross the Atlantic in acceptable time, we'd need a wind of more than hurricane force," I sighed. "And no ordinary broom can make that long a trip without recharge. Also too slow. And in either case we'd run into the border ward. No, we've got to put you on a regular flight, Fjalar. But the paperwork—"

"What is this paper?" the dwarf asked. "Let me see."

The best I could do was haul forth my passport. "This admits me to my homeland without question." He took several minutes to examine it, while the fires sank low and exhaustion overtook me.

At length he grinned and said, through the sword, "Why, this is only paper and a picture with marks on them. Show me what they must be—the Christian writing—and I will try what I can do."

I scrawled on a sheet off a notepad I carried. Fjalar took pity and led me to a bed of heaped sheepskins. He seemed tireless. Well, I'd worked twice or thrice around the clock myself on this or that technical puzzle. At the moment I was happy to collapse. I never felt the vermin.

I woke itchy from their bites, ravenous again, when a booklet flapped under my nose. And coffee was brewing, coffee! Bleary-eyed, I turned the pages. It was a perfectly valid-looking blue-bound United States passport, complete with photograph and the name *Dvergen Fjalar,* born in Norway at a plausible date, naturalized, et cetera, et cetera. "D'you see?" Fotherwick-Botts crowed. "Told you, didn't I? Splendid workmen, these dwarves. They can forge absolutely anything."

# XXVIII

We discussed plans over breakfast, which consisted of stockfish, flatbread, and that brown soap the Norwegians call goat cheese. Fjalar said he'd need the rest of today and tomorrow to make his arrangements. That was reasonable. He must pass out word to his assorted patrons that he'd be gone an indefinite while. Likewise it was reasonable that he take along the essential tools of his trade. However, when he wasn't content with hammer, tongs, runic whetstone, and such, but went on to anvils and cauldrons, we began a long wrangling session. I finally convinced him that if he required stuff so big and heavy, Barney Sturlason could have it fetched.

Leaving the sword with him for company, I found my way back to our broom, flitted to the hotel, had a late dinner, and turned in.

When the innkeeper next morning asked disapprovingly whether I'd located the dwarf, I said no, but I'd had a nice hike and campout. This was Sunday, but in tourist season enough shops were open for me to buy various items I figured we might want. Back in the room I used the phone to make travel reservations and call home with a very guarded account of what I'd accomplished.

Ginny said things were looking more hopeful for Will. The kids chattered about what we could do together in the all too few days between my return and the start of school. That was kind of heartbreaking, as busy as I expected to be. I vowed to myself I'd find some free time somehow. After we'd signed off I took a side trip to Svartisen, the glacier that's the main local attraction. The name means "The Black Ice" and it is in fact pretty grimy, but the hollows and crevices are a lovely blue.

Early on Monday I met Fjalar and Fotherwick-Botts at the high

parking lot as agreed. His luggage not only crammed the coffer, some must be lashed on top. I slipped the sword into a carrier bag and took out one of the things I'd gotten yesterday, the most adorable child-size fake-medieval costume. Fjalar made a noise of nausea. I made gestures and growled. At last I got him into it. His muscular build split the jacket up the back and the pants up the seat, but the mantle more or less hid this.

My thought was that an unreconstructed old-type dwarf would draw too much notice, too many questions. Now, I hoped people would assume he was bound for a pageant. Norwegians love pageants. They might even assume the nose and shag were fake and he a midget. Having shown him to his seat and buckled his safety belt, I climbed aboard. The overloaded broom lurched into the air.

He enjoyed the flight to Trondheim, bouncing and bellowing at the sights. If he'd made this sort of trip before, it would have been at night, maybe riding pillion with the Wild Huntsman. Not being stupid, he did keep quiet at the flyport while I turned in the rental and got us onto a domestic carpet for Oslo. After we took off, he was glued to a pavilion window till I hauled him back for landing. I'd reserved at a big hotel nearby, where the staff would have seen everything and be blasé. Nevertheless I must fend off several well-intentioned remarks and glimpsed a number of raised eyebrows. We went to our room and stayed there, ordering dinner sent up. Fotherwick-Botts told me the dwarf didn't like the food—not enough meat, too much green garbage—and complained the beer was thin. He demanded Scotch. I shuddered at the Norwegian price of a bottle, but it quieted him.

Mostly I was occupied with scissors, needle, and thread. Fjalar's costume had worked so far, but it'd make U.S. passport control wonder. I'd bought an outfit for a full-grown man with shoulders, waist, and thighs like his, as well as I could gauge. Now it had to be cut down to length. That including making the sleeves short, or his arms would pop them and stick out three inches past the cuffs. I'm no tailor, but I'd perforce learned a little sewmanship in bachelorhood and the Army; and nobody expects much of blue jeans and a khaki shirt. Fjalar griped that the socks itched and the shoes pinched. I told Fotherwick-Botts to give him a lecture on the stiff upper lip and biting the bullet.

Our flight to Los Angeles left Tuesday afternoon. I could have gotten an earlier one, but it would have been on SAS. Scandinavian attendants would soon have realized I was traveling with a sho'-nuff dwarf, and might have felt obliged to report this to the U.S. authorities. Americans probably wouldn't. So we lay low till departure time. Well,

in Hollywood I'd grown used to hanging around idle between takes or in producers' offices, while "Hurry up and wait" is the motto of the Army. As for Fjalar, he scribbled runes and diagrams on a sketchpad I'd obtained at his request, when he wasn't staring into space. The engineering of our moonboat—I knew the syndrome well.

The transatlantic flight was cattle-car crowded but endurable. Fjalar received no more than slightly puzzled looks. He was indignant that he hadn't been allowed to carry his bottle of Scotch with him and that I'd only spring for so much en route. More would have gotten conspicuous. But then the movie they showed enthralled him. Fortunately, he didn't understand the sappy dialogue. Me, I'd found a paperback about the Irish revolution and how de Valera raised pookas against the British. We both broke off to watch Greenland pass beneath us, austere and majestic.

Given the mob debarking at Los Angeles, Fjalar's passport got him by with no worse than a quizzical glance. I'd counted on that. Customs gave us a bit of trouble. With all his baggage, I couldn't well have checked "Nothing to declare" on his form. However, here too they were overworked. It was easiest to accept my explanation that the ironmongery was heirlooms and that my poor friend, besides being stunted, was deaf-mute. We'd practiced a few convincing-looking sign language gestures. Pity played its part in letting us through.

Again we must struggle with luggage and clerks, and then wait for our flight to Albuquerque. How I envied the Vikings. All they had to do was board ship, sail off, loot, and kill. Fjalar tugged my arm and pointed to his open mouth. I yielded, took him to a bar, and paid flyport prices for uncounted Scotches while I nursed a beer. They didn't seem to affect him much, though doubtless excitement had something to do with that. Nor do dwarves get hangovers, as far as I know. Lucky little bastards.

Dog-tired, malodorous, and unshaven, that evening I stumbled into Albuquerque International and Ginny's arms. The kids were there too. "Will is free," she whispered on my ear. "For the time being, at least." Happiness soared in me. For the time being, at least.

Fjalar and Fotherwick-Botts kept the children noisily occupied throughout the flit to Gallup. That is, the dwarf was silent but a sight to marvel at, while the sword told of battles, answered questions in excruciating detail, and harrumped avuncularly at exclamations. Meanwhile, in front, Ginny soft-voiced filled me in on events.

"Will would have joined us to welcome you, but he's utterly wrung out," she said. "They released him only yesterday. Besides, no doubt

a skulk of Fibbies would have tailed him. I'm as glad not to have them underfoot, aren't you?"

"More than glad." I gulped at the thought of what grief we might well have had on Fjalar's account. "We've got to keep the dwarf as close to invisible as inconspicuous will go, till we've made our arrangements and secured them." Against ghosties and ghoulies and long-nosed governments and things that go boomp at inconvenient times.

She nodded. "I rather expected that, from your hints on the phone, and encouraged Will to stay behind. Poor old dear."

"He, uh, he tested clean?"

"Absolutely, through every probe and exorcism they brought to bear. Oh, a certain faint aura of something undefined—I've caught it myself—but that's to be expected, considering his relationship to the Fair Folk."

"The inquisitors admit he's innocent?"

"No." Light from the nearly full moon showed her face gone as bleak as her voice did. "I heard babble about some kind of possessing spirit unknown to science, able to lie so deep, so dead, that none of our tests can touch it. Asian? But their references give them no information. I suggested a judicious application of common sense. Probably what won them over was judicious application of Nornwell's lawyers. In the end, it wasn't quite necessary to get a writ of habeas corpus."

"Uh, um, the physical evidence?"

Now she sighed. "Aye, there's the rub. Ordinarily, pretty damning. But in a case like this, where cunning, powerful Beings about whom we know very little are at work, the clues may well be a red herring."

"A frame-up?"

She chuckled harshly. "Framing a herring? To hang on the wall? Well, seriously, we do know the saboteurs have had *some* human ally. Implicating somebody else would protect his identity and prolong his usefulness, plus destroying the victim's. The gun dealer recognized Will's picture but would have had no way of knowing whether what he dealt with was a Seeming. Et cetera, et cetera. I put it to Bob Shining Knife: Wouldn't he and his people do better to set Will aside and go actively in search of the other parties involved, who remain on the loose?"

"How much did you tell him about our English expedition?"

"Barely enough. That we'd tracked Fu Ch'ing by proprietary methods, and Bob didn't really want to try for a court order that we reveal Guild secrets I'm sworn to keep, and we decided the trouble hereabouts has not been Fu's doing. The FBI knows about the anonymous tip and

the raid on those quarters, of course. What was found there doubtless tends to bear me out. I'm pretty sure Bob put in a word of his own on behalf of my brother.

"The upshot is that Will's free under bond and under surveillance. He must have permission to go anywhere more than fifty miles from Gallup. In other words, he's still a suspect—as an accomplice, if nothing else—and we still have to prove his innocence."

I glanced over my shoulder at the cold orb behind us. "For that," I muttered, "we probably need to land somebody on the moon, fast."

Fotherwick-Botts supposed I'd looked his way. "Ah, Matuchek," he blared, "want to hear, eh? As I was telling the children, there we were at Brunanburh, a thin hairy line—"

Eventually the lights of Gallup twinkled ahead of us. We landed at our house, unloaded the baggage, and went in. Fjalar promptly kicked off his shoes, ripped off his socks, and left tracks of ingrained soot across the carpet. Short, shaggy, redwood-burly, he fitted in that Southwestern American room about as well as an orangutan would. Edgar squawked. Svartalf bottled his tail.

The dwarf rumbled something. Ginny had drawn Fotherwick-Botts and stood him against the sofa. "He expects food and drink," the sword explained. "Chieftainly hospitality, y'know. And a gift worthy of him. Haven't got a gold arm-ring or some such thing lying about, have you?"

I went to the kitchen for a salami and a couple of beers. The drink poured straight down. Fjalar gave me a meaningful look. I resigned myself and fetched a bottle of Scotch. Glenlivet, it was, for appreciative small sips on special occasions. He glugged it much the same as the beer.

Afterward he belched, beamed, and made a remark to Valeria, who stood as hypnotized as Ben. (Chryssa was nodding off and Ginny preparing to tuck her belatedly in.) "Before we retire," Fotherwick-Botts interpreted, "Fjalar asks if your charming daughter would like to do him the honor of picking the lice out of his hair."

I'd failed to warn Ginny to lay in bug powder. "That, that's not the custom these days," I stammered, while Val giggled and said, "I'd better not tell any of the boys at school. They might get ideas."

The sword must have been tactful, whatever tact meant between those two—a four-letter word, I think—because the dwarf accepted the refusal cheerfully enough but stood expectant. I remembered about the gift. Thinking fast, I trotted to my study and brought back a carved meerschaum pipe, the last souvenir of my smoking days. My father

had given it to me and I'd miss it, but Fjalar obviously saw it as a kingly treasure. Okay, we needed all the goodwill we could collect.

I showed him to the guest room. Light switches were easy to demonstrate, but the adjoining bathroom took a while. Not that he didn't quickly get the hang of it. He wanted to know all about the engineering.

Around midnight I was able to join Ginny in our own bed. Neither of us slept well from then till morning. Several of the lice had accompanied me.

# XXIX

Things can move fast when money and determination like Barney Sturlason's push them. The next month or so stands in my memory like a string of sun-flashes, events, on a rapidly flowing river. The stream has its eddies, currents, and cataracts—no two days the same—but those brilliances blur the sight of it.

Will came around the afternoon following our return. He was gaunt and pale, he spoke barely above a whisper, his hands trembled slightly. "Rough go, huh?" was the best I could find to say as I let him in the door.

"Nothing abusive," he answered. His look evaded mine. "No torture, no bullying. But it went on and on, and in and in . . . and, and always I was afraid they'd find something—"

"Then they'd've freed you of it, wouldn't they? As for your personal secrets, I can't imagine you having any they'd think odd—barring your moon experiences, which weren't personally personal, if you follow me—and, though I don't like giving the government any credit, my understanding is that those guys keep confessions under seal same as priests or doctors. Now come in, man, have a drink, meet a couple of really odd characters, and hear about our gallivantings."

Fjalar and Fotherwick-Botts were guaranteed to take anybody's mind off his troubles, though doubtless it was a kind of shock therapy. "I'm setting up the spells to cram modern English into him," Ginny explained. "It's tricky when he's not Homo sapiens."

Will frowned slightly. Already his morale and strength were on the rise. He and the dwarf had lit their pipes and were companionably smogging the room. "Is that method ever satisfactory?" he asked.

"With humans, as a rule, no," Ginny replied. "They acquire a mere jumble of verbal reflexes, like parrots."

Edgar bristled on his perch. "Gruk, gruk," he objected. "Nevermore."

"I wasn't referring to ravens," Ginny told him. "Although they, like people, do have to grow into a language, experience it, to reach understanding. That's why instruction in the schools makes little or no use of goetics. Fjalar, however, is of paranatural stock, and has been involved with goetics all his long life. Once I've established the proper system, he should acquire English fast—his version, at any rate, whatever it proves to be."

As he listened to our story, of which he'd so far heard only the barest outline, Will revived more and more. "Then you have learned something about the nature of the ultimate enemy?" His voice shivered.

"Something." She spoke slowly. "I'm not certain what most of it implies. Fu Ch'ing was right, it takes a lifetime of study, asceticism, spiritual dedication, to gain mastery. Not common Western virtues nowadays, especially in me. I'll want to confer with you often."

"We'll want you for more than that," I added. "If we're to keep this project guardable—against demons, politicians, bureaucrats, and the news media—we have to keep it small, minimum personnel and everybody trustworthy. We can sure use your scientific skills. Not just your 'scope, though I daresay it's got important discoveries yet to make. Your knowledge of astronomy, physics, instrumentation— Are you willing?"

He stared at me the way Dante must have stared at Beatrice, Beatrice in Heaven. "Oh, yes. Oh, yes."

The doorbell rang next morning. Ginny was shut away in session with Fjalar. Val answered it. From my study, where I was trying to relate al-Bunni's design sketches to what the dwarf had seemed to propose, I heard her soft cry, "You, sir? P-please come in." Respectfulness like that, out of her, had *meaning.* I made haste to the living room.

Balawahdiwa waited there, dressed in plain shirt and Levi's, grizzled hair falling from a headband past the strong-boned face, an Indian such as you might see anywhere. But Val stood practically at attention before him, Svartalf very quietly a little behind, while Edgar had lowered his head and spread his wings. Maybe I felt what they felt even more. It was like wide skies and ancient lands and the silence that lies beneath all sound.

"Welcome." A snatch of Zuni came back to me. "*Keshi.* This is a, uh, a wonderful surprise."

He smiled and shook hands in ordinary style, but graveness tolled in his words. "*Elahkwa.*" I knew that meant "Thank you" and figured he wasn't showing off but had excellent reason to start with it. He continued in English: "Glad to see you home again. Your wife visited me while you were gone and told me as much as she knew then, but plain to see, much more has happened since."

"And you'd like to hear? Certainly. Do have a seat. Let me call Ginny and start coffee and, uh—"

"And introduce me to your friends, I hope," he said, taking a chair.

"Sure. Of course. Come to think of it, Val, you handle the coffee, okay? Just a minute, please." Collecting my wits as best I could, I went to knock on Ginny's studio door and tell her. She replied that she and Fjalar would be out as soon as possible. You can't safely break off in midspell.

On the way back, I fetched Fotherwick-Botts. We kept him sheathed in my study closet, having explained that if visitors saw him and marveled word would soon get around. For entertainment we left a book, which Ginny had 'chanted to read itself aloud in a low voice—Kipling's verse. He was happy.

I felt a tad anxious as I bared him in the living room, but needn't have been. He knew warriors, wizards, and wise men when he met them. "My salute, sir!" he barked in lieu of actually giving one; and after I introduced him he said, "I am honored, sir," with never a word about battles or natives.

The priest quickly drew us into talk. He could put people at their ease when he wanted to, no matter how serious the business. I'd answered a few questions about our doings in England and begun on my Norwegian travels when Val came in with a tray of coffee and cookies. Ben trailed her, bug-eyed. He'd been playing a reckoner game in his room, but unlike too many kids these days, he preferred reality. Chryssa was at the nursery center where twice a week she played with children her age.

"Thank you," said Balawahdiwa as the girl set his refreshments before him. His gaze captured her. I had a feeling it went deep and deeper. She stepped back, breathing harder, half scared but shoulders braced. Ordinarily Svartalf would have attacked any man who disturbed her. Now he stood motionless, back level and tail up.

"I'm sorry," Balawahdiwa said after several mute seconds. "I didn't mean to be rude. There is future in you, my young lady. I know

not what, but already I sense it, like the sharp smell of wind in front of a thunderstorm." He glanced from her to me and back again. "Do not be afraid. That future may well become glorious. We will watch over you closely and lovingly."

He could say that without going pompous or mawkish. I rose and laid an arm around my daughter. She smiled at me, snuggled close for an instant, then stood aside. The blood mounted in her cheeks. Ben looked jealous but kept his mouth shut. A good, solid boy.

"Bloody hell, yes!" Fotherwick-Botts blustered. "Thor hammer me if I let any whoreson knave touch a hair of your head. I'll cleave him from his filthy skull to his unwiped arse! If you will pardon an old soldier's language, miss."

"I had other guardians in mind," Balawahdiwa said.

"Bluff. True, though, true as the steel, straight as the blade."

"Of course. We value your help."

"None of those crooked, sneaky Oriental weapons, scimitars and yataghans and what the devil they call 'em. When I campaigned with the Varangians—"

"I am eager to learn about your background," Balawahdiwa slipped in smoothly. "Let's begin with the spells cast when you were forged and what they made of you. Rustproof, I expect? Unbreakable? How well do you keep your edge, if you don't mind my asking?"

"Not at all, sir, not at all. Happy to explain. Hr-rumph! Quite correct, what you say. Wasn't named Byrnie-biter for nothing. Cut right through chain. And plate if it's not too thick. Might need two or three strokes for heavy plate. Edge scarcely feels it. Must admit, when at last I've needed sharpening it's been the deuce of a job. If they hadn't turned Christian by then, they'd've known to send me back to the shop for it. As was, a month or more of grinding, whetting, and polishing—"

I admired how Balawahdiwa got the technical information he wanted out of the old gasbag. By the time he'd done so, Ginny and Fjalar appeared.

The dwarf was presentable. He hadn't refused to take a bath—in fact, he'd wallowed in the tub till the floor lay awash—and she had summoned forth a household-type Being to make neat new versions of his former garments. He too recognized the power in the priest, bowed till his beard brushed the carpet, and said in what English he'd acquired to date, "Ay ban glad to meet you."

In the course of the next several days he became fluent, but never got rid of that accent. He did get the two *th*'s right. They've dropped out of modern Scandinavian but exist in Old Norse.

"And to what do we owe the pleasure of this visit?" asked Ginny when everyone was settled down.

"We have thought about the work you mean to do," replied Balawahdiwa. I guessed he meant himself and his fellow leaders in Zuni. Were Others involved too? I still don't know. "We've prayed special prayers, gone on added retreats, made medicine." That last term was not properly Indian. He was showing the *Melika* a courtesy, a gesture of oneness with us. "We've confirmed it—great evil is loose, terrible Powers, and the trouble centers on the moon. I suspect you know more about those creatures than we do, while we know more about how they've misled the Beings of our land. We and you must come together."

Ben astonished me. "Maybe Val and me had better leave," he said in a small voice.

Balawahdiwa gave them a smile. "Later, yes, if and when we come to secret things. But we can't hide what I am about to suggest. We can only try to keep it quiet. I'm sure you won't blab. And—" His eyes sought Valeria. "—it's best you know this much."

The youngsters huddled on the floor and listened. From time to time one or the other stroked Svartalf, who'd crowded between them. Ginny said afterward that an experience of awe at an early age is healthy. I was too caught up to think about it just then.

"You need a site where you can work on your moonboat," Balawahdiwa said. "It ought to stand where it won't be generally noticed and casual pests can be shooed off. It should also be where we can bring our utmost strength to protect it.

"The Zunis offer you a place on our reservation, near Dowa Yalanne."

Corn Mountain, Thunder Mountain, their holy mountain.

Saving the world be damned, we wanted to get away and spend this long weekend, the last before school, with our children. Ginny decided she couldn't. Not only was she helping Fjalar with his English, somebody must look after him. In spite of his robustness and the cunning in his hands, the dwarf was pretty helpless here beyond his olden territory. If nothing else, he could too easily blunder into a mess that would bring publicity crashing around our ears. Besides, the sooner she started serious exchange of information and ideas with Balawahdiwa and his colleagues, the more our chances of outwitting the demons improved. Those chances were none too many at best.

We didn't know the nature of our foe, except vaguely and fragmentarily, nor their numbers, their methods, their operations on Earth and in space, how organized they were, even their long-range objectives. Yes, they wanted to keep humans groundbound and take over the moon for themselves, but what then? Given such a base, plus its goetic potentials, they could make life nasty for us mortals. And they would, they would. But beyond that, what? Had they thought it through?

Surely the Adversary had, I realized with a shudder. He was probably not directly involved in this—yet—but he must be watching. I could easily imagine the demons creating a situation he could take advantage of.

Not that I wanted to imagine it. His aim is always to lead us into evil, and we've fallen for it too bloody often. Think of what went on in the Belgian Congo in this very century. Or think of the persecution of Jews right up till the last century, and how readily it could revive—say in a strong, modern country that'd lost a major war and proposed to take its grudges out on the whole world, beginning with them. Or maybe a big but backward country, captured by an ideology that claimed human nature itself could be changed, setting out to do this with secret police, concentration camps, mass slaughters . . . Such things can happen. Demons with a lunar stronghold, striking out of it with tricks, temptations, lies, illusions, disruptions, despair, to set man against man, could make them happen.

Well, but we live day by day, taking whatever joys come by. Ginny, bless her, told me to go with Val and Ben. She'd stay home, looking after Chryssa besides the other stuff. Once in a while, I supposed, she'd sleep.

I took the kids to a little canyon we'd heard about, tucked in the highlands well off the usual routes. It's nothing spectacular, merely beautiful, ruddy walls above grass, piñon, juniper, and sweet herbs. A stream gurgles through, offering fly fishing as well as water. At one point it widens into a swimming hole, if your ancestors don't include any brass monkeys. Birds fly around. At night the sky is cramful of stars. There's a tiny, primitive campground. That's all I'll record, hundred-year seal or no. We three came back with memories that stood me in good stead afterward when I badly needed consolation.

Meanwhile I missed out on a fair amount of excitement. Right after Ginny briefed him, Barney Sturlason swung into action. Holiday weekend or no, money gushed, warehouses opened, carriers flew, and workers gleefully drew double-time pay. When I returned, a prefab workshop and living quarters were ready to erect for Fjalar on the

appointed spot and everything else he wanted was on its way from Norway, himself along to supervise.

He wasn't there for the actual start. No white person was. The Zunis performed their rites of purification and set their prayer sticks around the site. I saw those wands later, carved with faces, dressed in feathers bound on with cotton.

More securities were then added. Ginny handled the Western goetics, the Zunis their own spells religiously oriented rather than technologically. In the end we felt pretty sure that no Beings could make mischief around there. As for renegade humans, Fjalar had not only a phone but a siren to bring fast, well-equipped help. He loved making it scream. We must hope he'd control his impulses.

What could happen after our spacecraft left the protected area was less certain.

Construction, assembly, and installation proceeded in everyday fashion. Again for the sake of discretion, locals did the work. I pitched in alongside Indian laborers, carpenters, electricians, and whatnot. After years spent mainly at drawing boards and in laboratories, hammer, saw, and screwdriver felt mighty good in my hands. I was soon also enjoying the companionship—jokes, stories, lunch eaten together, maybe a beer after hours—of men with a common purpose.

Fjalar oversaw everything and bitched about most of it. Amazing, the amount of English profanity and obscenity now at his command. He didn't learn it from my wife. She's no prude, but she doesn't need that kind of language to put somebody in his place. She figured out that, considering the dwarf's character, the law of contagion had operated.

We hardly ever saw a Zuni priest anymore, and Balawahdiwa not at all. We wondered why, but were too busy to fret about it.

When completed, the smithy was a low building of cinderblock, sheetrock, corrugated metal, and so on, plunked down in the middle of sage, paintbrush, Apache plume, and so on. Fjalar's living space was tucked in one end. He didn't want a lot beyond a bed and privy; his work was his life. Nevertheless he appreciated the fridge that kept beer cold, the running water from a tank, the stove that made cooking easy, and the self-washing tableware. He'd also acquired a taste for a few modern foods, notably lutefisk and Limburger cheese, to say nothing of Scotch and tobacco. We kept him well supplied.

I doubt if he noticed how majestic the setting was. Around him reached the land, ruddy soil, bush, occasional tree, scarcely a trace of habitation other than a dirt road; Zuni lay beneath the northwest hori-

zon. Overhead arched the sky, deep blue by day, starful by night, its winds and its stillness. Nearby the enormous mesa, Dowa Yalanne, upheaved itself, two thousand feet high, more than two miles in length, sculptured red rock nearly sheer, white-banded through the middle, up and up to a thin woodland. Twin pillars were visible from here, in Zuni legend a brother and sister who had given their lives to save their people when a flood engulfed the world. Certainly those people had taken refuge on those heights in historic times. It was a hard day's climb to the top. I'd been told that only a few ruins remained—and an overwhelming sacredness. None but the purified were welcome, and they rarely.

Fjalar settled in. We left Fotherwick-Botts with him for company. The phone connection, which we hoped was secure, would keep them in touch with us. Of course, we and a few others would often come around in person: we especially, Ginny as a witch, I as an engineer. We thought that otherwise we could maybe, for a short while, get on with our own lives.

No such luck.

# XXX

Fjalar harked back to an era long before blueprints. A job did call for forethought, and he'd make charcoal drawings on bark or hides—in recent times, pencil on paper. But after that he went ahead and let things happen under his skillful hands. Always he had to improvise, for instance judging the state of the metal by its color as it glowed hot; and there were bound to be surprises along the way. So when I brought him the plans I'd developed on the basis of al-Bunni's preliminaries, I found him already at his anvil.

Stepping in from daylight to the gloom of the smithy, at first I was nearly blind. Heat and smoke rolled over me. The crash of hammer on steel went like gunfire. Coals in a rude stone furnace glowed white, fanned by a huge old dragonskin bellows that pumped itself. Metal rods above them had reached incandescence. Dressed again in wadmal, leather gloves, leather apron, and wooden shoes, beard and mane full of the soot that blackened his skin, the dwarf gripped a piece with tongs and banged it into shape.

We'd discussed technique, once he had English and I'd done some studying. I'd learned enough about wootz, case-hardening, pattern-welding, tempering, and the rest to understand that this was high craftsmanship and to appreciate how much I didn't know. Add the lore of 'chantment—songs, runes, special materials ranging from blood and snake venom to—what? bear fat and lingonberries, maybe?—anyhow, that shaggy little guy amongst the jumping shadows became pretty impressive. The sword had spoken well in advising that we engage him.

Nevertheless, he could sure be a royal pain in the rear.

"Halloa, Matuchek!" Fotherwick-Botts shouted from the wall

where he hung unsheathed. "Got something for us, have you?" Fjalar's eyeballs, red-lit white against the smudge, rolled toward me. He spat. The forge sizzled. He kept hammering. "He can't stop till he's done, y'know," his roommate continued unnecessarily. "Like fu—" He broke off. I gathered he was trying to refine his language for the ladies. "Like carnal congress, as I've noticed. Daft, you humans."

Remembering the latest scandals in Washington, I thought that that was where we Americans had our carnal Congress. I didn't say it. A reform movement was under way, as hysterical as the antispace movement, and many an errant legislator was now turning over a new page.

"At ease," Fotherwick-Botts invited hospitably. "Crack yourself a beer if you like. I'll keep you amused. Never did fill you in on that skirmish shortly before the battle of Buttington, did I?"

I fetched the brew, settled myself on sacks of charcoal, and made the best of things.

Eventually Fjalar laid the iron aside. I saw it was in fact three rods, twisted together and beaten into fusion. He went back for a bottle of his own. Rather, in proper Norse style, he carried several on a platter, plus a kippered herring between his teeth, which he let fall on the dish when he'd set that down. He hunkered on the floor. For a moment the only sound was the hoarse breath of the bellows.

"*Skaal,*" he toasted, lifting his drink.

"Wassail," I said.

"First, gentlemen, first the Queen, God bless her," Fotherwick-Botts reminded us.

"Sorry." I rose to my feet. "The Queen."

"Vich kveen?' inquired Fjalar. "Sigrid the Haughty in Sveden? She vas a great lady, she vas. Didn't like those little kings who came courting her, so she put them up in vun house and burned it. Married King Harald Bluetooth of Denmark. She made him vaylay King Olaf Tryggvason of Norvay at sea. *Ja,* there's a kveen vorth drinking to, by damn!"

Before Fotherwick-Botts could raise an argument, I said hastily, "I've brought you the plans."

We unrolled them on a workbench littered with wood and metal shavings. My eyes had adjusted to the murk and to Fjalar's it came naturally. For the most part, the design pleased me. I'm a scryotronic, not a mechanical engineer, but I'm fairly good at building things, and I'd gotten some help from a couple of close-mouthed fellows at the Point. Besides, this was basically just a broomstick. What was different

was the tremendous forces we meant to invoke, plus the capability of cruising through space and landing on places like the moon. For so small a vehicle to do this without being torn apart, we wanted the dwarf's metallurgy.

Straight off, he dashed my pride to the ground. "Vat the bloody blue blazes you mean by this silly box you got wrapped around the shaft?" he roared, in words more pungent.

"The cabin," I said. "For the crew."

"Cabin?" He bristled in all directions. An influence from the later years before he fell Asleep broke through. "Yesus Christ All-Father, ve send two men and you vant to sit them like in a king's hall? And vimmin bring mead and hop in bed with them? Hole in the head! Sailors don't need no stinking cabins. Your men, they don't even got to row. By Freyja's yugs, you ban yust plain crazy!"

I lifted my hands. "Calm down, will you? I don't like this feature myself. It'll play billy hell with the aerodynamics, and I hate to think how we'll gasket it around the shaft, but luxury accommodations it ain't. Look, would you send an unarmored man into combat?"

"Berserkers, *ja.*"

"Uncivilized thugs, the Vikings called 'em," Fotherwick-Botts reminisced. "No discipline. No tone. But what fighters! Absolutely fearless. The Fuzzy-Wuzzies of their day."

"Celestonauts are not berserkers," I tried to put in.

"Ah, if they could've been properly organized," Fotherwick-Botts sighed. "Sweep everything before 'em, they would have, a regiment of Norse berserkers. With white officers, of course."

"We're talking survival," I groaned. "I thought you knew, Fjalar. Lord knows we tried explaining. Between here and the moon, the air thins out to nothing. Our men couldn't breathe."

"*Ja,* Ay heard about likvid oxy-yen," the dwarf said. "They drink air from horns, okay?"

"Not okay! And with no outside pressure on them, their blood would boil. And the ultravi—its sunburn would fry them." Not to mention X rays, particle radiation, temperature extremes, the works. The Fair Folk themselves had to flee the sun. For us humans, raw space is a hell. The alien demons felt right at home. . . . "They've got to have metal around them."

"So they vear helmets and mail like Ay seen pictures of," Fjalar retorted. "The vay Ay vill make this *himinfar*—this sky boat, she can reach the moon in two-three hours."

I realized that. Acceleration and its pressure weren't a problem.

Thanks to al-Bunni's insight, the vessel ought to be in sympathetic relationship with the curvature of space itself. Everything and everybody aboard should be accelerated equally, except that we'd provide enough "downward" component to keep riders in their seats.

"The men can ride saddles," Fjalar continued. "This big, clumsy mass-mess you vant to stick on, it vill make the crossing ten times as long, and Ay think it vill make steering too hard."

"But spacesuits alone won't do," I maintained. "Can't you see what the whole mission is about?" *You stupid stump,* I did not add. It would've been unfair. If I'd had as much history and science to catch up on as he did, I might not have done as well. "They'll be gone for an unknown time. They're bound for unknown territory, with unknown hostiles there. Even a quick scouting flight calls for weapons, instruments, goetic equipment, and a refuge—a place where they can take shelter, rest, eat, drink, relieve themselves, for God's sake!"

"But Ay tell you, this cabin you vant is like putting an outhouse on a longship. The vind catches it, and down under the vater goes the lee rail. . . . The lee rail, *ja,* that's vere real seamen get their relief. That's how ve made it to Iceland and Greenland and Vinland, by yiminy."

"A point," Fotherwick-Botts agreed. "Austerity, y'know. Make do. Once, harrying along the Dutch coast, I think it was—Low Countries, at any rate, Frisia or thereabouts, my man Hog-Einar—"

"God damn it," I yelled, "I've been through the math on this and I can prove—"

The door opened on a dazzling rectangle of sunlight, broken by a silhouette. All but the bellows and the fire fell suddenly silent.

Balawahdiwa walked in. "How do you do, gentlemen," he said, as mildly as usual. "Am I intruding?"

"N-not in the least," I stammered. "We, uh, we haven't seen you for a while."

"Velcome," Fjalar greeted, ripped the cap off a beer bottle with his teeth, and reached it forth. "Please to sit down."

"Salute. Attention," Fotherwick-Botts said symbolically on his own behalf.

Balawahdiwa smiled. "At ease, General." He accepted the bottle and took a place beside me on the charcoal supply. I've never met another man who carried so much presence so lightly. "Thank you." He took a piece of kipper. I remembered that one should not scorn one's host and did likewise. A long swig of beer helped.

Fjalar went, shall I say, bluntly to the point. "Vy are you here, after this long time?"

"It's only been a couple of weeks, more or less," Balawahdiwa replied.

"It's felt longer," I said.

"Yes, you've been busy and in suspense, haven't you? I'm sorry. It was necessary. But I do seem to have appeared at a lucky moment. I heard you arguing, and believe I have an answer to your problem."

"Huh?" I exclaimed, and "*Haa?*" Fjalar grunted, and "Jolly good, by Jove!" Fotherwick-Botts declared.

The priest turned grave. It was as if the shadows deepened, the fire drew into its white-hot self, and the bellows shushed like a low surf.

"The story goes far back," he said slowly. "I may only tell you a little of it. We among the Zunis, and some in other pueblos, sensed evil afoot many months ago, more and more as time passed, but we could not discover what it was or what it intended. Though the moon was weak at midsummer, which should have aided us, my medicine society learned almost nothing when we made retreat. Nor did the others in their turns."

I knew almost nothing about that seasonal rite. The initiate men went into their kivas—heat, steam, sacred smoke—

"Then the disaster hit Cardinal Point, and everything else followed," he went on. "You know what my fellows and I have tried to do. It wasn't enough. The gods gave no dreams, no omens, nothing. You remember what Kokopelli told us, Steven. The other gods cannot have been ignorant of it, but they have not spoken to us. Now I have made a novena to Our Lady of Guadalupe."

The patron of the mission church. It had been restored, with murals that show something of Zuni life and faith. These people saw the gods, or God, in many shining forms.

"I did it on the heights of Dowa Yalanne," Balawahdiwa said very softly. "Then I was granted a vision, and there I found an eagle's egg, newly hatched, at this time of year when it should not be, a sign and a talisman.

"I returned to my fellows. After what the vision had shown me, we could make a new and stronger medicine."

We sat for a span in stillness.

Balawahdiwa relaxed and smiled. His tone became everyday: "Speaking practically, we here at Zuni understand that protecting the

scouts is critical. We think we've worked out a better way to do the job." He'd been carrying a manila envelope, which he handed me. "Take this home to your wife, Steven." Once more solemn: "Part of it is holy. But she will help you understand."

# XXXI

I'd told Ginny I'd probably be home for lunch, maybe a little late. Bursting in, I hollered, "Hey, have I got a surprise for you—" and stopped short. Not one but two redheads sat in the living room. "Why, uh, hello."

"I thought Curtice would like to join us and hear your progress report," my wife explained. The pair of them had become better friends than ever since she fixed the celestonaut's fundamental difficulty. I suppose that sort of experience forges a bond.

I hesitated. "Well, um—"

The big young woman stood to shake my hand. "Please don't worry," she said. "I know you have to keep the lowest profile possible. As far as the staff in general at the Point are concerned, what's left of them, they're under the same vague impression as the public is, what part of it gives a hoot anymore. Some privately funded, small-scale experiments going on at some offside location. Yawn. But Dr. al-Bunni decided a few of us ought to know the truth from the start."

"I see." Needless to say, we kept the chief himself posted, and he'd paid the smithy a clandestine visit. He had to be aware of what we were doing if he was to have any chance of covering up for us or even slipping us a little help. More important, he deserved to. Already he'd arranged for that pair of close-mouthed engineers to advise me on my plans for the vehicle.

"All are trustworthy," Ginny added. "They feel they have a personal stake in this."

Curtice Newton grinned. "Yeah, that stick of yours will want a couple of crew, I'm told. I hope to be one of them."

My doubts eased. "Couldn't ask for a better," I said.

"I'm touting myself for pilot. I'm not sure yet whom else to recommend."

"She's the only flyer let in on the secret so far," Ginny explained, "and I'm the one who did. We want to be sure we don't pick either a stickler for regulations or a glory hound who can't keep a secret."

I waved the envelope at her. "What's here may change everything," I blurted. "Fjalar dug in his heels against a life-support capsule, but Balawahdiwa showed up and gave me this."

The green eyes kindled. "I knew he was Seeking." Louder, firmly: "Lunch first. I'll have it on the table in a minute or three. You two entertain one another, please." Ginny left.

Curtice and I couldn't easily follow her suggestion. Neither of us was a glib talker. "How's life been treating you?" I attempted.

"Not often enough." The joke fell flat. She grimaced. "Terrible, frankly. I don't want to whine, but I can't help envying you and Ginny. You've been in action."

"And you've been idled."

"While my life's dream crumbles." She struck fist on knee. "No, I *won't* whine. I'm not alone in this fix, not by a long shot. . . . But oh, Steve, if only, if only."

Her burst of emotion embarrassed her, which embarrassed me. My mind cast about for something to say. My eyes hunted for inspiration. They spied a couple of books on an end table next to where Ginny had sat. "Hey, what're those?" I asked inanely.

"I don't know," Curtice said, equally anxious to fill the empty air. "She had one in her hand when she let me in."

"Must've been reading it, then. From the public library, I see, both of 'em." I reached over while my tongue clacked away on automatic pilot. "I didn't notice before. Been too busy with my design work, except Saturday afternoon when I took Ben to a ball game. She's been busy too, her consultations and— Anyway, we haven't had much conversation these past two-three days. I guess she checked these out meanwhile." Not to seem a total babbling idiot, I opened the books to their title pages. "Hm, a collection of Japanese folk tales by, um, Lafcadio Hearn. What kind of a name is that? And the fat one, uh, *The Tale of Genji,* translated by—"

Edgar had rested quietly on his perch. All at once he raised his hackles and spread his wings. "G-r-ruk," he croaked.

"What's the matter, bird?" I called. "Something spooky?"

"Haa, damn, hell, hell, hell! *Gr-r-ruk!*"

Ginny reentered before I could start seriously wondering. "Come and get it," she invited. Relieved, Curtice and I trooped after her.

A garbanzo and pasta salad with garlic toast and white wine broke the ice to flinders. My account of smuggling Fjalar from Norway gave Curtice a laugh. She couldn't wait to meet him. We must needs confess that he seldom received visitors gladly. Also, the less he was distracted, the sooner he'd finish. Better make the introduction part of a special event. She understood. "I've had to drop whatever I was doing and talk to this or that VIP too damn often. Pose for a picture with him too, likelier than not."

"What did you say?" I inquired.

She shrugged. "Polite noises. Some of them were human."

We left the table and repaired to Ginny's arcanum in a mood tense but hopeful. She spread the half-dozen sheets of paper on her desk and sat down. We brought chairs to either side of her. Our vision strained, our pulses fluttered.

The text was neatly hand-printed in English, with scattered Zuni words and a couple of diagrams. Yet after a while Curtice shook her head and leaned back. I surrendered a minute later. "It almost makes sense," I complained, "but as soon as I try to get the gist, everything dissolves, like in a dream."

"It is quite like a dream," Ginny answered low. "A vision. Call it highly technical or deeply theological, whichever you want. But Balawahdiwa wouldn't have sent it to me if he didn't expect I could . . . find out how to . . . comprehend it."

She pored and pondered. Sometimes her lips moved, or she stared off at the wall, or beyond the wall. Sometimes she consulted a reference work or her own notebooks from the pueblo. Sometimes her fingers traced a gesture. Curtice and I waited. This silence was not awkward, nor was it wearisome. It quivered.

Finally the witch crossed herself, laid the papers back in the envelope, and rose to stretch cramped muscles. We others bounced up as if a coiled spring had let go. "Whoo-oo," gusted from me. Curtice whistled.

Ginny's look gleamed from one to the other of us. "I've got it," she said. Triumph rang beneath the spare words. "The Zuni holy men have learned how to make medicine bundles—I may as well call them that—which provide complete life support, aside from food and water. No need for spacesuits or a capsule."

"What?" Curtice cried. "Are you sure?"

"If Balawahdiwa is, I am. The principles are valid, and of course everything will be carefully tested beforehand. Won't it?"

Curtice gulped. "Of course."

"How the—how in God's name does it work?" I faltered.

"From your viewpoint, dear, partly it draws on the same paranatural laws as the wind and weather screenfields for an ordinary broom. But this spell is far stronger and subtler. The field contains pressure, maintains temperature, and fends off harmful radiation, even excessive visible light." The engineer in me imagined the energy to do that as being copped from those very photons and charged particles. While still within the atmosphere, you might use its thermodynamic differentials. . . . "Air is recycled, renewed, by interaction with a stock of water and limestone, through a chemical conversion cantrip, though a unique one." *Ah, yes,* I thought, *a CCC.* "I doubt that NASA's scientists, no matter how brilliant some of them are, could ever have created anything like this."

"I do too," Curtice whispered.

"There's sacredness in it, you see," Ginny told us gravely. "The Zuni achieved it not only by thinking, but with prayer, fasting, rites, and sacrifice. They did it less for our sake than for land and folk, their children and grandchildren. Their native gods may not yet have responded to their appeals, but in native belief, humans aren't passive supplicants. They're integral with the world. They help maintain the balance of the universe.

"*We* have work to do."

Again, stillness. Afternoon light and heat blazed at drawn blinds.

"What?" I managed to ask.

Ginny smiled a bit. "Well, not too much immediately. The medicine bundles require certain things. Some the Zunis will supply. But we're to furnish water from each of the Four Oceans."

"The which?" said Curtice.

"These days they're interpreted as the Atlantic, the Pacific, the Arctic, and the Gulf of Mexico. We can sic Barney's men onto that. I'll write a manual of how they should collect and transport it. The Zunis will contribute aspects of the totem animals for five of the Six Directions, including eagle for Up. But we are to give several mole skins, for Down, because we are the people who mean to leave Earth . . . and return. I think you can take care of that, Steve. I'll brief you later. Then we stand by for further instructions, preparing our souls as best we can."

"Stand by," Curtice said woodenly.

Ginny patted her hand. "I know, that can be the hardest duty of all."

She took her leave soon after, telling us she didn't want to be underfoot. I suspect she was more wrung out than she let on. A session like today's was uncanny if you weren't used to such things. Or if you were. I felt it myself, and even Ginny seemed kind of subdued.

Having closed the door behind our guest, we passed to the coolness of the living room. My glance fell on the books. "Hey," I said to make conversation, "why this sudden interest in Japan?"

"What?" She hesitated, which wasn't like her. When she spoke again, the words dragged. "Oh, those. Just interested."

"Never heard of 'em."

We weren't ashamed to admit ignorance in the privacy of our own home. She'd had more formal education than me; I'd knocked around in places and situations foreign to her, and once in a while read something good that she hadn't. Being married to a dullard must get awful boring.

"Well," she replied—did I hear the slightest reluctance? "Lafcadio Hearn was an American journalist who fell in love with Japan in the late nineteenth century, settled there, became naturalized—practically unheard of—and wrote about the country and the culture, trying to show them to the Western reader."

" 'Unheard of' is right, from what *I've* heard. What about the other book? Japanese original?"

"Yes. The author, Murasaki, was a lady of the Heian court in the eleventh century. Her *Genji Monogatori* may be the first novel ever written, depending on how you define 'novel.' "

"So it tells about a world very different from any we know, I suppose."

"Absolutely. And yet some things have persisted—" Ginny broke off.

I clasped her elbow. "What got you hooked on this subject, with everything else that's piling onto you?"

She looked away. Her hands clenched. "Call it a hunch. Worthless, no doubt. I don't care to talk about it now. Anyway, the material is fascinating in its own right."

At that point Valeria and Ben arrived home from school and rescued her. Me too, maybe.

* * *

Wolf after dark, I sniffed around and located my spot. Next day, having given Fjalar the news and discussed it with him, I stopped by a bait shop and bought a can of night crawlers, which I emptied on the chosen ground. Rising well before dawn, I made my way back there.

Ginny had told me that for this I must be in human form. The town slept around the park I went into. Trees hulked black, shading out what lights shone along streets, and stars glistened in the west. Eastward the moonless sky had gone bleak white. Air lay soundless and cold.

Witch-sighted, my eyes caught the faint tremors under the soil. I plied my trenching tool. A mole flew up with the clods. I grabbed it in midair. The soft, warm body struggled in my grasp. "I'm sorry, little brother," I murmured as I had been taught, "and I thank you for what you give." Bringing my nose close to its snout, I wrung its neck with a single quick motion, breathed in its last breath, and felt it go limp.

I laid it aside and waited. Others, momentarily alarmed, should soon come back to the feast. I needed seven.

Valeria's fifteenth birthday fell in midweek. We made her favorite breakfast before she left for school, and planned a modest family celebration that evening. Come Saturday, we'd throw a party for her and her friends, and keep strictly in the background.

How young she was, slim, demurely dressed and almost shyly soft-spoken—for a change—and how beautiful. Memories rushed over me. Svartalf must have gotten sentimental too. He jumped onto her lap and purred till she had to go. Ginny and I stood in the door and waved. Edgar squawked, "Cheers!" Ben took the matter good-naturedly. Chryssa crowed.

Then business claimed us. For my part, I flitted to Zuni and gave Balawahdiwa the moles. He blessed them and took them elsewhere. Afterward we had a long conversation over coffee. Parts of it touched on our situation, though barely. He said he did not know the future. Nor, he believed, did the gods. (Well, the branching universes are so many, and each so strange, that probably none but the One God can keep track of them.) They could not have been unaware of evil Beings in their country, but Kokopelli's skepticism about us had maybe misled them as to the nature and danger of it. They might look on it as white men's business, and they were not white men's gods. We humans of every race must do our utmost; my wife had spoken truth, we have

our vital part to play in the cosmos. Then they might come to our aid, as Balawahdiwa knew a Christian saint had once done. Even so, the outcome was not sure and would not be. There had been planetary catastrophes in the past.

I nodded. There had also been times when evil simply bestrode Earth for centuries.

However, most of our talk ranged elsewhere, into war stories and other reminiscences, man talk, favoring anecdotes that were funny. No matter what happened, we had our past to cling to, and this shared moment.

Having said goodbye, I headed for the smithy to check on developments. A fair-sized tent a hundred yards west of it caught my notice, glaring white amidst gray-green brush and yellow flowers. Will Graylock had obtained permission to set up shop here. He'd been almighty withdrawn since last we saw him. I landed in front of his pitch.

He came forth dressed for desert and shook my hand beneath the sun-flap. I glimpsed portable instruments and rudimentary camping arrangements inside. "Hello, Steve, glad to see you. I was hoping you or Ginny or both would stop by soon."

I glanced around and didn't spot any Fibbies. Well, their surveillance no longer claimed top priority. They might well be carrying it out from Gallup, through a scryer attuned to his broom. He had to have a broom. Nobody but an Indian or a local-bred American would get far through this country on foot.

His tone had been listless, his handclasp loose. The skin, sallow in spite of the sun, stretched tight over the skull, the eyes were sunken and dark-rimmed. *Oh, hell and damnation,* I thought, *another downturn.* "How're you doing?" I asked mechanically.

He shrugged. "Surviving. Making ready to keep the moon under close observation away from city lights."

I thought about devils yonder and what they might intend. "You figure you might catch new, better indications?"

"Who knows?"

I glanced at the wan, waxing orb, almost lost in blue heaven. "What can you do before dark?"

"That's limited, yes. But I'll have another matter to keep me busy. The meteorites."

"Hm?"

"The pieces of them rather, that NASA—al-Bunni—gave us. In my opinion, they haven't been sufficiently studied. What goes into the moonboat is crucial, after all."

I nodded, recalling.

Most people never think about the pinch of sand embedded in a broom. It's there, it keeps the go-force from lofting you unsafely high, and so what? Racers use a stone from the destination area, to hurry them along contagionally. This is only for persons competent to handle it. Still more would be required for spaceflight.

"I want to ascertain beyond doubt that the alleged chip of moon rock did come from there," Will said. "Yes, I know about the chemical and goetic analyses, but I have finer tests in mind. Imagine that the identification is mistaken. Some of those specimens are purely terrestrial, some are from original orbits we don't know, the asteroid belt, the outer comet cloud, who can tell? Given the power that will drive the boat, what if the pilot stone should be wrong for the goal?"

I winced. Certain accidents in the early days of broomflight came to me. "Well, you're better qualified to double-check than anybody else I can think of."

"Can you arrange for the specimens to be brought here to me?" Will urged.

"Yeah, I guess so, aside from the moon rock itself. That is, uh, I expect you can look at it too—"

"Under supervision. I understand. Actually, I'm confident I'll confirm that it is lunar. But examination of the rest may help in future missions."

"Why not do it back at your place in Gallup? More comfortable."

"Too much interference. I need a low noise level."

"As you like. I'll speak to 'em at the Point. It shouldn't be any big deal." I paused. "Meanwhile, this is Valeria's birthday. You're her Number One uncle. How about dinner, with ice cream and cake and candles? No present necessary." Cliché: "Just your presence."

His hands lifted, as though in defense. "I'm sorry. I'd like to, but this is the autumnal equinox. The observations I make tonight, they, they may prove important."

I couldn't argue with that. The turnings of the year do matter. I promised to convey his regrets and proceeded to the smithy. There I was delighted to see how far along the work was.

Well, Fjalar forged tirelessly, with more than human strength. Besides, he didn't have to do everything. For instance, NASA was, under the counter, providing the titanium-alloy straws for him to weld to the shaft. A specialist would quietly come around to install the spirit crystal. Et cetera.

"Ay vill be done vith the main part before the full moon," the

dwarf told me. "Ay had better be, for that is ven ve can make sure she vill fly and Moon-Garm vill not shase her or any sush dumb stuff. This ban yust bare bones, you know. Later Ay add the fancy things." He rubbed his horny hands. "Haa, but you vill pay for your fancy things!"

I jumped through a quick calculation. Werewolves are naturally always conscious of lunar phases. "The full moon. That'll be Thursday next week, won't it? How about we schedule the first flight test the following Saturday?"

Fjalar hunched his shoulders. The fire behind him leaped and shadows through the gloom went wild. "No cackle-hens," he growled.

"News media? Positively not. A few of us, people who've helped make this happen and their immediate families."

What a birthday gift to promise Valeria today!

I didn't, then, think beyond it.

If NASA or some big corporation had been running Operation Luna, the first flight of our spacecraft would have been an Event. Farseers, newspapers, magazines, night club comedy routines would have been choked with it for months on end, everything from Our Destiny Among the Stars versus Our Arrogance and Neglect of the World's Real Problems to renewed impertinences about Curtice Newton's love life and taste in lingerie. On this Saturday, press and spectators would have packed the site from horizon to horizon, a site chosen to accommodate their numbers and what they'd buy. There would have been speeches. And interviews. And speeches. And a band. And speeches.

As it was, the group numbered a dozen. We weren't exactly being secretive, but we weren't handing out announcements either. Since we were a small, private outfit, we bore down on the "private" and the "small." Any more conspicuous, and we'd be entangled in politics and public relations. Any larger, and our defenses against demons would be spread dangerously thin. Surely *they* kept the closest watch on us that those defenses allowed.

Also, we'd decided our best strategy was to present what Ginny called a *fait accompli.* If we unveiled a broom that had repeatedly worked, nobody would have had a chance to hogtie us with regulations or pass a law forbidding the project. We could hope to keep a pretty influential voice in future developments. Yes, that included profits—royalties, licensing fees, shares in enterprises—for everybody in the partnership. The Zunis, above all, could find plenty of good uses for some megabucks.

But the greatest gains were not material. To al-Bunni, for one: vindication, the space program popular again, revived and strengthened.

And to humans in general. They'd be alerted to the menace on the moon, which so far had just been hinted at and met with scorn from most intellectuals—paranoid, racist, intolerant, absurd, same as prewar allegations about what the Caliph intended.

Okay, maybe we'd exaggerated the threat in our own minds, though if it worried people like Balawahdiwa and Fu Ch'ing it worried me. The point was, an expedition should determine the truth. Then the world could make ready to cope. Might that bring the nations together in a lasting alliance? Daydream, probably.

For sure, way too big a load to lay on this little trial jaunt. I told myself to relax and enjoy.

My glance traveled around the bunch who waited outside the smithy. The morning was bright, still cool. A breeze whittered, bearing touches of sage and, alas, rabbitbrush. Dowa Yalanne reared into utter blue, itself white-streaked ruddy, light and shadow at play across its carvenness. Ginny stood beside me, a fiery lock aflutter beneath her cap. On my other side quivered Val, and beside her Ben. We'd left Chryssa home—you never quite knew what could happen—with Hannah Becker to indulge her so she wouldn't care what she was missing here.

Will stayed a yard or two off, alone. He'd said hardly anything. A week spent mostly in the desert had tanned him, and it was as if the sun and the high stars had worked their peace; but how reserved he was, how unsmiling.

Likewise a disappointment was that Barney Sturlason and his wife weren't on hand. He was snarled in tax troubles like a dolphin caught in a tuna net. Meanwhile he must hold Nornwell on course, doing things of actual use to people. He couldn't spare even a weekend.

Nor was al-Bunni here. He'd been called back to Washington for more infighting. NASA's representatives were Curtice, who'd pilot today, and my friend and coworker Jim Franklin, who'd installed the control and communication systems on our broom. They too stood aside, a striking and handsome pair, his chocolate skin setting off her fair complexion. The cheery way they chattered made me wonder if something was developing between them. That'd be nice.

Balawahdiwa and two dignified old men, fellow priests, also held apart. They weren't being unsociable. I realized they were busy, though it scarcely showed on them. They didn't make a production of their—prayers?—and like us they wore plain outdoor garb.

The whole atmosphere was as informal as the lavender asters nodding in the breeze. Nevertheless, I felt more than the excitement usual

to a launch. Way down, underneath the fun and games, I had a sense of sacredness.

Ben's voice plucked my attention away. "Dad, how high's the spacecraft going to fly? How far?"

"They'll decide that as they see how she performs," I told him.

"If she works right, can we get a ride too?"

"Don't be a mudhead." Val sounded less superior than wistful. "This is a *test.*"

"But she's really only a broom, huh?" her brother argued. "She handles like any Ford or Volksbesen, doesn't she?"

"More like a souped-up Maserati." Val had swallowed every drop of information that came in range of her, and remained thirsty. This vehicle was meant for the regions where Magister Lazarus roved!

"And that's in low atmosphere, close to the ground," Ginny reminded them. "Crewed spaceflight has never been tried, you know. We'll have to feel our way forward."

"We," Val whispered. Her gaze went to Curtice, in envy and adoration.

"Hey, man, here she comes!" Jim Franklin hollered. Except for the Zunis—and maybe Will, who stood motionless and poker-faced—we all forgot about everything else.

Fjalar lugged his creation forth by himself. The weight wasn't too much for strength like his, and no thiefproofing spell resisted. Nevertheless, sweat runneled through the soot on him and breath tossed his whiskers to and fro. Sheathed at his waist, Fotherwick-Botts bump-bump-bumped over the ground.

At Fjalar's grunted word, the parking legs snapped down. They pulled the broom from his grasp and held it horizontally. A cheer lifted from us, small under the sky, big in our hearts.

There she posed, our craft, beautiful as clean design and fine workmanship always are. The shaft shone bluish white, with a damascene ripple that made me remember how bards once likened swords to serpents and fire. The single control crystal forward was not the standard globe but faceted, shattering light into rainbow fragments. Tucked under its eighteen-inch span, the communication relay glinted gilt. A subtlety of shadowings aft outlined the bundle of polished alloy straws.

But she was indeed not meant for Earth. The parking gear wasn't a mere quartet of rods, it was four slender machines made to adjust their own lengths and grip fast with claws; for the ground where they landed could well be rough, might well be strange, and would certainly offer no rack to stand the broom upright. There were no seats, only

two saddles, with stirrups and pouches; riders might have to get on or off in a hurry, and while flying could better shift body mass for close maneuvers. Beyond the single headlight the tip of the shaft ended in a safety-latched screw cap on which was etched a cross of four eagle feathers.

Fjalar had said it. As yet the vessel was bare bones. Aft, ahead of the straws, brackets waited for the coffer; we hadn't settled on the ideal shape. Somewhere along the line we must arrange for a license plate and whatever else would satisfy the law. First and foremost—

Ginny's thoughts had paralleled mine. "Defense," I heard her mutter.

What kind? A regular military machine gun, every tenth round argent? I imagined the laugh that the shen—kuei—evil Beings might get out of that. A 'chanted sword was a possibility. I'd wielded steel myself to good effect, long ago when we raided the Low Continuum. But a witch or warlock could do better than that, couldn't she or he? Have to be one who understood the demons and how to deal with them. Fu Ch'ing, riding behind Curtice, his wispy beard flapping in the cosmic winds. . . . Hardly.

Yes, our pilot needed a partner on her expedition to a moon where worse dangers waited than vacuum and radiation. A sorcerer or priest, who was also a qualified celestonaut and fit for any unforeseeable kind of combat. . . . No candidates were in view. Give us two or three years, maybe we'd find someone who could train for the mission.

I'd thought about myself and decided I didn't meet the specs, unless worst came to worst. Ginny— No, God damn it! If nothing else, we were trying to right an imbalance in the order of things. For that it was way preferable to have complementarity, Yang and Yin, male and female.

The world yanked me back to its immediate self. Fjalar had drawn the sword. He swung him past the bow of the broomstick and boomed something in Old Norse. "Ay name you *Skyfarer,* by yiminy," he added in English.

"I say," sputtered Fotherwick-Botts, "what d'you mean by that? *St. George,* by George. Bound off to slay dragons and devils and suchlike troublemakers, what, what, what?"

Fjalar grumped but didn't insist. Nobody else cared. Having no flacks, Operation Luna had never officially considered names for spacecraft. I doubt the question even occurred to the Zunis. In pillow talk with me, Ginny had once suggested *Owl,* honoring the totem of her order. That's what I'll use.

Curtice stepped forward. "Never mind," she almost sang. Her hand stroked the sleek metal. "This bird is what she is, which is wonderful. Thank you, Mr. Fjalar."

The dwarf blushed, especially his nose. Crusty old bachelor or no, he appreciated the appreciation of an attractive woman. "You ban vel-come." Grandly, he gave the key. "Ride her to Heaven and tell Thor hello from me."

"Um, well, not today, I'm afraid," said Curtice.

Balawahdiwa got her off the hook by advancing too. "Shall we make ready for the task?" he proposed. "Dr. Graylock, if you please."

Will started. It was as if his mind had been elsewhere, someplace far away and dark. "What? Oh, yes. Excuse me." He ducked into the building. A file cabinet had been brought there to keep the meteorite specimens and the notes on them. Already most of those notes were his. A couple of times, having had business here or in Zuni that kept us till after dark, Ginny or I had seen yellow lantern-glow or blue witchlight through the canvas of his tent. That was a lonely sight, but neither of us interrupted. She believed the work was healing for him.

Besides, it was valuable, if not right away then later on. We hoped for eventual voyages to the planets. That'd require stones from former orbits in their neighborhoods; and those stones had better be well re-searched beforehand.

While his colleagues chanted a prayer, Balawahdiwa unfastened and unscrewed the nose cap. I knew the cavity inside was lined with stabilized sea-foam. Carefully he packed into it the two halves of the newly hatched eagle's egg he'd found unseasonally on top of Dowa Yalanne. There they'd stay. My spine tingled; the hair stood up.

Will returned with a yellowish lump in his hand. He gave it to Balawahdiwa, who examined it closely before he and his fellows blessed it. He tucked it into the cavity and resecured the cap.

Just a chunk of local sandstone. If the charm on it was extra strong, that was because the go-forces driving the broom would be. It chan-neled and controlled them. As we gained experience and felt ready for longer tests, rocks from farther off would replace it, till the broom circled Earth carrying a tektite—terrestrial, but fused and scattered by meteorite impact.

And so at last the moon rock would go in, though of course the first ventures beyond atmosphere wouldn't try for the whole distance. That piece lay in its own drawer behind a special lock with an en-crypted alarm spell on it. This must have hurt Will, though he said nothing.

Today we forgot all unhappy things.

"Now, if you please, Captain Newton," Balawahdiwa said.

His companions brought over a box and laid it in his hands. He nodded to her to open the lid. Trembling very slightly at first, she took out an object. It wasn't pretentious: a furry brown cylinder made from the entire skin of a jackrabbit. Beadwork depicted a figure masked and winged, surrounded by feathers sewn to the hide. I didn't know whether the pattern was traditional or created for our use.

Packed inside were a container of mingled sea waters, the skin of a mole, and objects I knew less about, sanctified by what they stood for and by what had been sung over them. Here was a medicine bundle for a flyer bound high and far.

"Take this and bear it in reverence," Balawahdiwa said. "The favor of the Beloved Spirits lies within. It will give you clean air, comfort, health and strength wherever you travel. It is a shield against the deadlinesses beyond the sky. It shall bring you home to your loves."

"Thank you, sir." What other reply was possible? A belt with a buckle dangled from the fetish. Curtice slung it behind her left shoulder and made it fast.

Balawahdiwa took the box over to Ginny. "You get the rest," he said, his tone abruptly everyday. Or was it that to him the sacred and the ordinary were one and the same? "You'll know best how to keep them safe."

The bunch of us Matucheks crowded around and peered in at the half dozen bundles. Val reached deferentially to pat them. "Well, I expect right here, where the spacecraft and the rocks and everything else are, is as guarded a place as any," replied her mother.

"This'n's little," Val piped up. "You made it from a baby jack, didn't you?"

Balawahdiwa gave her a long look. "A thought came to us that somebody small might sometime have need of protection," he answered slowly.

"Oh." She didn't pursue the matter. I closed the box and carried it inside.

When I returned, solemnity and ceremony had given way to plain American excitement. The Zunis too were grinning and, I suspect, cracking jokes in their language. Fjalar and Fotherwick-Botts were singing some Viking song. Their voices were worse than Edgar's. The kids bounced.

Curtice had clamped earphones on her head and positioned an empathic pickup on her chest. She made an inquiring gesture at the

control globe. Jim gave her a thumbs-up and a blown kiss. She reciprocated, swung into the forward saddle, and snapped her safety harness together.

Will stayed expressionless but tense as a strung bow. Ginny moved across to him. I heard her ask, "Aren't you glad too?"

"Naturally," he said. "But I'm saving my huzzahs for her successful landing."

"She'll make it," his sister declared. "We've checked for the presence of hostiles anywhere nearby, we've warded against them, this is simply not a day when things will go wrong for us."

Nobody can foreknow everything.

Curtice inserted the key and switched on the main spell. "Off we go!" she cried. Her fingertips passed over the crystal. Its facets flashed brighter. The broomstick quivered.

She rose. The parking gear snapped down alongside the shaft. *Owl* arrowed aloft.

Jim carried a communication receiver with an amplifying speaker. "Hello," he called. "You all right?"

Curtice's words danced back to us. "Molly O'Kay. She handles like a dream. Screenfields perfect. Let's try a few maneuvers."

Already the craft was tiny in our sight. Those who had binoculars raised them. The broom soared, plunged, surged back, rolled and tumbled, frolicking in sheer bliss.

Balawahdiwa approached Jim. "Fly around the holy mountain and low above, if you please," he said into the phone.

"Really?" Curtice was surprised. "I didn't mean to."

"You will give no offense, Captain Newton. Think your thanks and your respects to the gods. They will know."

For a short while the great mesa eclipsed our little flyer. We fell silent.

A glint reappeared in the blue. It climbed and climbed. "Something spoke to me," the pilot called softly. "Not in words. But I learned I should go high, as high as I'm able today." Exultation blew away awe. "That's into the stratosphere, boys. Yippee!"

The glint vanished from us. I thought about those altitudes. Already she was beyond the point where she could breathe unaided. Jim's voice wavered. "You still there?"

His question reached her as he uttered it. Not that they'd have noticed any difference if it had gone by radio. But this was an empathic system, meant for interplanetary distances. Although I've been taught that "infinite velocity" is a meaningless noise, nobody's yet measured

how fast that kind moves; and, being keyed only to certain terminals, it isn't bothered by the inverse-square law. Before long, this would matter a hell of a lot to Ginny and me.

"Yes, oh, yes," rang Curtice's answer. "I could almost be astraddle a horse down where you are. Except the stick's *flying,* rising, alive. The sky's going deep purple. The sun-glare doesn't hurt my eyes. Thank you, Mr. Adams—uh, Ba-la-*wah*-diwa. When I look away from it I see a few stars. Earth's beginning to show curvature. Like a breast— Let me fly a while longer. Please!"

"Magniff," Valeria breathed. Her fists doubled. "But oh, cracky, how I wish I could."

I laid a hand briefly on her shoulder. "Someday, pony, if you want, you shall," I said.

"Hey, I just thought of something," Ben exclaimed.

"What, dear?" asked Ginny.

"This right now, sure, it's hyper. But what about when they go to the moon? What'll they do for supplies?"

"They'll have food and water along. If you're wearing a medicine bundle like Captain Newton's, you can eat and drink as easily as at home."

"Yeah, but there's no toilet."

Ginny smiled. "That's much easier than before. The celestonauts can—hm—void directly into the void."

Val giggled. "Tiny shooting stars?"

After a time that felt long but actually wasn't, Curtice descended. Besides taking pity on us, she was a pro and this was a test flight, not a joyride. She couldn't resist a few more power loops and such on the way down. They might have buckled an ordinary stick, but the dwarf-forged steel held firm. Or they might have broken her neck, but al-Bunni's design compensated. The only acceleration she felt was one steady gravity holding her to her saddle.

In fact, she told us this caused a minor problem. Feeling no tugs of motion, she had to rely entirely on visual cues. However, they included images and readings provided by the sprite in the control crystal, according to her mental orders—ample for a skilled flygirl.

"Coming in!" she yelled at last. Dust flew from the Valkyrie landing.

She leaped off. Most of us scrambled around to hug her. The Zunis, less demonstrative, offered handshakes. So did Will. "Jolly good show," said Fotherwick-Botts where he stood planted in the ground. Fjalar must tiptoe to embrace her. His hands started roving. Jim tapped his

head pretty strongly and he let go. Myself, after enfolding Curtice I laid a big, wet kiss on Ginny. She responded as enthusiastically as propriety allowed.

We all helped bring *Owl* and whatever else back into the smithy. Nobody spoke of debriefing. Curtice would write a report at her leisure. It would give us a basis for planning the next stage. Meanwhile we'd earned a celebration.

I said it first. "All right, ladies and gentlemen, let's go to Buffalo Bull's and open a keg of nails." Agreement whooped around me. It was a good thing we didn't know how the day would later blow up in our faces.

# XXXIII

The Zunis declined in friendly fashion. They'd rather party among their own people, who rated a share in the merrymaking anyway. I guessed that'd be quite a wingding. Pueblo Indians are only solemn when they need to be.

"I'm sorry, I'd better beg off too," Will said.

"Too bad," I replied sincerely, in spite of his flat affect. "Feeling punk again, are you?"

"Exhausted." His tone stayed machinelike, a machine that wanted oil. "My fault. I've been pushing myself hard in spite of this damned undiagnosed medical problem. Let me go home and rest."

"Yes, do," Ginny agreed. "Take a week at least. And then let's try to find a specialist in Albuquerque, a neurologist or some such."

He shrugged jerkily. "We'll see. I'll go pack my gear and strike my tent."

"Lemme help," Jim said, and "Me too," Curtice added. They were that kind of folks.

I made a move but Jim shook his head. "Thanks," he told me. "Any more, though, we'd get in each other's way." True, stowing things on Will's Völve was no contract job. However, I had a notion Jim would as soon be the only man there with our celestonaut. Poor Will hardly counted. The three of them walked off.

"Hoy, Ay come to town at last!" Fjalar roared. "Ban too damn long Ay had no feasting, by Freyja's rosy rump! They got visky there? And beer to vash it down?"

"Um, uh, wait a minute," I said, dismayed. "We're keeping this operation quiet. If you suddenly show up—"

Indignation flared. "You think Ay not ban nice? Ay ban good

enough to vork for you, but not sit in your hall?" Fjalar waved his outsize fists. "Loki fart me if Ay ban not a perfect yentleman! You vant me to prove it? Okay. *Einvigi?"*

"Hey, look, I didn't mean any—I mean—What're you talking about? Some kind of legal action?"

"*Ja.* Not like *holmgang.* In *einvigi* ve fight any old vay. Shoose your veapon. Ay vill take my hammer and, *ja,* my tongs too, for to pull your nose out before Ay smash your head."

The kids stared, appalled. "No, you won't!" Val cried. Before she could leap between us, Ginny glided in.

"Fjalar, dear, please," the witch purred. "You misunderstood Steve. Of course we realize how well and hard you've worked and how much you deserve to relax. We look forward to the day when we—when our whole kingdom can heap you with gifts and honors. It's simply that we'd best not draw attention to ourselves right now."

Fjalar's wrath collapsed. Instead, he felt wounded. "Ay ban funny-looking, ha?" he mumbled. My heart went out to him. He rallied. "Don't vorry, sveet lady. Anybody makes laugh of me, Ay skvash him like a bug."

Clearly, he was bound and determined to join the party. "Nothing of the kind," she told him. "Do come along. What Steve was trying to say is that your splendid work has left you grimy and sweaty. Honorable signs of honest toil, but you should sit in the . . . the mead hall as fine to behold as any of your peers. Why don't you dash inside, wash, and change clothes? Then the girls in town can see how handsome you really are."

Her smile bowled him over. "*Ja, ja!* Ay ban sorry Ay got mad, Steve. But you should have spoke more clear, like me. Yust a minute, and Ay vill be ready." He stumped into the building.

"Jolly good," exclaimed Fotherwick-Botts. "A feast, eh? Daresay you've no entertainment planned, on short notice like this. Never fear. I'll have stories to tell. And songs to sing, by Jove. Blood-and-guts stuff, fit for heroes. Or for the march. Boots, boots, boots, sloggin' over Normandy, whippin' along the pack animals. Troll the ancient muleside carol."

I staggered where I stood. "Hold on!" I gasped. "Buffalo Bull's is a cowboy sort of place, b-but they don't allow weapons in there, and—and—" With luck, Fjalar would pass. The class of people we'd be among generally mind their own business and practically never squeal to the cops. But a sword—and one that talks and talks and talks and then tries to sing—"No, sorry, impossible. The law forbids."

"Eh? No steel allowed in? What kind of fleshism is this? God's death! I'll not stand for it, I'll have you know. When Fjalar comes back, we'll see what my maker has to say about this bloody outrage."

"Lord help us," I whispered to Ginny. "Fjalar's still edgy. If he gets really mad he'll quit, if not worse."

"We beg your pardon, sir," she attempted. "No disputing, it is a foolish law. But if nothing else, valiant Byrnie-biter, we need you to stand guard. Nobody else will be here, and the enemy always watches for his chance."

Unfortunately, Balawahdiwa overheard. He stepped close and said, "That would be a good idea if the place were left alone for any length of time. But you're just bound for Gallup, aren't you? I imagine the dwarf will return tomorrow. The protective spells won't weaken overnight enough to matter. As for human intruders, lock the door. I'll arrange for boys in shifts to keep an eye on it. Anything questionable, and our men will arrive in minutes."

"Wait, wait," I muttered desperately. "You don't understand the situation."

His look reproached me. "I do, and it is ticklish. But the Beloved Spirits turn their backs on him who lies to a friend."

He and his fellows bade us a formal good-bye, mounted their battered Buick, and flitted off to Zuni.

"All right," Ginny sighed to me and the kids, "we'll have the party at our house and pray it doesn't get so noisy the neighbors call the police. Sending out for shishkebab will be a comedown, but I suppose a keg should smooth the disappointment."

Nevertheless we had the devil's own time getting Fotherwick-Botts to accept the compromise. He was still grumbling when Jim and Curtice returned. Though his own broom stood heavily loaded at his campsite, Will tagged along. At our quizzical glance, he told us, "I thought I should tell you, all at once I feel better. Yes, I'll stay home for a few days, but no reason why I can't conduct further research there at a less frantic pace. I have a few of those stones left to examine, and I also want to sit down and think about what the data imply."

"Why, that's great," I said. Hopefulness lightened my family's faces.

Yet now we had the awkward job of explaining the change in plans to the others without ruffling the sword's feathers more than they already had been. The figure of speech gives an idea of the general mess. As we began, Fjalar appeared. He'd showered and put on a clean pair of the jeans we'd had tailored to his measurements. His hairy toes stuck

out of leather sandals he'd doubtless made for himself in the past and taken along. Somewhere, maybe in a flyport, he'd seen a Hawaiian shirt and added several of those to his list of demands. This one was purple, with shocking pink hibiscus blossoms. On his shaggy head he'd crammed a Mexican sombrero. From his trip back to the old country, along with assorted tools and materials he'd brought a Norwegian flag as big as himself. It hung from a footed pole across his shoulder. True, it displayed the cross, but it was Norwegian.

"Yippee-yi-yay!" he thundered cheerfully. "Let's go, boys! The girls in the mead hall ban vaiting!"

"Uh, we've decided on our place instead," I made known, and actually felt relieved.

He bristled. "Vat you mean? You shame yourselves of me, ha? Vant you not to be seen vith me? You think Ay ban a lousy *dverg,* even ven you ban clad like thralls and Ay like a king."

"No, no, no, dear," Ginny said. "The house is more relaxed. You've worked so hard, you've earned a rest."

"A rest?" he bellowed. "You think Ay ban sush a veakling Ay need to sit and sip tea? No, by all the fleas on Fenris! After banging iron half a month, vat Ay vant to bang now is—"

"Well, uh, well," I stuttered, "you see, the trouble is, uh, Fotherwick-Botts—"

"Will bloody well not be left behind like a blasted ostler," the sword interrupted.

"Vat's this?" Fjalar snarled. I braced myself for the eruption.

Will moved in as quickly and softly as he spoke. He smiled. "Perhaps I can mediate. Certainly discrimination against either of our gallant friends is intolerable. But really, General Fotherwick-Botts, you wouldn't care for the taven originally intended. I've been there, sir, and believe me, you wouldn't. Lower classes, rowdy, no respect for their betters. All very well for colonials who feel like a bit of slumming, but for you, a ranking officer and a gentleman, definitely infra dig."

"Who you calling a colonial?" Fjalar demanded.

"He means the rest of us," I said in a stage whisper.

"As for the Matuchek home," Will went on, "you have seen it. You know how quiet and refined it is." *Huh?* I thought. "You will find the conversation today elevated and stimulating, devoted to science, literature, and the arts. If I'm not mistaken, the Santa Fe Ballet performs this afternoon. Perhaps everybody will watch it on the farseer."

Before the sword could notice us gaping, Will sighed. "Yes, General, enjoy yourself. I'd hoped to invite you to visit me. Perhaps some

other day. Everything I've heard about you has made me look forward to closer acquaintanceship."

"Eh?" barked Fotherwick-Botts. "Int'rested in me? You? I've been informed you're a lifelong civilian. I use the word in its kindliest sense, of course."

"But I am an amateur student of history. I gather you're full of . . . of the most fascinating eyewitness details. Things that never got into the chronicles and have escaped the archaeologists. I was hoping to ask you about them."

"Hey? What, what? D'you mean—*battles?*"

"The opportunity! Someone on the scene who partook, and who knows the real military significance. I could listen for hours. Days, if you might sometime honor me, sir, by being a guest at my humble abode."

"I will this very day, by Jove," said Fotherwick-Botts with ill-concealed eagerness.

"Gosh," breathed Ben. Valeria squealed and hopped. Fjalar beamed, as happy for the child of his hands as for himself. Curtice and Jim contained themselves, more or less. Ginny and I swapped a look. Mine wondered how we could repay her brother. Tears glimmered in hers. He was becoming his old, real, unselfish self again.

Will turned to the dwarf. "I do want to carry on my research at home," he said. I assumed he'd let the sword drone on meanwhile; he had powers of concentration. "Two meteor stones in particular. May I fetch them?"

*"Ja,* you betcha." All amicability, Fjalar accompanied him inside and watched while he opened the cabinet and dropped them in pockets of his field jacket. Regulations required that. "Thor-hated stupid Fibbies," the dwarf growled as they emerged. "They don't trust a man so smart like you? Henhouse!"

*Well,* I thought, *it's true that our wardings keep them from scrying him or anything in this immediate area,* and felt ashamed of myself.

Will sheathed Fotherwick-Botts as courteously as it is possible to stuff somebody down a long, narrow hole. Fjalar closed the single door of the smithy and locked it. The windows were barred. He moved with me and mine to our family broom, which he'd share. Jim, Curtice, and Will started for theirs.

Suddenly my brother-in-law galloped back. "Wait," he called. "Wait, please!"

We stopped. "I'm sorry," he apologized. "Like a fool, I quite forgot I'll want the notes I filed earlier. Could I pop in and fetch them?"

*"Ja,* sure." Fjalar gave him the key. Regulations didn't mention documents. Will left the sword with us. As though embarrassed, he opened the door barely wide enough to slip through. We hung around, chatting. He reappeared in maybe five minutes, a folder in his hand, relocked the door, and brought the key over.

"Took me a while," he said. "I found I had to sort out the papers I'll need. I *am* an idiot today. Left you standing here in the desert sun like this."

Fjalar chuckled. "*Aa,* ve grow a bigger thirst for beer." He gave the key to Ginny. The uneasy idea crossed my mind that he didn't want to be committed to any responsibility for the rest of today.

Will left with the sword. "There goes one swell guy," I said. "Come on, let's go have the fun he's bought for us."

And so our party flitted to Gallup.

# XXXIV

We landed in a tiny parking lot on the fringes of the preboom downtown, behind Buffalo Bull's. The hour was past noon and hot. We were glad to take shelter.

The joint was large and low, darkish, an old-style bar near the entrance, tables and booths beyond. Red-checked cloths, cheap and sturdy tableware, sawdust on the floor, just two farseers and their audio kept well down unless a major game or something was going on. A couple of big-game heads behind the bar, photos of ranch scenes on the walls, hundreds of yellowing business cards thumbtacked to the ceiling. The lunch crowd included families as well as singletons taking a break; the food was good and came in generous servings. A working-class place, which people from Cardinal Point had discovered. We spied none of them here today, in this bad time. Our seven pulled a couple of tables together.

Conversation around us dropped down to a beehive buzz when Fjalar planted his flagstaff on its base at the head of the board. Maybe folks in Minneapolis or Seattle would have taken it for granted, but the ethnology of New Mexico is different. I exchanged another glance with Ginny before I put myself on the dwarf's left, she on his right. Possibly between us we could keep him under some control. Ben settled by me, Val by her, Jim and Curtice opposite one another.

While a busboy established water, plates, etc., the sensation faded away. I began to feel optimistic. Probably we wouldn't touch off talk that'd reach official ears. Though the main tourist season was past, this state gets them the year around and locals are used to the occasional weirdo.

True, Fjalar roared, "Yust vater? Vat kind of *bondir* think they ve ban?"

Ginny shushed him: "It's to quench your first thirst. Wait a few minutes. Aren't your race as agelessly patient as the mountains where they dwell?" Though this was obviously on a par with the notion that every Hindu is a holy man and every Italian an incomparable lover, it worked on him. Not to let down the side, as Fotherwick-Botts would say.

A good-looking, dark-haired waitress arrived with menus. "Hi," she greeted. "Anything to drink before you order?"

"Hi, Conchita—" I began. We knew her from previous visits. This was a friendly place.

Fjalar broke through: "*Ja,* Scotch. Two doubles. Tightfist ban the innkeepers these days."

"He's from northern Minnesota," I murmured hastily. "Kind of, uh, rough-hewn. But an honest hombre." Before the dwarf could demand to know what that meant, I addressed the others. "Beer?" They nodded. "Okay, a pitcher of Cochise. And for the kids—"

"Vatever they vant," Fjalar said regally. "I give. Mead, rum, vat you like, my young lady and atheling?"

"Coke, please," they said together.

"*Haa?* That I have not heard of. Vell, don't drink too mush and start a fight."

We picked up our menus. "Vat's this?" Fjalar snapped. "Ay thought you said no spellcasting in here." We described the purpose and translated for him. Pork chops he understood. "Good, good. Like vat they have in Valhalla." Beef was more difficult, not in itself but the concept of such quantities. Wide-open range is scarce in Norway and cattle have always been dairy, eating them incidental until modern transportation brought imports. "Who has made so great a raid he slaughtered whole herds? Vy have you not told of this deed?" Some items, like fritos, salsa, and corn on the cob, we could not make clear. We ended by suggesting he watch and experiment.

Conchita arrived, balancing a tray. She set down Fjalar's whiskies first, with a smile. "Welcome to the West," she said.

He beamed. "Thank you. Freyja's brisket, you ban a toothsome piece!" Giving him the benefit of the doubt, I suppose he intended simply to pat her fanny; but the smack resounded across the room and she lurched.

Ginny sprang to steady the tray before it strewed its load across the table. "Judas priest!" I yelled. "I ought to call you out for that,

you oaf!" Curtice and Jim added their reproaches in softer language and their apologies to mine.

"All right, Ay ban sorry," the dwarf grumbled. He tossed off a jigger. "Ay should have asked your lord first, *ja.* It vas yust that maybe you vould sit in the seat vith me, and maybe later—"

Now I roared. "Pipe down, for Christ's sake!"

Fjalar nodded. "*Ja,* this is Hvita-Krist land, no? Ay do not vant to anger any god. As soon as Ay get paid, Ay buy a goat and kill it on his altar."

"I'm awfully sorry, Conchita," I babbled, standing before her. "We never expected— Won't happen again, I swear— We, uh, we want to make it up to you—"

That implied a substantial tip. Besides, she was a good sport. "Okay, Steve, we'll overlook it. A compliment of sorts, maybe." She lowered her voice. "I can't help feeling kind of sorry for him, you know? He must get pretty lonesome. And little guys like him don't live too long, do they?"

"You are forgiven," Ginny told Fjalar in her frostiest tone. "Be glad this is a Christian country."

"Ban it really? Ay have not seen any monks. *Ja,* vell, Ay forgive everybody too. Ay ban an easygoing fellow."

We sat back down. Conchita distributed glasses and put the beer on the table. "A-a-ah," Fjalar gusted. "A shaser ban yust vat Ay need." He reached forth a chimp-long arm, grabbed the pitcher, tilted it to his mouth, and glugged. When it was half empty, which took about thirty seconds, he lowered it and asked, "But don't the rest of you vant any?"

"Bring us another," I said resignedly to the waitress. "No, you may as well make it two."

She'd also given us a couple bowls of nachos. Fjalar made havoc of the nearest. Alarmed, the kids sped their hands to collect a share from the other. He smiled benignly at them. "You like those drinks you got?" he inquired.

"Oh, yes," Ben replied. On an impulse, he offered his. "Want to try a taste?"

"Thank you. You ban a high-born lad for sure." Fjalar gripped the glass. It nearly vanished in that knobbly hand.

Maybe the Old Norse never heard of sipping. Fjalar threw the Coke, ice and all, down his gullet in one swig. It spewed back across the table. "Poo-oo-oo! By every frog in Helheim, vat have the Americans done that they must drink this?"

We mopped things as dry as we could, refrained from commentary, and discussed the menu. Conchita brought Ben a replacement along with the fresh pitchers. They helped improve the mood. After all, we were holding a small gala. Fjalar mellowed. His joke about Odin and the giantess was pretty gross, but when he started reminiscing about early times it was very interesting—an utterly different world—and rather touching—an utterly lost world.

Lunch arrived. Not expecting anything from him in the way of table manners, Ginny had shrewdly steered him onto spare ribs, French fries, and tacos, finger food. Conversation grew lively. The kids took a polite but intelligent part. Too bad that nobody, first and foremost himself, kept track of how often the dwarf crooked a finger to order more beer, with a whisky now and then for variety.

At length Conchita cleared away the dirty dishes and asked if we wanted dessert. Adults felt full, but Val and Ben were ready for ice cream and Fjalar said he'd try some.

"—folk tell how the jotuns, the yiants, ban the oldest race there is," he declaimed, "but ve dvarves, by yiminy—"

The waitress set his bowl before him. He dipped a finger in and licked. "Ho, good," he exulted. "Vat do those cows feed on? But Ay make it better." He emptied a jigger of Scotch over it. "Ve vas the underpinning of the vorld, us dvarves. And the biggest smiths and vizards, too. The gods themselves vas customers of ours. Ve vere famous. The *Edda* got a list of us. It don't list no jotuns, no, nor even all the damn gods, but the *dvergar*—"

He dipped a spoon into his ice cream and swung it toward his mouth. Naturally, the alcohol had liquefied it. A thick brown fluid spattered his beard. "Vat troll trick ban this?" he bellowed. "Who makes spells at me? Ay vill hammer him in the ground like a tent peg! Ay vill—"

"Easy, easy." Once more people were staring. I grabbed his arm. When he didn't notice, I grabbed his whiskers. "No witchcraft, no harm done, you blockhead," I said into his glare. "You've seen ice melt, haven't you, and drunk the water?"

His wrath turned directly to sentiment. I should have recognized the danger signal. "Ice melts in spring," he crooned. "All things vept for Baldr's death. The ice cream too? How sveet. Ay drink its tears." He lifted the bowl and slurped. "Delicious soup!" he bawled. "More!"

To quiet him, I signaled Conchita. She approached cautiously.

"The list of the dvarves. Hark." Fjalar raised his forefinger. "First

Motsognir and Durinn. Then Nyi, Nidi, Nordri, Sudri, Austri, Vestri, Althjofur, Dvalinn—"

"Another ice cream," I rasped. "And could you bring the check?"

"—Veigur, Gandalfur, Vindalfur, Thrainn—"

"*Ay de mí,* you do have a problem, don't you?" the waitress sympathized. "The bartender's muttering about bouncing him. I hope it won't come to that."

I shuddered. "Me likewise, for the bartender's sake. Do move things along, okay? We are sorry. I promise this won't happen again." *Not in here, anyway.*

"—Fili, Kili, Fundinn, Nali—" Fjalar squinted cross-eyed from one of us to the next. "Ay not ban boring you? Ay don't vant to bore you. Friends don't let friends bore friends. Real kvick Ay vill finish. Hefti-Vili-Hannar-Sviur-Frar-Hornbori—"

Curtice leaned toward me. "Well, he did build our spacecraft," she murmured graciously.

"And we need him for the rest of the job," Jim added. "I reckon."

"—Alfur, Yngvi, Eikinskjaldi, Fjalar—Fjalar, that's me, Ay vas there, Ay vas—"

Conchita presented the last dessert and the bill.

"Frosti, Finnur, Ginnur!" The dwarf snatched the dish from her. "Now have Ay told the tale."

Overcome by emotion, he sprang onto the tabletop. An empty pitcher crashed. "Here's to the dvarves!" he trumpeted. "A *blót,* an offering, on our behalf, to good old Thor!" He hurled the dish at the wall. A fat spatter exploded. "Not blood, but you vill like it, thunderlord."

I'd been shoving money at Conchita. I shoved more.

"Mush can I tell!" Fjalar shouted. He started a chant: "*Geyr nu Garm*— No," he broke off. "You do not know. You do not understand. Nobody understands." Tears ran into the ice cream and Scotch on his beard. "Gone, all gone," he sobbed. Mustering heart: "But men still fight! Men need veapons! In Noreg—in Norvay they still ban mighty varriors!"

Last I heard, a committee of the Norwegian parliament chooses the winner of the Nobel Peace Prize.

"The steel shall clang, the volves shall gorge," Fjalar cried. *"Fram, fram, Norrmen!"* He grabbed his flag and waved it on high. Dust puffed off the tacked-up business cards.

"Let's clear out before somebody calls the cops," I said to Jim. He nodded. We each laid arms around Fjalar's knees—he weighed more

than you'd guess—and carried him away. Evidently he took this for a triumphal parade. He flapped his banner and howled violent verses.

Sunlight outside dazzled our vision. "Vat?" hiccoughed Fjalar. "The vorld on fire? Ragnarok already? Oh, vell." He crumpled into a heap. Jim and I almost dropped him.

Curtice retrieved his flag, respectful of the honorable nation for which it stood. "What'll we do now?" she asked.

"Steve and I will take him home," Ginny replied. "We'll put him in the guest room to sleep it off."

"You do know more about . . . Beings." Curtice was frankly relieved. "But if you need any help, give me a call."

"Uh, I thought maybe you and I might take in a show or something this afternoon," Jim said to her. "If that won't be, uh, an anticlimax."

She smiled. "On the contrary, I could do with some relaxation. Thanks, let's."

"Yeah, we'll manage," I told them. "We mainly need to have beer on hand for when he wakes up. Or, hm, maybe not."

We secured him on the rear seat of our broom, bade our companions good-bye, and started off. "I hope you weren't too shocked," I said to the kids. "He's a good guy at heart, and a great craftsman."

"Yah, sure," answered Ben with youthful loftiness. "I know. He just can't hold his liquor."

"The hell he can't," Val retorted. "Did you *see* how much he put down? And never went to the men's room once."

*Uh-oh!* I thought. *Better rouse him to take care of that before we tuck him in.*

What with one thing and another, an hour or so passed before Ginny and I sat down in the cool of our living room and drew a breath. The babysitter had left. Chryssa napped, more quietly than Fjalar. Since Ben was pledged to secrecy about what he'd witnessed and doubtless needed time to prepare himself not to share it with Danny Goldstein, he'd withdrawn to his own room and a book. Val went out to our mailbox by the street.

She returned thumbing through the stack. "Gas bill," she announced. "Something from the, hmm, Corn and Bunion Foundation—bulk rate—a pitch, right? And here's another worthy cause, Adolescent Council for Neatness and Elegance. And this envelope says you may have won five million dollars. And this—hey, for me." She flushed red and tucked it down her shirt front. From Larry, I guessed, with the muddle of worry and wistfulness that I suppose comes to every father of a young girl.

"What else, dear?" asked Ginny, lightly and smiling.

"Oh? Oh. Yes. A . . . a postcard from the vet, says Svartalf's due for his shots . . . More junk mail. . . . Hey, this'n's from the Insertion of the Royal Shaft."

"What?"

"IRS."

"That isn't nice."

Val grinned. "I'm quoting Daddy. I've heard worse from him."

"Well, let's have it, for God's sake," I said. My pulse jumped. Maybe it was a notice that we were in the clear. I ripped it open and read.

Edgar broke the silence with a doomful croak.

Ginny kept her tone level. "What's the bad news?"

I gave her the letter. "They claim we owe upwards of thirty thousand dollars plus penalties." Val was old enough and tough enough to hear. "They hint at criminal charges, conspiracy with Nornwell. It's signed Alger Sneep."

# XXXV

Yeah," said Barney when we got him on his phone at home. "I'm not too surprised." His face was haggard, his eyes were sunken and dark-rimmed, a tic jerked in his right cheek, and his voice plodded.

"Then why didn't you warn us, for God's sake?" I sputtered.

"I didn't know exactly what to expect, or I would have. Steve, it gets hard to think after a couple of weeks when they've had your most precious parts in a meat grinder."

"That bad, huh?"

"Agents everywhere, poking into everything, grilling everybody, demanding records and receipts from ten or fifteen years ago. No statute of limitations on some of the things they talk about. I haven't said a lot to you folks because I didn't want to dump on you. Now it seems they've undertaken that job themselves."

"But what in Satan's name are they talking *about?* You always griped at taxes, but you paid in full and on time, like us. Didn't you?"

"So I thought. The company and myself came clean through every audit. But this one— Well, for instance, you know how we've done a fair amount of business overseas, including some with organizations or regimes that have since gone belly-up, like Panchatantrics, Ltd. in India or the Pious Democratic Republic of Korea. We can't always now find somebody to corroborate that the deals were legitimate and the cash flows precisely what we reported. And then, there's no end to the labyrinth—maze—jungle—nightmare's nest of regulations. We may or may not have touched certain bases we're supposed to. Our own lawyers and diabolists admit they don't comprehend more than a fraction of it. They doubt the IRS does either. But the taxpayer is guilty unless proven innocent, remember."

"Any idea what they're after Ginny and me for? They claim the money you transferred to our account in August is income we haven't reported. But it's not!"

Barney sighed. "Of course not. It was to Operation Luna. Putting it in your name was just for convenience. You've kept records of outlays, haven't you?"

"Certainly," Ginny replied. "The whole matter would have been explained when we file next year. But we're accused of failure to file an amended return in September, plus some subparagraph—I forget which, though I called it up and tried to make sense of it—seems to have something to do with prevention of money laundering. Well, the bank was already required to report the transaction."

"I'll check with our legal staff." Barney's tone took on a little life. "Whatever happens, Nornwell will stand by you. Come worst to worst, you needn't go down with the ship."

Tears touched her eyes. Mine blurred for a moment. "Thank you, old dear," she whispered.

Then I remembered the threat of prosecution for us, too. Anger lifted afresh in me. "This is out-and-out harassment," I snapped. "Can't your Congressman do anything?" Ours was a freshman. The only weight he swung was his belly.

"He's trying," Barney said, "but he tells me he's up against something as slippery as it is powerful."

"Something that's out to get us, no matter what. Right?"

"Well," Barney said carefully, "I haven't gone paranoid yet. My guess is, this started as a routine, maybe even random checkup, and snowballed." *But who might have nudged the random factors?* I wondered. "They thought they smelled big game. The more heads a tax agent takes, the better for his career." He paused. "But, yeah, some interests would like to see Nornwell ruined. Certain competitors. Certain politicians, whose opponents I've given strong support. The assorted types who hate the space program. One or two of them, or a coalition, could be cheering the IRS on from behind the scenes."

Ginny nodded. "And as for us here, I suspect that little Sneep creep has seen a chance to make our lives miserable."

"Personal malice does often enter in," Barney agreed. "A big reason why the framers of the US Constitution tried to put strict limits on the powers of government." He sighed again. "Enough for now. We'll slog on, okay? At least you've told me how well the test went today. Keep up the good work."

*If we're allowed to,* I refrained from saying. We three spoke a few

more words that meant nothing objectively and a great deal emotionally before we signed off.

Though Ginny and I did our best to assure the kids that everything was under control, dinner became a fairly cheerless meal. Afterward Val comforted Chryssa with a lighthearted bedtime story about how Moldylocks overcame a wicked wizard, Soapy Wilberforce, who'd been making people feel bad by convincing them they were made from nothing better than dirt.

Neither Ginny nor I slept well that night. The children did, to judge by how bright-eyed and bushy-tailed they were in the morning. Well, youth bounces back fast, and although Fjalar's snores had reached every eardrum, they were deep and steady, like geological forces.

He too was energetic and cheerful when at last he woke. "Good morning, good morning, good morning," he boomed, bursting in on us and the Sunday paper. "And how ban everybody this lovely morning?" I suppressed an urge to kill him. "Ah, Ay sniff hungry-making grease." We'd finished our bacon and pancakes. "My belly yawns like Ginnungagap and rumbles like Thor's car wheels. First a shot of Scotch, no?"

Ginny started to rise. "Never mind," I said. "I'll feed him." He wouldn't recognize her gourmet touch, and I needed something to do. I led him into the kitchen, gave him his eye-opener, and busied myself at the stove.

He aimed his nose at me and sighted down it from under his brows. "You got a face on you as long as the Midgard Vorm. Vat ban wrong? A foeman of yours ban happy?"

I didn't want to discuss our troubles and spoil the breakfast taste in my mouth. However, sooner or later I must, so I might as well get it over with. "Trouble with our taxes."

"*Haa,* ban its yeomen rebelling? Ay didn't know it ban yours, Steve. Ay thought it ban a *len* of this kingdom."

I stared from the frying pan to him. "What're you talking about?"

"The Taxes folk. East of here, no? They raiding you?"

The English vocabulary laid on him had holes. "No, I mean the, the tribute we have to pay."

"Ah, the scot. *Ja.* You pay the king every year so he can feed his household varriors and make gifts to other kings and to skalds that praise him. If you don't, the household varriors come vith fire and sword."

"Worse than that hereabouts. But you've got the general idea."

"Vat kind of payment he vant? Not fur or amber, Ay bet, not from this land. Maybe hides? Ay've seen herds of kine."

"Money. You know about money, I'm sure."

Fjalar nodded. "Gold, silver, *ja.* Vat's the matter? You can't skveeze enough from your underlings to glut the king? Maybe you should rise against him."

Ever tried to explain income tax to a complete outsider? Especially while cooking? Smoke soon hazed the kitchen, fans whirred, alarms beeped, Ginny came in to see and retreated after one glance. Luckily, the dwarf didn't mind if his food was scorched. Or maybe he was polite in his way—in olden times, the obligations between host and guest were sacred—or maybe he was too hungry to care. Anyhow, he wolfed the result down, say I who have knowledge of that subject. Meanwhile he listened to me and asked questions. Though naive, they were not stupid.

Having cleaned his plate, he poured another whisky, sat back, and unloosed a philosophical belch. "*Ja,* Ay see," he ruminated. "Foul men have done trollcraft on the law till they can tvist the vords around to make it say anything they vant it to."

"I don't think it was on purpose," I replied slightly reluctantly. "It just happened. Congress—the, uh, the Thing—" I had a brief vision of a mindless, insatiable Thing rising from the grassroots. "—it keeps changing who has to pay what and why. This forces the, uh, the scot gatherers to make their own rules more and more complicated . . . though, true, doing that comes natural to such people."

Fjalar shrugged his massive shoulders. "No difference. Vat you vant is the exact vord of the law on your side. Like vun time in Iceland, a man who had done wrong got the doom that for vun year he must stay in bowshot of his house. His foes lured him farther. This made him outlaw and they could lawfully kill him. But his son vent on a kvest for a stronger bow, and in the outlands he found vun. He came home and shot it from the house. The arrow flew longer than his father had gone. So the killers vas now in the wrong, and they themselves became outlaw, and the son took his revenge."

"Great, if only it were that simple," I said. "As is, though, we, Ginny and I, we're not the main targets. Operation Luna is, and its backer, Nornwell. I'm very much afraid our moon flight will be derailed."

I didn't bother to correct myself. Besides the dashing of a lifetime's dreams, I was thinking of demons unhindered on the moon.

"Vat?" Fjalar roared. "All for nothing? The boldest faring ever

made, stopped before it leaves the dock?" His fist crashed on the table. The plate jumped. I looked at him anew. Yes, he'd been interested in the job for its own sake, a challenge. I hadn't realized how the dream had caught him too.

I struggled to explain the ins and outs, to the extent I grasped them myself. He brushed this aside. "Vat ve vant is the strong bow," he growled. "Not to shoot nobody. Too bad. But the vord, the . . . reading of the law that shows you are right, and none can gainsay."

"Barney Sturlason's retained some of the highest-paid tax experts in the country, and so far they aren't getting anywhere," I said dully. "Oh, they may win out in the end, or reach a compromise or something. But that could take years and cost our side a fortune, when the IRS has unlimited tax money to draw on. We might end up in the clear, but Operation Luna will have died on the vine, and as for whether Project Selene can be revived—I doubt it, without us to demonstrate a success."

"Then—" Fjalar brooded for a minute. Sunlight seeped though the window and the air grew less acrid as the smoke thinned away.

"Mimir!" the dwarf shouted.

"What?" I asked through the ringing in my ears.

"The head of Mimir. The vise jotun, who can answer all kvestions. Come on!" Fjalar hopped to the floor. "Ve go tell your vife the vitch. She vill know vat you don't, you anvilhead."

I felt too battered to resent that and followed him out. Presently we were in the arcanum with Ginny.

I saw her come alight from within. "Mimir," she breathed.

Both the *Elder* and *Younger Edda* were on her reference shelves, along with the *Heimskringla* and other such stuff. She leafed through them. Fjalar and I stood still in the shaded room among the curious objects and waited.

"Mimir—or Mim—he kept the well of wisdom beneath Yggdrasil. . . . Sent as a hostage to the Vanir. They cut his head off and returned it to the Aesir, which almost renewed the war between the two tribes of gods. . . . Odin embalmed it and cast spells that brought it alive again. Thereafter he often consulted it. . . . The sybil foretold how as the end of the world draws nigh, 'Odin takes counsel with the head of Mimir.' As well he might, seeing that Mimir at the beginning of the world had allowed him a drink of that water. . . ."

She laid the last of the books down and turned to us. "Yes," she murmured, "I have a feeling—call it a hunch, at this stage—I'll have to research much deeper—but I have a feeling we may find help there."

My spine chilled. I'd known Ginny's hunches in the past.

"Another universe, right?" she put to Fjalar. "A continuum coexistent with ours, but different, distant in hyperreality, where your gods and Mimir exist."

"Vell, Ay dunno," replied the dwarf, bewildered. "You talk too fancy for me. All Ay know is, Ay have gone there and seen the roots of Yggdrasil. Other dvarves told me how Mimir's head still lies at the vell, and Ay think a vise voman like you can find the vay. Me, Ay have seen the Tree rise up and up like forever." He gulped.

Ginny nodded. Half to herself, half to us, she said low and slow: "That cosmos was once closely entwined with ours, and surely with others. Or, rather, the crossing was easy from Northern lands. The belief factors . . . Christianity changed things. In a way, Beings like you, Fjalar, were left stranded here, like their counterparts in related universes."

*And meanwhile the Low Continuum, Hell, became more accessible,* I thought with a shudder. But no, like every faith, the Old Norse religion had its own hells and horrors. Its gods were in fact only Beings, however powerful. They'd withdrawn before the One God, though what His real nature is, I do not pretend to know.

The point was—my spirit surged upward—Mimir still lived, in at least one universe. Ginny could figure out how to reach him, probably with less difficulty than we'd had going to the Inferno. If he was the chief advisor to the chief of those gods, he must be a genius at unraveling the word games of skaldic poetry and Icelandic law—

And maybe, even, the United States tax code?

Ginny seemed to think it was possible. Her voice rang. "I'll look into this. Steve, can you take care of the household for the rest of today?" And keep Fjalar out from underfoot, she did not add. "Perhaps I'll know by evening. Meanwhile, do not, repeat not, disturb me."

The doorbell sounded. Already obedient, I went to see who was there. The dwarf trotted behind me. Val and Ben were ahead of us. They'd admitted Balawahdiwa.

# XXXVI

"Welcome, sir," I greeted when my surprise had settled down. For such a guest, of course Ginny postponed her research. We led him to a chair and started fresh coffee brewing. Edgar dipped his beak, then perched at attention. Svartalf strolled in, stopped, raised his tail for a moment, and took a seat on his haunches to look as Egyptian as possible. Fjalar hunkered on the rug beside him, Val, and Ben, who sat there in very respectful silence. But Chryssa ran over to the priest and hugged his knees. He smiled and ruffled the yellow curls. She put herself at his feet with a proprietary air, though she also refrained from prattling.

I groped for words. *To what do we owe the honor of this visit?* seemed too damn highfalutin. There he was, grizzled and leathery, dressed in a denim shirt, faded Levi's, and shoes worn into comfortable shapelessness. The Ford he'd parked outside stood aged and dusty. But he wouldn't have come unannounced like this on a social call.

"I hope everything's okay at the pueblo," was the best I could think of.

Balawahdiwa nodded. "Yes. For now. But you're troubled here."

"Well, we shouldn't cry on your shoulder."

"You needn't," he answered softly. "Trouble is overtaking us all." He glanced at the children. "I don't want to frighten you," he told them. "But not knowing is often worse. Your parents will decide."

Valeria doubled her fists. "I'd rather know." Can someone speak both stoutly and thinly? "Sir."

"Yeah, I can take it," Ben declared. "Sir."

"Me too, me too," said Chryssa. I doubted she'd understand, but figured that being with us would give more comfort than exile to her

toys. Or did she already have an inkling? She closed a hand on Balawahdiwa's ankle.

"We'll wait for your mother," said the priest. Drawling: "Did you have fun at your party yesterday?"

Val couldn't suppress a giggle. "Mr. Fjalar got drunk," Ben blurted. "That was funny."

"Ay did not," protested the dwarf. "Yust yolly. Drunk is ven you make vows like you vill sail to Italy, take the Pope for ransom, kill the other men, loot, burn, take the vimmin and—"

"Never mind," I interrupted. "We'll stipulate that we had a long and lively lunch. How'd it go at Zuni?"

"Enjoyable." Balawahdiwa launched into an account, concentrating on polite but colorful details. I saw the children forget their fears while he talked.

True to pueblo ideas of courtesy, Ginny had gone to the kitchen to prepare refreshments. She returned, put them on the coffee table, and took a chair next to mine. At once she became the professional, her husband's and visitor's equal.

Balawahdiwa cut his story short without making it obvious that he did. He turned grave. His gaze locked with ours. "Then as I slept, a dream came to me," he said slowly. "That's what's brought me here."

He must have detected my flicker of doubt, because he added, "There are dreams and dreams. Most are nonsense. This one was what you call a medicine dream."

"You'd know it when it came," Ginny agreed low.

Balawahdiwa sat still for half a minute. The brightness and warmth seemed to drain from the sunshine in our windows.

"I can't tell you much about it," he went on. "That is, I mustn't. Not yet. But I can say it warned me that time grows short for us. The enemy know what we intend and they're marshaling their forces. Already they've begun to strike."

"*Ja,* they have, by Hel's blue boobs!" Fjalar exploded.

For an instant I wondered how he acquired his vulgar American slang. Maybe by some slight rapport with the vulgar American mind? "At least, we're suddenly in deep, uh, sheep dip," I said fast. "Though I wouldn't accuse anybody of being in conscious conspiracy with demons."

"Nor I, on the basis of evidence to date," Ginny rejoined, "but that doesn't mean the enemy have had nothing to do with it."

"Tell me about it later, please," Balawahdiwa said. "What I can tell you right away is that any strike at you must be only a beginning.

The demons have their agents on Earth, but the moon's become where their real strength is. They're gathering, organizing, to hit all of us, all humans who could give them serious resistance, while the hitting's good."

Through horror, I looked from Val to Ben to Chryssa. The older two sat huge-eyed, breathing quickly and shallowly. We, their parents, would have plenty of explaining to do, not in detail but not mendaciously either, and plenty of reassurance to give, to Ben still more than Val.

Chryssa scrambled over to me. I gathered her onto my lap and held her close. "Do you mean an actual attack?" I rasped.

"Not a material war like the Caliph's, I'm sure," Ginny declared. "Demons are subtler than that. They have to be. But overwhelming our goetic, even our religious defenses and subverting our souls—"

"There, there, honey, you hear?" I crooned to the little one. "No boogies are coming to bite you."

"After they've gotten a strong foothold in us, we'll take care of physical destruction ourselves," Ginny said in as bleak a voice as I've ever heard.

Balawahdiwa nodded. "That's about the size of it, I reckon. We need the help of Powers that can match them, we need it bad, and we need it soon. So my dream made clear." His eyes swung back to me. "You and I have to seek it, Steven."

*"What?"* I nearly dumped my child on the floor.

Sitting back again, I heard him explain: "We're to go on retreat. I'll initiate you in certain things. Then together we'll call certain Ones."

"But-but-but," I protested like an old-time outboard motor, "I'm not any kind of adept or— My wife—"

"You are the man of this household and the male chief of Operation Luna. We have to follow the Ancient Way."

"But Ginny—her and me—we may be bound for another universe. I can't let her go alone." My will stiffened. "God damn it, I won't."

"Huh?" Val piped up. "Another universe? Like Magister Lazarus—like you did once yourselves?" Fox-quick, her mind grabbed the idea and ran with it. "Why can't Mom wait here till you get back, Dad?"

I eased a trifle. "Well, yes. How long will this . . . this retreat take?"

"A few days." Balawahdiwa frowned. "However, that may be as much time as we'll have. Right now, when the first full moon after the fall equinox is waning toward the half, is best for a Seeking like ours. I don't guarantee the Ones I'm thinking of will come to us, but

the medicine for calling them is stronger than it can be again for months." He hesitated. On him that was a scary thing to behold. "Nor do I guarantee they and their kind can defend us and clean away the evil by themselves. But the enemy will be ready soon, soon. We need every help we can get. Pray to your Christian God."

Chryssa's voice wavered from the circle of my arms. "Jesus loves us."

I didn't doubt that, nor doubt that the Almighty could end our woes with a word. But He wouldn't. Bismarck said once that the Lord looks after fools, drunks, and the United States of America. That, though, was just a joking remark about luck. Sooner or later luck runs out. Always we mortals have to do the best we can with whatever we've got. And each of us must wage the fight for his or her soul alone.

"We have to take every possible action," Ginny said crisply. "Very likely, if I stay idle till you return, whatever I can do will be too late to save Operation Luna. Then what are our chances of prevailing? We'd never get clear information about the enemy, or get at them. But if Mimir's head really can advise us, perhaps we'll forestall that part of the attack."

"You don't know if you can reach him, let alone make it back alive!" I cried.

"That's the question I intend to study today," she answered.

"It ban not too dreadful," Fjalar maintained. "Ay don't think ve vill meet vith any trolls, and unless ve get lost among the roots, ve von't come too near the dragon Nidhöggur."

"Hey, wait just a damn minute—" I began.

Balawahdiwa's quiet words cut across mine and killed them. "In my dream, you traveled a long and strange way, Virginia. More than that I don't know. Would you care to explain?"

For a while the talk grew pretty chaotic, as might be expected when three cultures meet head-on. I don't remember enough to record, and it doesn't matter. The upshot was that Balawahdiwa received a thumbnail education in Eddic lore, and I promised to be at his place the next morning.

He declined our invitation to lunch. "Thanks, and I'm sorry, but you'll be busy making ready, Steven, and you learning, Virginia. Me, I'd better go home, think, and speak with a few others. Maybe their spells and prayers can help you."

*If* she went. Inwardly I hoped to blazes she'd discover the scheme was as hairy-brained as it looked. Bloody idiot dwarf!

No, that wasn't fair. I'd snatched at the idea myself, before it turned out I couldn't be at her side.

Balawahdiwa paused in the open doorway, looked past me at the children, and said gently, "It's for them. It always is. . . . See you tomorrow, Steven. Fare you well, Virginia." He took both her hands in his and breathed on them, then mine. The gesture held enormous meaning and love. Turning, he walked to his stick and flew off.

Ginny told me she'd skip lunch, and disappeared into her studio. There was no big hurry about my packing, which wouldn't amount to a lot. The kids stood by watching: how silently. I suggested a picnic excursion. Rather to my relief, Fjalar said, "No, Ay think Ay stay here. Yinny may vant my redes."

"Won't you get bored waiting?" asked Ben, maybe recalling what beer and whisky had done.

"No, Ay vatch your—farseer, you call it?" Fjalar stroked his beard. "But first, because you may come back from your trip before Ay from mine, Steve, Ay should make extra keys to the smithy and moonboat for you."

I conducted him to my workshop in a corner of the garage. His skillful, powerful hands required no jig or grinder, simply a hacksaw and file, to turn out the duplicates from an L-brace of the right thickness that was lying there. Naturally, he also needed to 'chant them properly, but those were simple spells, though none that I could follow as he sang in his rusty basso—on which account no intruder could likely circumvent them. I took the keys to my study and left them in a desk drawer.

The kids trailed us everywhere. Then they helped me prepare the picnic lunch. Chryssa made the job take twice as long as necessary, but nobody complained. We were together.

Red Rock State Park was the right place to talk reality. The air was mild and sweet, sunlight dappled the shade under the tree where we sat, sandstone cliffs sheered ruddy behind it, and everything bespoke enduring strength and peace. First renewing pledges of secrecy, I told them as much about the basic situation as it seemed I must. I left out the nastier features and emphatically downplayed the danger. Balawahdiwa was a good man but too pessimistic, I said. Though the aid of the Zunis was invaluable, none of them fully realized what resources we Americans had to call on. Never forget how we'd defeated Kaiser and Caliph and thwarted the Adversary himself. As for the immediate future, I was simply bound off on an interesting field trip. If their mother did go to Yggdrasil—if—why, that wasn't anything to

worry about. Not at all like going to Hell. Merely seeking advice. Like visiting a doctor's office—no, I meant a lawyer's—no, I meant like dropping in on Uncle Will to ask him something about the stars.

I got Val and Ben kind of soothed. They could be trusted to keep quiet. Chryssa might forget to, but who'd take her seriously or even know what she was babbling about? In fact, she didn't really understand what I related, only that it wasn't happy. She still fretted. Her sister heartened her with an impromptu story about Moldylocks and the Pig Baby.

After that we could eat and play games and sing songs and look in on the museum and hike around some. Those hours were good. I wished there could have been more. But if nothing else, the kids were too tired to be overly worried when at last we flew homeward through the long light of a westering sun.

We entered into a thunderstorm of hoarse laughter. "Haw, haw, haw!" Fjalar rolled on the floor, slapped his thigh, kicked his legs aloft. The farseer was concluding an English-language performance of Gounod's *Faust.* Since that's a favorite opera of mine, I asked what was funny.

"That man, he got run through, he ban dying, and he sang!" whooped the dwarf. He wiped his streaming eyes. "He sang and sang. He fell down, he stood back up, he fell down, he stood up, he fell down, he flopped like a landed fish, and alvays he sang! Now they ban going to burn that poor girl alive, and she *sings!*"

Different folk, different tastes.

"Has my lady called on you?" I finally managed to inquire.

"*Ja,* yust vunce, a few kvestions. She vill come out soon and tell us Ay vas right. You got any more humorous shows?"

Our music library contained some audiovisuals. I wondered about Wagner's *Ring.* No, Fjalar might rupture himself guffawing. Ginny saved me from making a decision when she appeared.

She was exhausted, white-faced, her hands trembling slightly, but fire burned green behind her eyes. "I'm done," she said, her voice not quite level. "We'll go, Fjalar."

"Ay knew it," replied the dwarf smugly.

She took my hands. Hers were cold. I told myself that was from weariness. "It's all right, darling," she whispered. "I verified the cross-over is possible. Ordinarily it's hard. There's no body of belief here anymore, and the time lines have branched far apart. But given Fjalar's presence, his affinity, I can make it more easily than . . . the one we made before. And we'll meet with no hostility."

*Oh, yeah?* my mind groaned. *What about trolls and dragons and giants and drows and the rest of that merry crew? I wouldn't trust old One-Eye much, either.* For the sake of the youngsters I kept it to myself. Nothing was ever certain anyway. Maybe here at home drunks on brooms were a worse hazard.

Dusk was filling the room. The glare and noise of the farseer deepened it in every other corner. Ginny squared her shoulders. "We should start making arrangements," she continued. "First about the children. Let's see if Will can take over again."

Action is the best medicine for anxiety. We phoned her brother and he said we'd be welcome. Leaving Valeria in charge, we flitted with Fjalar to his house. The sky was turning purple and windows had come aglow among shadows beneath. The lights on other vehicles bobbed past like fireflies. The air was as cool as a stranger's kiss.

Will guided us into his cluttered quarters, fussed about with cups and a pot of tea, finally sat down opposite us. He seemed frazzled, his smiles mostly mechanical. However, when we asked he said that, sure, he could move back to our house anytime and stay as long as we wished, "if you don't mind the FBI making eye tracks all over it. But what's the occasion?"

That I was bound off with Balawahdiwa couldn't be hidden. I told him about seeking native help against the demons. Maybe he'd have a suggestion or two. Instead, he lost what cordiality he'd shown. "That doesn't strike me as a very hopeful idea, or even a wise one," he snapped.

"Why not?" I replied, surprised. "You know something you haven't told us?"

"No. But remember what happened when last you invoked one of those Beings."

"It wasn't any of them that tried to kill us!" At once I regretted my outburst. Did he flinch? "Sorry, Will. I shouldn't have said that." I fumbled for better words. "Seeing as how you've been falsely accused, why shouldn't you cheer us on in anything that might clear you?"

"I feel dubious. Call it an intuition."

"I'm afraid we engineers haven't much training in intuition," I argued, trying for lightness. "I'm going, regardless. Nothing to lose."

Maybe.

He looked at his sister. "You too?" It sounded almost like *"Et tu?"* Why?

She shook her head. "No, I'll be working on the tax mess. That'll take me . . . out of town."

"Where, please?"

Fjalar opened his mouth. Ginny's tap on the shoulder warned him and his teeth thumped together. "I'd better not speak about it yet, except that the prospect seems good." Pain was in her voice too. Deciding to keep this from him had not come easy. It was like admitting to Will that our trust in him was not quite a hundred percent. Oh, close enough, or we'd never have requested his services. But he could just possibly, unknowingly, act as some kind of information conduit. . . .

In fact, this was in a way the case. "Yes, I am under surveillance," he said with a shrug. "Possibly the stakeouts hear everything uttered in this house. I wish them joy of it."

"We've nothing illegal in mind," I declared hastily.

Fjalar broke the embarrassed silence that followed. "Vere ban Brynjubítr?"

"Ah, Fotherwick-Botts? It—he's back in the room I use for a laboratory." Will's withholdingness broke. He brightened as the sea does when a sunbeam strikes through a fog bank. "Do you want him along on your venture?"

"No, better not," Fjalar opined. "He don't know his vay around yonder, and maybe he says the wrong thing. He's not tactful like me. And if ve meet real trouble, no veapon vill help mush."

That was great news for my ears. Will's smile died. His eyes narrowed.

Before I could introduce a motion to cancel the whole crazy junket, Ginny cried, "Nonsense, Fjalar!"

Her relief was plain to see when the dwarf proceeded: "But ve should hang the sword in the smithy to keep vatch and call an alarm if need be vile ve ban gone."

Will's gladness revived for a moment. "Absolutely! Why don't you take him out there tonight, to make sure?"

"He talks a lot?" I asked redundantly.

Will winced. "I didn't realize how much. It has eroded my powers of concentration. He's gotten as far as some tenth-century affray in Yorkshire."

Ginny smiled compassionately. "Poor dear. Yes, we'll release you, with many thanks."

"Ve shouldn't bring him avay tonight," Fjalar cautioned. "He'd think you didn't like his tales, and be hurt. He's sensitive, you know."

"Tell him you're worn out and have to turn in early," Ginny sug-

gested. Her glance at Will said that he certainly looked it. "Fjalar and I will fetch him in the morning. You get your stuff together, and as soon as I'm ready to leave you can move over."

Will's face locked into the mask we knew too well. "Ah, yes. You may rely on me."

I worried a smidgen, and Ginny admitted to me later that she did too. But whatever his problem was, it hadn't caused him to do anything really erratic. The psychoscopy had proved that the evidence against him must be a frame-up. The FBI monitored him as much in hopes of getting a clue to the somebody or something responsible as because of lingering suspicion.

The kids loved their Uncle Will, he'd done fine by them the last time around, and . . . in the event of an emergency, Val was mature enough to call for the right kind of help. Ginny told me privately she'd brief her in more detail, just in case.

What with all this, my renewed objections to the Mimir expedition were brushed aside.

Before then, Will had declined our invitation to dinner, saying that he was in truth fatigued. We returned home and actually had a rather pleasant family evening. If the cheer was a tad forced, it wasn't fake. Eventually Ginny and I were alone together and made our own farewell.

# XXXVII

Now the story splits again, three ways this time. I'll have to reconstruct two of them from what information came to me later, most of it brokenly, and the best guesses I can make. Nor may I say much about my own experiences. They're branded on my memory, but I gave my word of honor I'd keep certain things secret.

Ginny had been awake and active for hours while I still slept. At the earliest decent time she flew back to Will's. He let her in, himself also fully clad. "I hope I haven't disturbed you," she said for politeness' sake.

"Oh, no." He spoke dully. "I've been up for two or three hours."

She looked at the wan face. "You sleep very little these nights, don't you?"

"I manage. I thought the dwarf would come with you."

"Why pummel him out of bed and coffee him? I've a great deal to do in the shortest possible time."

"Such as?"

"Just now, taking the sword to the workshop. Frankly, I'd as soon not have Fjalar along. Those two can get into dialogues so long and rambling you wouldn't believe it. And he would doubtless criticize my work, as if it weren't perfectly simple and straightforward."

Did Will stiffen? "What work, if I may ask?"

"Well, you remember the idea is to leave Fotherwick-Botts there on watch, to notify the Zunis if anything untoward happens. But I'm not entirely satisfied with the alarm system. This is a busy time of year for them. They may not be able to respond at once. Or if the 'something untoward' is more subtle than a burglar or a vandal, they may feel confused, unsure how to react. That's especially true while

Balawahdiwa, the man among them who's worked most closely with us, is absent the next several days. It occurred to me that I can provide a direct line of communication to Steve. Whether or not he can come immediately in person, he can give advice. I have to have it ready for him before he goes."

Will seemed to turn the idea over in his mind, weighing and peering, before he nodded. "Yes, a reasonable precaution. I'll fetch the garrulous glaive." Sometimes his academic humor still flickered.

The blade had been sheathed. Ginny left it so, said good-bye—with the slightest catch in her voice—and went out into the chill, hushed morning.

Nobody else was in sight when she landed at the smithy. Shadows stretched westward from sparse grass, brush, and wildflowers. Dowa Yalanne dreamed in the offing, red-and-white, rugged, mighty. A few insects buzzed. Somewhere a mountain bluebird cried *teww, teww.*

Fjalar having reclaimed the keys, she let herself in with the spare for the padlock, leaving the door open for light. Nevertheless the space reached cavernous and gloomy. Poised on her parking gear, *Owl* shimmered, beautiful. Ginny took the sword forth. Steel gleamed likewise. She laid the scabbard on a workbench.

"I say," Fotherwick-Botts exclaimed from her hand, "what is this farce, eh, what? Thought I was a guest of Graylock's. Suddenly he boots me out. After casing me before nine in the ruddy P.M. yesterday. Right in the middle of my describing that set-to on Barmby Moor."

"I'm sorry," she replied. "We arrived and caused him to interrupt. But that was an emergency. You understand."

"Emergency? Hah. He didn't say. Certainly I understand emergencies. What kind of weapon would I be if I didn't understand emergencies? Tell me that, eh? What are weapons for if not emergencies? Yes, display and taking of oaths and whatnot, true. But fighting's what it's about, egad. And after you'd gone, he didn't unsheathe me, that Graylock. Is this your American idea of hospitality?"

"He was exhausted. He had to sleep."

"Hrrumph, he was awake bloody early, I can tell you. Didn't so much as say good morning. Left me gagged. No other word will do. Gagged, by thunder. Hah! Bah!"

"I'm sure he was too preoccupied." Ginny set him on the bench, leaned against the wall. "He had hoped for leisure to hear you out later today."

"Indeed? Tchah! If he was really int'rested— How could he not be? There I was, telling how I clove that scoundrel from left shoulder

to right hip. Tasted terrible, he did. Hadn't bathed in months, I'll wager, and shaggy as a dog. How could any thinking person wait to hear the rest of the tale? Anyone but a, a born-and-bred *civilian!*"

"But General, sir, I had dire need of you," she cried piteously.

His wrath puffed away. "You did? You do? Dire need, m'lady? Why didn't you say so at once? At your service, madame! Just bring me to the villains and I'll spill their rotten guts for 'em. I'll sending 'em yelping down to the Devil. If you'll pardon an old soldier's language."

"No, thank you very much for your kindness, but that won't be necessary. At least, not yet. We want—we request you to keep watch here for some days while everybody else is away. You're tireless. If someone tries to break in or otherwise make trouble, you'll sound the alarm and the Zunis will come."

Fotherwick-Botts grew suspicious. "Everybody else? Going away? The dwarf too? What for, ha?"

"Oh, er, various errands."

"Errands? What sort? Bad business, this, that we're in. I smell danger skulking about." The sword paused. "You—are you bound off on a—a quest?"

"Well, in a way."

"A quest! And I'm to hang behind like the tail on a ruddy cow? Bleat for help from a pack of natives? No, by Cross and Hammer both!" he roared. "If you suppose I will, little do you know what a Fotherwick-Botts is full of!"

Ginny thought fast. Though he had no power over her, a surly sword could well prove a sloppy sentry. "But this is different, sir. The quest is only for knowledge. More like a pilgrimage. Yes, that's it, a pilgrimage. Here is the stronghold the foe must take if he can. I wouldn't ask anyone who wasn't totally fearless to stand guard. You, ringed in by the forces of darkness, standing your lonely vigil—"

His volume dropped. "Vigil, did you say?"

"Come worst to worst, you will blow your horn, so to speak, like Heimdall on the walls of Asgard or Roland in the pass of Roncesvalles."

"Hum, ha, see your point, m'lady. A vigil, eh? And a call to rally the troops. And then I'll join in the battle."

"When this need arose, we thought of you first. You are superb at blowing your own horn."

Thus she won his agreement. She hung him by two pegs above the bench before she adjusted and tested the alarm system. It was

merely an open phone to the pueblo governor's dwelling. Somebody was always there, doing housework if nothing else. That person could holler for the tribal police. A number of able-bodied men had been deputized to strengthen their tiny band. The system could also call for assistance from the sheriff's office in Gallup. Since those people hadn't been briefed—discretion—reinforcements might take a while to arrive.

However, we didn't expect any huge assault. The enemy could have only a few humans working for them, maybe only the slippery customer we were trying to find. As for demons and other Beings, the protective spells remained potent. Ginny knew better than to tell Fotherwick-Botts that we thought of planting him here as nothing more than a cheap precaution against an unlikely contingency, like buying a life insurance policy from a vendor before boarding a commercial flight. And it'd keep him out of Will's hair, which was plenty gray enough.

So we thought.

She went on to operations that involved *Owl.* Quick and easy for a witch of her skill, they did not demand any physical or goetic examination of the spacecraft. That wasn't unfortunate, it was much worse.

Having bidden the sword a ceremonious farewell and received a gruff godspeed, she flitted home. When she walked in I was about to fix breakfast for the kids. She took over and made it good. She always made everything good.

We were almost casual as we saw Val and Ben off for school. I was going on an excursion, sort of, and their mother wouldn't leave today. Yet I stood at the door and watched them till they were out of sight.

Inside again, I met Ginny as she came out of my study. Chryssa trotted at her heels. "I returned the smithy key to your desk drawer," she said, "in case you have use for it when Fjalar and I aren't here."

The reminder spoiled my mood. "Hey, didn't you figure your jaunt might be shorter than mine?"

"Might. I still have much to learn and do. In any case, we can't foretell how things will go." She smiled and patted my hand. Sunlight streamed down the hall where we stood, to make ripples of fire in her hair and ripples of shadow across the curves beneath her clothes. "Don't *worry* so, dear old woof. C'mon, I've got something for you."

She led me to the living room. From the jacket she'd taken off and left lying there, she drew a pair of flat rock crystal discs about an inch in diameter. I stared. There was nothing obviously special about

them. Probably every working thaumaturge has blanks like this in stock, to carry assorted kinds of everyday spells.

"Communicators," she explained. "That's why I roused myself at an unsanctified hour. I got the idea last night, after—" She glanced down at Chryssa. "As I was falling asleep. It's simply a portable, untappable phone line. Naturally, it had to be made ready before you start off today."

Such a device wasn't "simply." I wondered just how long and hard she'd worked on it. Eagerness drove that out of me. "We can talk while you're in yonder universe?"

"No, I'm afraid not. Nobody's developed the capability." Transcosmic expeditions had been mighty few, I recalled. Some had never been seen again. " 'Untappable' is the operative word. I've sympathized both these to *Owl*'s communication globe, which is unique, you know. Through it, you and I can be in instantaneous touch across any distance—in this continuum—and nobody and nothing not in actual earshot should be able to listen in on us."

"Unless in possession of *Owl*. . . . But we've provided against that, haven't we?" I couldn't help thinking of the hopeful applications. "Say, this'll come in handy when she's in space. Ought not to need all that apparatus to transmit voice in airlessness."

"Yes, it's mind-resonant, though given air it does audio. In case one of us has to be aroused, for instance."

"Smart girl. Um-m, but Balawahdiwa and I are supposed to be in spiritual retreat."

"I realize that. Matters will get grim indeed before I yell for you. What I mostly considered was the situation after we both come home."

"Yeah, when we try carrying the war to the enemy. But it's nice to have this gadget already. Thank you, darling."

Chryssa clutched my leg. I rumpled her curls. "Hey, honey, nothing to be scared of. This is only a funny phone. We'll let you talk on it later, okay? The boogies are far away. As far as Moldylocks is from the soap works. Want to come watch us make jewelry?"

We took her along into the studio. Ginny kept a supply of rings, fine chains, and suchlike stuff. Best not let untrained hands put talismans in their settings. Mine were reasonably competent under her supervision, and we worked together. It didn't take long. Both crystals went into lockets, to hang around the neck. I placed Ginny's on her. If our daughter hadn't been there, I'd have felt around for the exact right arrangement.

As we came out we heard a bass bellowing. Fjalar was awake at last. He wanted to know where we and his breakfast were.

Noblesse oblige, or some damn thing to that effect. We fed him and left him as our babysitter while we flew to Zuni on separate brooms. We'd leave one there for me to return with. We didn't linger in the pueblo. Well-meaning though the dwarf was, neither of us cared to have him in charge for any length of time. For instance, out of the kindness of his heart he might conceivably offer the child a beer.

Landing by the church, we spoke a few low-voiced words, took a hasty kiss, held hands for a minute, and went our different ways.

# XXXVIII

At Balawahdiwa's command I'd brought a minimal outfit, backpack filled with the usual gear and clothing, sleeping bag tied to the frame. It goes without saying that besides my new communicator I kept my wereflash under my shirt. When I'd asked about a pistol, he'd replied, "No. Wouldn't be any use, and might give offense."

He waited at his home, broom heavily laden. The food, which he'd said he'd supply, had little volume or weight, traditional Zuni fare. His priestly things were likewise deceptively few and simple. But water for several days filled as many large clay *ollas,* padded against breakage in a net lashed to the coffer. We boarded, lumbered into the air, and flew slowly east.

I mentioned Fotherwick-Botts' presence at the smithy. "Good," Balawahdiwa said. "We really can't spare even a boy any longer to stay in view. Busy time—the regular duties of the season, the Doll Dance coming up, and preparations for the Shalako under way in earnest."

The casual-sounding words gained power from the grave tone. He and his people lived their religion. Not for the first time, I wondered if my family and I should do likewise with ours. Had not a veritable saint once come to our aid? But he didn't seem to have been—dispatched; he'd heard our appeal and responded, being the kind of spirit he was. And the business had had some ridiculous mixups. And if we'd been, oh, Shintoists, might it have been somebody like Susano-o? And in, say, the Kaiser's War both sides had called on the same Christian God. And if He really wanted anybody's prayers, why was there so much pain and evil and outright horror in the world? . . . If you trace such questions no further back than the prophets of Israel, I'd still have

to set my poor wits to pick and choose from three thousand years of thinking. That wasn't my natural bent. For now, at least, I'd take the guidance of this old medicine man.

"Where are we bound, please?" I ventured to ask.

"Same place where Kokopelli met us," he answered.

My belly muscles tightened. The aftermath of that encounter—

"They're different, those I'm hoping will come to us now," he added. "You'll need your courage."

After a moment, while the air flowed warm and the uplands lifted stark ahead: "It's permitted that we land on the site and unload our stuff. But then we have to fly down and walk back up." He glanced at me. "Don't worry about being attacked on the trail like last time. The enemy don't repeat their mistakes. Also, Virginia isn't with us. I think they wanted most to eliminate her."

"And you," I replied around a thickness in my throat.

"That's not for me to say."

Nor may I say what followed, unless in words so bare as to be nearly meaningless. Let me try, though, within the limits laid on me.

By the time we'd returned to our things, the sun was low. I unpacked and made camp while Balawahdiwa gathered dry wood, kindled a small blaze with a fire bow, and blessed it. After he'd given me basic instruction in the proper prayers, we ate and drank frugally. I did the cleaning, as befitted an acolyte. We both made reverence while sunset burned away in enormous gold and red. Later we sat watching the stars come forth, impossibly bright and many. He told me of much. We hailed the rising moon before we went to sleep.

Understand, I wasn't being converted. My puzzled, partial religion stayed the same. It wasn't incompatible with his. I just had to make myself worthy.

Tuesday was hard.

On Wednesday I began to use a little of what I'd learned and, more important, to feel it.

This went on through Thursday. That night they came to us.

The moon rose gibbous, only half an hour later than before, for it was waning down from Harvest, to be reborn as Hunter's. Against the icy brilliance of Milky Way and crowding stars, its glow barely touched the soil, rocks, and sparse growth around us with gray. Below our ridge the mountainside plunged into a darkness that upheaved itself on the other side of a dry arroyo. Embers in our banked fire lay like drops of blood. Balawahdiwa and I had stripped down to kilt, sash, and paint. A breeze stroked my skin with a chill that seemed far distant.

It fluttered the feathers of our prayer sticks. The silence in which we stood belonged to the rite we performed, and the rite had taken possession of me.

Beyond this, I can't really tell what happened, what was said, or how. Even if I were free to, I wouldn't be able to. Words, images, ideas don't reach to it.

Did the wind go from a whisper to a whistle, or was that a flute at the lips of a hunchback? Did thunder roll through these unclouded hills, or was that a drumbeat?

I felt them approach, without knowledge of how they did. Balawahdiwa scattered sacred meal from a bowl he held onto the ground they would tread. Then it was as if the night thickened there and became the pair of them.

Short they were, but hugely muscled and cougar-lithe. Ugly they were, but flintily majestic. Clad like hunters they were, in skin tunic and leggings, bow and quiver slung behind the shoulders, but gourds in their belts rattled the measures of a dance, plumes nodded tall above leather caps, each right hand bore a spear and each left hand a shield. The markings on the shields glimmered with tracings I could not follow, lines and curves and emblems in which my gaze lost itself till I ripped it free. The priest had taught me well and I knew them—once the Divine Twins, now the Twin War Gods.

We spoke with them.

—The Beloved Ones know what is our need and our prayer.

—*We know what the Fluteplayer told. We know that Coyote has consorted with strange Beings. What is that to us? Again and again have we raised the hearts of our peoples. Again and again they were crushed. Their war cries resound no more. Their lands have fallen to those who love not Earth our Mother, but flay her alive. Why should we help the invaders?*

The Twins were not only gods of the pueblos. Folk venerated them across our whole West and far into the South. The Maya told how in the underworld they once played ball with the Lords of the Dead. Everyone told how they had led the ancestors of humanity from below to the sunlight. There could be truth in that belief, the same kind of symbolic truth there is in Genesis.

—Forsake us not, we pray.

—*How faithful do* you *remain? After the Fluteplayer revealed his news, we searched. Yes, terror is on the moon, and this is unholy. But may it not scourge the world clean, as terror did over and over in the*

*ancient past, and purify those who live through it, that they may begin anew?*

—What threatens is worse than death, worse than pain and loss. Hear what my friend has to tell.

The Twins looked coldly upon my soul.

And somehow, I don't know how, I found—not the facts; those they scanned at once—but the will to speak up, clumsily, foreignly, but as honestly as ever I did.

—Sirs, if you please, is this the worst of all possible worlds? Are my people really such monsters? A long time before us, wave after wave of newcomers crossed over from their old countries. Did they always mingle peacefully with those they found? Who wiped out the mammoth, the giant bison and bear and sloth, the sabertooth, the American horse and camel, any big game that didn't learn fast enough to fear them? Who, in these very parts, stripped the land till at last they had to move out? Did one tribe never come with slaughter, torture, rape, and enslavement to drive another from its home?

—And today, how dreadful is it to have eyeglasses when your vision weakens, books to read, teeth in your mouth for life, no more hours and hours spent over a metate to grind the corn, an excellent chance that a woman will live through every childbirth and every child live to have children?

—Sure, we whites have done horrible things and made horrible mistakes. We're still at it. We're human, after all. But more and more of us are trying to do better; and we've worked out a few guidelines, like the Bill of Rights; and—

—And, God damn it, we're not about to fold our hand and quit the game! I said it, we're human too. Best would be if we had you and your people at our side in this mess. It makes sense. The disaster would also fall on them. If we win together, they'll have more say in what to do with the victory. If we lose—we'll go down together, and you won't have sold out to Hell.

I straightened before the Twins.—Sorry, sirs. But with respect, that's what I mean, and I'll stand by it.

—He speaks truth, as well as he grasps it, Balawahdiwa said.

—*We see that. . . . And, yes, a monstrous evil is indeed gathering here in our motherland and upon the moon, the holy moon. The Flute-player did not believe but could not long keep still. Then we made medicine, we sought, and we learned. At this meeting we have learned more.*

—*We will speak with Others.*

Can gods feel anxious, even afraid? That's not for me to judge. What I imagine I remember, and retell as a shadow-scrap of the reality, is:

*—We will call Coyote to task and hear him out. He is mischievous, sometimes stupid, but he is not at heart evil. And he is among the Creators.*

*—But all of us together cannot by ourselves fend off the demons who are abroad. They are too strange to us, and too strong. Once more, humans will have their part in upholding the world . . . if you and we can . . .*

Presently the Twins left us. The air blew frosty, the stars gleamed keen.

"We, we aren't sure how they'll help us, or when, or anything?" I stammered into the stillness. My breath smoked white under the moon.

"It depends on what happens, which they can't foresee either. I'll hope for another dream, come the time." Balawahdiwa laid a hand on my shoulder. "Let's turn in, Steven. It's been a long day and a longer half a night."

Suddenly I felt how wrung out I was. I barely made it to my sack.

My dreams were weird, though not as terrorful as I'd expected. Slowly they settled down into normal gibberish. One almost roused me, a formless fear. My eyes opened. I saw stars, heard silence, felt the cold on my cheeks, and toppled back into sleep.

Medicine outfit or no, I'd kept the locket Ginny gave me on my breast. Now it woke me for keeps.

"Daddy, Mother, help!" the girl-voice cried, small, remote, desperate. "Please, can you hear me? Anybody? Help!"

# XXXIX

For the next three days after she saw me off, Ginny worked harder than you'd dare work a mule. Transit to another continuum—another cosmos, another reality—isn't like flitting cross country or even paying a call on Dr. Fu Ch'ing, especially if you'd prefer to come home alive and sane. Fjalar provided important information, plus manual skill and muscles when matters got that far, but she had to do the goetics all alone, research, planning, preparation, everything.

True, he'd made the journey before. However, that was long ago, when the sympathetics of human belief kept the connection close and the passage fairly easy between the Nordic region and that universe. Besides, he'd gone with a bunch of his kind, led by their chief wizards. Most dwarves lived yonder, as they presumably still did. Those on our Earth went to persuade the gods to send more business their way.

When the Christians took over their stamping grounds they were left stranded here. In his rough-hewn style, Fjalar was pathetically eager to see the old scenes again. It made him do his damnedest to help. It also made him discount any dangers.

Along with a lot else, Ginny obtained a complete file of Nornwell's tax records and papers pertaining thereto. She didn't tell Barney why she requested it, because he didn't need concern about her on top of the woes already besetting him, but he trusted her. She added the same from Operation Luna and the Matuchek household. Thereafter she tapped into the public lorebase for the United States tax code. Transmitting that took about twenty-four hours and, despite the modern miracle of atomic-level recording, presented her with a lorestone weighing two pounds.

Meanwhile she flew to Albuquerque. In a big hardware store she bought a disassembled tool shed. Collecting Fjalar at our house, she took him, his kit, and her purchase to a spot she'd discovered. She left him there to assemble the structure and prepare certain items for it, returned home, and cooked dinner. That was Wednesday evening.

Thursday morning she sent Val and Ben to school as usual. Though she had assured them and their sister that everything would be quite safe and she expected to come back in a day or two, she hadn't gone into detail. The dwarf had likewise kept mum. They did their best to believe her. Nevertheless, I can imagine that stoic little "So long" scene. I can't make myself write it.

Will arrived shortly after she phoned him, suitcase in hand. She made it an occasion to smile. "You'll hardly need that, I hope," she said. "With luck, this jaunt of mine will only be an overnighter." She paused. "If it does run a bit longer, don't worry . . . and don't let the children worry . . . or Steve, if I'm not here to meet him."

"Won't you give me an emergency line?" he asked.

She shook her head. "I'm sorry, Will. I can't. You know our family doctor and the police and— I'd better be on my way."

He followed her to the garage. Chryssa tagged anxiously along. Several containers were secured on the rear of the Jaguar. His thumb gestured at them. "The coffer must be full," he observed. "Rather a lot of baggage for an overnight trip, isn't it?"

"Professional apparatus."

"That much, to cope with the tax collector?" He saw her lips tighten and shrugged. "As you wish. I'll look forward to hearing about it someday. Bon voyage."

"B-b-bye, Mommy," Chryssa gulped.

Ginny hunkered down for a hug and a kiss. Edgar hopped from her shoulder to the broom and perched there in a marked manner. He disapproved of sentimentalism unless it focused on him.

When Ginny straightened, Will bent toward the child. "Let's go inside, sweetie," he proposed. "How would you like a brand-new story? Perhaps later, if you want, we can go to the park playground." Ginny signed the garage door to open. She boarded the broom and slipped out. Her brother and daughter waved farewell.

It was a lonely flight to Mount Taylor and a lonely place, high on its northern flank, where she landed. There was nothing illegal

about camping here, and nothing against bolting a temporary shelter together from corrugated steel panels. Nobody did, because no trail ran anywhere near, nor was water to be had. No Beings were likely to come by, either. But she had more on her mind than secrecy. The public menace afoot was great enough without her adding to it.

Like every licensed thaumaturge, she knew her physical sciences, including the conservation laws. Nature keeps exact accounts—well, pretty exact, say the quantum mechanics experts. If mass goes to a different continuum, an equal amount must go the opposite way, plus or minus whatever balances the energies. As Ginny, Fjalar, Edgar, and their gear crossed over, several hundred pounds of Old Norse stuff would appear where they'd been and stay till they returned.

No telling what form it would have, except that a load of plain dirt and rocks was ruled out. The second law of thermodynamics must be satisfied as well as the first. It's more lenient; surrounding matter, such as air and soil, can take up considerable entropy slack. In fact, since a demon's basic structure is chaotic, junk will serve. She knew, all too well, of one that had exchanged with the contents of Svartalf's catbox. But true life is highly organized. There was bound to be at least some living matter from the other side. It wouldn't necessarily consist of vegetation and bugs. The books mentioned pretty formidable creatures.

Ginny had studied those books in college, along with belief systems from around the world, history, and anthropology. The more esoteric a symbolism a witch employs, the more powerful are her spells. In an irreverent mood once, she and a classmate had composed a ballad to the tune of "Jesse James." They called it "The Childish Edda." The chorus went:

*"Yggdrasil, where nine worlds flash,*
*Is a noble piece of ash*
*That shelters Norns and gods and all that crew.*
*There's a dragon gnaws the base*
*Of an eagle's resting place,*
*And a squirrel and four harts complete the zoo."*

Fun. But who knew what else might happen to be running around in the vicinity?

As for it, given Fjalar's recollections and the rheatic effect of his presence, Ginny had figured out a scheme that ought to land them reasonably near the well of Mimir. She had a certain amount of control over the time parameter too. If they made it back, they might have spent some hours more or less than had passed in our world, but the difference shouldn't be major. If they made it back.

First they needed the shed for a cave in which she'd cast her crossing spell. Afterward they'd need it to contain whatever exchanged for them. Its isolation added a trifle to a safety margin that was thin at best.

"Hail," hailed Fjalar as she got off her stick. He doubtless enjoyed the sight, though she was dressed for the field in heavy shirt, jeans, and boots, with her hair falling loosely gathered from beneath a battered old hat. Belted to her left hip was a canteen, to her right a pouch for things she might want in a hurry. A light backpack carried the remaining essentials. The dwarf's outfit was similar, in a medieval fashion. "You brought visky?"

"I left a fifth with you yesterday," she said.

"That vas yesterday. Vat if ve meet poison snakes?"

"I've a first aid kit," she told him firmly, "sandwiches, meat pies, and two thermoses of hot coffee." Relenting: "Oh, and candy bars. Here, have one now. You've done a good job, I see." She took it from a shirt pocket and handed it over faster than Edgar could snaffle it. "We'll ration the rest. They supply quick energy."

For a moment she stood still, looking out at the sky and down the mountain to the land below. Junipers rustled darkly green in a wind whose coolness they sweetened. Clouds loomed like snowbanks against an unending blue. Desert reached subtly colored to ocherous cliffs afar. Two or three vultures hovered on broad wings. Here and there she saw human works, very small. She sighed and turned about. "Let's get going," she said.

Fjalar helped her unload and arrange what she'd taken along. It amounted to considerably more than what we'd had on our Hell expedition. Mainly it was to safeguard the shed against attack from within or without. The occultics of the destination universe bore scant relation to ours; a pentacle surrounded by blessed candles wouldn't contain an angry monster from there. Besides, Coyote or one of his alien buddies just might happen by, spot the setup, and investigate. It had to withstand the kind of forces they could bring to bear.

I don't know what she deployed, nor what she used and did to make the crossing. I do know better than to ask. I can guess at a spear; rods of oak, ash, and thorn, carven with runes; chants, gestures, horse blood splashed from a horn onto the ground—guesses.

The gloom of the locked shed deepened. Lightning flared, thunder cracked, stones shivered underfoot, waves ran wild before a sleetful gale, a noise of galloping hooves and hawk-shout of female voices passed by, a maelstrom raged, the wayfarers whirled down and down to the bottom of night.

# XL

They stood beneath vastness. Fog drifted in low, smoky streamers. Light seeped wan from an unseen sky. Silence brooded.

"Quark!" screamed Edgar and rocketed from Ginny's shoulder. He flapped to and fro above them, hoarsely expressing alarm, indignation, and doubts about this whole business.

"You come back," Fjalar called to him. "Vat kind of familiar ban you, getting scared by a little frighteningness? You shicken or something?"

Edgar braked to a hover, glared, and returned. On his way he gave the dwarf a smart beak-rap on the head. "Ow!" Fjalar bawled. "Surt's fires sizzle you black, you foul fowl!"

Ginny refrained from pointing out that the raven was already black. The ruckus had diverted her, steadied her shaken mind and body. She looked around.

A root rose slightly above the soil. That part of it loomed like a curving silver-gray cliff. The moss underfoot, wet and cold but a green richer than she had ever seen before, grew halfway up the bark. Where the root met the trunk, sight ended. Too broad for eyes to make out any curvature, the bole ran right and left until it faded into the mist. Upward it reared, as if forever. Somewhere aloft the boughs began. She glimpsed one through a twilight of leaves on branch above branch, overshadowing all.

And yet she felt a warmth, a sense of life like a tide, of strength and abidingness. Did her ears capture a ghost of the soughing where a wind blew between the worlds? Did she glimpse a gleam, brighter than gold, a dwelling of gods? She had found Ash Yggdrasil, the Tree whose roots go deeper than death and whose

crown is among the stars. The Earth she knew seemed remote, unreal, a half-forgotten dream.

Fjalar drew her back from helpless awe. "Look," he rumbled. "The traces of vat vas svapped for us."

"Oh, yes." She peered through the mist. A wide, shallow depression showed where turf and sod had been torn away. "But what about animals? Did the transition force scoop up some birds that happened to be flying by?"

Fjalar squatted. He had lived close to nature throughout his many centuries. "No, see here, tracks. They come but don't go." Now she could identify them, faint in the resilient moss though larger than her own. Not human—claws— "Yumping yiminy," Fjalar breathed, "Ay think we caught Ratatosk himself."

Her mind wobbled at the thought of a giant squirrel bouncing around and chittering in the tool shed. Well, for that while he wouldn't be carrying nasty words between the dragon under the Tree and the eagle on its heights. . . .

"This ought to scare off volves and bears and drows and such," Fjalar opined. "They von't know vat happened, or if it can grab them too. This patch ought to ban pretty peaceful till Ratatosk gets back."

"But we'd better not waste time anyway." At first her voice sounded strange to her. She ordered her strength to the forefront. "Let's find the well. It should be somewhere near."

Reaching into her pouch, she withdrew her wand and extended it. The star-tip lit and strewed brightness through the dusk. "Gruk," said Edgar, obviously encouraged. "Good bird. God damn."

They trudged along the root toward the bole. A hole gaped where those joined, the mouth of a tunnel. Fjalar indicated a trail, hardly more than a slight flattening across the bark, switchbacking down the root from above. "Ay think this ban the path Odin takes ven he goes to speak vith Mimir. *Ja,* ve should keep moving. Ay vould not like to meet him, especially in the dark."

*So much for the benevolent All-Father of the kiddie books,* Ginny thought. The real Odin had hanged himself on the Tree and swung in the wind for nine nights, as the price of gaining the runes of power. That was how it got the name Yggdrasil, the Horse of the Terrible One. That was why the human sacrifices to him were hanged, and he known as the Lord of the Gallows. Pagan gods weren't very nice people.

Well, maybe those of the Pueblo Indians—some of them—

And she had her part to do. She entered the opening.

A passage sloped downward. Rootlets matted its sides and hung

from above, snaky, dead-white. Water dripped, runneled, puddled the clay floor. Soon only her wand gave light. It leaped in and out of monstrous shadows. A cobweb as big and thick as a carpet draped halfway across the corridor. Fjalar, in the lead, brushed against it. The spider that scuttled into view was the size of a dog. Edgar shrieked and flew to attack. His wings snapped, his beak jabbed. The spider retreated into the dark. Edgar settled again on Ginny's shoulder.

"Brave bird," she said. "Noble bird." He gave her a stare and presented his bill. Sighing, she handed him a candy bar. He held it in his beak while one foot clawed the paper off. She stopped to collect those scraps. Even pagan gods think ill of littering.

Winding ever deeper, the tunnel burrowed into rock. She heard water clink where it hit and chuckle where it ran. An underground chill gnawed through her clothes. Breath gusted white in the forlorn radiance she carried.

"How much farther?" she asked.

"Ay dunno," Fjalar replied. "Ve dvarves don't never come *here.* Ve got better sense." Nonetheless he stumped stoutly onward.

The star-point of the wand seemed to pale. Likewise did the murk around. Light had begun to glimmer from ahead. Ginny's feet quickened with her heartbeat. The tunnel dipped, curved, and opened.

A cavern lay before her. She could not tell its size, only that it was huge. The rock itself shone, to make a bluish gloaming, shadowless and windless. Some distance off, black moss ringed silvery water, a pool, no, surely the well. A squared-off block of stone lifted man-high beside, with one side a ramp leading down to it. Something rested on top.

Fjalar jarred to a halt. After a paralyzed moment, he took off his woolen cap. Edgar hunched down where he sat. Ginny's wand flickered. She needed none of these tokens. Witch nerves shivered with the knowledge that she had reached her goal.

Slowly she advanced, the dwarf now at her heels. The silence grew and grew. As she neared, she saw runes graven in the block, but could not read them. She drew as close as she dared, stopped, and met the gaze of the head.

Had it somehow turned on its altar to confront her? Larger than human it seemed, though she could not give a measure to it. Hair and beard fell white over the stone, around livid skin tight across jutting bones. Eyes deep-sunken under the brows did not gleam like living eyes; they had had no tears since Mimir died. Odin embalmed the head

and called the awareness back, to counsel him with insight from the Otherworld; but nothing was left that wept or laughed, feared or loved.

Ginny heard Fjalar's teeth clatter. He set them and trod gamely forward, bowed till his own beard brushed the ground, and stuttered a salutation in Old Norse.

Lips parted. A dry tongue stirred behind them. The words that rolled forth were deep, iron-hard, with an eerie hiss. Ginny did not try to wonder how that throatless, lungless thing formed them. She knew a sword that did likewise.

Nor had she spent scarce time filling her brain with this language. The words and phrases she used professionally had given her a hook on it, which she expected Mimir could seize. From her pouch she drew a crystal into which his speech and hers had been 'chanted. She held it in her left hand, waved her wand around it, and uttered the activating charm.

Light blazed briefly out of it. The grating sibilance became English: "I have learned. Put that toy away."

She obeyed. "Hail and honor to the Wise One," she said, faintly surprised at how steady her own voice was. "I am Virginia Graylock Matuchek, witch, come from across space and time to seek your help."

She'd considered using a johnsmith but decided it would be useless here. Mimir would surely realize it was false and might well feel insulted—that she'd imagine he'd stoop to casting a nymic spell. She dared tell him nothing but the naked truth.

Naked. . . . An impudent thought sparked. She barely choked back a giggle. At least the disembodied head wouldn't mentally undress her. She supposed.

"That you are not from any of our Nine Worlds, I see, I hear, I smell," answered the harshness. "But do you think me a mere corpse, to be raised and questioned?"

"No, no, no!" yelped Fjalar. "There ban nothing mere about you, sir!"

Ginny made a shushing gesture. "Of course not, my lord," she said. "My kin and friends are in desperate need. Enemy wizards have made a riddle no man in our homeland can solve, and laid it on us. Unless we find the answer, and so unbind ourselves from it, we and our works will go under; and what we're waging is a fight against wicked trolls. Recalling how Odin himself seeks to you for advice, I trusted you might grant it to me. Then the name of Mimir and the fame of his great-heartedness—er, his intelligence will always be remembered in our country."

"Hm." The uncanny stare shifted. "You do bear the bird of Odin with you."

"And gifts, sir, such as a guest should bring." Ginny emphasized the word "guest" a trifle, a reminder that hospitality was sacred. "May you find them worthy."

She took off her backpack, opened it, and lifted them out. Considerable thought had gone into the choice. Gold must be plentiful hereabouts; the head couldn't put weapons or fine clothes to use; what then? Well, the Zunis carved beautiful small images, mainly stylized animal figures, in assorted gemstones and minerals. Though many were fetishes, they were often made for sale. Ginny had acquired several fine specimens, a jet buffalo, a pipestone buck sheep, a dolomite deer, a black marble fish, a serpentine snake . . . She spread them on the block before the head.

Mimir studied them. "Yes," he admitted. "Handsome work. And foreign indeed. Contemplating them should pass time for me. You must tell me more about them."

"Gladly, my lord, since you will so generously counsel us."

For the first time, the dead face showed expression. At least, it raised its brows. "Counsel? Did I say that? What you have given will probably oblige me to grant you safe conduct out of here, after you've satisfied my curiosity."

It didn't describe how it proposed to stop her if it wanted to, and she didn't ask. "The fame of your wisdom will reach farther than the boughs of Yggdrasil," she urged. "And I truly believe you'll find the riddle interesting. A challenge nobody in our whole world can meet, a word-skein no mortal man or woman can unravel. I came because I had no doubt that Mimir can," she finished slyly.

The head considered. Silence pressed inward, except for Fjalar's repeated gulps. The dwarf had never seemed daunted before. Ginny wondered if he sensed, still more than she did, how formidable their host really was.

"Well," murmured Mimir after a gape of time, "you have traveled far, with tidings new to me. None else but Odin has ever dared. That deserves something too. I must admit, existence can get tedious, all alone here. . . . Yes-s. Sit down, tell me about it, and I'll see if I can help."

Gladness danced. "Thank you, my lord, thank you!"

"Of course," Mimir said, "I charge for advice."

Fjalar moaned. Edgar bristled his hackles. The cold struck deep into Ginny's bones. "Charge?" she faltered. "What is the price?"

"An eye is customary."

Shock staggered her. "No! I mean—you're joking, my lord."

The head scowled. "I never do."

*Yes,* Ginny thought at the back of her mind, *it must be hard to keep a sense of humor when you've lost your body.* She grabbed after words. "Is it honorable, my lord, to, to set a price on prowess?"

"Odin paid it. I can take no less from you."

"Awrrk!" croaked Edgar. "Lawyer!"

The retainer Mimir demanded did seem excessive. However, Ginny felt that that line of argument would lead nowhere. She heard: "His eye lies here in the well of wisdom. Each day I drink from it."

*How?* she wondered wildly. An unpleasant vision arose, of the head rolling down to the water, the eyeball rising, the tongue lapping. . . . And how did Mimir know day from night? . . . "I, I'm not prepared—"

"If your fingers tremble, your raven can pluck it out for you," Mimir suggested. "Right or left, whichever you prefer," he added with fine old-world courtesy.

The images before her became ridiculous. "Edgar? He'd swallow it."

Her wits leaped. "Lawyer!" the raven had cried. She hadn't trained him as a familiar for nothing. The nonhuman life in him strengthened her in her sorceries. And sometimes he *knew.*

She recalled the hairsplitting legalisms of the Icelandic sagas. "But Odin wanted more than I ask for," she protested. Through her rang a verse from—how long ago?—"The Childish Edda."

*"Odin said to Mim, 'I think that I would like a drink.'*
*Mim said, 'That will cost you your left eye.*
*You have come so very late to the well at wisdom's gate,*
*And the setup prices after hours are high.' "*

Not exactly lines to sing in this presence. Yet poetry was potent among the Old Norse.

Poetry. Shakespeare. *The Merchant of Venice.*

She rallied, clutched her wand tighter, and told the head: "Besides, if you must have an eye, that doesn't include any blood, does it? Impossible."

Was Mimir actually taken aback? "What warrior counts a little blood loss?"

"That's beside the point. A deal is a deal. You've named it, you

should stick by it. Furthermore, I repeat, I don't need any of your water. Just your words."

"What words can you give *me?*" asked the oracle sullenly.

She had made ready for that. A poem of praise was itself a valuable gift. "I am no skald, my lord," she said, while hope rose within her, "but I did do my best to make staves that puff—that compliment you."

The tone brightened a trifle. "You did?"

"The form is different from any that your bards use," Ginny explained. "It is short and end-rhymed. But my people consider it their most powerful way to express the generative force of life."

"I listen," said Mimir almost eagerly.

Ginny took stance, drew breath, and recited:

*"Mimir who dwells by the Well*
*Is the wisest 'twixt Heaven and Hell.*
*Since his head lacks two hands,*
*A heart, and some glands,*
*It more thoroughly thinks, I can tell."*

Fjalar braced himself against he knew not what. Ginny waited.

"That is . . . unusual," Mimir said.

After a moment: "Nobody ever made a poem for me before."

Abruptly: "Yes, you shall have your skald-gift, witch. I'll read you your riddle."

She fought down a gasp and a wave of weakness. If necessary, for her children's sake and mine, she would have paid the price. It was not necessary.

"You are my guests," Mimir said. "I have no food to give you, but sit down and let us drink together."

*Oh, no, you don't,* Ginny thought. Once she'd partaken— And yet shared mead or wine sealed the bonds of hospitality. If only she'd packed along some Scotch, as Fjalar wanted. "We are not worthy of this water," she replied. "May we offer you something from our homeland?"

Mimir grunted. Probably he was disappointed that his trick had failed. He might still go temperamental and refuse to cooperate.

She broke out a thermos bottle. "Would my lord like to taste?" She unscrewed the cup, pulled the stopper, poured a serving, and held it out to him.

Did his nostrils dilate at the aroma?

His tongue reached forth. She tilted the cup to his lips. Where the coffee went, she didn't know, but it went fast.

"Aahh!" The stony voice had gone soft. The lips—by every god everywhere, the lips curved into a grin. "This they quaff not in Valhalla! Where's it from? Do you have more?"

"Oh, yes, two jugs."

"Good, good," Mimir purred. "I'm sorry I've no bench to seat you, but do make yourselves comfortable. Ask what you will, my dear. And we'll drink together, won't we?"

"*Ja,*" Fjalar muttered, "Ay should have known."

Ginny realized that she too could have foreseen. Mimir was a Scandinavian, after all, a Scandinavian who had just had his first cup of coffee. Naturally he grew quiet and refined.

From then on, events proceeded with the utmost cordiality. The only trouble was that it took so long. Mimir needed to be filled in on the situation. That involved many searching questions and complicated explanations. As hour and hour and hour went by, living flesh wearied. Mimir was tireless; Ginny wouldn't risk upsetting the mood by calling a break; he didn't mind when his visitors ate, and declined a share, but he drank every drop of the coffee; Edgar could tuck head under wing, Fjalar could stretch out his sleeping bag and snore; Ginny must keep on. Exhaustion dragged ever more heavily. The stones beneath her bottom got harder and harder.

Much of the time, the part that felt infinite, she didn't even talk. She sat waiting, or rose to stretch and pace, while Mimir pondered the playout of the tax code. He admitted it made the ultimate Eddic question—"What did Odin whisper in the ear of Baldr when Baldr lay on his pyre?"—look easy. He mumbled and muttered and gnawed his beard, which he caused to float up to his mouth for the purpose. Maybe he'd have been baffled, were it not for her sustaining brew.

In the end, though, the end of endlessness, he worked out the answer. He told her the basics of it—her spirit sang for a minute, before sinking back into ashen weariness—and spoke the technicalities—which took quite a while itself—into the three recording stones she'd brought.

By then she could find nothing to say but, "Thank you, my lord."

"A pleasure, my lady," Mimir replied. "I'll throw in a warning. You war with Powers unknown here; but what you have told shows me they are mighty and crafty. I think one of them has possessed one among your band, hiding too deeply for any skill of yours to find it. Beware—and seek stronger help."

Ginny shuddered.

"I further counsel you to be well rested before you return home," Mimir continued. "There is no foresaying what awaits you, yet I feel some great onslaught is nigh." His solemnity turned amiable, maybe slightly wistful. "You are welcome to sleep here."

"Thank you, my lord," she said, "but, well, I think we'd rest better above ground."

"Yes, this is a hard and cold floor," Mimir agreed. *And a spooky place in general,* she did not remark. "Fare you well, then. Do feel free to come back if you have any other little problems. You'll bring coffee, won't you?"

# XLI

Val's day at school became a disaster. Her attention kept running away, hounded by fears for us. I was supposedly on a safe errand in strong and knowledgeable company; but what if something went wrong, like a bunch of evil Beings getting on my tail? Her mother claimed she'd be all right too, but hadn't really said much about what she intended, had kind of glossed over her destination. . . . Those squarehead gods were *violent.* Every day at that Valhalla place, a drunken brawl. And the reasons for our gitzy expeditions—hostile demons, the Internal Reaming Service—negative plus! Meanwhile she herself, Valeria Matuchek, was supposed to sit and listen to Miss Prickett dissect *David Copperfield* like the book was a frog in biology class. Unseelie!

So when Mr. Nakamura in history period asked who had been the Spanish conquistador of Mexico and called on her, she blurted, "Coyote." In gramarye Mrs. Kaltfuss sprang a pop quiz and Val totally mangled the conjugation of *venefacio.* In goetics lab, which she'd always loved, they did an elementary pyromantics experiment, mainly to learn safety. Her flame sputtered bilious green. She blew on it and spoke the controlling words, but scrambled those as well. The flame rose, took the form of a clenched hand with an upright middle finger, and vanished.

That broke her. She couldn't hold back the tears any longer. Everybody stared. Larry Weller moved toward her. She waved him back as if she were striking him. Half of what caught at her was rage.

Mr. Escobedo drew her aside. "Are you ill, Valeria?" he asked gently. "You've never made mistakes before."

"I, I, I'm sorry," she gulped, knuckling her eyes. "No, I'm not sick, but—" She couldn't go on.

Being a wise and compassionate man, he didn't inquire further. "I think you should take the rest of the day off," he said. "No blame, no fault of yours. Everybody feels overwhelmed now and then. I'll inform your other teachers." He smiled. "We'll hope to see you happier tomorrow."

"Th-thanks." She walked out with her cheeks wet but her head high.

Bicycling home through indecently cheerful sunlight, she won back her self-control, sort of. Too bad she'd miss geometry period. They were studying Pythagorean significances, which was fascinating. But probably she'd also have cowfooted there today. At least she was free of sex education. That sex could be made boring had been beyond belief till Mr. Tupper started in on the subject.

Stewing and fretting were no help to anybody. Might even cause trouble for the people she loved—bad sympathetics, maybe— She wasn't sure. So much she didn't know. At her age, that thought came as a shock.

Well, she'd take shelter in her room and try to uncoil. How about rereading a Magister Lazarus book? And, after dinner, playing some music to fall asleep by? Who knew but what Daddy and Mom would both be back when she woke, carrying the strange treasures they'd gone in search of?

A breeze blew fragrant off flowerbeds about the neighborhood. They were still brilliant and leaves had not begun to fall. Yet somehow a breath of winter reached her. It conjured glistening blue-shadowed whiteness, snow men, snow angels, snowball fights, sledding, skiing, a fire in the fireplace where chestnuts roasted, and if she and Larry went on a hike and he stole a kiss—she'd make like it was his idea, of course—how extra warm and cider-spicy!

Though not exactly blithe when she reached our house, she felt better able to cope with herself. Dismounted, she wheeled the bike to the garage, whistled the door open, and entered by the adjoining storeroom. Her sneakers made no noise and she wasn't in a mood to shout, "Hi." In fact, she'd have some explaining to do to Uncle Will. He'd understand, the old darling, but she didn't want to bare her soul or anything like that. Pondering what to say, she passed through the kitchen into the hall.

His voice drifted from the living room. "—caution your agents not to fly it off. The ergodics are known only to the designers and builders, but powerful forces are obviously latent. Furthermore, at the

moment I don't know where any key is for either vehicle or building. Let me suggest that two men carry it out and put it on a truckrug—"

Val came in. Will sat at the phone. The face before him was Alger Sneep's.

"Oh!" burst from her.

Will twisted about. His features, briefly slack and bloodless, froze. A hand made a chopping gesture. He turned back to the other man. "I think that covers the situation," he said fast.

"We appreciate—" Sneep began.

Will cut him off. "Pardon me. I have to disempath. An urgent personal matter. We'll talk later." He cut the resonance and swung again toward Val.

She quivered under the impact of a world falling apart. "What's that about?" she cried.

"What brings you home so early?" His tone could have slashed chaparral.

"I, I felt bad—they excused me—but, but, Uncle Will—"

"This is unfortunate," he said across the distance between them. "Are you sick?"

"No, I was just worried and scared and— You and *him!*"

"I see." Will stayed mute for a minute. She watched his face soften. Somehow, though, it and his voice never quite became what had cheered and enlightened and comforted her in the past.

He rose, approached, stopped a yard off as if wary of seeming to press himself on her. "I meant to keep this from you, Ben, and Chryssa," he said dully. "Why load bad news onto the fears you already suffer? Your parents will know best how to break it, after they return." He sighed. "Well, you've overheard. I can't be other than honest with you. But will you promise not to tell your brother or sister?"

She had no choice. "Yes, I do."

Will constructed a smile. "Very well." Once he'd have said something like, "All right, then, soldier," and made a gesture, such as knuckles barely touching her shoulder. "The IRS called. The examiner wanted to speak with your parents. When I explained that they're out of town, I don't know where, it apparently catalyzed the agent's suspicions. His office is putting a lien on the property of Operation Luna. Tomorrow they'll seize the spacecraft."

"They can't wait a couple of days?" Val wailed.

"Evidently not. I suppose their superiors have ordered direct action."

"How'd they even *know?*"

He shrugged. "Your parents and their associates haven't tried to keep things strictly secret. Agents may have put two and two together and instigated inquiries. Or they may simply have asked of the FBI. It has me under surveillance, remember. In any case, seizure of a crucial article from a small group like ours is easier than proceeding full tilt against a company like Nornwell."

"And it hurts everybody just as bad! Or worse! Why were you *helping* them?"

"What use, an attempt to lie? Yes, I did volunteer a warning, as you heard. Not that I know precisely how the spacecraft works, but the test flight suggested it can be, hm, tricky. Best play safe. Suppose an agent did try to flit with it and came to grief, perhaps was killed. Wouldn't that prejudice our cause? Also, he wouldn't be a devil, merely a civil servant, probably with a family of his own, doing a job. Let us not be malicious, Valeria."

"And, and not meek either." She whirled and ran from him.

I can't say what went on in the next several hours. I'm a man, not a girl. I no longer feel the storminess of youth. No doubt she wept for a while, alone in her room, raw, racking sobs. Probably Svartalf went "Mneowrr" at her door till she stumbled over and let him in. He'd have joined her on the bed and butted his big black head against her till she curled around him. Then maybe he groomed the disheveled hair. Not that he was ever what you'd call sentimental. Tomcats aren't. However, time had somewhat mellowed the arrogant old bastard.

Unless—well, for most of his life he'd been a witch's familiar. He'd known sorcery, combat, dealings dark as well as bright. Once, for a while, he was the vessel of a spirit who in life had been as rowdy as himself; and together they'd gone along on a harrowing of Hell. Anyway, he wasn't in full retirement. He partnered the witch's and werewolf's daughter as step by step she moved toward her own mastery of the Art.

Maybe he foresaw something. Or maybe he lusted after one last piratical adventure. His purring presence may have done more than console and encourage. It may have generated an idea. Val would only have been aware of the turmoil in herself and a resolution that slowly—or lightning suddenly?—crystallized out of it.

At dinner time she washed her face, combed her hair, and came to the table.

Will had cooked his usual good meal. It went stonily. Ben and Chryssa sensed the tension in the other two. It kept them short-spoken, stiff. Will tried to jolly the party up and failed. He lacked the whimsy

they'd formerly enjoyed. His remarks fell wooden, his jokes as flat as a frightened soufflé.

"I'm sure your sister would like a bedtime story from you, Valeria," he said at last.

"Sorry," Val answered, staring at her plate. "I don't feel inspired."

The cloud in Chryssa's eyes threatened rain. "Please," she begged.

"Well, I'll do my poor best," Will offered.

Val raised her head. "No, I guess I can," she decided.

The tale she invented was fairly sinister, Moldylocks getting chased by a vampire. She'd have won to safety by crossing a brook, but was unwilling to wade through water. Barely ahead of pursuit, she came on an Italian restaurant and ducked in. The vampire couldn't pass the crucifix over the door. He lurked outside. After eating a large meal, Moldylocks stepped forth and breathed on him. He started to flee, turning himself into a bat. In his panic he got it wrong and became a baseball bat. Since now he could neither speak nor gesture, this condition was permanent. Moldylocks gave him to a bush-league player she met on her way home to belch. Chryssa fell asleep reasonably content.

Val joined Will and Ben at the farseer for the "Alice the Goon" show. Though it was pretty funny, nobody laughed. She said goodnight before it closed.

In her room she set the alarm clock for silent awakening at four, changed to pajamas, and crept into bed. Svartalf crouched beside her. His eyes gleamed yellow in the gloom. She didn't fall asleep soon, and then fragments of dream gibbered.

It was almost a blessing when the clock sprouted an arm and shook her. In spite of the uneasy night, she woke keenly alert, charged by excitement. Stealing forth—she could always claim an errand to the bathroom—she found the house lightless and soundless. Returning, she switched on an edison; no unnecessary, revealing goetics. "Shh, Svartalf," she whispered. The cat arched his back and bottled his tail.

She dressed quickly: underwear, warm shirt and jacket, Levi's, wool socks, again the sneakers, a hat to shade her after sunrise. A wallet with some allowance money went into a rear pocket. Svartalf padding behind, she entered my study, where she took the keys to smithy and spacecraft that she knew about but Uncle Will didn't.

Nothing stirred. Poor man, he slept so much and so heavily these nights. Not to rouse him. He'd have to forbid her enterprise. This way, he, like her parents, would be uninvolved.

They'd get terribly worried, of course. Having shut off the kitchen

and illuminated it, she scribbled on the reminder pad, "I'm sorry. I had to try and save your moon boat. The broom will be at the workshop. I will be okay. You will hear from me real soon. I love you. Val." Her vision blurred. She blinked fiercely. No, damn it, she would not cry anymore.

Food. She constructed sandwiches, wrapped them, and stuck them in her jacket. Candy would be helpful too, when her strength flagged. For a moment she grinned. The best excuse in the world to scarf down some Venus Bars and Elf Mounds. Never mind if they gave her a few zits.

From the storeroom she fetched a saintelmo and a couple of canteens, which she filled with water and belted on her flanks. Dousing the kitchen light, she tiptoed out into the garage. Svartalf ghosted alongside.

Both Matuchek brooms were elsewhere. The saintelmo picked Uncle Will's staid Völve out of the murk. She lifted the cat—he felt heavier than before—and put him on the front seat. "Okay, fuzzface," she murmured. "You know what I want. Do your stuff."

She set up the conditions for him with a simple cantrip such as she'd learned in school. It was quite insufficient, especially since her inhibitions about misuse weakened it. Svartalf wasn't burdened with morals. He'd acquired some powers during his long association with Ginny. Given a preliminary charm, he needed just a short meow-song and a gleeful gesture of his tail to hotspell the vehicle.

The girl quelled her conscience and boarded. A skulky trick to play on Uncle Will. She'd considered using her bicycle, but thirty-odd miles over bad road in the dark would have wiped her. Nor could she be sure of arriving at the right time, dawnlight to pilot by and nobody around to notice. She was only borrowing this stick. Uncle Will could easily get a lift with somebody and retrieve it. He was bound to forgive her as soon as he understood why she must go. Wasn't he? And the police would overlook the fact she didn't have a flyer's license. Wouldn't they?

She definitely had the skill. Very quietly, she commanded the door open and steered the broom forth.

What about the Fibbies? If they were watching— But their detectors would show it wasn't Uncle Will leaving the house, and her mother's wardings blocked them from seeing or hearing anything that happened inside. She didn't expect they'd trail her. Regardless, her heart thuttered.

She left the town behind. It was as if her doubts and fears stayed

there. More and more exultant, she flew south. The moon stood high, well-nigh at the half. The Milky Way swept crackling bright among uncountable stars. The land below intermingled shadows, dim grays, and ruggedness. Each cold breath she drew sparkled through her blood.

No, she swore, the IRS monster wasn't going to grab *Owl* away from her folks and trample on their dreams. She'd flit her—*her,* by the Aegis, not *it*—to a safe hiding place. That obscure canyon where they'd enjoyed a span of peace. . . . She could leave the spacecraft tucked beneath trees, hike out, and take a bus home. Unless she phoned. . . . No, probably better not. Keep the location as secret as possible. Meanwhile Dad and Mom and Uncle Will and honorary Uncle Barney could seek court orders or something. They'd be clearly innocent of this removal, and who'd persecute—prosecute a kid for a, well, a prank? Possession was nine points of the law, she'd heard. She was buying time in which nobody had possession, above all the monster.

Everything is so clear-cut, so certain to work out happily, when you're young.

The east was faintly paling as she passed over Zuni pueblo. Dowa Yalanne sheered across it. Val slowed. Her breath smoked into a tremendous silence. There, the smithy! She slanted to a landing.

Svartalf jumped straight off and relieved himself, unless he was putting his sign on a clump of rabbitbrush. Val dismounted and pulled the keys from her pocket. Numbed, her fingers fumbled before she got the door unlocked.

She stepped into utter blackness. Her saintelmo limned *Owl* against it, lean and taut. Scattered light flashed off the blade hanging nearby.

"Who goes there?" she heard. "That's *'Qui vive?'* if you're Norman. Stand and deliver!"

"Me," she called shakily. "Don't sound any alarm. It's a-a-all right."

"Eh? You, princess? What the devil are you doing at this unsanctified hour? Risky for young ladies, let me tell you, risky, traipsing abroad unescorted after dark. I mind once on Stromsay—became the occasion of a rather pleasant battle, it did—"

"Hush, please hush, sir." She groped toward Fotherwick-Botts. "Later we'll talk. B-but right now we've got to escape."

"What?" roared the sword. "Leave my post? Slink off like a, a, a slinker? Isn't done, I'll have you know. Not British. Or Norwegian."

"You're supposed to guard the spacecraft," Val pointed out. "We've been, uh, betrayed. The enemy'll soon come to steal her. I want to—to—"

"Forestall them. Yes, that's the word, forestall. Unless 'outmaneuver' fits better. Which d'you think, 'forestall' or 'outmaneuver'?"

"I think we'd better get away from here."

"I see. Strategic retreat. Of course I must accompany you."

"Sure. They won't snatch you either, you good old fighter."

"P'r'aps we should make a stand instead?" wondered Fotherwick-Botts. "Your mother wielded me well, except she wouldn't go for the kill. Let me drill you till the villains arrive, and—"

Val sheathed him.

Slinging him at her side, she looked around for the medicine bundles. Just in case. She wasn't about to shoot for the stratosphere. Anyway, probably she couldn't get that high when the pilot stone was just a boringly ordinary piece of local rock. Curtice and everybody said that in low-level flight the craft wasn't much different from a regular broom, aside from being able to go a lot faster if you wanted.

However, Dad had often told her that engineers thought well of—what was the word?—redundancy. Following his principle would feel a tiny bit like having him at her side.

She found the bundles and buckled one onto her back. Another, a miniature, caught her eye. Yes, Svartalf ought to have redundancy too. Abruptly she remembered Balawahdiwa's remark about this, that a small person might need it. Caution, guess, hunch, or something unconsciously heard from someone or something unknown? Eeriness walked the length of her spine.

Therefore she took time to locate the jewel Curtice had used to link herself with the communication crystal and slipped its necklace over her head. Be prepared.

Svartalf didn't object when she fastened his packet on his back. He sprang readily to the rear saddle. His whiskers stood stiff. Did he feel a hunch of his own? She verified that the go-force would provide a steady one gravity beneath him no matter what. It was almost an afterthought to check her own.

She climbed onto the forward saddle. Fotherwick-Botts clunked against a canteen. She inserted the key. "Rise," she pushed past the knot in her throat. "Go straight ahead." *Owl* glided out the door. "Park." She got off, relocked the building, and remounted.

Her hand flicked for a northwest course at a hundred-foot elevation. Once aloft, she'd evoke a map in the control crystal and aim properly at her goal. The broom lifted.

The broom tilted heavenward and took off.

"Hey, wait!" Val screamed. "Stop! Back!"

There was no sense of acceleration. That made the headlong rush all the more horrible. Air boomed around the screenfield. Its noise dwindled to a whine, ever thinner. Stars that dawn had been drowning crowded again into sight. The moon stood hard-edged. Sunrise blazed suddenly behind her. Earth fell away as if down a hole.

She tugged at the key. It stayed frozen in position. No gesture, no command worked. Tumbling upward through terror, she roused the communicator. "Daddy, Mother, help!" she cried. "Please, can you hear me? Anybody? Help!"

# XLII

"Val!" I shouted. "That you? What's wrong? Where are you?"

"I, I don't know— The broom's gone runaway."

"Huh?" I scrambled from my sleeping bag. "The hell you say!" *The Hell indeed,* I thought. "You mean—oh, no—"

Balawahdiwa was already on his feet. He gripped my hand. Steadiness flowed into me. I became aware of the world. Stars glistered in blackness, but eastward the sky was lightening. The air cloaked me in cold, the dirt gritted beneath my soles.

"Okay, honey," I said. "Calm down. I'm here. Are you in any immediate danger? Aside from your problem, that is. Are you hurt? A prisoner?" I choked on a killing fury. If some creature had dared— "Tell me everything you can, and we'll go to work on it."

"No, I—we—we're alive and, and well. Svartalf and me and . . . the sword." I heard how she swallowed. There was a silence of an infinite half minute or so. When she spoke again, her voice was low, almost a monotone, as if she talked in her sleep. "Earth's big, huge, but shrinking so fast. Mostly it's dark. I can still make out bunches of lights, cities, I guess. Some strung like pearls. . . . A thin bright curve, all blue and white. The sun's just above it . . . beside it. . . . I can look straight at the sun and it doesn't hurt my eyes. Like looking through a filter. That's the medicine pack protection, isn't it? Everywhere else I look, more and more stars. I've never seen so many. And they're *around* me. The Milky Way goes clear around the sky."

"Jesus Christ!" I yelled. "You're in space?"

"Y-yes. Moving faster and faster, I think."

"You're aboard *Owl?* Bound for the moon?"

The voice gathered strength and clarity. "No, we're heading

straight away from Earth and sun. The moon's falling behind too. I have to turn my head back to see them."

My mind, gone quick and sharp, detached from the fear and grief in my heart, drew a diagram for me. My tone flattened. "Then you're bound into really deep space. Probably your acceleration vector points straight outward. Your speed's increasing second by second. Don't panic. Think hard. What made this mess, and what have you tried to do about it?"

She replied straightforwardly and to the point. *That's my girl,* thought the feeling part of me. "The IRS was going to seize your spacecraft and all the other stuff before you or Mother came home. Wouldn't that ruin everything for you? I decided I'd fly her to a hiding place. Then you'd have time to figure out what to do. But as soon as I took off from parking stance, she zoomed straight up. The steering crystal is blank. Nothing responds except, I guess, the communicator."

My soul groaned, wanted to turn her over my knee, wanted to hug the valiant lass close to me and weep. Any of it, a waste of time. "That should certainly not be. You ought to've been able to fly her the way you intended. Or if for some reason she did run wild, she ought to've headed for the moon. Something's radically wrong. Okay, let's try this. Listen and repeat back to me."

I led her through what spells and other procedures I knew that she could do without special equipment. They should have restored control. They didn't. The sun rose over me. Earth dwindled behind Valeria. I had her estimate the rate from the constellations the disc occupied. By then she was cool—I shied back from that word—and, within her limits, competent. About two gravities of boost, I reckoned. *We* hadn't planned a moon flight that hot.

At least the part of the system that kept a steady one gee on the normal to the long axis was still working. Otherwise—no, I would not think about that.

"All right," I told her. "One or more major parameters have changed, and I've got no way where I am to discover which. Balawahdiwa and I are off in the Zuni Mountains. Our only outside link is with you. Your mother hasn't returned yet, or we'd have heard from her through her connection. Our stick is miles from here. I'm going after it as fast as possible, which means wolf shape. It'll take an hour or more." By which time she'd be approaching the orbit of the moon. "Evidently your medicine bundle is preserving you. Hang on, sweetheart. I can't answer you while I'm running, unless you'd like a yip now and then. But put together an account of what's happened

and how, and give it to me as I go. The more information we have, the quicker we can bring you home."

*If ever we do* stayed unspoken.

"Sure," she replied. "I'm awful sorry about this. Thanks for everything, Daddy. Love you."

"Love you right back."

"I'll wait," Balawahdiwa said quietly. "I'll pray as best I can."

"Thanks," I mumbled.

"Before you transform, Steven, let me suggest you drink a quart or two of water. Even werewolves can overexert and dehydrate."

"Good idea. Thanks once more."

Having gulped a bellyful, I crawled back into my bag, pulled the cover over my head, and changed. Balawahdiwa stroked me as I emerged. His other hand made a sign of blessing. I loped.

Brush, rock, soil fled past. Sometimes a jackrabbit bolted. The sun climbed. Odors of growth awakened. Air warmed. Toward the end it was like a furnace blast in and out of my gullet. I paid no heed to anything but the running.

Valeria told her tale. My wolf brain couldn't follow it closely, but stashed it in memory for later attention. My wolf body wanted to rip throats. My wolf spirit wanted to howl for my mate. Pointless. Nor had I breath to spare.

When at last, nightmarishly at last, I reached the stick, I fell on my side and struggled for air. My heart hammered. A were recovers fast, though, from whatever doesn't outright kill him. Soon I could lurch up, crawl into the coffer, and transform.

"How're you doing, Val?" I croaked.

"The same," she said, "except Earth and the moon, they've really shrunk, and they're both the thinnest crescents, with the sun between them. Everywhere else, stars." After a moment: "Space is beautiful. More beautiful than I imagined." Did I catch the ghost of a laugh? "Even Svartalf looks awed. He jumped from his saddle to me. I caught him and put him on my lap. He sits there and stares out of big, round eyes. How are *you,* Daddy?"

"About to set things in motion, I hope."

"Mother?"

"Not yet. We'll know it when she does report in."

"Oh, won't we! And Mr. Sneep and NASA and everybody." The forlorn gaiety faltered. "If she—"

"No ifs," I decreed. "She will. Now I've got to fetch Balawahdiwa

and analyze what you told me and start calling around. Break in anytime, if anything changes. Understand?"

"Yes. I understand."

"I'll check with you every chance I get. Not to make a pest of myself, but—"

"You can't. It's lonely here." Again she paused. "I'll be fine. Honest, I will."

"If you grow desperate for conversation," I said absurdly, "you can draw Fotherwick-Botts." Since the sword, lacking a mouth, spoke by goetic generation of sound waves, he should be able to affect the communication crystal, which would act on the jewel mike, which in turn would vibrate her eardrums. My locket should pick it up also. Not an elegant system, from an engineer's viewpoint. No matter. *Owl* was what we needed to make work—right.

Her answer came grave. "I guess I should. It must be lonely for him too."

I had no better response than, "Okay, pony. I'm on my way. Hang tight."

The flit to camp was quick. I considered what Val had told and sketched plans. On landing, I drank a lot more water. Balawahdiwa gave me some jerky and Zuni-style bread. I realized, dimly surprised, that I was hungry. He'd arranged our things. We didn't stop to load most of them, just what was sacred or otherwise essential. I dressed. We lofted.

"Ha!" brayed on my breast. "Bound from the flinkin' mortal world, are we? Hardly for Heaven. No offense, young lady, but I doubt you've made sainthood yet. Besides, how the deuce could I and the cat? And we have evil at work. I sense the traces of it on this steel steed. Stinks like the dead horse I once saw a trebuchet throw into a besieged city. Well, well, courage. Keep up the side. We won't likely crash through any crystal spheres. What say you practice with me? Against enemy ambuscade, y'know. Good for morale, a round of drill, if it's not punishment drill, and even that teaches a lesson, what? We'll begin with presenting arms—"

I lowered the volume to bare audibility. If Val needed my counsel, she'd yell loud enough for me to hear and tune up.

As if seeking a moment of shelter, my thoughts stayed with Fotherwick-Botts. Originally Ginny and I meant to return him to St. Oswald's, the same clandestine way we'd borrowed him, assuming either of us got through this brannigan alive. But having learned what

his nature was, we couldn't condemn him to lie in solitary confinement, gagged, for more decades, maybe centuries.

Events might bring our role to light regardless. Then we'd have to confess, plead necessity, and hope for leniency. No doubt we'd be fully pardoned if the kuei had been exposed and expelled. If.

Victorious, we'd rather not endure the publicity. The aftermath of our Hell foray had shown us what that meant. Well, we could lay the sword back in his case as we'd first planned. Then Frogmorton could claim a scholarly interest and request to examine him, which would surely be granted. We'd have gotten the promise of both not to say anything about us.

However the revelation happened, Fotherwick-Botts' future was guaranteed. He'd be a treasure for historians. I visualized him going on the lecture circuit—where he wouldn't have to eat creamed chicken—before accepting a professorship. The only question would be whether he chose a famous university or a military academy.

Provided, of course, that he survived and our cause did.

The subject dropped out of me as Zuni hove into sight. We set down at Balawahdiwa's house. He anticipated my words: "By all means use the phone here, Steven. Don't lose time, go straight in. I'll take care of the stuff."

Tribesfolk in the lane on their early morning errands gave us curious glances. I ignored them and opened the door. "Excuse me, Mrs., uh, Adams," I said to the lady. I couldn't remember her native name. Ought to be ashamed of myself. No, under the circumstances, who could blame me? Anyhow, maybe the Anglo one was more respectful, coming from a *Melika*. Never mind. I went to the phone and called home.

Will's face appeared. He didn't look well rested. "Oh . . . Steve. What's this? You woke me."

"None too damn soon," I snapped. He'd have had to leave the feathers shortly anyway, to fix breakfast and otherwise start the kids on their day. Unless he relied on Val. No, negligence wasn't like him. Not that he'd been much like himself very often of late.

The possibility that Ginny and I had recognized and denied, with the psychoscopic results to give confidence, rose again. Half of me struggled to hold back a sickness. Couldn't be, mustn't be! The other half somehow went on: "Emergency. Rouse Ben and Chryssa. Pack clothes and teethbreesh for them. I'm asking the Goldsteins to come take them in."

Instant alertness peered back at me and demanded, "Why?" in as cold a voice as I'd ever heard.

"No offense, Will. But there's hell to pay, and I don't want the bill collected from my children."

"A demon? This house is secured, I'm told. They should be safer here than anywhere else. Particularly if it's under federal observation."

"I'll decide that. Neither you nor those Fibbies are trained to know every trick evil can play. Besides, we may need your help." If this man was harmless—*Please, God, let him be*—his knowledge could be valuable. If not—against that *if,* the youngsters must damn well clear out of there.

"I notice you didn't mention Valeria," he said.

"Tell you later." He was bound to find the note she'd left. I guessed he'd guess her vulnerability was what terrified me, not anything concerning him. "Take too long right now. Make Ben and Chryssa ready. Sam or Martha Goldstein should arrive in a few minutes. Or somebody else, if I can't raise them. The police, if need be. Move, man! And then sit tight. You'll hear from me again. Savvy?"

A stiff nod replied.

I disempathed and touched our friends' glyphs, Martha answered. "Why, good morning, Steve. How are you? Frankly, you look terrible. Something is wrong, maybe?"

"You bet it is," I grated. "I can't explain, not right away, but Ginny's not here and our two younger ones need a place to stay. Immediately."

"You had a fire or—" The plump features steadied, the tone firmed. "No. I can see. A guest bed we have, and the crib from when Esther was little is in the attic. I'll tell Sam. He'll be right over. Don't worry, Steve. We'll be delighted. Danny especially, having his friend Ben here."

"Don't send mine to school or the nursery. Keep them indoors. It should be just for a day or two, or less, till Ginny gets home and things straighten out."

She regarded me closely. "They are very tangled, *nu?* I won't say this is what comes of dealing with the Darkness—"

"We didn't, Martha. It, well, it wished itself onto us."

She raised a hand. "Hush, Steve. I know. You and Ginny would never make bad. What I'm saying is, if you don't mind, we will ask Rabbi Levinson to come and give our house a new *barucha.*"

"Do I mind? Y-y-your God bless you," I stammered, blinking back tears.

This was why I'd turned first to this family. Not only were they good-hearted and reliable; they believed, and practiced their belief. I didn't see how wicked spirits could pass through the holiness that guarded those doors.

They might lay siege. But they wouldn't, I calculated. That would expose their game too blatantly. Ginny's and my house, however well antihexed, wasn't the same case. Its defenses were purely goetic, and technology can outwit technology. Moreover, it was a focus of the enemy's interest.

And maybe it had already been invaded.

No, I would not accept that notion, not yet. *Not ever, please.* Was my wordless agnostic prayer worth anything? If only we too could sincerely believe. But we were what we were; in our minds, belief was a powerful force if you really had it, with no doubts or reservations, an attitude we'd never managed to reconcile with a slew of disturbing questions. Intelligence had nothing to do with that. Sam, for instance, was smarter than me, more widely read, better at math, and so on. It was a matter of psychology.

Enough! What next? Recalling Val from the outer deeps. Which I should approach as an engineering problem. Else helplessness and hysteria would grab me.

I glanced at my watch. Amazingly, the hour was still too early for anyone who mattered at Cardinal Point to be on hand. Not that much help was available there. Sure, everybody would be sympathetic, in the emotional sense of the word. But how many of them had knowledge, let alone experience, of Operation Luna? Not Incanted Here. They'd call meetings, at which I'd have to appear, and—

Al-Bunni was supposedly in Washington, where people weren't quite ready to go to lunch. I unscrolled the national directory and reached an office where they might be in touch with him. They weren't. Having testified before Congress (again!) and done whatever other lobbying he'd come for, he'd taken a long weekend off, leaving no information about his itinerary. Not unreasonable. I'd probably have done the same.

But by Monday Val would be half a billion miles or so from us, among the farthest comets, her speed maybe at a point where the medicine bundle could no longer fend off the hard radiation of collision with atoms and dust. Before then, she'd have run out of food and water.

What use calling al-Bunni, anyhow? He'd given Operation Luna ideas that made all the difference. However, by now I understood them as well as he did, if not better. Cut-and-try experience counts for more

than theory. Jim Franklin had contributed, but mainly to communications, which were functioning well in spite of everything. Ginny and Fjalar were those we most needed. How much longer would they be out of touch?

A thought hit me.

First I checked back with the Goldsteins. They'd collected the kids, who were bewildered and sort of scared but well on their way to being comforted. Then I called Will.

He'd found the note. I saw him white, shivering, appalled. "Valeria actually did it?" he whispered. "Yes, my broom is missing. But she— What have you heard from her?"

I'd had my fill of pussyfooting. "The spacecraft went crazy. She's bound for outer space. I mean outer. Any ideas for getting her back?"

"No . . . no. . . ." Face and voice stiffened. "This is incredible. How may I help?"

"For the time being, stay put. We don't need your Fibbie shadows while we try to cope with this." A reminder, just in case, that they were there. "Think. Pray, if you're able." After a few more words, I cut off.

Balawahdiwa had entered the house. He stood above me like an image of its austerity. "My fellows and I will seek knowledge," he said. "Maybe the Beloved Ones will speak to us."

Why utter more thanks? He knew how I felt. "Good, I expect I'll be in the smithy. That's where everything is that we Anglos can use, plans, records, apparatus. I might find a clue to what's wrong and how to turn that damned shaft around."

"Your technics won't be all that's necessary, I suspect," he said. "But they won't be useless either. Yes, go and work on them," and find what consolation I could in the work.

"One more call from here, if you please."

I got hold of Curtice Newton. "Hi," she greeted. "You caught me barely in time. I was about to take off for the Point and yawn my way through another day." Like Martha before her, she looked closer. The image of the red head leaned toward me. "Hey, this isn't fun anymore, is it?"

"No." I explained. By the end, I was gulping and stuttering. "Y-you know things about *Owl* nobody else does. And, uh, and you're a good technician. Could you come and, well, help me figure this thing out?"

"Judas priest, Steve," she exclaimed, "why did you suppose you had to ask? Sure. The workshop, you said? I'll be there pronto. Fast as I can finish in the kitchen."

"Huh?"

"Poor man, I'll bet you've forgotten about lunch. I'll pack a basket for us, and coffee and such. You want a clear head, not a growling stomach. Wouldn't hurt if I stuck a couple of beers in the cooler, too."

# XLIII

The sun wheeled higher. The land warmed, but not much more, because a wind blew from the west. Clouds were massing on that horizon. Drifts of them passed overhead. Light and shadow played across Dowa Yalanne, as though the rock of it stirred.

Curtice and I hardly noticed. Even before she arrived, and she'd burned the air on her way, I'd been occupied. Besides Fjalar's tools, forge, runestones, and whatnot, the smithy was loaded with the scientific and engineering equipment that had analyzed, measured, and tested as the spacecraft came into being. Strain gauge, voltmeter, tarot, polarimeter, dowser, reckoner, mummy dust, microscope, you name it, probably you could find it here. I set about arranging things for use.

Curtice strode in. She spent one second giving me a smile full of compassion, then asked, "How can I talk with the girl?"

"Through this." I took off my locket, tuned it up, and handed it to her.

"—slantwise," we heard. "You've no shield, y'know—bally carelessness—so my blade'll have to defend as well as attack. I'm no la-de-da rapier, but it is possible. Yes, like that. Now, a slicing cut. . . . No, don't hew. Draw across. A feint, but with luck you might take off his nose. Again. Again. Hup, hup, hup—"

Curtice stared at me. "What in the jumping blue dickens?"

"She's got a talking sword along," I explained. "And our old tomcat."

"Well, I knew it's weird out, but I didn't expect—" The woman shrugged, brought the locket to her lips, and said crisply: "Hello, Valeria Matuchek. Curtice Newton on the line. Stow that drill and listen." Her tone softened. "How are you, honey?"

Fotherwick-Botts sputtered to silence. Val's reply trembled. "You, Captain Newton? W-we're alive. Still speeding away. Earth's nearly lost in the sun-glare. B-but you—" I pictured a few tears breaking forth, tears of sudden joy. She idolized the celestonaut.

"Good. Your father and I aim to turn you around and haul you home. For openers, we need to discover what's caused this. Stand by to answer questions as they occur to us. We may ask you to make some observations too, as best you can. Okay?"

The voice rang—thinly, but it rang. "Yes, ma'am."

"Keep on with what you're doing, Steve," Curtice told me. "I want to get the details for myself." I obeyed. My hands and most of my mind made a complex of instruments ready. With half an ear I heard inquiries more incisive than any of mine.

"All right," Curtice said at length. To me: "I have a hunch of sorts, but we need confirmation and more exact data. You know better than I how to handle most of this gear."

"And you know better what to look for." I leaned close to the locket, which she'd hung about her neck. The scenery was admirable, but I didn't stop to enjoy. "This is a technical problem, Val. It may take a while to crack. Don't think we've gone cold and unfeeling. Time enough to hug you—" My words stumbled. "—when you're back with us."

"Sure, Daddy. Er, General Fotherwick-Botts, sir, excuse me, please, but I think I ought to sheathe you. Svartalf, if you don't stop kneading my lap you can go back to the rear saddle!"

I won't describe the next half hour or so. To you it would be a dry list of procedures, tests, readings, calculations; to me the recollection would be hurtful. That's twice true of when we had to call on Valeria. An eyeball estimate from her seat wasn't worrisome. However, when she must crawl along the shaft, both backward and forward, to lay hands on straws and on nose cap, gathering impressions that the resonance sent for us to interpret— No. I see her too clearly, silhouetted against the unforgiving stars. One blunder and she'd drift free, to fall among them forever.

Oh, sure, she made light of my fears, and Curtice vowed that any agile young person could easily manage. "Do you suppose I'd have asked her to, otherwise?" Nevertheless—

The report stabbed: "I'm unscrewing the cap. . . . Reaching in. . . . The stone— Yow-w-w, I'm dropping!"

"Keep your legs wrapped around the shaft as I told you to," Curtice answered. "Don't lose that hold, whatever you do."

"But what's happening?"

"Free trajectory. When the pilot stone's removed, acceleration stops. You've still got the field giving you a one gee pull, but when the shaft is all that's under you, you can too easily slip off. In fact, most of you is bound to be out of line and feeling the weightlessness. Are you all right? Any nausea or dizziness?"

"N-no. I was just surprised. It feels. . . . it feels fun." *What a girl,* I thought dazedly. "I almost let go of the stone, but curled my fingers in time."

"Well done. Look at it. Describe it."

"The sunlight and shadows here, they're kind of confusing, but— It's blackish, lumpy. When I look close, I see. . . . like little grains embedded."

Curtice's face had become a bloodless mask. "Very well. Put it in your pocket and return to your saddle. Better fasten your safety harness."

"Svartalf's first."

Panic grabbed. "Hey!" I yelped. "That's not a—"

Curtice waved me to keep mum. "I'm back," Val called after a few minutes. The sweat on me reeked.

"Good," the celestonaut said. "I didn't want to risk startling you so you lost your grip on the stick. That's probably a chondrite. It's positively not terrestrial or lunar."

I leaped to the cabinet, unlocked drawers, yanked them open and slammed them shut again. Yes, one of the samples was missing. Its identification label mocked me.—*believed to have come from a collision in the asteroid belt, but there are some indications of an origin more remote, possibly the Kuiper belt—* The ring of comets beyond the orbit of Neptune.

"That bit of Earth sandstone was supposed to be still in the nose," I moaned. "Somebody switched it for—for—" My throat seized up on me.

Curtice nodded. "For a rock with an outwardness so great it overrides all ordinary control. A counterspell would have curbed it, but no one imagined any would be needed yet. The next test flight, you remember, was only planned to check maneuverability at low altitudes. Chances are, our pilot wouldn't have bothered with a medicine bundle. Death within seconds, as the craft shot beyond breathable atmosphere. With no living person aboard, we'd have no hope of recalling her. End of Operation Luna, very likely of Project Selene too."

"But who—"

"Later. Valeria, did you hear? Don't be afraid. You *are* alive and well. We *can* get you back."

"I know," said the brave, dear voice. "Daddy and Mother got me back from Hell once, didn't they? This should be a, a cracklesnap."

"Not exactly," I must confess. "We don't know offhand how to do it. But we'll find out, by God. Hang in there."

"At least she's no longer adding to that huge velocity," Curtice muttered. "As for reversing it—"

A new sound broke in from the locket on her bosom. "Steve? Fjalar and I have returned. What I heard— What's the matter?"

"Ginny!" I exploded. "You're okay?"

"We're fine, except hungry. But what's wrong here?"

Valeria, Curtice, and I told her. Well before we finished, she and the dwarf were demolishing speed limits in our direction.

"Oh, if only I'd come back sooner." Never before had I heard her wail. She mastered it and continued steadily. "Our mission was successful but exhausting. We decided we'd do best to arrive home rested, and slept the night through beside Yggdrasil. If I'd known, if I'd even guessed—"

"You couldn't have," Valeria said.

"Nor could you control the exact time when you'd return," I reminded.

"Or vat Ratatosk, or whoever it vas, did to the shed," Fjalar added. "It held, but it vill never be mush good again."

As always when the chips were down, Ginny became straight business. "We'll see you in about half an hour. Phone Balawahdiwa and inform him."

I tried, but as well as I could understand his wife, she said he'd left for a while. Making medicine, I supposed. "Shall I let Will know?" I asked.

*"No."* Ginny's tone was like sudden midwinter. The suspicions that had been nastily floating in me congealed.

Before my guts quite felt the weight and chill of them, Curtice said, "Uh-oh. We've got visitors."

I looked through a window. Tatters of cloud sent shadows scything across the desert. Brush stirred to the breeze. A broom and a truckrug had set down by the other vehicles. Dust puffed and blew away from their extended legs. Each carried two men. Three were big, neatly dressed but like laborers, the fourth small and in a business suit. He had a briefcase along.

Memory rammed through my tension. "Yeah." Words I'd once seen

on a tombstone in an old New England graveyard: "I expected this, but not so soon."

"What?" Curtice asked.

"Our wonderful government. Its income tax tentacle. Precisely what we need."

"They'll be disappointed!" laughed Val from her aloneness.

Anger put a good, clean taste in my mouth. I opened the door. Alger Sneep jarred to a startled halt. His companions stopped more slowly. They carried a sledgehammer, a crowbar, and a spell checker. The air that sighed around them seemed to have gotten a touch less warm than when I arrived.

"Mr. Matuchek!" Sneep yelped. "What are you doing here?"

"I'd like to hear the same from you," I replied.

He drew himself up to his full, negligible height. "I have an order to seize this alleged spacecraft and any other relevant material, and sequester the site."

Ginny was bound for us. She'd said her expedition had succeeded. I'd better play for time. Lounging in the doorway, I drawled, "Would you mind telling me the reason? I'm kind of curious. Maybe you'll agree that's natural."

"You have received notice that you, your associates, and your business are under investigation—"

"Have we?" I interrupted. "Sorry, but some troubles have driven a lot of things out of my head, Let me think a bit." I made a production of running fingers through my hair, rolling my eyes, and similar foolishness. "Um-m . . . yes, I do seem to recall something like that. But really, we're honest, law-abiding citizens in these parts. We might not always agree that our taxes are remotely in proportion to what we, or anybody except the favored few, get in return, or that the founders of this nation would condone the method of collection, but our returns are complete and accurate."

"That is what is in dispute, Mr. Matuchek. Please let us by." Sneep's plug-uglies, who'd been obviously disgruntled that they weren't going to bash their way in, began to look hopeful.

"Of course, of course. I wouldn't dream of obstructing justice. Assuming it is justice. Actually, my objections to the system are basically, uh, philosophical. Plato doubtless wouldn't have shared them. But he was a totalitarian, as his *Republic* makes plain, and an idealist, meaning he imagined the world around us is all in our heads and only his abstract archetypes actually exist. Those positions often go together, you know. The idea that our experience of reality is more direct leads

to the concept of the human being as a, uh, maybe not a Cartesian monad, but a separate individual with individual rights. For instance, Locke—" I was fudging it from a couple of vaguely remembered college courses.

Sneep suppressed a yell. "I am not here to discuss philosophy!"

I nodded. "Or, as Anthony said to Cleopatra, 'I am not prone to argue.' "

"Will you step aside, Mr. Matuchek, or must I invoke the law?"

Before his troops could lick their lips, I made an expansive gesture and declared, "Far be it from me to interfere with an officer in the performance of his duties. That's what I was trying to tell you. Come right into our humble shop. Make yourselves . . . at home, I mean. But first, just so you won't suppose we aim to spring anything on you, let me introduce the lady. Curtice, would you step out for a minute?"

She did. "How do you do," she said. Her voice implied she was not remotely interested in the answer.

"Curtice Newton, please meet Mr. Alger Sneep of the Inquisition for Revenue Securement. I'm sorry, I don't know you other gentlemen. If you'll give me your names, I'll do you the honor of introducing you, too."

"Never mind," snapped Sneep. "How do you do, Miss Newton."

"Captain Newton," I corrected him. "The distinguished celestonaut. You must have seen her on the farseer. Her record goes back to well before the space program. She was a test pilot with Boeing, and set a still unbroken record for—"

"Yes, yes. Let us *by.*"

"Certainly. Curtice, would you go back inside? And now me. This is a pretty narrow door, but then, we're on a tight budget, as you doubtless know. I should explain that Captain Newton is here to give advice on a problem. We're always getting surprises in this business." I winced. "Some are unpleasant."

Did I hear Valeria gulp and Ginny snarl?

The agents entered. For a moment they blinked. In spite of the cloud-rags, the outside was brilliant compared to the interior. Fjalar liked his workplaces gloomy.

"But—but where is the spacecraft?" Sneep said.

"That's what we're trying to learn," I told him, not untruthfully. We didn't have an exact fix.

"Somebody busted in and stole it?" growled one of the bruisers.

"No," I said. "She was taken out—" My glibness broke down. "For damn good reasons. Now she's lost."

Sneep's eyes needled me. His followers glowered. "Is this an attempt to forestall seizure?" he demanded.

"How could it be? No papers had been served on us. And by the way, I want to see those you've got."

"Do not raise more obstacles, Mr. Matuchek. I warn you. And you, Captain Newton. We shall have to investigate your involvement in this matter."

Even in the dimness, I saw her tauten. Rage flamed through me. I struggled to keep it down. "Ever hear of the Fourth Amendment, Mr. Sneep?" I rasped.

"That is for a tax court to interpret. Thus far, judgments have generally been in favor of our service." Sneep turned to the others. "Load as much of this material on the carpet as you can. I'll be asking questions meanwhile." He produced a minirecorder from his jacket. "You will be well advised to give prompt and correct replies, Mr. Matuchek, Captain Newton."

My eyes went toward an upright cabinet in the rear. It had room to hold a man. Curtice grabbed my arm. "No, Steve!"

"I'm here," Ginny called, maybe barely in time.

She stalked through the doorway. Edgar hunched black and ominous on her shoulder. Fjalar stumped behind, hair and whiskers bristling like a porcupine, nose a crimson beacon of fury.

"Ah—Mrs.—ah, Dr. Matuchek." Sneep retreated a step. His thugs stopped in their tracks. "Welcome. We have come to—"

"Kindly do not bid me welcome to my own property," she said. "And I know what your wretched errand is. Listen, Sneep and the rest of you. Listen well. You'll regret it if you don't."

She thrust a lorestone into his shivery hands. "I have just returned from a long session with a very special advisor. He analyzed our case not only item by item, down to the last cent, but from every aspect of the entire United States tax code. Take this back to your office and play it. I will dispatch a copy to Mr. Sturlason of Nornwell Scryotronics and retain one for myself. It will take you some time and effort to go through the calculations and logic, but I assure you they are steel-clad. You will find we are absolutely in the right. I do not claim we followed every jot and tittle of the technicalities. That would be impossible for any mortal. Furthermore, as this report demonstrates, there are numerous contradictions. But it turns out that none of us owes a thing. Rather, the Nornwell company has, over the past three years, overpaid by a total of approximately fifteen thousand dollars. This includes Operation Luna, which under the regulations is a legitimate subsidiary. My hus-

band and I, as individuals, have overpaid by approximately nine hundred dollars. Refunds will be expected, with interest."

"Y-you assert this," he stuttered, "but until we, we have gone through the analysis, it's only your word." He stiffened. "Meanwhile—"

She smashed him flat. "Meanwhile, sir, you are delaying the rescue of our daughter, an innocent child." Did I hear Valeria squelch a giggle? "Your overbearing tactics drove her to desperation. She took the spacecraft. No papers had been served, no official notice of any kind given. Therefore the sole possible charge against her is flying without a license, which is not within your jurisdiction. It is trivial. In fact, it's debatable, because this is not an ordinary vehicle. If the charge is considered at all, you know perfectly well it will be dismissed."

"What, what, what do you mean?"

She told him no more than that the flight had gone out of control and astray. Her words were few but whetted. He cringed. His threesome mumbled and bunched their muscles, till Fjalar took his favorite hammer from a bench and tossed it to and fro, rippling his thews at them.

"Our Congressman and both our senators will hear of this," Ginny finished. "We would prefer to keep it from the news media. However, I suggest you think what the consequences will be if we can't. Here you are, as I said, endangering a child's life the more for every minute you inflict yourself on us. I do believe that if we must resort to forcible measures—" She had drawn and extended her wand. The star flared wickedly. I bared teeth, wolf style. "—a jury will find we were justified. Best you return to your office at once and study what I have been kind enough to bring you."

"But I—I didn't know," Sneep half sobbed. "I'm so sorry. I have children too and— I'm sorry!"

Ginny gestured at the door. "Good day, sir."

"Grech, kh-hui," added Edgar.

They shambled out. The sunlight glinted off tears in Sneep's eyes. I almost sympathized. There's little doubt in my mind that the Sixteenth Amendment was inspired directly by Hell, but its agents are human, most of them decent at heart. The jobs they have were the best they could get.

The stick and the rug took off.

Ginny gusted a long breath. The ice fell from her. "They're gone," she said low. "How are you, darling?"

"I'm okay," Val called across the gulf, "but, oh, Mother, I'm sorry too. For giving you this trouble."

"*No importa.* What matters is to free you from it. I think we can, but let's not waste time on sentiment." Ginny turned to Curtice. "Pass that locket back to Steve, please. I'll tune mine down. You and I have work to do. He can keep her company."

"*Ja,* me too," Fjalar boomed. "Ay vill give her heart, songs and stories and visdom."

"No, we'll want you on tap—" He perked up for a split second, then saw what she meant. "—ready to fill us in on any technical questions that may arise. You're the wright, Curtice is the pilot and, in a way, engineer, I'm the thaumaturge. Between us, we'll find an answer. How lucky that Svartalf and Fotherwick-Botts are with her. Both carry a strong ergodic charge. That should give us a handle on the forces, in the absence of a proper lodestone."

Edgar flapped to a stool. The trio went into a huddle around him. I found a corner, sat down, and talked with my daughter. I won't write what we said. She was too gallant; I was fighting too hard to keep up a light and optimistic front.

Ginny interrupted a few times and spoke directly—for instance, when a sortilege revealed that Val should toss away the piece of meteor. May the damned thing orbit into the sun.

Light went down as a man-shape filled the doorway. I surged to my feet and went to meet Balawahdiwa. He'd returned to Zuni and gotten my message. Ginny explained to him that this wasn't his kind of goetics, but begged him to stay because we really would need his help soon. I joined him outside and we continued the conversation with Val. He spoke of beautiful, secret places he'd guide us to, once our troubles were past. The clouds piled higher in the west, snow-bright on top, blue-black in their depths. The wind piped louder and colder.

Brilliance flared in the shed. Something sang like a trumpet. "Hey!" Val shouted. "The . . . the boat's turning. . . . The sun, Earth, they're *ahead* of me! Daddy, Mother!"

Curtice emerged from the shed. "We've done it," she gasped. "Reversed acceleration— She's coming home, Steve."

Ginny appeared behind her. She didn't whoop and dance like everybody else. Her expression brought us to a dead stop. "It'll take seven or eight hours, if not more," she said. "There's a matter we must deal with immediately. Curtice, Fjalar, will you hold the fort here? Steve—Balawahdiwa, sir—will you ride with me?"

# XLIV

The wind of our passage brawled louder than the wind over the desert. Road, heights, brushy flats unreeled around us. Edgar crouched on Ginny's shoulder, beak forward, spearlike. Balawahdiwa and I crowded together in the rear of the Jaguar. His fingers clutched a medicine bag, which he had brought along from Zuni, with needless tightness.

When the stick was steering itself, Ginny twisted around and regarded us. The look of her terrified me. "My fault," she said. Each word fell like a stone. "I should have seen from the first. But no, I let wishful thinking take me over."

"Me too?" I mumbled. My vision blurred; I tasted salt on my lips. "Will seemed impossible."

"Everything pointed to him."

"No, but—that time somebody tried to kill us— He isn't capable of any such thing! For sure he couldn't have left his house and returned unobserved, hotspelled that carpet, or shot so well. I— Remember when I took him out on the target range once? Just once. The other guys were laughing too hard."

"The evidence—"

"Frame-up."

"The physical evidence is *there.* Oh, yes, Will never would or could have done any of it. The thing that's possessing him did."

"He passed the psychoscopic exam."

"It's no ordinary demon. I think now it's not strictly speaking a demon at all. It lies deep in him, intertwined with his whole being like a latent virus. When it goes active, it takes him over, body and brain. *He* isn't aware of what happens then, and afterward he doesn't remember."

Balawahdiwa nodded. "Indeed he cannot," he said, "or he would have revealed the truth, or taken his own life if he saw no other way out. Only his spirit knows. Horror and heaviness are upon it."

"Yeah, that depression," I admitted. "But when the thing's using him, it does a great job of faking his real self."

"No demon could control him that cleverly," Ginny said. "This is an infection of the very soul."

*Whatever the thing was,* I thought, *it needed some practice to begin with. When it entered him, and when it first really used him, it left traces in the form of nightmares. Not anymore.* Desolation gripped me. "It must plant false memories of those times, now that it knows its way around in him."

"Obviously. Harking back, I realize how vague his accounts were. To his conscious mind, whenever the possessor is lying low, it must feel like some kind of mental lapse. That alone would worry him sick." Ginny shook her head. "But he's not one to dump his fears and woes on others. Not Will."

The grief in me was turning to vengefulness. It was as if I heard a clangor and a shrilling inside my skull, a blade forged and honed. "That thing—yes, plain to see—now—it switched lodestones the day we test-flew *Owl.* When he ducked into the smithy. Later on, though—"

"I think it decided to try an alternative approach. It could acquire skills like shooting and evading surveillance from demons that know how. But they and it are not native to America. In many respects it must be naive about this country, learning gradually and piecemeal from Will's brain—who's pretty naive himself—and by observation. It came to understand that if *Owl* took off and killed her pilot, investigation would incriminate him. He's too useful to abandon until it becomes absolutely necessary. Nor would anyone else with such potentials be as easy to invade as he was. Another kind of infiltration looked more promising. I neglected to quiz Sneep, but it seems clear that, when Valeria caught him on the phone, Will—his body—wasn't simply responding to an IRS initiative as he claimed. He had tipped them off and proposed that they sequester the boat."

Ginny had left her communication locket with Curtice. I'd kept mine, and hadn't reduced the gain. Our daughter's voice wavered from afar: "Yes, he, he—*it* warned Mr. Sneep they shouldn't try flying her."

"Uh-huh," I grunted, the way a wild boar might. "Doubtless it could've persuaded them to dismantle her in the course of bankrupting Nornwell and us."

"But Uncle Will, old Uncle Will, how could something that wicked get into him?"

"Because he was—in his heart still is—so innocent," Balawahdiwa answered. "His studies, his previous contact with your Fair Folk, drew the attention of the enemy. He was one they needed to subvert, for his research strongly aided the space program. Possessed, he could be a major force in undermining it. Besides his trustfulness, the work itself had made him vulnerable."

"He never thought to have protective spells cast," Ginny added. Agony: "I never did."

"For God's sake, don't blame yourself," I begged. "Who outside of Hell could have known? Just cure him!"

The steel of her stood forth. "I mean to try, with the help of you two."

Balawahdiwa leaned over, halfway across me. "Valeria," he said gently, "you'd better not hear the rest of this."

"I wouldn't yell," the girl protested.

"No, but it would be hard on you. Besides, you'll likely need to exchange information with Captain Newton from time to time. That would come through to us and be distracting."

"He's right," I said. "Hang in there, punkin. We'll call as soon as possible."

For that instant, Ginny's tone was tender. "Yes, so long, darling. Fare luckily. We love you."

I snapped the off switch on the locket. Part of me wished it were somebody's neck.

"Do you believe we can exorcise the thing?" Balawahdiwa asked. His question sounded stupid to me till I realized how it probed.

"I think that between us we have a chance," Ginny replied. "But first we must secure him."

Gallup appeared ahead, tiny when we glanced at the cloudbanks on our left. She slowed to a legal speed. Getting pulled over and ticketed would eat time.

*No doubt the spirit's controlling him at this moment,* I thought. *Probably it's been continuously in charge for at least the past couple of days. And we left the kids alone with it.* A knife twisted.

*But harming them would've been pointless and could've given the game away,* I told myself. Ben and Chryssa were safe now, Val distant a couple of million miles and homebound, homebound. She'd taken his broom. Anyway, the FBI maintained watch on him. True, the possessor had outspelled and eluded them before. However, that was at Will's

house. I supposed the charms on ours would complicate, quite possibly forbid any such stunts. And it didn't know what we, Ginny in particular, had been up to. And although I'd removed the kids, I'd left the impression that I trusted Will same as always, because in fact I did . . . then. I imagined it'd figure its best bet was to lie low, alert.

Lightning flickered in cloud-caverns. We landed at our place and dismounted.

"I'll go ahead and catch his attention," Ginny said. "You follow a minute later, Steve, and grab him. He'll resist. Try not to hurt him."

The Medusa mask of her dissolved. She tossed her red locks back as if casting off a burden. Her smile beamed. I don't know how she managed that, sorcery or an innate gift. Balawahdiwa stood impassive. I had all I could do not to howl and attack.

Feather-lightly, Ginny ran up the walk and the front steps. She flung the door open. "Hallo, Will!" she caroled. "I've got news!"

Counting seconds under my breath was better than staring at my watch. One hippogryphius, two hippogryphius, three hippogryphius . . .

The door remained ajar. Words drifted to my tight-strung hearing. "—we routed the tax pack. We're in contact with Val—"

*Sixty.* I moved. *Easy, easy. Don't rush. Amble.*

Will confronted Ginny in the living room. He saw me enter and nodded absently, his mind on her. "—not sure what the trouble is," she was saying, "but I have a guess. I expect we'll want your help."

Did the brush of gray hair faintly bristle, did the green eyes flare behind the innocuous spectacles? Approaching, I caught a stench of anxiety and . . . malevolence? He nodded. "Of course," he said. "Anything I can do."

*Anything the spirit can do to ruin the undertaking and leave our girl adrift.*

Balawahdiwa came in, cat-footed, and closed the door. I found my position and pounced.

At Will's back, I caught his arms. I brought them together, pinned them with my left, and swept my right around his throat till that hand joined its mate in a choke hold.

"What—what's this?" He sounded so shocked and bewildered, so Will, that I nearly relaxed and apologized.

Ginny restored my strength: "Stand fast, Steve. Goryo, we are here to drive you out. Will, if you can hear me, if something of you understands, we mean to set you free."

He shrieked, a horrible saw-toothed noise. He threw himself to and

fro against my grip. He kicked my shins; the heel of his shoe bit and raked.

*Try not to hurt him.* The fury became unbelievable. Enough to tear bones from their sockets. I hooked an ankle in front of his, pushed his shoulders, and hung on to keep him from falling too hard. I followed him, though, and lay on top, using my weight to control the writhing, jerking, raving mass.

Ginny had darted off to the storeroom. She returned with a length of stout cord. Tears whipped down her cheeks. Balawahdiwa helped me hogtie the prisoner.

"Be quiet," I growled. "You want the Fibbies to hear and bust in?"

He choked the racket off. The air whined in his gullet. Spit drooled into his beard. He'd lost his glasses. Nothing stood between us and the utter hatred in his gaze.

Ginny squared her shoulders. "All right," she said, "Take him to my arcanum."

Balawahdiwa and I carried him. Edgar, who'd flown to his perch, descended and click-clicked along the floor after us. Ginny, in the lead, drew the blinds. We laid the body on the couch. Its frenzy had passed. The sweat was drying on skin grown cold. Only the ribs moved, and those terrible eyes that followed us.

Ginny spread books and certain other things on her worktable, Balawahdiwa unpacked his bag beside them, the raven settled on the edge: shapes dark and strange in the dimness. I waited aside, listening to my heart knock. My mouth had gone dry as a dead man's.

"What do you think the possessor is?" Balawahdiwa asked hushedly.

"A goryo," Ginny answered as low. "I began to wonder a while ago. Things Will had told us at times when he was himself—I threw the idea from me, but it wouldn't stay gone. Mostly for reassurance, I read some Japanese lore. Parts of it fitted hideously well. Still I denied. But Mimir seems to have done more than solve a secondary problem for me. One like that—" Her voice faded.

"I too have met with Powers," he said. "You don't come away unchanged. What is this you speak of? A kind of—shen, kuei, do they name them in China?"

"Not quite. It could perhaps become a kami, a tutelary spirit, but its malice locks it into what it is. A vicious ghost, oftenest a woman's, self-tortured, trying to avenge the miseries of its past life on the living. Goryo have driven people to madness, violence, suicide. Like the rest

of the paraworld, they were helpless during the Long Sleep, but old tales remembered them. Since the Awakening, a few seem to have reappeared—or newly come into being."

*And the demonic conspiracy co-opted them,* I thought.

Ginny went on, Fimbul-bleak, iron-hard. "I suspect we have here the late Princess Tamako. We'll find out, I hope."

I'd never before seen Balawahdiwa hesitate. "Necromancy is vile."

"Necromancy is rubbish, at least as my civilization defines it. But the soul, the spirit— Yes, I admit we don't know much more about it than that it exists." Ginny's manner went professional, impersonal. There was an odd comfort in that. "I favor the theory that it's formed by the living organism, an energy structure within the universal web of forces, and outlasts its matrix. You may consider this crassly materialistic. But surely you'll agree that it, like everything else, is subject to the great law, whether you call that the law of nature and logic or the law of God and morality. Demons have been exorcised. Between us, you and I should be able to expel a ghost."

Balawahdiwa nodded. He murmured in Zuni and crossed himself. They got to work.

Again I won't tell of the next two hours. I mustn't, and I couldn't. While I watched, frozen, they studied, conferred, planned, prepared. Sometimes they drew on Edgar, in ways I am not sure of—he, a member of the nonhuman natural world, kin to the birds of Odin and to the mighty Creator and Trickster of our Northwestern Indians. Once they laid hands on my head, and for a moment I whirled off into infinite abysses.

It passed. I sat in the shadows and waited. Inside, I felt as lonely as Valeria. Maybe more; she had company, yonder in the void.

They lighted sticks of incense and a bowl of dried herbs. The smoke drifted bitter through the dusk. Ginny's wand glowed star-fierce. Balawahdiwa chanted. A small drum throbbed beneath his right hand, his left shook a feathered rattle. Did I also hear the notes of a cedar flute, the beat of dancing feet? The sorcerers went to stand at Will's side, her familiar again on her shoulder. They began an incantation.

His throat shrieked. His face contorted to a troll's. He writhed, strained against his bonds, would indeed have broken himself while he wrecked the room if he hadn't been restrained. I tensed for a battle.

No need, thanks be. The songs joined, Latin and Hebrew, Zuni and Shoshonean; fingers beckoned; the raven spread wings as if to fly to the Underworld. Blue fires blazed icy and died. A wind that smelled of thunderstorm whistled by. The floor quivered. And the spirit passed.

I glimpsed it go. Did I see the image of a woman, faint and tattered as fog in that wind, robe and hair streaming wild, mouth drawn back from dreadful teeth? Did I hear her scream, did I feel the wrath and spite and despair? I don't know. I don't want to know. Enough that she was gone.

Will collapsed where he lay. His eyes closed, his breath shuddered and steadied, his face became his, and he slept. Edgar flapped to the bookshelf and sat a-droop, exhausted. Ginny sank to the floor and wept. I groped my way over to hold her close. Balawahdiwa stood above us while he spoke his final prayers. Glancing up, I saw that there was not yet any real peace in him.

A long while afterward, a short while by the clock, Ginny and I with our arms still around one another, we watched Will rouse. He sighed, blinked, looked nearsightedly around. She disengaged and bent over him. "How, how are you?" she stammered.

"Free," he whispered. "The horror . . . no more . . . like escaping from a fever nightmare, back to . . . reality. . . . I can never thank you. . . ."

She kissed his brow. "No need to, old dear. Take it easy. Rest. Sleep. Or what do you want?"

"First, I suppose, to be untied," I said. Prosiness was a blessing. "Can you roll over, Will? I'll undo those knots. Sorry 'bout them, and if I was kind of rough."

"No, you saved me, you called me back from Hell—" I took the cord off.

He stirred. His head lifted. "Take it easy, I said," Ginny urged. "You've been through an ordeal as bad as cancer. Give yourself time to recover. Would you like some food or drink, maybe some broth? You should certainly take plenty of water."

"Wait, wait," he pleaded. "I have . . . memories . . . not suppressed anymore. . . . What *she* thought and did. What she told *them,* and heard from them."

"Later, Will. You're free. Val's returning to us. That's all that matters right now. That, and healing you. Lie down. Rest."

"I can't," he gasped. "Not till— You've got to know. *They've* kept track of you. Not everything. They don't know where you went, Virginia, or what you did, nor the dealings of our shaman friend with his gods, nor—But they know plenty else. Already they're reacting. Valeria—"

His words trailed off. He lowered his head, completely wrung out.

Balawahdiwa stepped forward. His own voice chopped. "He speaks

truth. In my Seeking this morning, I felt a hint. While we worked our spell here, the Beloved Ones spoke again, more clearly, and I begin to understand what they said. The demons can't keep your daughter from returning toward us, but they can set their strength against her."

*They can apply a vector to the forces,* I thought. Sickness rose in me.

"I do not see how we can counter it," Balawahdiwa finished. "She will not land on Earth, but on the moon. They will be waiting for her."

# XLV

Oh, no," I begged.

Ginny turned on the priest. "You're quite sure?" she demanded.

He nodded. "I wish I weren't."

Same as earlier, she had become all business, like a sword drawn in anger. "We might have foreseen." She spoke flatly, except for the barest quaver, while her lashes blinked away drops that sparkled in the dusk. "It makes sense. They want to destroy *Owl*; Val's incidental. They can't stop her in her course, but the original mission, a lunar landing, gives them the goetic leverage to redirect it that much. Can we change it back?"

"That's your department. But I'm afraid the answer is no."

"Can your Beings help at all?"

"I will go out beneath the sky and pray." Balawahdiwa gathered his things and went from us. After a minute, while our eyes and Will's met in silence, I heard the door to the back yard open and shut.

I shook myself and managed to say, "Maybe it has an engineering solution."

Ginny touched my cheek. "Always the engineer, aren't you, Steve? Still, yes, we'll see what we can do."

"We and Curtice."

"Absolutely." She stepped to her desk and resonated the phone. The celestonaut's image shone at us, pale and expectant.

"Will's rid of the ghost," Ginny said. "The possessor, I mean."

"Why, wonderful!" Curtice cheered. "Did you hear that, Val?" The girl shouted jubilation.

"We have bad news as well," Ginny went on. "I'm sorry, darling,

this has to be confidential. We'll explain soon. Turn the communicator off, Curtice."

The other woman obeyed. Ginny gave her the facts. She let loose several words that shocked me, then steadied. "Yes," she agreed, "we must break this to the child as calmly and optimistically as may be. But break it we must."

"Have you any ideas?" I asked with scant hope.

"Not really. Without navigational instruments, Val can't give me the data to determine her position and path any closer than a ballpark estimate. I'll try for a fix here, groundside. If that succeeds, and assuming your Zuni partner got the straight goods from his gods, maybe we can work some trick. I honestly don't see how, but— When can you join me?"

"As soon as my broom can manage." Ginny's glance fell on her brother. "No, I'm sorry. Not immediately."

"Eh?" he wheezed. "Go. Don't delay. I'll be all right."

I looked down at the drawn face and replied, "Nonsense. You're convalescent, son—yeah, and in the earliest stages of it. You've got to have rest and care. Not to mention protection from any attempt to repossess you."

He shuddered. Either he was too scared or too weak to argue further. "We have to wait for Balawahdiwa anyway," I remembered. "We'll call you later, Curtice." I disempathed and touched the glyphs for the Goldsteins.

Martha saw me, sucked in a breath, and asked compassionately, "All right, Steve, so what's gone wrong now?"

"I can't explain yet, but—I'm sorry, it is an imposition, but can you take in another refugee for a day or two?"

"Refugee? This sounds like a war or a pogrom." She wasn't joking. "You bring whoever it is straight over. We will be very hurt if you don't."

"Thanks and—and God bless you," I wished once more for her and hers.

"God help you, Steve, Ginny. Sam's at work, but I will be making up a cot we have. Before you ask, yes, your children are fine, though naturally anxious. They will be glad to see you. I will too."

Doing something, anything, was a relief. We collected Will's pajamas and stuff. He leaned heavily on my arm as I led him to our broom and helped him onto a seat.

Martha, Ben, and Chryssa waited at the Goldsteins' front door. Their uncle's condition frightened the kids. I said he was sick but re-

covering; their mother and I had to take off for another little while but ought to be back shortly with everything made right. I'm skilled at hiding my feelings when necessary, legacy of wartime and of countless poker games. I convoyed Will to his bed, got him into his bedclothes, spread sheet and blanket over him.

"You're kind," he whispered.

"I'm family," I said.

"Yes. The Graylocks are honored." He smiled a wee smidgen. "Excellent chromosomes you've brought us."

Martha promised as I left: "The Sabbath begins this evening. We will pray for you." She gave me a quick hug, kissed my cheek, and let me go.

I returned home. Ginny was at her books. The look she threw me was desperate. "I've found nothing that might work," she said.

Balawahdiwa came back in a few minutes later. My pulse jackrabbited.

He regarded us gravely. "Behind my eyelids I have had a vision," he declared. "Within my head I have heard. The Beloved Ones, yes, with Coyote himself, will do what they can against this thing that menaces all Earth."

He paused. "What they can. They are not the Single True God, you know. Their powers are not unbounded. We too must give what we are able, we humans, everything we are able to.

"They can't stop the spacecraft from landing on the moon. But once she has, they can sing her home—if she has a living pilot, if Valeria escapes the trap laid for her. The demons will surely pursue. The Beloved Ones will try to give her the speed or the trickiness to keep them from overtaking her. If the chase goes clear to Earth, the Beloved Ones will fight. But they can't do it alone. We must be there ourselves, in body and in soul, prepared to stake our lives."

Through my pounding blood I heard my voice recite the rough calculation that was all I had at this hour to offer. "At two gees, braking, Val should reach the moon about, oh, about nine or ten o'clock. If she can then take off again, same acceleration to midpoint and equal deceleration, well, roughly an hour and a half to here."

"She probably can't leave at once or go that fast. The demonic forces will drag on the vehicle."

"Wouldn't a new lodestone help? An object from Earth. Like a coin, a pocket knife, anything?"

"Yes, after a fashion," Ginny said. "It would be much better if she

had a paranatural or poetically charged thing. Perhaps the Fair Folk can give her something of theirs."

I scowled. "Dicey. But we'll have time to talk with her. Maybe somebody will get an idea. Where do we meet our allies, Balawahdiwa?"

Sternness responded. "On the sacred mountain. There the Beloved Ones have their greatest strength."

"Well, that figures, I guess. When should we flit?"

The priest shook his head, a slow weaving to and fro. "You don't understand, Steven. Dowa Yalanne is holy. We don't set foot atop it casually or even easily. That would be sacrilege. For us, our mission, it would damn any hopes we ever had. This isn't a simply practical matter. It's also spiritual, and sacrifice is always required in an appeal. It may be as little as a pinch of meal, it may be as much as your whole life, but it is what you must give to become, for a while, one with a Power higher than yourself, and what the Power must have for this to happen.

"We'll walk up the mountain. A small beginning to whatever sacrifice we must make. How great that will be in all, I do not know."

A stiff six- or seven-hour climb, I'd heard.

Balawahdiwa hadn't been preaching a sermon, just telling us how it was. Nevertheless I badly wanted some plain old practicality. Ginny beat me to it: "When shall we start?"

He frowned. He wasn't entirely used to the white man's scissored-off concept of time. After a moment he replied, "We should take a particular route. I'll tell you how to find the trailhead. Suppose we meet there at three-thirty. You see, it looks as though we'll have trouble along the way. Did the demons brew this weather? Or is it an accident? Or a test, a part of our sacrifice? I don't know."

"Very well," I said. "Three-thirty p.m. Meanwhile, uh, no disrespect, but we'll try to redirect *Owl* ourselves."

"Go ahead," Balawahdiwa answered starkly. "However, I believe this is our only chance."

"Let's go!"

Ginny shook her own head. "Be sensible, Steve. I wasn't at first, but that was an impulse. We're starved, we're tired, we'll be worthless without some food and a nap. You too, sir?"

Balawahdiwa nodded. "We're mortal."

We made sandwiches in the kitchen and swallowed them while we discussed details, carefully keeping them mundane. We called Curtice.

She told us her observations seemed to confirm the priest's warning. She'd been searching for an answer herself and gotten nowhere.

"Bring Valeria in," Ginny said.

I haven't the heart to write exactly what went on between us and our daughter. She took the news like a trooper. I suggested she draw Fotherwick-Botts and continue the swordsmanship drill. She said Svartalf was already sharpening his claws on his saddle. We bade farewell for now.

Ginny laid a sleep-and-arousal spell on the three of us. We stretched out and toppled.

Someone spoke to me in my dreams, someone good. I don't quite recall.

Much refreshed by that hour of siesta, we prepared for the trek. Food and extra garments, including rain ponchos, went into backpacks, sleeping bags onto the frames, water into canteens. Ginny foresightedly borrowed Val's and Ben's back-country gear and did likewise for it.

Edgar with us, we reached the workshop about three. Balawahdiwa took off on his own stick. He needed to fix a pack, too. I suspected he meant to do more than just that. Ginny, Curtice, Fjalar, and I conferred, briefly and without result.

"If there is a straightforward method, we'll never find it soon enough, and probably there isn't." Curtice sighed. "Okay, we'll go the religious route."

"You're coming?" I asked, not surprised.

"*Ja,*" the dwarf boomed. "Ay'll ask Thor he hammer those trolls."

"Why not?" Curtice said. "And I'm a Christian. Not awfully devout, but I do attend Congregationalist services most Sundays. I'll be praying."

*And the Goldsteins,* I thought. *And Fotherwick-Botts, who's a Catholic of sorts. And Will and Ginny and me in our uncertain ways. And Balawahdiwa, powerfully. And Valeria out of her innocence.*

We locked the workshop, mounted our brooms, and set forth.

# XLVI

Balawahdiwa waited at the trailhead. He was as plainly outfitted as us, except for a weblike pattern of paint on his face and a prayer stick tucked in his belt. I guessed that his backpack held other sacred objects and that he'd spent his time here blessing the way we must walk.

Naked red rock loomed steeply from the desert scrub. Up and up it sheered, buttresses, ravines, cliffs, crags shaped into fantasies by a million years of weather. Beyond glimmered the pale strata, then layers again ocherous, on to the final heights. From the bottom we could only glimpse jumbled great fragments of what reached ahead of us.

The sky also hindered sight. Clouds covered it, gray and blue-black, the lower ones scudding like smoke. What light seeped through was turning an eerie brass-yellow. Wind whistled and boomed. It thrust around us, stronger, louder, colder every minute.

Balawahdiwa addressed me through the noise. "I think you should come along as a wolf, Steven. We may well need that strength and toughness on the climb and in whatever happens afterward."

Disappointment flickered. I'd be under animal limitations. Ginny laid a hand on my arm. Resolution and an odd, savage glee drove off any qualms.

I gave her the communicator locket I'd worn. She kissed me. I kissed her back. I'll carry those few seconds with me through my life—but probably not Edgar's beak grooming my hair from her shoulder. He meant well.

"You guys start," I suggested. "I'll catch up."

Curtice nodded. "Yes. We're in for a tough stretch at best, and the weather may make it worse than tough." She glanced at Fjalar. "Will you be okay?" she asked. When the dwarf tried on Ben's rain poncho,

the smallest we had, he'd said it was too long for him to do any scrambling in.

"Oh, *ja,*" he replied. "Yust Thor making merry."

He didn't know how violent Southwestern thunderstorms can get. Often outright cloudbursts, they generally hit in summer but are not unknown as late as October. I doubted today's conditions were pure chance.

My friends began their ascent. Winding among rocks, they were soon lost to view. I stowed the pack I wouldn't be able to use in the coffer on one stick and laid my garments beside it as I stripped to my skinsuit. Chill ripped at me. I crawled into another coffer and made the changeover. Maybe that wasn't needful, as murky as the scene had grown.

Wolf pelt and wolf vigor warmed me. I bounded out and yelped defiance at the wind. It still bore faint scents of blowing grit, wildly tossing brush, deer. . . . I quelled an urge and loped ahead.

Nothing but feet had carved the trail, century by century. A greenhorn could easily lose it. Narrow, strewn with stones, pitted and gullied, it twisted skyward like a snake about to strike. Maybe the Zunis usually took a different, better path. Maybe this route, the difficulty and danger, were part of our sacrifice. I didn't know. In my present state I wondered only vaguely. The question slipped from my wolf mind. I ran on my hunt.

Soon I overtook the party and fitted my pace to theirs. They all knew how to move on a mountain, long, slow strides, aware and wary of everything that might make them slip or stumble. Fjalar's short legs had to swing faster, but he seemed unweariable. His right hand clutched a heavy hammer he'd taken along from the shop. Token of religion, lucky charm, or just a comforting reminder of tasks less uncanny? He grinned at me. Ginny stroked my head, Curtice ruffled my shaggy neck, Edgar cawed a hello from Ginny's shoulder, which he must hang onto tightly. Balawahdiwa, leading, turned his head to give me a smile. We climbed on.

Occasionally my companions stopped to rest, drink from their canteens, munch on a handful of raisins or other trail food. Ginny would pour some water into a depression for me to lap up and give me a piece of jerky. The interludes were brief, in that bitter, tearing wind. At the priest's signal we'd rise and resume the hike, ever higher.

The sky went black. Lightning flared, over and over. Each white blaze showed the mountainscape in shadowless sharpness. Thunder

rolled like monstrous wheels, down and down across the world, echoing off scarps, shaking our bones. Wind roared, skirled, keened.

The rain came, a cataract around us, upon us, against us. Hail mingled, slingstones to bruise and draw blood. We couldn't make out Balawahdiwa's shout, we barely saw his gesture through the flying silver, but we did as he did, cast ourselves flat on the slanted ground, lesser targets for the lightning. First Fjalar brandished his hammer aloft. "Fun ban fun," he bawled, "but, Thor, this ban ridiculous!" I suppose he used English to inspire us. Edgar took refuge under a concave boulder.

Water runneled in the trail. Its stream swelled, a torrent, mere inches deep, yet a force that clamored, foamed, dragged. The sudden mud gave way beneath Curtice. She slid aside and downward. Runoff plunged over the edge of a nearby bluff. Jagged rocks lurked below. She flailed after a handhold to stop her skid. Whatever she caught pulled free.

I sprang up and bounded. My pads and claws kept an uneasy grip. I reached her, grabbed her poncho between my jaws, and hauled. We stopped on the brink. I fought to keep us there.

That kind of berserkerdom seldom lasts long. As abruptly as it had exploded, the chaos ended. Rain and hail ceased, wind dwindled, the sky lightened as clouds broke apart, the spates gurgled away to naught. Both of us on all fours, I helped Curtice back to firmer footing.

She clambered erect. Her hand caressed my drenched head. "That's another I owe you, Steve," she said shakily. "I hope you'll be best man at my wedding someday—the groom's bound to ask you—and, later on, godfather."

Even wolf, I was touched. Even human, I couldn't have mumbled more than, "Aw, shucks." I wagged my stump of a tail. Ginny came over to lift my muzzle and kiss me right on my black nose. "Yumping yiminy, Grettir the Strong never did any better!" Fjalar exclaimed. Balawahdiwa signed a blessing.

We labored onward. The dwarf and I were a sight, my pelt and his hair and beard waterlogged, both of us black with mud. We could take it, though. Wind chill might have been too much for the others, but their ponchos had kept them from being soaked and now gave some protection. However, neither Ginny nor Curtice were at their glamorous best.

The going became marginally easier. With just the thinnest small patches of soil on the high slopes, the trail was again solid underfoot, aside from where the rain had washed scree across it. The clouds scat-

tered, opened an infinite blue to us, at last were quite gone. The wind died off. Only the scrunch of stone beneath soles and the often harsh sound of breath remained. The cold deepened, but it was a quiet cold, which exertion held at bay.

The sun set behind Arizona. We lost sight of the lowlands as night fell quickly, glorious with stars. They gave light enough to travel by, through a world gone dim and shadowy. With my other animal senses to help, I could have gone faster than any human. But I stayed close to the women and listened.

From time to time they had spoken with Valeria. Hitherto the girl had been hopeful, almost cheerful. When you're her age and healthy, you don't really believe you can die. She'd caught naps, supported by her safety harness, taken food and water, attended to Svartalf's needs, and dutifully practiced wielding Fotherwick-Botts. As Earth and moon waxed, blue and gray-white, her excitement had mounted.

Now, though, the lunar disc hung huge, a blackness cut out of heaven, edged with dazzlement where steeps and craters stood brutally forth. "She's coming in for a landing," Ginny told us. Her words trembled beneath the stars.

"Sooner than we estimated." I heard the anguish in Curtice's voice. "Oh, if only we'd had exact data—"

"Yingle, yingle, yingle," Fjalar moaned. "How mush longer ve got to go?" Edgar added a croak.

"About two hours, I'd guess, if we can hold to this pace." Balawahdiwa's answer tolled iron-steady. "Once on top, we have to continue to where the Beloved Ones are gathered. When the maiden has landed, they'll sing their recalling song. They don't know when she'll actually be able to depart; and without a lodestone of Earth in her craft, she will fly slower than otherwise. I'm not sure how effective an ordinary, uncharmed object out of a pocket can be."

"I've been advising her," Ginny said. "If she can't avoid setting down on the moon, she can steer, choose her spot. In daylight there'd be nobody but demons. She's aiming for the dark side, well beyond the sunset line."

"In any case, we ought to reach our goal before she arrives here." Balawahdiwa's tone had turned equally, deliberately commonplace. "We couldn't help her right now, wherever we were. If it comes to a fight, that's when we'll be most wanted.

"Keep going."

# XLVII

Again I have to reconstruct the story from bits and pieces, what I heard at the time and afterward, what I myself experienced, and—because witnesses' memories are notoriously unreliable—what I rightly or wrongly infer. How much of history do we really know?

*Owl* slanted downward across a moon that was no longer ahead but below. The terrain reached gray and black under the soft bluish light of Earth. Our planet stood high in the western sky, slightly gibbous, altogether beautiful, clouds a swirled and banded white marbling azure ocean, glistery polar caps, greenish-brown Asia. Its brilliance drowned most stars out of Val's eyes. She wondered whether she glimpsed lights like them, city lights, sown on the night half. Maybe an illusion, a glint of tears caught in her lashes.

Joy warred with fear. First lunar landing ever! And, God willing, the nastards, taken by surprise, wouldn't reach her before she'd fixed the craft and left for home.

Mountains, gentler contoured than Earth's, fell aft. She swept above a lower stretch of stone, where craters peered from shadow, down toward a darkling plain. "Mare Tranquillitatis," said Curtice's voice from Dowa Yalanne. "The name a good omen? Anyhow, safer to settle on than the highlands westward, and farther from the sun."

"Yes," rang the command of Valeria's mother. "Take it."

*Owl* handled easier than in an atmosphere. Of course, allowing for the low weight was kind of gitzy. . . . She'd show them. Too young for a license? Ha!

Savagely braking, *Owl* hawk-swooped at her goal. Her liberation. When she touched yonder soil, the spell that compelled her was ended. Val need simply put a piece of terrestrial matter in the nose cap, and the Zuni gods would call her to them.

"Yee-hi!" she shouted. She stole a glance aft. Svartalf arched his back and bottled his tail. She didn't hear him through the vacuum, but she well knew that yowl from of old. *Here I come! Make way, rabble, or I'll gut you for fishbait.*

The broom slammed to a halt, yards above ground. Val lost her saddle. Ashen desert and luminous Earth spun across her vision. The stick rebounded and toppled. She struck. Black dust billowed.

"Val!" Ginny cried. "Are you there? What's happened?"

Dazedly, the girl sat up. She'd fallen next to the vehicle. For a second she noticed only how fast the dust settled, no air to lift it, and that it'd gotten all over her, a fine powder that clung, an unseelie mess. Svartalf had sprung clear. He trotted toward her, equally disarrayed, furiously indignant.

"Valeria, Valeria—" And, less loud and clear, she heard her father howl.

Her sense came back. She rose to her feet and stared. "We hit something. Something invisible, I guess. We dropped."

"Are you hurt?"

Val moved arms and legs, twiddled fingers and toes. "No, don't seem to be." She was most conscious of how light she had become. The collision had occurred at perhaps five miles an hour, while the forces held the riders secure. Given lunar gravity, the fall had corresponded to a couple of feet on Earth. It was well, though, that she'd unbuckled her harness before starting her descent. The broom would have hit ground with her astride. That mass would probably have broken any bones caught underneath it.

Ginny swallowed a sob before she asked, "The spacecraft?"

"Lemme take a look." Val stooped, peered, and felt. "Okay, I think."

"Sure she ban fine," Fjalar snorted. The whole gang must be clustered around the locket bearers. "Ay do honest vork. Volund the Smith could have took lessons from me."

"The fact you can still communicate, that the crystal wasn't knocked out, yes, that's encouraging," Curtice said. "Think you can fly?"

"Well, she's lying on her side," Val reported, "but I don't expect she weighs too much here for me to right her."

"Have you any idea what you struck?" Balawahdiwa inquired.

"N-no, sir." Val gripped the hilt of the sword at her hip. "I, I can try feeling of it."

"Don't linger," Ginny ordered. "The demons must have tracked

your path. They'll be on their way. This could be a barricade or a trap of theirs. Get out!"

"I wonder—" Balawahdiwa mused.

"Oh!" Val gasped.

A touch, light as a breeze, tender as a kiss, on brow, eyes, lips, bosom, hands. And there *they* were, at hover before her and around her. Seven figures, male and female, less tall than her, slim, big-eyed, features grave and exquisite, long silvery hair and translucent billowy garments afloat though there was never a wind. . . . Earthlight shone through their locks and robes; it seemed almost to pass through them. Above them reared a wall surmounted by slim towers, ivory-hued, playfully filigreed, a high ogive gate at its middle that shimmered like mother-of-pearl. To the left of this gaped a hole. The shards showed how thin the wall was, how delicately formed.

Svartalf halted his prowlings. He settled down on the ground, alert but much as he would have at a fireside.

"The Fair Folk," Val whispered. "It's got to be. They've appeared to me."

"Hush," came Balawahdiwa's word to his companions. "Don't disturb the meeting. Listen, only listen. Let's us keep on."

Valeria gulped. "Hi," she breathed. "Can you hear me, people? I'm sorry I damaged your building."

She heard the reply within herself, dream-speech, a melody, a birdsong, a running brook. —You are not at fault. How could you have known? Welcome, welcome.

"*Are* you—"

—Yes. And now we know who you are and what your need is. A fate is in this. What it may be, we know not. May it bring deliverance.

"You, once you showed yourselves to my Uncle Will."

—Your kinsman, aye. For we saw that humans might well follow us to the moon. We wished that someone would give them forewarning. Then perhaps when they came they would show us mercy. We could not speak for ourselves. Few are the haunts remaining on Earth which have not become horrible to us. Nor do we understand anymore the souls of most men, who no longer walk in awe and worship, but question everything and seek ways to bend the whole world to their will. Here was a youth as pure in heart as any son of Adam can be, his yearning already turned heavenward. We hoped he would be our friend.

Val shuddered. "He was. But later those scabrous demons went for him."

—With sorrow did we learn this from your mind, and with gladness that he is again free. But you, child, are in terrible danger.

She gulped. "When w-will they get here?"

A male frowned. It was not natural on a face meant for carefree happiness. —We cannot say. But we think that if they have lain in wait for you, they are not together. For they must know that while they could command you to this sphere, you, wisely counseled from Earth, could find harbor wherever you chose. Thus they would not gather at a single place, but spread themselves over great distances. Is that not what hunters would do?

Val nodded.

—The number of them is not large. No more than a hundred, belike fewer.

"What?"

A female, with unwonted grimness: —We have found out much in the years since they first arrived.

*Well,* passed through the girl's head, *that figure must be about right.* Besides what observation had shown, it just wasn't reasonable that China, Japan, Mongolia, Tibet, any country had ever been overrun by fiends. Most Beings were benign, or at least neutral, or at worst sort of mischievous. Didn't the old stories say so? How could the world have survived if good didn't always outweigh evil?

Then how could these devils, kuei, oni, spooks, hoodoos, and screaming meemies have caused the grief they did?

*Because it doesn't take many,* she thought. Anywhere in the human or nonhuman worlds, nature or paranature. One stalking murderer can terrorize a city. One self-infatuated dictator can turn entire nations into prison camps and torture chambers. One warped prophet can preach a creed whose fanatics butcher millions of the harmless. Why, one honest but pushy bureaucrat—

Her tension and fear erupted in laughter. She had remembered Alger Sneep.

She grew aware of the Fair Folk's puzzled regard and realized that her merriment was half hysteria. But it had rallied her like a dash of cold rain.

A female told her: —That is why they have not destroyed us and our homes. We withdraw from their warlike bands, as we withdraw from the sun. Being too few to ransack widely, they seldom discover our dwellings, whether we take shelter there during the day or depart for others.

She gestured. The gate swung open. Val saw gardens where flowers

glowed beneath arching argent trees, fountains soared in white plumes, a pool shimmered full of twilight. One building stood amidst them, as fragile as everything else, wholly strange yet in its way as lovely as the Taj Mahal.

—We make our homes and ourselves invisible to all who menace us.

That shouldn't be hard for Beings so ethereal. Indeed, this couldn't be ordinary, material matter. What was it composed of? Starlight and enchantment, perhaps?

—Sometimes the wicked, casting about, come upon a place by chance, as you did . . . if your advent truly was by chance. They wreck it. Sometimes they sorcerously find traces of us and hunt us down and . . . we will not say what then happens. Give the demons time, and they will slay the last of us.

*Like humans hounding whole races of animals to extinction,* Valeria thought.

—And always, from their lunar stronghold, they will wreak harm on your kind.

*No, they needn't really be many. Plenty of mortals are, well, easy marks for them, Dad would say. Some would choose to be their allies.*

—We will do what we can to aid your escape, before we too must flee.

Her blood throbbed. "Oh, thank you!"

—You bear not only your own hopes, but ours.

Svartalf jumped up, squalled, and spat. She couldn't hear him. He tugged at her jeans. She looked down and saw him crouched for battle, eyes and teeth agleam in the stiff-standing ebony fur. Sparks snapped through its dustiness.

Her gaze swept west. Over the near horizon, across the pockmarked plain, under serenely shining Earth, three forms bounded toward her. They went in flat leaps, hurtling like cannon shells. A hairless giant, nude but for a loincloth, blunt horns sprouting from a narrow brow, fangful mouth agape; a fish-scaled monkey with a split head and an obscenely erect phallus; a human skeleton, clattering its jaws: nightmare become as real as a gallows.

"They're at us," Valeria cried to father and mother and friends, unreachably distant. "The nearest of them—they didn't wait for more—"

She heard me bay. There was no time for terror. It was as if she stood aside and watched. She drew the sword.

"Haro!" Fotherwick-Botts trumpeted. Him she could talk with,

more bluntly than with the Fair Folk, who scattered back appalled from the oncoming enemy. "God send the right!" He began scolding her. "None too soon, young lady. D'you think I liked sitting in that confounded sheath, mute while plan after plan came to me? Bally insubordination, I call it. Never have happened in the Widow's army, I'll wager." His attention went outward. "Bloody heathen, those. Not even natives, are they? Let 'em break themselves on us. Remember, no roundhouse swings, no silly overhead cuts leaving your belly wide open. Slantwise. Go for the neck, the arm, the thigh. If you must stab, strike below the rib cage. . . . Yoicks! Tally-ho!"

The demons arrived.

Svartalf sprang, hooked claws into the giant's skin, climbed up him and set about tearing out his eyes.

The monkey was more agile. It bounced to and fro, dodging the blade. Its muzzle leered and soundlessly gibbered what its phallus threatened.

"Fight, Val, fight!" Curtice shouted from Earth, as if she were still a college cheerleader. I could not yawp anymore, merely, in my dumb animal way, implore. Fjalar futilely shook his hammer. Edgar flapped and screamed. Ginny's wand wove spells, Balawahdiwa lifted his prayer stick to the stars and chanted—to what avail?

The skeleton attacked on Val's left side. Its fingerbones grabbed her and jerked her around. Its teeth clapped.

The monkey leered and doubled its legs for a pounce.

Three misty shapes blew over to swirl around and blind it—Fair Folk, with the desperation of the timid when they are cornered. It swatted at them. They wavered like a fog.

"Backbone," Fotherwick-Botts directed.

Val hewed. The blow shocked through her. The skeleton's vertebrae parted company. It fell in two pieces. They sprattled for a minute, then lay still. Kicked-up dust settled back onto the bones.

"Now that beastly little ape, while it's hampered," Fotherwick-Botts said. Val clove it. Blood gushed onto the ground, black under the blue light, and seethed off into vacuum.

"The big fella," barked the sword. He was clearly enjoying himself.

The giant staggered, groping for Svartalf. The tomcat clung but shifted to and fro. Val summoned what force remained to her. She sliced across the abdomen. Guts spilled, blood spouted. The demon collapsed.

"I—we whipped them," Val choked aloud. She knelt and vomited.

"Good Lord, m'lady, what's wrong?" Fotherwick-Botts wondered.

"You slew 'em, didn't you? A shield maiden, by Jove! I've never seen a woman do neater work. Nor many men. My compliments."

Svartalf raised back and tail. He caterwauled his triumph into airlessness.

"Val, how are you?" her mother pleaded. "Pull yourself together. You've got to get out. They'll be after you in a horde."

"Uh-huh." Strength returned from deep inside the girl. She lurched to her feet, steadied, and approached *Owl.*

"I, I have to right her and put an Earth thing in to guide her back," she told the returning Fair Folk. Her throat burned, her mouth was foul. Well, once embarked, she'd swig from her canteen, spit the puke into space, and—and—

—Yes, quickly, before more of them come, she dream-heard. —But they will pursue. We believe every last one of them will pursue.

*Bound to,* she thought. For the demons it was now or never. If she came home bearing her news, exorcists would soon land here. But if she didn't, how many people would take our unsupported word? There would at least be endless argument and shilly-shalling. Meanwhile the demons could sap all space enterprises beyond revival.

—It is your cause and it is ours, the Fair Folk sang.

"If you must sheathe me, first wipe me clean," Fotherwick-Botts interrupted. "Military neatness, y'know." Numbly, she took a handkerchief from her shirt and obeyed.

"Now don't hesitate to draw me again," the sword added. "We've won a skirmish, not the war. I've seen battles lost because of overconfidence. F'r instance, once when campaigning with the Varangians—"

She slid him into his scabbard and dropped the handkerchief by the slain. It fell slowly.

—Make haste.

She bent her knees, took hold of the shaft, heaved the broom off its side. A push on the rune key released the parking legs. *Owl* stood.

Val fumbled in her pockets. What did she have for a lodestone?

The Fair Folk gathered around her. —Whatever you carry has not been long in space. Therefore it has little power. The Beings on Earth cannot by themselves move you swiftly. The enemy will overtake you in midpassage.

She looked upon death and said, "I've got to try."

—But we, we are also children of Earth. Thence we came. There we go back from time to time, renewing ourselves at what is left of her springs and streams, her wildwoods and wild meadows. She is our mother too.

The girl unlatched and unscrewed the nose cap. She had decided on a silver dollar, a birthday gift from long ago which she still carried.

Beauty drifted close. —I am Rinna, it sang. —I will give myself to this. May we both outlive the flight.

The Being went small. She slipped into the cavity. Val had no words. She replaced the cap.

The rest of the fays hurriedly kissed her, one by one, a token of love she barely felt. —We must go now. Fare you well. Fare you always well.

They vanished from Val's sight. She swung to her saddle. Svartalf jumped to his post behind her.

Ghastly shapes swarmed over the horizon.

Val took off like an upward meteor.

# XLVIII

By then we were on top of the mesa. We stopped for a few minutes to offer tears, prayers, wishes. The air went hoarsely in and out of us. Otherwise it lay still, thin, freezing cold. Stars gleamed in their thousands, the Milky Way as a river of frost.

"Our girl is free." Curtice's sigh trembled.

"No, she ban Steve and Yinny's," Fjalar corrected.

My wife shook her head. "Tonight Valeria is everybody's."

"Well spoken," Balawahdiwa agreed. "Everybody of good will. Deliver her from evil. Come, we'd better move."

Again he took the lead. Though the growth was fairly sparse, piñon, juniper, low bushes, it made the going gloomy. Ginny didn't give us witch-sight or even light a saintelmo. Balawahdiwa had not told her she might. This was holy ground. That didn't stop Fjalar from ripping out Old Norse oaths when he stubbed his toe on a rock; and with wolf-keen ears I caught occasional muttered words from Curtice that weren't ladylike.

I found my own way easily, by cues captured in nose, ears, hairs. Ginny did likewise; though not kindled, her wand thrilled in her hand. But this freed our minds to be afraid for our daughter. I felt almost grateful for the limitations on my intelligence in my present form. I could only hurt, inwardly rage, and mutely try to keep courage. Ginny could visualize, calculate, weigh odds all too clearly.

Val had blurted an account of herself after she was spaceborne. Later Ginny called and asked how things were going. "Fast," she answered. "I can nearly *see* the moon shrink and Earth grow." After a pause: "I d-don't see . . . anything else . . . behind me."

"You wouldn't, across that many miles," Curtice told her. Unspoken: *Yet.*

"She rides at a mounting pace," Balawahdiwa said. "Maybe the demons can't match it."

"Thanks to that little spirit who came along," Ginny couldn't help observing.

"True." Balawahdiwa's tone reproached. "Nevertheless, do you imagine this was happenstance, that the Beloved Ones had nothing to do with it?"

"I'm sorry. Their inspiration— But Rinna, she accepted, didn't she? How can we ever reward her?"

Memories from humanity passed through me. I heard my father's voice: "Some good turns you can't pay back. What you do is pay them forward." I thought of cleansing the moon for her people—the image was wolf, snarls that challenged, fangs that tore—and, necessarily vaguely, of afterward starting a movement to restore woodlands and flowery meadows on Earth, so the Fair Folk could visit their mother more often.

"Now hush," Balawahdiwa commanded.

"We'll call again when we can, darling," Ginny finished. "You call if anything goes wrong. But don't fear. We love you." I licked her hand, as if somehow she could transmit a caress. Edgar made a sound like a rusty purr.

We traveled on.

It took about three-quarters of an hour. At last the trail entered a thicker stand of evergreens, you might call it a grove, which ringed a broad open space with its low boles, gnarled boughs, and murky needles. Starlight fell hoar on grass, a few shrubs, scattered rocks, and the remnant of a stone house. I could still remember that the whole Zuni tribe had taken refuge from their foes for years on Dowa Yalanne. As they had done in the mythic age of the Great Flood. . . .

Silence, cold, emptiness brooded over us. Balawahdiwa halted and made a sign of reverence. We had arrived.

Edgar's cheekiness got away from him. "Wot, no gods?" he croaked. I don't know where he picked up that British gag.

"Quiet, you!" Ginny rapped. "My humble apologies," she added to our guide.

He smiled. "They are not humorless, you know." Solemn again: "They watch and wait. Calm your hearts, open your spirits, receive." From his pack he took kilt and sash and donned them.

We grew very still, under the galactic arch and the wheel of heaven. Ginny bowed her head—yes, and Edgar too. Curtice folded hands over

breast and murmured. Fjalar took off his stocking cap, bent a knee, put the cap back on but held the hammer as a Christian might a cross.

I also felt it, awe, awareness of a vast presence, like communion in a cathedral—no, not really that. They were not One but many, not infinite though ancient and strong, friends and guardians of life, to which they gave a meaning that went beyond it. As I was, I could not fully feel, nor understand at all; but I lowered my head and stumpy tail in submission to an alpha.

The feeling passed. "They have withdrawn a small way for this while," Balawahdiwa told us softly. "We have to do our own work, our own thinking, before we can play whatever part will be ours."

Fjalar was first to go pragmatic. "Ve can't help the girl vile she flies in space," he growled. "If the trolls and drows ban far behind, somebody like you, Herr Ballavalla, can take her to a safe place. Ve others, vell—" He hefted the hammer. "Ay'd like to crack a few skulls, Ay vould."

"If Valeria escapes, I doubt they'll attack us," Ginny replied. "Not worth the risk, when they've lost the prize."

Curtice scowled. "But I'm afraid it'll be a near thing at best," she said. To the priest: "What do you think?"

It was dismaying to see him taken aback. "I . . . don't know. I should imagine—moving as fast as before—"

"If the spacecraft is boosting that hard now. I don't have the data to say for certain. However, from what Val's told us, probably she is. It's pretty much her performance limit. Can the enemy match that, Ginny?"

"I don't know either," the witch said raggedly. "Their powers are limited too. If Fu Ch'ing were here, he could give us an estimate. But I'd guess, from my own slight knowledge, they can, or better. Otherwise, why would they give chase?"

"Vich they maybe are not," Fjalar proposed.

She struck down his note of cheer. "We don't dare assume that. We can simply hope and pray that Val has enough head start and enough capability that they won't overhaul her."

"She has to make turnover and decelerate," Curtice reminded. "About a two-and-a-half-hour flight, total. No, worse. The moon's not in this sky yet. The only refuge for her is right here. To reach us, she has to apply vectors—curve around, in effect. I'd better advise her soon."

"Can the pursuit cut across that arc?" Balawahdiwa's question was not quite even.

"They may well," Ginny said. I bristled and bared teeth.

"Maybe we can do somethin' about that thar problem," drawled a new voice. "Maybe we jest can."

We stared. A man sauntered out of the woods and across to us. While clad in Western clothes—ten-gallon hat tilted back on his head, fancy bandanna, plaid shirt that would have been loud in a light that showed colors, silver-buckled belt, crisp jeans, tooled-leather boots—he was an Indian. Or was he? He seemed too lean for a Southwesterner, if not a plainsman. Certainly his features were too narrow, his nose too bladelike for any full-blood anywhere. And was it a trick of shadow, or did his outline somehow waver, like smoke or a desert mirage?

Balawahdiwa's firmness broke apart. "Suski!" he cried.

The stranger nodded. "The same." With a glance at us: "Otherwise known as Coyote. At your service, ladies and gents."

And he wasn't there. In his stead posed a canine smaller than me, gaunt, prick-eared, sharp-muzzled, with a scruffy pelt that we knew was sandy-brown and with eyes that mocked us as they had done a flicker ago. He lolled his tongue and grinned.

Balawahdiwa lifted his prayer stick, Ginny her wand, Fjalar his hammer. Edgar cracked his wings up and down and cawed, I tightened my muscles. Curtice alone kept aside. She brought her locket to her lips and in an undertone told Val what was happening.

Coyote flashed back to human appearance. "Whoa, podners, take it easy," he said. "Didn't mean no harm. Jest innerducin' myself."

Ginny exchanged a look with Balawahdiwa. He nodded. She stepped forward to challenge the demigod. Loosened and tangled by the storm, her hair seemed to crackle with the starlight it captured. I stalked at her side.

"No harm?" she retorted. "You, sir, brought this trouble on us. You allied with the common enemy of man, the creatures of the Adversary. You helped them wreck the Selene spacecraft. That no lives were lost wasn't your doing. That a maiden's life and soul are now in mortal danger traces back to your mischief. And you don't give a curse, do you? What more evil have you raised?"

"Hey, you really are mad." He didn't act remorseful or even apologetic. "Calm down, why don't you? We're different, that's all. You're you and I'm me."

He switched to animal shape, I suppose to underline his point. I drank in the feral smell and bristled my ruff.

He changed back to man. "I was jest havin' some fun," he went on. "Though I got to say, if you'll excuse me, you folks been crowdin' in mighty hard on my range." His speech continued slow and amiable.

"How'd you like it if squatters moved onto your spread, yay, right'n your garden, and brought along their prairie dogs to burrow through it and their buffalo to graze and trample it? My folks ain't too happy with what you done to their country. Or to them."

"We were never your people, Suski," Balawahdiwa declared. "You never belonged to or cared for any but yourself."

Coyote gibed by swapping forms back and forth for a minute.

Human, he replied, "Wall, now, they do say as how I had a little somethin' to do with the Creation. 'Course, the *Melika* claim that's a kid story, and I reckon they've got most of you believin' so. Truth's a tricky maverick, though, like I was tryin' to demonstrate jest now."

"You said it yourself. We are what we are, which is what history has made us. You have betrayed us to the enemies of everything rightful."

"Aw, that's puttin' it purty stiff." Coyote held up a palm. "But okay, mister, I made a mistake. Not my first, I admit. You folks never made any?"

Recollections rose in me, easy for a wolf with a half-human brain to grasp, some of the countless old tales about him. If he was the Trickster, he was also the Bungler, the schemes he thought so clever ending more often than not in a pratfall—or in death, from which he always arose, apparently unable to learn any lesson whatsoever.

Ginny must have remembered too, for she smiled starkly. "Are you here to try setting things right?" she demanded. "Dare we let you?"

He fished in his shirt pocket, brought out makings, rolled a cigarette between his fingers and struck a match on his heel. "I did have a session or two with the Beloved Ones," he replied, unabashed, after the first drag. "Yep, turns out those waddies are a real mean gang, and shore, none of us wants 'em in charge. I come up with a notion they'll go along with if'n you agree."

A scream sounded from Ginny's and Curtice's lockets.

Startled, the newcomer changed shape. Not entirely. I'd never before seen a coyote with a cigarette in its mouth.

"I spy them!" Valeria cried. "I think I do. I looked behind and . . . like dust-glints over the dark side of the moon—Daddy, Mother, is that them?"

Ginny looked straight at doom and stared it down while she said, "I can't imagine what else it might be."

I howled. Edgar screeched.

"Darling, keep going," Ginny urged. "Don't give up. We're here, we have friends greater than they are, we'll save you."

"A minute." Curtice turned off her communicator. She signed Ginny

to do the same before she stated, "If they've become naked-eye visible, that means they're boosting faster than the spacecraft is. I don't have figures to work with, of course, but I expect they'll intercept her before she arrives, especially if they shortcut across her change of direction."

Coyote had resumed man shape. "Beg pardon, ma'am." Suddenly he showed excitement. His eyes flashed starlight. "The little lady don't need no two hours. I reckon she can get here inside of one more, even allowin' for that thar switcharound you talk of."

"In God's name, how?" Ginny exclaimed.

"Why, she don't need to slow down till the very end. Tell her to keep tumbleweedin' along, faster'n faster. The gang can't match that nohow, can they?"

I barked a protest. Curtice voiced it for me: "The whole distance at two gravities? Have you any concept of what her speed will be? If somehow she stops within a few miles, our forcefields can't withstand such a deceleration. She'll be smashed like a beetle under a boot."

"*Ja,*" Fjalar added heavily, "Ay guess the boat vill crumple and break in shunks. It's good steel, none better, but the sword of Sigmund the Volsung shattered against Odin's spear."

"The demons will for shore have to put on the brakes," Coyote said. "I reckon they can do it faster'n a human could stand. But it's bound to take them a while, and that's when they lose ground. For your gal, though, why, we've got the Beloved Ones handy. You reckon they can't cradle her to a soft landin', easy as turnin' a flapjack?"

I saw Curtice frown. In my dim way, I wondered too. Nobody short of the True God can repeal the conservation of energy. Those gigajoules would have to go somewhere, damn near instantly.

But Coyote *was* smart. And he doubtless knew what his superiors could or would do. And—

"The gang may be close on her tail, mind you," Coyote warned. "But I got a notion about that." His laugh yammered. "Oh, but I got a notion!"

Ginny's chin lifted. "We'll try it," she said, as impersonal as the sky. "It seems to be our only chance."

"I think it is," Balawahdiwa answered.

# XLIX

For a short span our hearts rose. Something was being accomplished. The rest of us listened while Curtice talked Val through the maneuvers that would aim her at America and us. Formerly I'd have claimed that such piloting by second-hand eyeballs, with neither instruments nor reckoners to help, was impossible. But Ginny had judged that the combined influences of the Beings here and the spirit aboard made a crucial difference.

Then once more the agony of waiting set in. The shift in path would give the pursuit opportunity to shorten its own. What we couldn't predict was whether the two would meet.

And then Val told us, and we heard in her voice and felt in her bones how she shuddered: "They've gotten close. M-maybe a mile. I can't stand to look at them. But I'll have my blade ready."

"Into Thy hands, O God, we entrust our souls, in the name of our Lord and Savior Jesus Christ," her weapon said. "Remember, cut right and left both, or they'll be at your undefended side. Whatever the outcome, I wager those scoundrels won't soon forget who they dealt with. St. George, haro!"

And *then* Val: "They . . . they . . . yes, they're dropping behind. They are! S-slowly, but . . . they are, they are!"

I howled. Coyote yipped. "Khr-r-r, quark!" Edgar gloated. "Good bird. IRS nevermore."

"They've got to start deceleration," Curtice said like a machine. The demons couldn't tap this line of communication. "But they'll take for granted it's to prepare for a course change. They can't expect you'll dive straight at Earth. They must suppose you'll apply a vector to slip past, and they'll line out after you."

"You won't," clanged Ginny's word.

"If you stop instantaneously and they're on the same track, they may not be able to sheer off," Curtice cautioned. "They may have no choice but to follow you down."

"Still hoping to catch you," Balawahdiwa said.

"Yup, that's how I figured," Coyote bragged.

Fjalar chewed his whiskers. "If it vorks," he muttered. "Ay dunno. Ay yust dunno. A gale, a riptide, and a lee shore."

"Yes, go ahead and cry for a while, dearest," Ginny called to the sounds of weeping. "You've earned the right."

Time crawled.

In an eyeblink, time was no more.

"Earth's enormous," Val said from the stars agleam over us. She didn't sound altogether calm—who would have?—but she was done with tears. "Fills half the sky. Dark, dark, the seas and clouds like silver, there's a kind of blue rim—the air, I guess. No sun, but the half moon's off yonder. Earth growing, faster and faster."

When she hit the outermost atmosphere at that velocity—

She knew. "You better stop me soon, I think." A gulp. "If . . . if you can't, make a wish on the shooting star."

No wishes would be left that were worth making.

The Beloved Ones appeared.

Their host filled the meadow. They were as if gently luminous, yet blinded no sight of heaven from our vision. Balawahdiwa made reverence. We companions gave them the honors we had earlier given an unseen nearness. Their presence overwhelmed. Coyote himself took off his hat.

The Twin War Gods glowered at the forefront, squat, ugly, shields and spears to hand. Kokopelli stood offside, the hunchbacked wanderer, flute to his lips. Some of the rest I knew from books, pictures, dolls, costumes in ceremonies that whites may watch.

The warrior Salimo:beya, face hidden in his collar of crow feathers, yucca-bundle whip in his grasp, guarded the Longhorns. Hu:dudu, also masked, strung his bow. The ogres of discipline stood like stones. The torch of the tiny fire god burned close to six bird-headed Shalako, each twice the height of a tall man. Grotesque, heads plastered with mud, the sacred clowns kept unwontedly still. And more kachinas and more, rank upon rank, not human to behold but intertwining with human lives and the life of the land, had come to save what they preserved and blessed.

The Ko:koshi, earliest rain dancers of the year, raised their rattles

and evergreen boughs. Kokopelli's music piped. Somewhere drums and a chant both shrill and deep-throated made response. Feet moved. All were now dancing, most of them gravely and in place. The Mudheads capered and somersaulted, ululating. The ground thundered.

Valeria hurtled at our planet. Her forcefield clove the outermost wide-strewn molecules of air. Incandescence blazed around her.

Something like tremendous invisible hands closed on it. They took the shock into themselves. Val found herself hardly more than a mile above the mesa, flying hardly faster than an eagle upon its prey.

That energy did have to go somewhere. Sky roared, earth shook. The Mudheads got much of it. They flew on high in every direction. Their gleeful shouts pierced the boom and bang. This was fun! They crashed on treetops, tumbled to the ground, skipped back to their pranks unhurt.

*Owl* arrowed from aloft. The spirits must have helped Val steer. Her own skill, though, gave aim; her own dear form was silhouetted on the broom with Svartalf's, a Hallowe'en figure athwart the stars. She still clasped the drawn sword.

"Flit for yonder house," Ginny told her beneath the music. "Land inside. Stay."

Balawahdiwa had said an altar for prayers and sacrifices stood there. The ruin was holy. Bounding toward it, I watched her glide to a near halt and through the doorway. Balawahdiwa advanced to stand in front. Two kachinas flanked him.

"Yahoo!" Coyote yelled. "Here comes the stampede!"

It was he who had proposed, "We shouldn't ought to jest disappoint them. Let's see if we can't bushwhack them." His overlords had evidently agreed.

Svartalf darted forth between Balawahdiwa's legs. His pelt and tail stood straight, his eyes were a tiger's, he yowled the challenges of his tomcat youth.

From within the house a basso blustered, "What is this farce? I demand my bally honor. There'll be questions in Parliament if I'm confined, there'll be courts martial, and you'll jolly well deserve to lose your confounded fight!"

"He's right," Curtice said. She sped to the doorway. "Pardon me." She edged past the sentries. I'm sure she grabbed a moment to hug and kiss our girl before she returned brandishing Fotherwick-Botts.

"That's better," the sword grumbled. "Were you concentrating on the drill I gave the lass? Should've been, damme. Well, keep your head, obey my orders, and by all the merciful saints, woman, strike to *kill.*"

"I went in for saber fencing in college," the celestonaut replied. "This isn't the same, but I can get the hang of it."

Fjalar tossed his hammer, limbering up. The star-tip on Ginny's wand kindled to a hellish blue-white. Edgar flew to perch alert on the head of a Shalako. The giant didn't seem to notice. I unreeled my tongue, cooling off against the heat to come.

Something like a sheaf of lightning bolts burned lurid aloft. *—It is they,* went through our minds.

*—ma' lesi tewanane*
*a-winakwe*
*awan tse'makwin aka*
*tetse'makponolkwina—*

"The prayer before war," Ginny whispered.

The demons streaked at us. Curtice and Coyote had guessed truly. Not foreseeing that Val would plunge directly to Earth, they hadn't decelerated enough in that direction. Superhuman though their power of goetic movement was, it couldn't check them before they hit the atmosphere. So, wild with the chase, the blood lust, they followed her onward. If they caught her on the surface, they'd tear her to rags and carry away our craft.

I wished for an antiaircraft battery—rumor claimed the Army had developed some firearms that shot more than silver bullets—but Val would've been dead and forever lost before we'd gotten through the bureaucracy and clearances and politics and—

And here we were: mortals, who are nonetheless born with the power to resist evil; weapons and tools charged with paraforce to match its own; gods of the land and the people.

Too late, the demons saw.

They attacked anyhow. Their numbers were close to a hundred, and scorn for others dwells at the core of the satanic. I glimpsed the grisly and the graceful, the crazy and the cruel, mingled together in a swarm that stank of death and corruption. I felt the bow wave of their passage, cold, cold. And they were upon us.

Nobody ever sees a combat whole. It's clamor and confusion, fear and fury, stab and stagger, shoot and take shelter, the world narrowed down to you and your nearest foes or friends, sometimes a flash from a scene elsewhere that sears itself into your memory for as long as you live, which may be only till that unawaited dull shock and amazed

understanding. Maybe I, wolf, sensed more of it than my civilized self would have; but it was in fragments flying by.

A man shape came at me. For an insane instant I thought it was Fu Ch'ing, tall, thin, stooped, solemn, in mandarin robe and cap, with mandarin nails as long as a finger joint. No. When I rushed in, those nails slashed me like whetted steel. My were-flesh knitted. My teeth raked. They closed on a fold of the robe. It was not clothing, it was the very body of the Being. Blood gushed icy. The features never changed, the throat never cried out, as we fell to the ground and struggled.

The wounds he gave me went deep. I barely felt them. They healed while I tore him open. After a time he sprawled, empty. I coughed a vile taste from my mouth and glared across the field.

Nearby, a short, squat demon in a coat of mail might have been a benign temple guardian. But his pop eyes and grinning gape radiated hate. He swung a curved sword at Fjalar. The dwarf's hammer met the blow in midair and turned it. He smote the wrist behind. Bones cracked. Fjalar waded in and beat the creature to shapelessness.

Svartalf sprang at a cat twice his mass. *Off my territory, you!* They mixed it up, a tumbling, spitting whirl. Fur and blood flew. Our old guy got the worst of it. He hung in, though, and worked some havoc of his own. I ran over and bit through the devil's neck.

Svartalf crawled free and threw me a dirty look. What'd I mean, butting in? His injuries didn't seem too bad. A couple of rat-sized horrors scuttled by. Svartalf took off after them. Edgar joined him.

A man shape seven feet tall and broad to match charged Curtice. Its head was like a wild boar's. Hunched over, it went to gore her. "Ha, swine to hunt!" exulted Fotherwick-Botts. His blade whirred. It shortened those huge tusks. The monster reeled back. Curtice took a two-handed grip and stabbed it in the lower body. It sagged, threshed, and went limp. "Excellent," Fotherwick-Botts approved. "Modern pigsticking."

A different sort assailed Coyote. Like a deformed woman with needle teeth and claws at the end of webbed hands, the rear half a shark's, it swam through the air as it had swum in space. Coyote leered. It raked at him. He became a coyote, lower case. *Duh,* it maybe thought. Coyote turned man again. And beast. And man. And beast. When he had it thoroughly confused, he worked his way around, got onto its back, rode as he'd have ridden a bronco, and broke its neck.

Farther off, Ginny's wand swept to and fro. She dueled something I could not see from here. I loped toward her. Terror grabbed me. That

misty, ghastly phantom, hair and kimono tossed by no wind I could feel, mouth stretched open, the silent shriek— I cringed. The racket of battle elsewhere rolled over me.

I recalled that this was my mate who fought. I forgot everything but rage and bounded forward.

Too slow. Just as well. I'd have been no use in such an engagement. Ginny's left hand gestured. She spoke words of power. Her wand smote. The goryo wailed one last time and blew apart like fog before a dawn breeze.

I joined my witch. Sweat ran down her face and soaked her shirt. She breathed hard. The wand shivered in her grasp. But she spoke gravely. "I believe I've given peace to Princess Tamako."

We stared around us. Demons dashed again and again at Valeria's refuge. Always they recoiled from the priest and his companions. However, those were having an awful time keeping her where she was. She wanted to get out and join the fracas.

With spear and shield, the Twin War Gods raged. Arrows whistled and struck. The fire god darted about, the touch of his torch setting foes aflame. The ogres of discipline clubbed. The kachinas pressed in, smiting. The Mudheads bounced like rubber balls; they let no bunch of our enemies rally. The Shalako ponderously trod the wicked underfoot.

And it was as if others loomed behind, above, as if every well-wishing spirit of Earth and Earth's life was with us. Six arching legs across the stars and a body at the zenith where they met—Water Strider? A hint of a web that bound the stars together—Grandmother Spider, mightiest and most caring among the Hopi? Edgar, silly Edgar, was something of the Northwest's Raven in him? Even Coyote—

My wolf sight blurrily saw the half moon rise over the trees.

I saw the demons break. Panic swept through the survivors. They scattered aloft as sparks fly from a dying fire when you stamp on it.

Arousal drained out of us. Weariness and awareness of the cold crept in. Ginny put away her wand, clasped her shoulders, and shivered. I nuzzled her while calling up the last of what heat was in me. Fjalar strutted, Svartalf limped to us across the hideously strewn field. Edgar landed and sat, wings drooping, as if glad to be again no more than a bird.

Curtice followed. Fotherwick-Botts hung low in her shaky hand. "Jolly good show," the sword deemed. "Milit'ry lessons. Yes, by Jove, this should go into the textbooks."

Curtice slumped down beside us. "Chilly con carnage," she sighed.

Did a trumpet peal, did a chorus sing? A radiance filled the sky. His wings reached across constellations. The glory around his head lighted his face, his eyes, the wisdom and compassion. His great hand moved. The slain and the blood vanished from the sacred meadow. The final fleeing devils became nothing.

And he was gone.

"Cambiel," Ginny breathed. "The fifth archangel. He who watches over discoverers."

Did our deeds and our dreams mean more to the cosmos than we had known?

—*Farewell,* we heard. *Blessings.* Coyote, kachinas, and the Beloved Ones vanished. We rested alone on Dowa Yalanne.

Balawahdiwa led Valeria out by the hand. "It's all right if *Owl* flits us to our brooms," he said. "Let's go home."

I sat on my haunches and howled my happiness at the pure moon.

D0390064